Managing Foodservice and Food Safety

by Susan Davis Allen, MS, RD

Association of Nutrition & Foodservice Professionals
406 Surrey Woods Dr
St. Charles, IL 60174
800.323.1908
www.ANFPonline.org

ISBN 0-9753476-9-1

Printed in the United States of America

Preface

Managing Foodservice and Food Safety focuses mostly on non-commercial foodservice. Non-commercial foodservice is typically not for profit and the role of foodservice is secondary to the overall mission of the facility. Non-commercial foodservice is changing rapidly. The lines between commercial and non-commercial foodservice are blurring as hospitals, schools, and long-term care provide more choice for their clientele. In hospitals, retail sales are becoming an increasingly important part of the overall foodservice budget.

This textbook may not be organized in the way that other foodservice management textbooks are; it may not contain all of the topics that other foodservice management textbooks do. That is because a team of Certified Dietary Managers have identified a series of tasks that are common to most foodservice operations. These tasks represent current practice in the United States. The *Managing Foodservice and Food Safety* textbook follow those tasks including the unit organization.

Today, Certified Dietary Managers are responsible for the daily operations of their department while helping the facility fulfill its mission and goals. They coordinate the service of food and nourishments among various departments, such as dining services and nursing. Certified Dietary Managers ensure that clients are satisfied with their dining experience and that the meals are meeting their nutritional and emotional needs. In addition, they oversee food safety, the inventory and ordering of food, equipment, and supplies, and arrange for the routine maintenance and upkeep of the foodservice equipment and facilities. Certified Dietary Managers are generally responsible for all administrative and human resource functions of the foodservice department, including recruiting new employees and monitoring employee performance and training. This textbook walks you through the daily management operations of your foodservice department.

Acknowledgements

We would like to express our appreciation to many individuals who have contributed to the development of this textbook, including Sue Grossbauer, RD; John Knight, PhD; Ruby Puckett, MA, RD, LD, FCSI; Jack Ninemister, PhD; and James Kinneer, MA, CDM. Much of their original work has been retained in this edition.

In addition, we would like to recognize the contribution of the review team who generously invested their professional expertise and valuable time to offer many recommendations for achieving the educational objectives of this textbook:

Julie Abernathy, DTR, CDM, CFPP
China Grove, NC

Marian Benz, MS, RD, CDE, CD
Wauwatosa, WI

Michael Braun, MS, RD, CD
Madison, WI

Janet Burtch, CDM, CFPP
Toledo, OH

Jolene Campbell, MEd, RD, LDN
Baltimore, MD

Sharon Doughten, MS, RD, LD
Cleveland, OH

Juanita Gunnell, MS, RD, LDN
Dallas, NC

Cindra Holland, RD, LD
Perrysburg, OH

Laura Horn, MEd, RD, LD
Cincinnati, OH

Floristene Johnson, MS, RD, LD
Desoto, TX

Judy Kaplan, MS, RD, LD
Cleveland, OH

Tama S. Krause, MS, RD, LMNT
Norfolk, NE

M. Theresa Leo, RD, MAS, LDN
Morgantown, PA

Fran Lukacik, RD, MS, CDM, CFPP
Lafayette Hill, PA

J.J. Marcano, RD, LDN, CSG
Ambler, PA

Linda Eck Mills, MBA, RD, LDN, FADA
Bernville, PA

Monica Perry, RD, LD
Boise, ID

Marla Prytz, MS, RD, CD
Rice Lake, WI

Ruby Puckett, MA, FCSI
Gainesville, FL

Beth Ringlein, BA, AOS
Milan, OH

Tim Roberts, PhD, RD, LD
Auburn University, AL

Brenda Rubash, RD, LD
LaPorte, MN

Becky Rude, MS, RD, CDM, CFPP
Grand Forks, ND

Joanne Seid, RD, MS
Valhalla, NY

Sharon Smith, RD, LD
St. Paul, MN

Loretta Spangler, RD, LMNT
Ewing, NE

Jane Valentine, MS, RD, LD
Champaign, IL

Linda Waite, MS, RD, LD, CDM, CFPP
Quincy, IL

Meshele Wyneken, RD
Fort Wayne, IN

Mary Louise Zernicke, MS, RD, MPH, CSG
Berkeley, CA

Furthermore, the ongoing efforts of the developers of the Nutrition and Foodservice Professional Training Curriculum, Susan Davis Allen, MS, RD; Marion Benz, MS, RD, CDE, CD; Becky Rude, MS, RD, CDM, CFPP; Katherine Church, RD; and the Certifying Board for Dietary Managers have done much to focus the development of this textbook.

We also wish to express gratitude to Mercy Ehrler for graphic design and production and Sue Moen for editing this textbook.

Finally, thank you to Pam Himrod, MS, RD, CDM, CFPP; Association of Nutrition & Foodservice Professionals Director of Professional Development; and the ANFP staff for their support, direction and ongoing commitment to enhancing the profession, and their dedication to the members of Association of Nutrition & Foodservice Professionals.

A Personal Invitation

We at The Association of Nutrition & Foodservice Professionals (ANFP) would like to extend a personal invitation to every student enrolled in the Nutrition & Foodservice Professional Training Program to join ANFP. We recognize the value of your career choice, and would like to offer you the many benefits of ANFP membership. As a student, you are welcome to join today and establish your professional footing through your participation in this professional association.

The Association of Nutrition & Foodservice Professionals is a national not-for-profit association established in 1960 that today has 15,000 professionals dedicated to the mission: "promoting career development, setting standards for foodservice best practices, and enhancing and strengthening the overall profession of foodservice management."

ANFP is the premier resource for foodservice managers, directors, and those aspiring to careers in foodservice management. ANFP achieves its mission through:

- Professionalism
- Integrity
- Advocacy
- Best Practices

ANFP members work in hospitals, long-term care, schools, correctional facilities, and other non-commercial settings. The association provides foodservice reference, publications and resources, employment services for members, continuing education and professional development, and certification programs. ANFP monitors industry trends and legislative issues, and publishes one of the industry's most respected magazines, *Nutrition & Foodservice Edge.*

ANFP national and regional meetings also offer a unique opportunity to enjoy timely educational sessions and network with colleagues. ANFP also provides industry leadership in the area of food protection and offers online resources about food safety and sanitation.

For more information about ANFP, please contact The Association of Nutrition & Foodservice Professionals by telephone at 800.323.1908 or 630.587.6336; or visit the ANFP website at www.ANFPonline.org to join online.

Table of Contents

CHAPTER

(Continued...)

Table of Contents *(Continued...)*

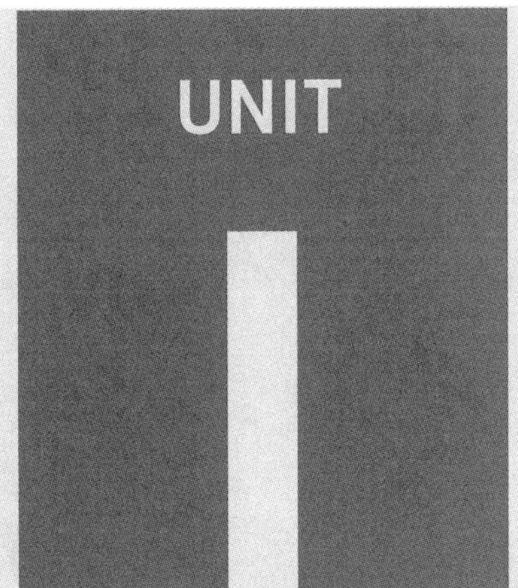

Provide Foodservices

This unit provides information for managing the actual service of food to your clients. It will cover topics on food quality, diet accuracy, preparation and service of special nourishments, determining client satisfaction with food, and then modifying menus to meet client's needs and preferences.

Check Meal Service for Food Quality, Portion Size, and Diet Accuracy

Overview and Objectives

How do you know that your clients are receiving the appropriate diet, appropriate portion sizes, and quality food? This chapter takes you through the steps to assess and validate food quality, calculate staff efficiency, and assure compliance of modified diets.

After completing this chapter, you should be able to:

✓ Define procedures for mode of foodservice

✓ Assess attractiveness of food served

✓ Validate the type, quality, quantity, and temperature of food served

✓ Calculate efficiency (time, cost) of foodservice system

✓ Assure compliance of meals served as posted

How you provide food in your facility is considered your method of foodservice. There are many different methods or modes of delivering food. There are many types of service and delivery methods for non-commercial foodservice. A Certified Dietary Manager needs to use judgment to design and/or revise systems. In addition to the needs of clients, the manager must consider:

✓ The physical design of the kitchen

✓ Locations of dining rooms or service areas

✓ Requirements for off-site service (if any)

✓ Objectives of the facility

✓ Staffing resources

✓ Budget and operating costs, and

✓ Timing requirements for service.

The implementation of culture change in foodservice is changing meal service. One of the biggest changes is away from traylines and to dining room services.

Culture Change

In an article in the *Dietary Manager's Magazine*, June, 2010, on "Culture Change in Dining and Regulatory Compliance," Linda Handy, MS, RD, explains that "never before has the Certified Dietary Manager been needed more as a manager to use your skills to implement a more person-centered, resident-driven dining program." The choices for healthcare communities for older Americans are expanding and the type of food and nutrition care will need to expand as well. With 2010 CMS regulations, F242, "your facility has to demonstrate that it's allowing residents' choice and self determination in dining." At the same time, it is important to tailor a menu to the dietary requirements of the client. How do we accomplish this? This section will describe the culture change movement and menu options to support culture change.

Culture Change in Language

Culture change begins with changing some of the language we use. Karen Schoeneman wrote about this in an editorial for the Pioneer Network Culture Change project. She asked people to come up with alternative words for, bibs, feeder, elderly. Figure 1.1 lists samples of dining terms that were suggested to help older adults maintain their dignity and healthcare facilities to become more person-centered.

Culture Change in Dining

The culture change movement in dining is driven in part by the large numbers of Americans who are aging and who will be entering the various healthcare communities as they age. It is also being driven by the change in regulations to implement more person-centered, resident-driven dining programs. This is indeed an opportune time to showcase dining services and your ability to enhance the quality of life through food and dining choices. One service option change is to offer restaurant or buffet style service in the dining room instead of the traditional trayline.

Figure 1.1 Terminologies in Culture Change

Old Terminology	Suggested Terminology
Elderly	Elder, older adult, individual
Wing, unit	Household, neighborhood, street
Institutional care	Individual care
Feeder table	Dining table
Feeder	Person who needs help eating
Facility, institution, nursing home	Home life center, living center
Foodservice worker, Hey You	The person's name
Dietary service, foodservice	Dining services
Trayline	Fine dining
Nourishment	Snack
Bib	Napkin, clothing protector
Diabetic	Person who has diabetes
Mechanical soft food	Chopped food
Trays are here	It's dinner time; dinner is served

Source: http://www.pioneernetwork.net Used with permission.

As with any change, there is resistance based on concerns about cost, staffing, and coordinating the changes with regulations. The California Culture Change Coalition piloted a project in 2007 in 11 participating facilities. The purpose of the project was to identify and implement a new food-related practice in their facilities. They have provided information about their projects, lessons learned, and resources at this URL: http://www.calculturechange.org/services-dining.html. One of these resources is a decision-making tool with questions they needed to answer to move forward with restaurant style dining (see Figure 1.2).

As you begin to adopt this culture change, there are many questions that need to be answered. Start with questioning your clients to help you decide what they want for dining services. You might ask questions such as:

- ✓ What time of day do you like to eat your meals?
- ✓ Do you snack regularly?
- ✓ How frequently during the day do you want coffee, tea, or water?
- ✓ Where do you prefer to eat your meals?
- ✓ What foods do you usually eat at breakfast, lunch, and dinner?
- ✓ Where should you begin with the culture change? (expanded snack program, restaurant services, selective menu)

Next, you will want to choose appropriate resources for changing your dining and/or menu options. The California Culture Change Coalition materials are a good start. You could survey other facilities in your area to determine how/if they have begun to implement a culture change. The Association of Nutrition & Foodservice Professionals (ANFP) published a position paper in 2011: *The Role of Certified Dietary Manager in Person-Directed Dining.* This position paper is located in *Management in the News* at the end of this chapter. Remember, the changes you make need to reflect your client's food and dining preferences.

Once you have data for what you want to do and why, the next step is to work with all of your facility departments. This will be a change for them as well and you want them to support your changes. Specifically, other departments that might be affected are maintenance, fiscal, and nursing. You will want to develop a policy and procedure that outlines every department's responsibility for each type of change you initiate. Communication and training will be key steps as you begin to implement a culture change in your facility. It is important to note that a culture change is a process that takes some time to implement.

Figure 1.2 Decision-Making Tool for Culture Change to Restaurant Style Dining

Decision-Making Tool: Critical Element—Restaurant Style Dining
• What equipment is needed for restaurant or waiter dining?
• Where will the mobile equipment be stored when not in use? Does it need to be locked?
• Is there adequate electrical and plumbing access for your plan?
• What existing equipment can be re-purposed for restaurant or waiter dining?
• Are there any physical plant changes that will be needed?
• Who will approve the expenditure?
• Can restaurant or waiter dining be operated on an interim basis with existing equipment while waiting for the capital budget?
• How many different food items can be offered?
• Will these menu food items be available to residents who do not dine in restaurant or waiter dining?
• Are there any resident safety concerns such as pouring hot beverages?
• How will menu be communicated to residents?
• Will waiters take orders at the dining table or will menus be pre-selected the day or meal before?
• Can physician ordered diet restrictions be liberalized?
• How will items be labeled or designated for various dietary restrictions?
• Does the current facility budget cover the anticipated costs?
• How will costs be monitored or reported?
• What serving utensils or equipment will be needed?
• What glasses, dishes or utensils will be used by the residents?
• How will condiments such as salt, pepper, sugar packets be handled for residents on "No Added Salt" and diabetic diets?
• What disposable or re-usable items, including napkins, staff uniforms, table linens and clothing protectors will be needed?
• How will cross-contamination be avoided when serving residents?
• How many residents will participate in restaurant or waiter dining and how long will it take to serve them?
• How will staff be assigned to restaurant or waiter dining?
• What is the cost of staffing restaurant or waiter dining?
• How will dietary restrictions be communicated and provided?
• Who will monitor and document the resident choice/consumption of food?
• Will this be documented in the medical record?
• Will staff track the waste, over-production or shortage of food?
• Do the facility policy and procedures need to be updated and approved for restaurant or waiter dining?
• Are there any forms needed for restaurants or waiter dining?
• Will you do resident satisfaction surveys?
• How will you communicate about the new restaurant or waiter dining? To whom?
• Will you do a pilot test of restaurant or waiter dining?

Source: http://www.pioneernetwork.net Used with permission.

Service Options

Restaurant Style Service

This is another way of implementing a culture change in a nursing home, even with a nonselective menu. Your regular cycle menu entrée can be the daily special with an option of sandwiches, grilled items, vegetables, and salads. Restaurant style dining might include the following:

✓ Foodservice staff waiting on tables

✓ Food ordered and delivered in courses

✓ Food plated in the dining room

✓ Specials such as sandwiches, salads, or desserts offered tableside from a cart.

Buffet Style Service

Buffet style service is offered in some long-term care facilities as a way to implement culture change. Be prepared to offer extra help for those clients who cannot serve themselves. Facilities offer the same number of choices as with restaurant style service, only clients can serve serve themselves.

Whatever menu or service style you use in your culture change, make sure there are adequate policies, staff training, and oversight to be able to justify when clients choose foods that are contrary to the therapeutic diet that was ordered for them. In addition, a facility needs to devise procedures and provide adequate staffing to assist with person-centered dining.

Trayline Service

In some facilities, clients are not physically able to go to a dining room or cafeteria for meals. In a hospital or skilled nursing facility, for example, clients may not be well enough to leave their rooms for dining on a mandatory or routine basis. Or, they may be able, but the logistics of care may make going to an other location impractical. Trayline systems are also common in correctional facilities.

A trayline system is one in which trays move through an assembly line and employees place items on trays. Afterwards, individual trays are delivered to clients. During a tray assembly process, trays may move along a straight line, or along a circular trayline, with the help of a conveyor belt beneath the trays to move them along. Some conveyor belt systems are powered by electric motors whose speed can be regulated. Also, there is a switch that can be thrown to stop the movement. Other facilities operate manual roller systems.

Serving meals through a trayline system involves a number of steps that are tightly integrated with a menu management process. How these steps are implemented varies from one operation to another. Figure 1.3 provides a sample flow for a traditional trayline service using a selective menu and computer support.

The system described in Figure 1.3 is an example of a centralized meal service. **Centralized meal service** means that food is portioned onto trays in a centralized location, such as the non-commercial kitchen. An alternative is **decentralized meal service**, in which food is distributed to other locations for finishing and service. In one decentralized model, trays are prepared and chilled. They

List at least three steps you would take to implement a culture change in your facility.

(Check your answer at the end of this Chapter)

Figure 1.3 Trayline Service: The Steps

1	Clients may receive a selective menu for upcoming meals.
2	Clients indicate their choices on the menu and/or foodservice staff interviews them to obtain their menu choices and collect menus/choices for the food-service department. In a "spoken menu" system, employees skip Step 1 and simply interview clients for selections.
3	Foodservice staff enter menu choices in a handheld computer (in the room) or on a computer system in the foodservice department, referencing each client's diet order and care plan. They review the choices and assure that special dietary needs are met, making any adjustments required to meet the diet order.
4	Shortly before service, foodservice staff prints individual tray tickets for each meal. The tray ticket printing follows a defined sequence, and trays are grouped by unit or location.
5	Staff send menus or tray tickets down the trayline for assembly. Food items and supplies are organized by station on the trayline. An employee at each station adds items to the tray, as specified on each individual menu.
6	Staff place trays on a cart or trayveyor or subveyor system for delivery.
7	Nursing or foodservice staff deliver trays.

are delivered in temperature-controlled carts to kitchens or pantries on nursing units. Next, the hot items are **rethermalized**, and sometimes additional items are added. Then, designated staff members deliver the trays to client rooms.

In yet another decentralized service model, food is prepared and transported in bulk to serving locations. Again, staff may use unique hot and cold transport units to maintain temperature. Hot products may be transported and served hot, or rethermalized from a chilled state at the point of service. This can be a useful way to provide service for designated group dining areas in a nursing home when implementing culture change. It is also a model used by some school systems, where food production is centralized and food is transported to individual school cafeterias.

Meal delivery systems integrate with food production systems. Many decentralized tray services incorporate cook-chill technologies, in which food is produced in quantity, chilled, and later re-heated for service.

In both centralized and decentralized trayline systems, the equipment used must support the service and delivery model. Temperature control from the time of assembly to actual delivery is of paramount concern. To help ensure food safety as well as quality, food must be kept out of the danger zone (41° - 135°F).

For a centralized tray service, when trays will be produced and served immediately, some of the most basic temperature control systems are insulated trays, heated base systems, and temperature-controlled transportation carts. Insulated trays contain indented compartments for food. Each compartment is insulated, so that cold foods can be placed in some compartments, and hot

Glossary

Centralized (Delivery) Meal Service
Foods are prepared and portioned onto trays or plates at a central location in or adjacent to the main kitchen.

Decentralized (Delivery) Meal Service
Bulk quantities of prepared foods are sent hot or cold to other locations for finishing and service.

Rethermalize
Reheat

Putting It Into Practice: 2

When working in a school system, you decide that food will be prepared in a central kitchen and then shipped in bulk to the other schools in the district to reheat and serve. What type of meal delivery system is this?

(Check your answer at the end of this chapter)

foods in others. A lid or cover helps to maintain temperature and keep hot and cold separate, while also protecting food from contamination during transport. Figure 1.4 illustrates insulated trays and dinnerware.

A new heated base system today is called "heat on demand." This is an instant heating system that transfers heat into a base plate while keeping the edges cool. Food is then portioned onto the base plate, covered and ready for service. Figure 1.5 illustrates a heat on demand base heater.

Trays assembled for immediate service can reach their destinations in several ways. One is a conveyor system that moves trays directly to service units that are close in proximity. This is typically an expensive system to build, and generally must be part of the initial design of a building. It also creates maintenance and sanitation concerns. For example, if trays are moving through a vertical conveyor, what happens if foods spill or trays fall? Spilled food is difficult to clean through such a system. If the conveyor malfunctions, there must be an alternate delivery method in place.

Another choice is cart transport. Some carts are designed to provide thermostatically maintained heat for maintaining temperature, while others are designed for providing refrigeration. One specialized system may have both a hot side and a cold side in one cart. It integrates with specialized trays that have designated hot sides and cold sides. During assembly, employees place hot

Figure 1.4 **Insulated Tray and Dinnerware**

Insulated Dinnerware

Insulated Tray

Figure 1.5 Heat on Demand

© Aladdin. Reprinted with permission.

Figure 1.6 Rethermalization Systems

Bulk Rethermalization System

Tray Rethermalization System

© Dinex International, Inc. Reprinted with permission.

foods on the "hot" side of the tray, and cold foods on the "cold" side. A dividing seal helps maintain temperature control. Some units can plug into a controller unit to rethermalize hot foods on trays immediately prior to service.

If an operation is using a cook-chill system, in which foods are delivered cold and rethermalized just before service, trays may still be pre-assembled and delivered on carts. Some carts and related technologies are designed to heat the food very quickly, using induction or convection heat, just in time for service. Some are rethermalized using a microwave on each floor or wing. Figure 1.6 illustrates some rethermalization systems. Note that tray rethermalization can occur in a centralized location (in the kitchen just before tray distribution), or in a decentralized location (on nursing units).

Also, specialized rethermalization systems generally require specialized dinnerware to integrate with the systems. In selecting equipment, it is important to review related needs and costs for dinnerware. Many are available in a range of colors and designs.

With today's service equipment, a manager can use software support for meal delivery systems to track temperature data, to program rethermalization features, and even to control and monitor remote delivery systems and generate reports through a desktop computer.

Beyond equipment, there are additional service considerations related to the trayline system, particularly in healthcare. We will examine delivery to clients in a trayline system.

Delivery to Clients

Even with well-designed equipment and well-planned systems, foodservice departments sometimes face delivery challenges with trayline systems. For example, in a healthcare facility, if trays reach their destinations through a cart service, staff then need to distribute trays to clients. This task may often be the responsibility of nursing or foodservice staff.

Staff who deliver trays need to accomplish several things:

- ✓ Be available as trays arrive and distribute trays promptly.
- ✓ Verify that each tray is reaching the right client. They check a client name against the name on the menu or ticket on the tray. Some tray tickets include client photos for easier verification.
- ✓ Be alert to any diet changes that have just occurred.
- ✓ Help the client set up the tray and open any packaging.
- ✓ Help the client with feeding, as needed.
- ✓ Obtain substitutes or make adjustments if a client has any difficulties with the meal.
- ✓ Make sure food is arriving to the client at the appropriate temperature.

You have heard from your hospital director that clients are complaining about receiving cold meals when their trays arrive. Your staffing plan is to have the nursing staff deliver the trays to the room. What are some steps you should take to resolve this problem?

(Check your answer at the end of this chapter)

These tasks require training. In addition, they can take a lot of time. When nursing staff are required to assist, there can be time conflicts. A nurse may be involved in another clinical task at the time that trays arrive, and this can cause delays. An effective staffing plan takes into account the skills and timing requirements of the job. In addition, it typically involves sound coordination between nursing and foodservice departments.

Delays in the distribution process are a common reason for complaints about food temperature and/or quality. In addition, there is a food safety concern with trays that sit at room temperature too long. How can a Certified Dietary Manager tackle this challenge?

There is no single best answer. However, some healthcare organizations have begun using additional auxiliary staff to assist with tray distribution and client feeding. Some have begun switching tray distribution from nursing to foodservice staff to avoid timing conflicts. In addition, some of the rethermalization systems described allow staff to control temperature much closer to the time of service. So, in one case, staff may heat only a few trays at a time—and then distribute them. Likewise, a cart that holds food temperatures helps to provide a longer window of time in which to accomplish the job without sacrificing safety and quality.

Furthermore, the Certified Dietary Manager needs to review schedules carefully to assure that they are reasonable and feasible with respect to client schedules and staffing patterns. Meal delivery schedules must also comply with additional regulations to assure that frequency and timing fit prescribed needs. For example, the time frame between supper and breakfast cannot be more than 14 hours. Also, to facilitate delivery, sequence menus or tray tickets to assure that trays are assembled and grouped in a meaningful order.

If delivery problems arise, it is up to the Certified Dietary Manager to review them with a nursing supervisor or administrator to help assure that the entire meal delivery system functions effectively.

Performance Measurement in Service Systems

Performance Measurement in Culture Change Systems

As the chapter objective stated, you are expected to assess the attractiveness of food served. This is the first part of measuring performance in a service system and it is the easiest part. Remember, we "eat with our eyes first," so assessing the attractiveness of food served begins with using your eyes:

- ✓ Look for one or two colorful items on each plate (or use a colorful garnish).
- ✓ Look for a variety of shapes (i.e. peas, a dish of mashed potatoes, and meat balls would be too many round shapes).
- ✓ Look for a variety in food textures (unless the plate is a texture modification).
- ✓ Look for a variety in cooking methods (i.e. offer something stir-fried with something steamed).
- ✓ Look for foods arranged attractively on the plate (avoid food hanging over the edge or spilled on the edge).

You might want to develop a quick checklist and offer the opportunity for other staff members to assist you in assessing the attractiveness of the plate service.

In addition, both productivity and accuracy are key concerns. Three productivity measures in foodservice are meals per labor hour, minutes per meal, and labor hours per meal. These indexes are used to determine productivity and may be used to determine appropriate staffing. There are several factors that need to be considered when using productivity indexes:

- ✓ Type of service provided (restaurant service, room service, cafeteria service, trayline)
- ✓ Amount of convenience food used
- ✓ Skill level of employees
- ✓ Complexity of the menu.

As you assess the efficiency of your department, ask and answer these questions:

- ✓ What food cost data will be used to determine actual client meals served: client trays, Meals on Wheels, meals for physicians?
- ✓ What food cost data will be used to determine a meal equivalent for non-client meals: cafeteria, floor stock, caterings from outside groups, staff, supplements?
- ✓ Which labor hours will be used in the calculation of meal productivity: all staff involved in producing meals, management staff, clinical dietetics staff, support staff?
- ✓ Are break times paid for by the facility? If so, then break time should be included in the labor cost.

Once you have determined the answers to these questions, you can calculate the productivity indexes. To begin, a Certified Dietary Manager gathers the following information:

- ✓ Number of meals and meal equivalents produced
- ✓ Number of labor hours worked.

The calculation for each index is as follows:

- ✓ **Meals per labor hour**—This is calculated by dividing the total meals served by the total number of labor hours

  Total meals served ÷total number of labor hours=meals per labor hour

- ✓ **Minutes per meal**—This is calculated by dividing the total labor hours times 60 minutes by the total number of meals

  Total labor hours x 60 minutes ÷total meals served=minutes per meal

- ✓ **Labor hours per meal**—This is calculated by dividing the total labor hours per meal by the total meals served

  Total labor hours ÷total meals served=labor hours per meal

- ✓ Hints—Meals per labor hour is <u>always</u> a number greater than 1. Labor hours per meal is <u>always</u> a number less than 1.

See Figure 1.7 for a sample form to measure meal productivity.

Meals Per Labor Hour
A productivity standard that is a calculation of the total meals divided by the total number of labor hours for a given time such as a week, month, or year (total meals ÷ total labor hours for a given time = meals per labor hour)

Minutes Per Meal
A productivity standard that is a calculation of the total minutes in producing meals divided by the total meals served (total minutes to produce meals ÷ total meals served = minutes per meal)

Labor Hours Per Meal
Total labor hours per meal divided by the total meals served

By now you can see that checking meal service for food quality, portion size, and diet accuracy includes measuring productivity or calculating efficiency. When it comes to providing service and delivery to your clients, you have many options for the mode of service. Whatever options you choose, include standards and measurements for assessing food quality, portion size, diet accuracy, and productivity.

Putting It Into Practice: 4

You are managing a school foodservice program that serves 558 meals or meal equivalents and you had 40 hours of paid labor for the day. How many meals per labor hour did you have?

(Check your answer at the end of this chapter)

Performance Measurement in Trayline Systems

Both productivity and accuracy are key concerns in trayline service. To monitor these, a Certified Dietary Manager may conduct several types of studies. One is a productivity analysis, showing the rate of assembly as trays per minute. Very simply, **trays per minute** means how many trays are produced during each minute of a tray assembly process, on average.

To calculate this figure, a Certified Dietary Manager gathers the following information:

✓ Start time of tray assembly
✓ End time of tray assembly
✓ Total number of trays assembled.

Figure 1.7 Measuring Meal Productivity—Sample Form

	January				February				March			
Variables	Week 1	Week 2	Week 3	Week 4	Week 1	Week 2	Week 3	Week 4	Week 1	Week 2	Week 3	Week 4
Total Actual Trays/ Client Meals												
Total Non-patient/client meal equivalents												
TOTAL MEALS												
Total hours worked for selected staff												
Meals per labor hour OR												
Minutes per meal OR												
Labor Hours per Meal												
Facility Standard												

Source: Allen, Susan, "ANFP Practice Standards: Measuring Meal Production & Calculating Meal Equivalents", Dietary Managers Magazine, *January 2010.*

The calculation is as follows:

✓ Determine total time elapsed for tray assembly from start and end times. Identify this figure in minutes.

✓ Divide the number of trays by the total number of minutes. This is the trays per minute figure, which tells you how many trays were made in one minute.

For example, let's say you operate a lunch trayline for one hour, or 60 minutes. You produce 240 trays. Trays per minute = 240 trays ÷ 60 minutes = 4 trays per minute. This figure serves as a meaningful benchmark which you may monitor and strive to tweak over time.

Another measure you might make is turnaround time for delivery. This measures time from assembly of trays until they actually reach clients. Quick turnaround is a key objective in trayline systems, and can be challenging to achieve. Many managers measure this by timing trays. Using a list of selected trays on the trayline, mark the time assembly of each tray is completed, follow tray to destination, and record time of delivery. By examining the two figures, it is possible to list turnaround time for each tray delivery. Coordinating this process requires the assistance of several people.

It is important to review the range of timing, or what is the quickest and the slowest turnaround time. Particular service areas with long turnaround times merit special attention to the process in place. In addition, a Certified Dietary Manager may average values to obtain a generalized performance measurement. Over time, a manager can use this information to evaluate system revisions and other interventions in the distribution system.

Tray/Plate Accuracy and Appearance. Finally, **tray/plate accuracy** is an important aspect of service for monitoring. Tray accuracy means how accurately tray assembly staff followed the menu, tray card, or tray ticket in assembling the tray. Accuracy is challenging in a fast-paced trayline. Plate accuracy means how accurately the plate follows the menu or diet.

Whether you use tray service or plate service, accuracy also includes the quality, appearance, and temperature of food served. For instance, does the plate or tray have a pleasing appearance with a variety of color? A meal of roast beef, mashed potatoes, and cauliflower would not be an attractive plate. Besides color, the meal should have a variety of shapes and texture. Picture a meal of meat balls, tater tots, and peas. This meal needs a better variety of shape and texture.

The quality of food served is equally as important. Foods should be cooked to the proper temperature, texture, and flavor that guarantee client satisfaction. Vegetables are best cooked **al dente'** but many older clients prefer their vegetables to be softer than al dente'. How do the foods taste? For every meal, a test tray or plate should be prepared and tasted prior to service. Some facilities allow staff to receive a free meal if they are the 'official taster.' Temperature of food is critical for older clients. Not only do you have to meet temperature requirements for food safety, but many older clients expect their food to be hot when it is served.

Glossary

Trays Per Minute
A measure of efficiency of a trayline foodservice system

Tray/Plate Accuracy
How accurately staff have followed the menu, tray card, or tray ticket in assembling the tray

al dente'
An Italian cooking term meaning cooked until still firm but tender to the tooth; not soft. Even though it was originally intended for pasta, it is also applies to vegetables.

How do you validate the type, quality, quantity, and temperature of food served in a trayline service?

To measure tray accuracy, you may briefly intercept trays between the time of assembly and distribution. You can also do a test tray to an area having service issues. In this case, your test tray is tested after the last tray is removed from the cart. Review each item to be served (as indicated on the tray ticket, menu, or tray card), and compare it with what is actually on the tray. Often, it is helpful to group items by trayline station. This way, if you discover a high error rate for a particular station, you can follow up as needed with an individual employee who staffs the station, and provide additional training or coaching if required.

Some managers calculate a rate of error. To do this:

1. Count the total number of items named on the menu or tray ticket for each tray you are reviewing. Example: You are checking five trays. Look at items appropriate for color, shape, texture. Tray #1 has 12 items; Tray #2 has 10 items; Tray #3 has 10 items; Tray #4 has 8 items; Tray #5 has 11 items. Your total item count is 12 + 10 + 10 + 8 + 11 = 51.
2. Count the number of errors you discover on these trays. Example: Trays 1-4 were completely accurate. Tray #5 was missing one item and had another item present that should not have been there. This counts as two errors.
3. Divide the number of errors by the total number of items. Example: 2 ÷ 51 = 0.039, or about a 4% error rate.

Alternately, you can define this as an accuracy rate. To do this, subtract total number of errors from total number of items served. This is the number of items served correctly. Divide number of items served correctly by the total number of items. Example: 51 - 2 = 49. This is the number of items served correctly. 49 ÷ 51 = 0.96, or a 96% accuracy rate.

To validate the temperature of foods prepared using a trayline, prepare a test tray as the last tray assembled. Measure the temperature of the food. Place it on the cart that goes to the farthest dining room or client. Follow the cart, retrieve the test tray and take a second measurement of the temperature. The temperature should still be above the danger zone for hot foods (above 135° F) or below the danger zone for cold foods (below 41° F).

If you are using a computerized diet order system, you can also compare actual diet orders to trays. Routine monitoring through measurements such as these are important tools that allow a Certified Dietary Manager to monitor performance of the system in place. Measurements of temperature, error counts, and comparison of actual diet orders to trays are also types of data that can help implement continuous improvement procedures for foodservice operations.

What is the tray accuracy rate in the following example? You are reviewing the trayline for diet accuracy, color, and food temperature. Your staff prepared 102 trays. There was a total of 1000 items served with a total of 12 errors.

(Check your answer at the end of this chapter)

Menu Options

A **selective menu** is the way to implement current federal regulations emphasizing client rights, and more importantly, enhance the quality of life and quality of care for your clients. A selective menu is one in which clients have the opportunity to make choices or selections in advance of meal service. For example, a selective menu usually offers at least two choices for an entrée and multiple choices for most items on the menu. Typically, a selective menu is distributed to clients in advance of the meal (about a day or half a day before service, depending on the system). Clients note their selections, which are retrieved and used in the kitchen as trays or meals are prepared. Computer-based selective menu systems may use handheld computers and/or telephone systems for entry of choices into an automated system. Figure 1.8 shows an actual selective menu with options for general, carbohydrate counting, clear liquid, and full liquid diets. Notice that the modifications for the carbohydrate counting diet are the numbers of 'carbs' found in specific menu items. That way, the client, who knows how many 'carbs' they can have, still has many choices. Menu options on a selective menu in a hospital should rotate daily for variety.

In healthcare facilities, or in any environment where the foodservice department is responsible for honoring therapeutic diets, it is standard practice to review menu choices before they are served. If clients make choices on a selective menu, a member of the foodservice staff then reviews these choices against a nutrition kardex card or computerized tray ticket. Common adjustments on selective menus that may need to be made are:

- ✓ Portion sizes of products that count as fluid, for a fluid-restricted diet
- ✓ Portion sizes of high-carbohydrate foods, for a carbohydrate counting diet
- ✓ Consistency of foods and liquids for specific dysphagia diets
- ✓ Special adjustments for diets with multiple restrictions
- ✓ Adjustments to incorporate a standing order, such as the addition of a liquid nutritional supplement to meals.

What happens if the client does not request enough food on a selective menu? What if the client selects food that is not on his/her diet? Foodservice staff should be trained to address a client's diet when they drop off the menu, e.g. "Good morning Mrs. Smith; I know that you are on a sodium restricted diet and here are your menu selections for today." This helps remind the client of their diet and sets the stage for their menu choices. If they see that the client has not selected very much food, the foodservice staff might say, "Oh, Mrs. Smith, our roast chicken is very tender and moist today; may I add that to your selection?" If the client insists on selecting something that is not on their menu, such as bacon on a salt restricted diet, gently remind the client that their diet does not allow them to have bacon. Always treat the client with respect and respond in such a way that they don't become defensive.

On a **selective menu**, there may also be items a client writes in as a special request. How this is handled depends on the facility policy. In general, health

Figure 1.8 **Sample Selective Menu with Carbohydrate Count**

Room Number: ______ Pt. Name: ____________________ Diet Order: __________

DOB: __________ Meal: **B** **L** **D** Time if advance: __________ Total Carb Choices: __________

Breakfast	Cereals	Fruits/Yogurt	Bakery/Breads
• Scrambled eggs • Egg beaters • Pancake = **1** • Waffle = **4** • Bacon • Sausage link	• Oatmeal: ½ cup = **1** • Malt O Meal: ½ cup = **1** • Cream of Wheat: ½ cup = **1** • Bran Flakes: 1 box = **1** • Cherrios: 1 box = **1** • Cornflakes: 1 box = **1** • Frosted Flakes: 1 box = **1** • Fruit Loops: 1 box = **2** • Raisin Bran: 1 box = **2** • Rice Krispies: 1 box = **1**	• Apple = **1** • Banana = **2** • Orange Slices = **1** • Fresh Fruit: ½ cup = **1** • Applesauce: ½ cup = **1** • Stewed Prunes: 4 = **1** • Flavored Yogurt: 6 oz. = **2**	• English Muffin: ½ = **1** • Muffin: small = **2**; large = **4** • White Toast: 1 slice = **1** • Bagel: ½ = **2** • Coffeecake: 1 piece = **6** • Dinner Roll: 1 = **1** • White Bread: 1 slice = **1**
Entrees	**Soups**	**Sides**	**Salads**
• Roast Turkey • Baked Chicken • Roast Beef • Chef Salad = **1** • Taco Salad: 1 pkg. = **1** • Cafe Special (Noon M-F) • Ham	• Chicken Noodle: 1 cup = **1** • Tomato: 1 cup = **1** • Cream of Broccoli: 1 cup = **1** • Chili: 1 cup = **1** • Crackers: 3 = **1** • LS Tomato: 1 cup = **1** • LS Chicken Noodle: 1 cup = **1** • LS Vegetable: 1 cup = **1** • LS Crackers: 3 = **1**	• Mashed Potatoes: ½ cup = **1** • Baked Potato: ½ = **1** • Rice: ⅓ cup = **1** • Carrots or Peas: ½ cup = **1** • Corn: ½ cup = **1** • Green Beans: ½ cup = **0** • Broccoli/Cauliflower: ½ cup = **0** • Gravy: regular or large • Baked Beans: ½ cup = **1.5**	• Tossed • Dressing • Coleslaw • Cottage Cheese • Potato Salad: ½ cup = **1** • Pasta Salad: ½ cup = **1**
Sandwiches	**Desserts**	**Beverages**	**Milk/Juices**
• White, Whole Wheat, Bun* • Hamburger • Cheeseburger • Sliced Meat • Turkey, Ham, Chicken: ⅓ cup = **1** • Grilled Cheese • Grilled Chicken • Ham and Cheese • Ham (hot, cold) • Grilled Ham & Cheese • Tuna salad, Egg salad • Ham salad **Each bread =* ***1****, Bun =* ***2***	• Angel food cake: 1 piece = **1** • Pie: 1 piece = **3** • Ice cream: ½ cup = **1** • Sherbet: ½ cup = **2** • Cake: 1 piece = **2** • Cookies: 1 = **1** • Vanilla Wafers: 5 = **1** • Pudding: 1 = **2**	• Coffee • Decaf Coffee • Black Tea • Green Tea • Decaf Tea • Iced Tea • Lemon Juice • Crystal Llght - Lemonade - Raspberry	• 2%: 1 cup = **1** • Skim 1 cup = **1** • Chocolate: 1 cup = **2** • Apple Juice: ½ cup = **1** • Cranberry Juice: ⅓ cup = **1** • Diet Cranberry Juice: 1 cup = **1** • Grape Juice: 1/3 cup = **1** • Orange Juice: ½ cup = **1** • Tomato Juice: 6 oz. = **½** • V8 Juice: 6 oz. = **½** • Prune Juice: ⅓ cup = **1** • Pineapple Juice: ⅓ cup = **1** • Hot Chocolate = **1** • SF Hot Chocolate = **½**

(Continued)

Figure 1.8 Sample Selective Menu with Carbohydrate Count *(Continued)*

Condiments*	Clear Liquids	Full Liquids
• Butter	• Apple Juice: ½ cup = **1**	• Any clear liquid items
• Margarine	• Cranberry Juice: 1/3 cup = **1**	• Orange Juice: ½ cup = **1**
• Cream Cheese	• Grape Juice: 1/3 cup = **1**	• Milk, White: 1 cup = **1**
• Light Cream Cheese	• Diet Cranberry Juice: 1 cup = **1**	• Milk, Chocolate 1 cup = **2**
• Sour Cream	• Beef Broth	• Hot Cereal: ½ cup = **1**
• Creamer	• Chicken Broth	• Cream Soup (strained)
• Non Dairy Creamer	• Plain Gelatin: 1 = **1**	• Pudding: ½ cup = **2**
• Salt	• Pop Treat: 1 = **2**	• Ice Cream: ½ cup = **1**
• Salt Substitute	• Crystal Light	• Sherbet: ½ cup = **2**
• Sugar: 3 = **1**	• Coffee/Tea	• Creamer
• Splenda, Equal, Sweet-N-Low	• Creamer Breeze: 8 oz - 54g = **3.5**	• V8 Juice: 6 oz = **½**
• Syrup: 1 = **1**		• Tomato Juice: 6 oz = **½**
• Diet Syrup		• Prune Juice: 1/3 cup = **1**
• Jelly: 1 = **1**		• Pineapple Juice: 1/3 cup = **1**
• Pepper		• Boost: 8 oz - 41g = **~ 3**
• Mrs. Dash		
• Catsup		
• Mustard		
• Mayonnaise		
• Peanut butter		
** Condiments are okay: salt, sugar, Equal, Splenda, Sweet-N-Low, syrup, diet syrup. NOT PEPPER*		

Source: Southwest Health Center, Platteville WI, 2010. Used with permission.

facilities attempt to honor write-in requests as practical. Many facilities develop a standardized list of write-in options to provide greater choice for clients.

A **nonselective menu** is one in which clients do not have the opportunity to make choices for main dishes. Instead, they receive a standard, predefined menu. This is more common in a group dining experience such as a nursing home or assisted living. Even with a nonselective menu, you can focus on the clients by following their individualized food preferences with appropriate substitutions. You may be able to work with the medical staff to implement more liberalized diets so that all clients receive the general diet except for texture modifications.

In a nonselective menu system, it is also important to review and modify standard menu choices to accommodate specific diet orders. If your facility has implemented a liberalized diet, there may be very few diet orders, other than texture modifications. You will still want to follow individual food preferences, which may mean substituting a food item. Menu substitutions must be of equal nutritional value. For instance, if someone doesn't like cabbage, the substitute should be a food that replaces the vitamin C, such as tomatoes. Since menus are planned to incorporate color, try to replace a food with a similar or additional color. Your facility should have a list of approved substitutes

Selective Menu
One in which clients have the opportunity to make choices or selections in advance of or immediately prior to meal service

Nonselective Menu
One in which clients do not have the opportunity to make choices for main dishes

Figure 1.9 Food Substitutions*

Food Item	Substitute Choices	Vitamin A Content (per 1/2 cup serving)	Vitamin C Content (per 1/2 cup serving)
Dark Green Vegetables	• Asparagus, boiled • Broccoli, frozen, boiled • Brussels sprouts, frozen, boiled • Green beans, canned • Green peppers, boiled • Kale (use in soups) • Mixed vegetables, frozen • Pea pods, boiled • Peas, frozen and boiled • Romaine lettuce, 1 cup	• 50 μg • 50 μg • 36 μg • 129 μg • 13 μg • 260 μg • 195 μg • 43 μg • 84 μg • 163 μg	• 7 μg • 50 mg • 35 mg • 4 mg • 60 mg • 16 mg • 3 mg • 38 mg • 8 mg • 14 mg
Bright Orange Vegetables	• Carrots, sliced, boiled • Sweet potatoes, boiled and mashed • Winter squash, baked	• 671 μg • 1000 μg • 268 μg	• 2.8 mg • 21 mg • 10 mg
White Vegetables	• Cabbage, boiled • Celery • Parsnips • Rutabaga • Turnips • Wax Beans	• 11 μg • 13 μg • 0 • 0 • 0 • 7 μg	• 30 mg • 2 mg • 10 mg • 16 • 9 mg • 3 mg
Red Vegetables	• Beets • Tomatoes, fresh, diced	• 1 μg • 38 μg	• 3 mg • 11 mg

* *Note: Vegetables are often the foods that clients will have an aversion to. Remember that substitutions have to be equivalent in nutritional value so choose another vegetable (s) that is roughly equivalent to the content of the leader nutrients, vitamin A and vitamin C*

for your menu cycle. When making substitutions, always document the substitution and keep a record. This helps to prove during surveys that you are meeting client needs and preferences. See Figure 1.9 for food substitution choices.

Putting It Into Practice: 6

What would be an appropriate substitute if a client does not like broccoli?

(Check your answer at the end of this Chapter)

Legal Implications

Not only do you want to check meal service for food quality, portion size, diet accuracy, and productivity to help satisfy your clients, you also want to monitor this for legal reasons. CMS (Centers for Medicare & Medicaid Services) is a federal agency that administers the Medicare programs and monitors the Medicaid programs offered by each state. All healthcare facilities also have mandatory state licensing requirements. CMS provides investigative protocols

Figure 1.10 CMS Regulations

Frequency of Meals

1. Are staff preparing, serving, and assisting with dining in the scheduled time frames?

   ○ Yes ○ No F353, F362

2. Does the facility provide meals that are no greater than 14 hours between the evening meal and breakfast (or 16 hours with approval of a resident group and provision of a substantial evening snack)?

   ○ Yes ○ No F368

Meal Substitutes

16. Are meal substitutes offered when foods are refused?

   ○ Yes ○ No F366

19. Does the facility serve the meals in an attractive manner (foods not combined together, variety of textures/colors)?

   ○ Yes ○ No F364

Liquids at Mealtimes

20. Does the facility provide the residents with insufficient liquids and provide assistance when needed?

   ○ Yes ○ No F327

If question 20 is marked "No," conduct staff interview(s) for additional information to determine staff awareness of the need for maintaining adequate fluid intake:

- Were liquids provided?
- Were liquids within the resident's reach?
- Were the residents encouraged (or reminded) to consume liquids?
- When residents refuse liquids offered, does staff offer different beverages and/or foods with high fluid content (e.g., soup or broth, ice cream)?
- Are residents assisted with their liquids as needed (e.g., cued to drink, handed glasses, offered a variety of fluids)?

that provide guidance for the surveyors. CMS guidelines use "F-Tag" numbers to identify specific guidance for long-term care. Regulations cover all areas of a healthcare facility, including the following examples that are specific to checking meal service. These are questions the surveyors will be checking during a survey. Note the F-Tag numbers in Figure 1.10. Check with your administrator to review the regulations that cover foodservice. Make sure you and your staff are aware of all regulations and their implications for meal service.

The Role of the Certified Dietary Manager in Person-Directed Dining

"Person-directed care" is a philosophy that encourages both older adults and their caregivers to express choice and practice self-determination in meaningful ways at every level of daily life. Values that are essential to this philosophy include choice, dignity, respect, self-determination, and purposeful living. These values are also at the core of desirable medical care and are embraced by many medical providers. Yet practices that conflict with these principles are common in the long-term care setting. Examples include waking residents at times that are determined by staff convenience, modifying residents' diets without discussion, and inflexible mealtimes and medication pass times. In addition, care plans may be created without truly understanding a resident, their history or previous occupation, their recreational and personal preferences, wishes regarding lifesustaining treatment, and other likes and dislikes.[1]

(Continued...)

The Role of the Certified Dietary Manager in Person-Directed Dining *(Continued)*

The discipline of geriatrics emphasizes medical care in the proper context, where there may not be a right or wrong decision, but rather a weighing of the impact on quality of life, potential for decline, and personal preferences. Advocacy groups such as the Pioneer Network promote person-directed care in the long-term care setting.[2] In addition, alternative approaches to nursing home care have become more prevalent over the past decade. Examples include the Eden Alternative, the Green House Project, the Planetree Model, and the Wellspring Model.

The American Dietetic Association's Position Papers on Liberalizing the Diet[3] and Individualized Nutrition Approaches for Older Adults[4] have supported these concepts. Many Certified Dietary Managers (CDMs) have embraced the application of these philosophies and assisted their facilities in providing residents with more choice in their care.

Initially, the federal OBRA '87 regulations and accompanying survey process were intended to ensure that residents were provided dignity, rights, and self determination in their care. Over the years, these dining rights (mainly identified as the right to have food preferences honored) were supported if they did not interfere with what was perceived as regulatory compliance with all the other nutrition and dietary requirements. Facilities became more and more institutionalized as they focused on ensuring "good dietary/nutrition care." Surveyors were evaluating facilities based on these nutrition and dietary regulatory requirements.

Physicians ordered the therapeutic diet restrictions that had been assessed or recommended for a resident's diagnosis or medical needs. Kitchen tray lines operated like clockwork to provide resident trays with exact portions of a planned menu and modified diets, and only the acceptable condiments. Trays were sent to dining rooms to be placed before residents, usually without place settings being removed from the tray. Staff schedules revolved around getting residents ready for mealtimes (bacon and eggs or breakfast menu at 7 a.m., lunch at noon, and dinner at 5 p.m.). Mealtimes were planned for staff convenience (all trays needed to be back before the dishwasher clocked out) and to meet the stated regulatory requirement (F-Tag 368: No greater than 14 hours could elapse between the evening meal and the breakfast meal). An evening snack was required to be offered (hs snack usually offered at 8 p.m., then lights out). Families often brought in food for a specific family member, but it could not be shared. Residents were never invited to staff potlucks—though residents could smell the aromas of the event—as these were potentially unsafe food preparations and transport that did not have the trained dietary staff supervision.

Greater emphasis on resident rights and choice was emphasized in the revision of the guidance to surveyors of the Quality of Life tags in June 2009. The Centers for Medicare & Medicaid Services (CMS) revised the State Operations Manual, Appendix PP—Guidance to Surveyors for Long Term Care Facilities as it relates to several federal tags concerning quality of life and environment. Noteworthy changes to the interpretive guideline for F-Tag 242 (Self-Determination and Participation) included the statement:

> *"Residents have the right to have a choice over their schedules, consistent with their interests, assessments, and plans of care. Choice over "schedules" includes (but is not limited to) choices over the schedules that are important to the resident, such as daily waking, eating, bathing, and the time for going to bed at night. Residents have the right to choose health care schedules consistent with their interests and preferences, and the facility should gather this information in order to be proactive in assisting residents to fulfill their choices."*[5]

F-Tag 325 (Maintaining Nutritional Status) emphasizes the requirement to consider the resident's preferences in determining if a therapeutic diet or restriction is to be ordered. The revision of September 2008 states:

(Continued...)

The Role of the Certified Dietary Manager in Person-Directed Dining *(Continued)*

> *The intent of this requirement is that the resident maintains, to the extent possible, acceptable parameters of nutritional status and that the facility: Provides a therapeutic diet that takes into account the resident's clinical condition, and preferences, when there is a nutritional indication.*[5]

In May 2009, a CMS memo on Food Procurement and Guidance was provided to facilities. It clarified the following:

- That residents have the right to choose to accept food from visitors, family, friends, or other guests according to their rights to make choices of self determination.
- That these non-facility foods are not subject to regulatory requirements of F-Tag 371 (Sanitation & Food Safety).
- The responsibilities of the facility in providing food safety information to family/staff and the safe handling of visitor foods once it is in the facility.[6]

Concerns

Identifying the proper balance between medical complexity—which may require medications, modifications, and restrictions—and allowing for personal choice, is the essence of good geriatric medicine. Individualized care should seek to understand the entire person, to focus attention on the medical, functional, and psychosocial aspects of the resident. The interdisciplinary team (IDT) should consider the potential effects of proposed interventions on the resident, rather than simply the treatment or protocol's effect on a disease. For example, some residents who remain in bed until they wake on their own may develop pressure ulcers or lose weight, although most will not. Most residents will appreciate having these choices, and the team can weigh the benefits against the risks and work with the resident and/or family/POA to establish an effective individualized plan of care.[1]

An elder's right to have a liberalized diet, or even the elimination of caloric and other dietary restrictions, has slowly been embraced to enhance quality of life. But many dietitians and CDMs, along with the interdisciplinary team, resist the elder's right to have an informed refusal of an ordered diet (texture modified or tube feeding) that might put them at aspiration and choking risk. Often this is based on the long held, preconceived notion that federal regulatory requirements (and possibility of a deficiency finding) are for safety first, and quality of life decisions take a second seat after that. It is also based upon years of not informing the resident that these choices were his/her rights, and not including the resident's voice or preference in the dietary planning and decision making. Yet, the F-Tag 151 federal requirement states its intent regarding the facility's responsibilities toward rights:

> *"Exercising rights means that residents have autonomy and choice, to the maximum extent possible, about how they wish to live their everyday lives and receive care." This includes the right of refusal of an ordered medical therapy or diet. The surveyor is to "Pay close attention to resident or staff remarks and staff behavior that may represent deliberate actions to promote or to limit a resident's autonomy or choice."*

Each facility must answer the questions: How is the resident informed about dietary/dining rights? Does the resident have a voice or is it limited? Is there educating and informing the resident about alternatives and consequences of choices? Is there a mutually agreed-upon plan recognizing the resident's choice? Is there adequate resident support and monitoring once that informed refusal is made? Remember the challenges when there were federal mandates for removing physical and chemical restraints for a resident's quality of life? There will always be safety issues and concerns. We are facing some of the same challenges in supporting a resident's informed refusal and right of choice.[7]

(Continued...)

The Role of the Certified Dietary Manager in Person-Directed Dining *(Continued)*

In 2010, CMS/Pioneer Network held their second cosponsored national symposium, Creating Home II National Symposium on Culture Change and the Food and Dining Requirements.[8] Please see symposium topics and their pdf files in the Bibliography reference at the end of this paper. Two of the numerous recommendations for future consideration were:

- National stakeholder workgroup develop guidelines for clinical best practice for individualization in long-term care living to provide regulatory overview and interpretive protocol and investigative guidance, and prepare related education materials to facilitate implementation.
- Each profession serving elders in long-term care develop and disseminate standards of practice for their professional accountability that addresses proper training, competency assessment, and their role as an active advocate for resident rights and resident quality of life from a wellness perspective, in addition to quality of care from a medical perspective.

These recommendations were acted upon, and in 2011 the national stakeholder groups (including Dietary Managers Association) participated in developing and agreeing on new individualized standards of practice moving away from traditional diagnosis-focused treatment to individualized care supportive of self-directed living. (Anticipated out in fall 2011.)

The Certified Dietary Manager can have an effective role in ensuring resident rights, choice, and self determination. The CDM is often the first responder in interviewing residents, gathering appropriate information, informing residents of their rights, and in ongoing reevaluation of their nutrition/dining status. The CDM can be an effective collaborator with the dietitian and IDT to implement person-directed dining. DIETARY MANAGER magazine has provided many articles on resident-directed dining, including an article titled, "Your Role in Ensuring Culture Change in Dining and Regulatory Compliance," (June 2010) that defined the role of the CDM and a review of the CMS/Pioneer Network Symposium topics.[9] As best practices and new standards of practice for resident-directed dining are identified, the CDM is in a pivotal role to help implement them.

Competency

Dietary Managers Association supports the philosophy of person-directed dining and believes that it can promote improved quality of life for long-term care residents. The Certified Dietary Manager has an essential role in promoting this individualized nutrition/dining care, as well as helping to ensure quality of life and quality of care.

A Certified Dietary Manager, Certified Food Protection Professional (CDM, CFPP) has passed a nationally-recognized credentialing exam offered by the Certifying Board for Dietary Managers. Continuing education is required to maintain these credentials. The exam is written by content experts, and administered by The American College Testing Program (ACT). The CDM, CFPP credentials indicate that these individuals have the training and experience to competently perform the responsibilities of a dietary manager. CDM, CFPPs work together with registered dietitians to provide quality nutritional care for clients, and perform the following tasks on a regular basis: (CDM, CFPP Scope of Practice)

- Conduct routine client nutritional screening which includes food/fluid intake information
- Calculate nutrient intake
- Identify nutrition concerns and make appropriate referrals
- Implement diet plans and physicians' diet orders using appropriate modifications
- Utilize standard nutrition care procedures

(Continued...)

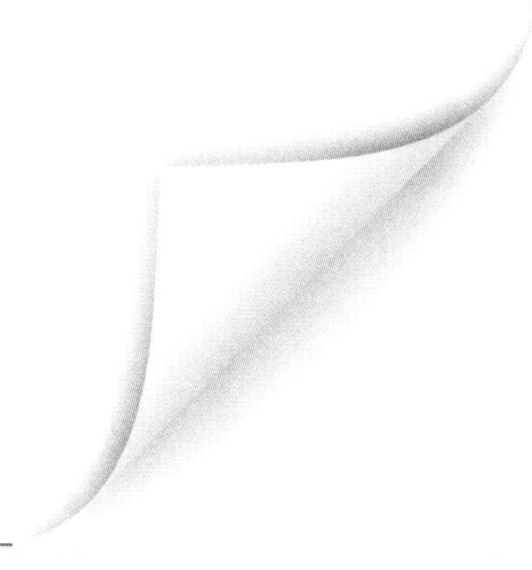

The Role of the Certified Dietary Manager in Person-Directed Dining *(Continued)*

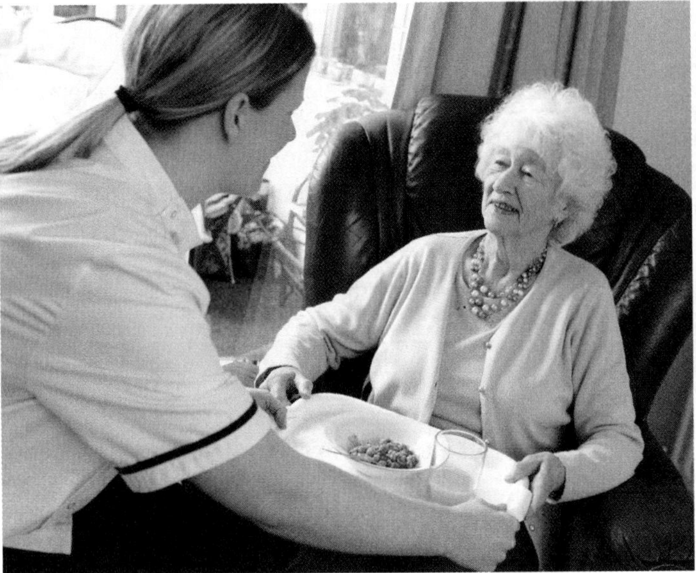

"An Elder's right to have a liberalized diet, or even the elimination of caloric and other dietary restrictions, has slowly been embraced to enhance quality of life. But many dietitians and CDMs, along with the interdisciplinary team, resist the elder's right to have an informed refusal of an ordered diet..."

- Document nutritional screening data in the medical record
- Review intake records, do visual meal rounds, and document food intake
- Participate in client care conferences
- Provide clients with basic nutrition education[10]

The Certifying Board for Dietary Managers believes it is in the best interests of the profession and the public it serves that a Code of Ethics provides guidance to Certified Dietary Managers in their professional practice and conduct. Following is an excerpt from the CDM Code of Ethics:

- The Certified Dietary Manager practices dietary management based on professional principles
- The Certified Dietary Manager assumes responsibility and accountability for personal and professional competence in practice
- The Certified Dietary Manager exercises professional judgment within the limits of his/her qualifications and seeks counsel or makes referrals as appropriate
- The Certified Dietary Manager provides sufficient information to enable clients to make their own informed decisions.[11]

The CDM who works in long-term care is expected to seek continuing education and information in order to implement the best practices and recognized standards of practice for elder nutrition care and person-directed dining.

Summary

Person-directed dining promotes resident choice and self-determination in ways that are meaningful to the resident and, hence, their quality of life. The Certified Dietary Manager, in collaboration with the dietitian and the interdisciplinary team, has an essential role both in facilitating this process, as well as in monitoring it for desired outcomes.

The Role of the Certified Dietary Manager in Person-Directed Dining *(Continued)*

Task Statements for the Certified Dietary Manager

1. Empowers and honors the resident and quality of life first and foremost by getting to know the resident, listening to the resident's preferences/goals in dining, and informing the resident of dining rights.
2. Builds an ongoing relationship with the resident that includes quality of life markers such as satisfaction with food, mealtime service, level of control, and independence.
3. Collaborates with the dietitian, other interdisciplinary team (IDT) members, and the family/POA or surrogate decision makers to create a person-directed environment and maximize resident choice in dining, quality of life, and quality of care.
4. Recognizes that all dining decisions default to the resident, works toward removing traditional or institutional decision making, and implements creative, effective solutions based on person-directed decision making.
5. Encourages active resident participation in changing the language of nutrition care plans away from the problem-goals-approaches format, to promoting the incorporation of resident preferences and goals into development of an individualized plan of care.
6. Collaborates with the dietitian and other IDT members to develop, implement, and review policies and procedures that ensure residents offered dining choices that promote dignity and self determination (e.g., choices regarding waking times and breakfast dining, evening snack times, availability of preferred food between meals, liberalizing diets, discussions of risk/benefits in making informed choices/refusal of therapeutic diets).
7. Participates in orienting, training, and monitoring staff in promoting individualized dining care.
8. Participates in maintaining and continually improving the quality of care (e.g., helps develop quality assessment and assurance projects that monitor the success of person-directed dining approaches).
9. Continues to seek information in order to implement the best practices and recognized standards of practice for elder nutrition care and person-directed dining.
10. Ensures regulatory compliance for a resident's dignity, rights, and self determination in dining areas, as well as supports the maintenance of nutrition markers, food safety, and other dietary requirements.

BIBLIOGRAHY

1. The Role of the Medical Director in Person-Directed Care, White Paper G10, March 2010, http://www.amda.com/governance/whitepapers/G10.cfm
2. About Us. Pioneer Network Website, http://www.pioneernetwork.net/AboutUs/ Accessed February 2011
3. American Dietetic Association's Position Paper Liberalization of the Diet Prescription Improves Quality of Life for Older Adults in Long-Term Care 2005, http://www.eatright.org/About/Content.aspx?id=8373
4. American Dietetic Association's Position Paper and Practice Paper Individualized Nutrition Approaches for Older Adults in Health Care Communities 2010, http://www.eatright.org/About/Content.aspx?id=7181
5. State Operations Manual for LTC Facilities, Appendix PP, F-Tag 242 Self Determination (June 2009 Guidance) & F-Tag 325 Nutrition (September 2008 Guidance) Accessed February 2011, www.cms.hhs.gov>manuals(online)>100-07 SOM>Appendix PP

The Role of the Certified Dietary Manager in Person-Directed Dining *(Continued)*

6. CMS Memo SC 09-39 on Food Procurement, www.cms.hhs.gov/SurveyCertificationGenInfo/downloads/SCLetter09_39.pdf
7. Handy, Linda. Culture Change in Dining and Regulatory Compliance DMA Webinar, www.DMAonline.org 2011
8. Creating Home II National Symposium on Culture Change and Dining Requirements, sponsored by CMS and the Pioneer Network, February 2010 Background paper: www.pioneernetwork.net> Conferences>Creating Home II: Dining* (see Symposium Topics at right.)
9. Your Role in Ensuring Culture Change in Dining and Regulatory Compliance by Linda Handy, MS, RD, DIETARY MANAGER Magazine, June 2010 http://www.DMAonline.org/Members/Articles/2010_06_cultureChange.pdf
10. Certified Dietary Manager Scope of Practice, http://www.DMAonline.org/Training/CDM_CFPP.shtml
11. Certified Dietary Manager Code of Ethics, http://www.DMAonline.org/Docs/codeEthics.pdf

CMS/Pioneer Network Symposium Topics:

The Food and Dining Side of the Culture Change Movement: Identifying Barriers and Potential Solutions to Furthering Innovation in Nursing Homes by Carmen Bowman, MHS, http://www.pioneernetwork.net/Data/Documents/dining%20symposium%20background%20paper%201-28-10.pdf

Food for Thought: The Missing Link Between Dining and Positive Outcomes by Dr. Judah Ronch, PhD, Interim Dean of the Erickson School, http://www.pioneernetwork.net/Data/Documents/CreatingHomeOnline/Paper-Ronch.pdf

Survey Interpretation of the Regulations by Linda Handy, MS, RD, Consultant, Retired Specialty/Trainer Surveyor CDPH, http://www.pioneernetwork.net/Data/Documents/CreatingHomeOnline/Paper-Handy.pdf

The Role of the Physician Order by Matthew Wayne, MD, CMD, Medical Director University Hospital Health System Senior Services, Geriatric Services Southwest General Hospital, University Hospital Foley ElderHealth Center, Legacy Health Care and Provider Services, Karyn Leible, MD, CMD, Chief Clinical Officer for Pinon Management and Vice President for the American Medical Directors Association, http://www.pioneernetwork.net/Data/Documents/CreatingHomeOnline/Paper-WayneandLeible.pdf

The Deep-Seated Issue of Choice by Linda Bump, MPH, RD, LNHA, Culture Change Consultant and Trainer, http://www.pioneernetwork.net/Data/Documents/CreatingHomeOnline/Paper-Bump.pdf

Outcomes of Choice in Dining—Home-Style Dining Interventions in Nursing Homes: Implications for Practice by Robin Remsburg, PhD, GCNS, FAAN, Director, School of Nursing, and Associate Dean, College of Health and Human Services, George Mason University, http://www.pioneernetwork.net/Data/Documents/CreatingHomeOnline/Paper-Remsburg.pdf

Food, Pharmacy and Culture Change: A Recipe for Success by Denise Hyde, Pharm.D., RP, Community Builder Eden Alternative Inc., http://www.pioneernetwork.net/Data/Documents/CreatingHomeOnline/Paper-HydeandOgden.pdf

Enhancing the Quality of Nursing Home Dining Assistance: New Regulations and Practice Implications by Rosanna Bertrand, PhD, Abt Associates Inc., Sandra Simmons, PhD, Vanderbilt University, Center for Quality Aging, http://www.pioneernetwork.net/Data/Documents/CreatingHomeOnline/Paper-SimmonsandBertrand.pdf

The Food Code and CDC Infection Control Guidelines (only webinars, no papers), Glenda Lewis, MSPH, FDA Office of Food Safety, Nimalie Stone, MD, MS, Centers for Disease Control

END OF CHAPTER

Putting It Into Practice Questions & Answers

1. List at least three steps you would take to implement a culture change in your facility.

   A. *1. Interview your clients*
   2. Review/research resources
   3. Decide what your facility can/will offer for a culture change in dining
   4. Meet with other departments
   5. Refine ideas
   6. Communicate, communicate, communicate, train

2. When working in a large hospital, you decide that food will be prepared in a central kitchen and then shipped in bulk to the other wings/floors to reheat and serve. What type of meal delivery system is this?

   A. *Decentralized because food is shipped in bulk for final preparation away from the central kitchen.*

3. You have heard from your hospital director that clients are complaining about receiving cold meals when their trays arrive. Your staffing plan is to have the nursing staff deliver the trays to the room. What are some steps you should take to resolve this problem?

   A. *1. First, use a test tray to test the temperature of the food as it leaves the kitchen and when it arrives to the client. Observe the process of delivery.*
   2. If the food was proper temperature when it left foodservice, was delayed by nursing staff, and arrived to the client below temperature, ask to meet with the Director of Nursing to work together in solving the problem.

4. You are managing a school foodservice program that serves 558 meals or meal equivalents and you had 40 hours of paid labor for the day. How many meals per labor hour did you have?

   A. *Divide 558 by 40 = 13.95 or 14. You can measure this index by the day, week, month, or year depending upon the data that you gathered. Once you have the index calculated, it becomes a benchmark to compare to other schools or track within your facility.*

5. What is the tray accuracy rate in the following example? You are reviewing the trayline for diet accuracy, color, and food temperature. Your staff prepared 102 trays. There was a total of 1000 items served with a total of 26 errors.

   A. *1. To determine accuracy rate, subtract the number of errors from the total number of items served: 1000 – 26 = 974*
   2. Then divide the number of items served correctly (988) by the total number of items (1000) = .974 or 97%
   3. Compare this number to your facility standard or desired goal.

6. What would be an appropriate substitute if a client does not like broccoli?

   A. *Green beans, asparagus, mixed vegetables with peas, beans and corn.*

Manage the Preparation and Service of Special Nourishments and Supplemental Feedings

Overview and Objectives

A large percentage of clients receive some type of between-meal supplements. Certified Dietary Managers have to be prepared to manage the preparation and service of these supplements as well as manage the burgeoning cost of supplements.

After completing this chapter, you should be able to:

- ✓ Identify clients who need nourishments or supplemental feeding
- ✓ Define schedules/needs for special food preparation/foodservice
- ✓ Monitor implementation of special foodservices
- ✓ Identify appropriate supplemental products
- ✓ Monitor cost of supplements
- ✓ Monitor the passing of nourishments and supplements
- ✓ Use a system to audit the passing of nourishments or supplements

Nutritional Support

The dual role of meeting nutritional needs and satisfying the personal menu requests of your clients is a challenge. Protein and calorie malnutrition is fairly prevalent today and you will have clients who need additional nutrition support. The diet order will be the tool you use to identify clients who need nourishments or supplemental feedings. You may also gather information for the Registered Dietitian (RD) on clients in poor nutritional status or with high nutrient needs. These clients are often in need of concentrated sources of nutrition. **Nutrition support** is a general term describing providing foods and liquids to improve nutrition status and support good medicine.

Generally, there are two approaches to providing added protein and calories. One is to use conventional foods, selecting those that are particularly nutrient-dense. Another is to add commercial nutritional supplements to menus. Each has its pros and cons. Conventional foods have the advantage of familiarity, and are often readily accepted by clients. To make effective dietary recommendations, it is important to complete a diet history and discuss food tastes, preferences, and tolerances with a client. This helps to identify good candidates for menu enhancements. See Figure 2.1 for menu planning techniques for nutrition support.

Figure 2.1 Menu Planning Techniques for Nutrition Support

- Use margarine liberally on bread, toast, vegetables, rice, pasta, and in sandwiches.
- Add gravies or sauces to entrees and side dishes.
- Add sour cream to potatoes, casseroles, and fruits.
- Use real whipped cream on top of desserts and fruits.
- Add 2 tablespoons dried milk powder to each cup of whole milk. Use for drinking and when making cream soups, hot cereal, pudding, custard, hot chocolate, mashed potatoes, casseroles, milkshakes, and creamed dishes.
- Add dried milk powder to scrambled eggs, gravies, casseroles, meatloaf, and meatballs.
- Spread peanut butter or other nut butters on toast or English muffins, on crackers and cookies, and on apple slices and celery sticks.
- Add cheese to sandwiches, scrambled eggs, casseroles, vegetables, and sauces.
- Add chopped eggs and diced or ground meat to salads, sauces, casseroles, and sandwiches.
- Use mayonnaise liberally on sandwiches.
- Choose desserts such as custard, bread pudding, rice pudding, and fruited yogurt. Serve with real whipped cream or ice cream.
- Offer whole milk products or cream in place of skim milk, or, offer milkshakes as beverages.
- Cook cream soups or hot cereal with whole milk; add margarine or butter.
- Serve six small meals rather than three large ones.
- Add ice cream to enteral products as a milkshake.
- Use enteral pudding supplements as a topping for cake desserts.
- Add olive oil or flavored oils to potatoes and vegetables.

Enteral nutrition refers to the feeding, by mouth or by tube, of formulas that contain essential nutrients. It requires that the gastrointestinal tract be functioning. Specialized commercial products exist for providing nutrition support. A standard enteral formula provides one calorie per milliliter (ml). (About 240 ml equals one cup.) Other enteral formulas may provide 1.2, 1.5 or 2 cal/ml. A complete enteral product contains a nutritional balance of protein, carbohydrates, fat, vitamins, and minerals. Some are flavored so they can be taken orally.

Incomplete nutritional supplements offer another way to boost nutritional intake. For example, a product of carbohydrate powder with minimal flavor can be stirred into beverages, soups, applesauce, and other foods to add almost invisible calories. Another commercial product is protein powder used to boost protein content when added to mashed potatoes, hot cereal, soup, or other products.

A third type of nutrition support product you might be purchasing are the formulas for **parenteral nutrition.** Parenteral nutrition is the administration of simple essential nutrients into a vein. Parenteral solutions may contain dextrose, lipids, amino acids, electrolytes, vitamins, and trace elements. They may be used in cases where the client's gastrointestinal tract is no longer able to digest and absorb food properly; to maintain fluid and electrolyte balance both

Glossary

Nutrition Support
General term describing providing foods and liquids to improve nutritional status

Enteral Nutrition
Supplemental feeding, by mouth or by tube, of formulas or food that contain essential nutrients

Parenteral Nutrition
Administration of simple essential nutrients into a vein

before and after surgery; or when a client is not receiving enough nourishment by other feeding methods.

Implementation of Special Nourishments and Supplemental Feedings

Work with your Registered Dietitian to select special nourishments and supplemental feedings. In selecting an enteral product for oral or tube feeding, a nutrition caregiver should consider the following:

- ✓ taste, texture, and individual client acceptance
- ✓ product concentration
- ✓ the need for nutritionally complete formulation
- ✓ needs for modification in carbohydrate, fat, or protein composition
- ✓ tolerance of lactose
- ✓ location of the feeding tube if tube fed
- ✓ whether or not to include fiber
- ✓ cost

Advantages and Disadvantages to Commercial Supplements for your own Facility

Does your staff have the expertise and/or the time to prepare your own supplements and nourishments? Perhaps you can combine commercial products with conventional foods. For example, a client who does not enjoy a liquid supplement may enjoy a milkshake made from the supplement plus ice cream. Instead of purchasing protein powder, consider adding Non Fat Dry Milk (NFDM) to mashed potatoes, soups, and desserts. For your clients who prefer it—or for certain dysphagia diets—specialized nutritional pudding products represent another choice. Pudding supplements that are nutritionally similar to liquid products are available. A garnish of real whipped cream, chocolate shavings, or fruits may also make these products more appealing.

Putting It Into Practice: 1

You are working with the Interdisciplinary Team in the nutrition care process for a client who needs additional nourishment. In spite of being served the nourishment three times a day, she has not gained the desired weight. Upon inquiry, you find that she doesn't like the taste of the nourishment. What steps would you take to help resolve this concern?

(Check your answer at the end of this chapter)

Some disadvantages to commercial supplements include acceptance and cost. Client acceptance may vary, as clients may perceive a flavor described as "medicinal" or tasting "like vitamin supplements." On the other hand, these products are available in a variety of flavors and textures that may help to overcome this drawback. When offering commercial supplements, it is important to allow a client to taste several products and choose what seems most enjoyable. Some facilities have a client taste panel to help determine what supplements the foodservice department purchases.

Blenderized whole foods are now being suggested as an alternative to commercial enteral products. Anecdotal evidence in one Milwaukee case showed increased growth for an infant using blenderized whole foods.

The cost of nutrition supplements can range from almost "at cost" to being outrageously expensive. As the Certified Dietary Manager, you may be expected to manage these costs as part of your food costs. Some facilities purchase their supplements through the pharmacy and the cost is not allocated to dietary. In some cases tube feedings are paid for by nursing and oral feedings by

foodservice. Whatever purchasing policy your facility has, remember cost cannot be the only consideration; it is just one of them.

Nourishment Delivery Systems

Many of the liquid supplements are better accepted when served very cold. If your delivery system isn't efficient, those supplements may arrive too warm and therefore, may not be consumed. When managing nutrition supplements, it is important to consider when and how they are delivered to clients.

Nearly all healthcare facilities provide an evening snack to clients. Snacks at other times of the day may be part of the routine system, or may be offered only to clients with specified dietary needs, such as a diet order for six small feedings each day, or a snack coordinated with insulin injection for a client with diabetes. Nourishments must comply with the diet order, and may be pre-assembled by an assigned staff member or team. These may be delivered as a group to each nursing station for delivery by nursing staff, or delivered directly to clients' rooms by foodservice staff.

Even in facilitiies using traditional tray service systems, a point of service or a service-on-demand approach can be used to handle between-meal and evening snack needs. In some organizations, the nursing units contain locked pantries from which nursing staff withdraw items requested by clients. In others, foodservice employees travel from room to room with a rolling cart, and offer diet-appropriate snacks. These mechanisms eliminate pre-selection and turnaround issues. They allow clients to choose what they want at the time of service, and receive personal attention to their requests. In many cases, they improve turnaround time for processing requests, and may also streamline labor requirements. Foodservice staff providing snacks on demand must be familiar with special diets and must assure that foods offered meet the diet order.

Part of your supplement system should be to give supplements between meals and not with meals unless the supplement is part of a fortified liquid diet. This is to encourage the client to eat the meal and not just drink the supplement.

Use food first as a supplement. Providing foods at meals that the client likes will encourage them to eat better. In some cases this may not be the menu of the day. If a resident wants a sandwich at every meal and they eat it, that is better than giving the meal of the day and only having a 25 percent meal completion.

Every facility will have a different variation on their nourishment delivery systems. It will be important to meet with your Interdisciplinary Team to discuss the best process for your facility. Then, develop a policy and procedure that outlines what part the foodservice department plays in this process. See Figure 2.2 for a sample policy and procedure for delivery of between-meal snacks.

An audit of your nourishment delivery systems shows that nourishments are being delivered to the floors/wings but clients are not receiving them. What are some steps you should take to address this concern?

(Check your answer at the end of this chapter)

Legal Implications

CMS (Centers for Medicare & Medicaid Services) is a federal agency that administers the Medicare programs and monitors the Medicaid programs offered by each state. All healthcare facilities also have mandatory state licensing requirements. CMS provides Investigative Protocols that provide guidance for the surveyors. CMS guidelines use "F-Tag" numbers to identify specific guidance for long-term care.

A Certified Dietary Manager is responsible for making sure that clients know what their diet is and be offered the choice of whether to receive the diet (e.g. a choice about whether to receive nourishments or tube feedings). If the client refuses a tube feeding or additional nourishments, the client, facility and Registered Dietitian collaborate to identify pertinent alternatives. Recently, during a survey, an F-tag was issued for a tube-fed client who had asked to receive food and drink by mouth. (F 151: The facility failed to address one resident's right to refuse a physician ordered treatment.) With the 2010 CMS guidelines, you have to acknowledge the following:

- ✓ Promote care in a manner and in an environment that maintains or enhances each resident's dignity and respect. CMS F-241 Interpretive Guidance: Promoting resident independence and dignity in dining
- ✓ The resident or representative has the right to make informed choices about accepting or declining care and treatment, CMS F-325

According to Linda Handy, Retired Specialty Surveyor/Trainer CDPH and RD consultant, F 322 Tube Feeding is being revised, Spring 2011. Check with your administrator to review the regulations that cover foodservice. Make sure you and your staff are aware of all regulations and their implications for meal service, including the service of nourishments and tube feedings.

Figure 2.2 **Sample Policy and Procedure for Delivery of Between-Meal Snacks**

POLICY: Between-meal feedings will be available at established intervals, upon request, or when prescribed to meet the specialized nutritional needs of the resident/patient.

DATE EFFECTIVE: ________________

DATE REVISED: ________________

DATE REVIEWED: Annually

APPROVED BY: ________________

ISSUING DEPARTMENT: Nutritional Services

APPROVE FOR USE IN: ________________

PROCEDURE:

1. A variety of nourishments/snacks is available at each Nursing Unit daily. Each Nursing Unit will order nourishments/food supplies for residents.
2. Planned nourishments are delivered to the nursing unit front desk at 10:00 a.m., 3:00 p.m. and 8:00 p.m. (HS) for nursing staff distribution.
3. Individual patient nourishments will be available when alterations in the usual feeding pattern are required due to the dietary prescription or patient need. These may be made by patient request, by nursing request, or as recommended by the Nutrition Professional (or approved designee).
4. The Nutrition Professional (or approved designee) and nursing staff will routinely refer to the nourishment intake record and MAR to determine if nourishments and supplements are being consumed and at what level. Changes will be made as needed to ensure acceptability by the resident.
5. Rotation of stock and sanitation of the nursing pantry areas is the responsibility of the respective nursing units and Nutritional Services.
6. Procedures for cleaning and care of the nursing pantry area have been developed by Nutritional Services and are posted in each pantry area.
7. All individual nourishments should be covered for transport to residents. Each is labeled with the resident's name, room number, date and time of delivery.
8. Nourishments or snacks are defined as food and/or drink singly or in combination from the kitchen that are offered between meals to all residents whose diet order allows it. These foods are from the basic food groups.
9. Nutrition Services personnel will maintain a log of residents who receive between-meal nourishments and supplements. This list will be used to prepare nourishments. Nursing staff will distribute the nourishments and record intake.
10. The Nutrition Professional will refer to the MAR to determine if supplements are being consumed at what level (i.e., percentage). The Nutrition Professional will refer to the approved facility form to determine if nourishments/snacks are being consumed and what amount.
11. If a nourishment or supplement is not being consumed, the Nutrition Professional should review the meal pattern and overall care plan approaches; visit with the resident and/or family member; and make changes to help ensure intake and acceptability by the resident as much as possible.

Source: RD411.com (used with permission)

END OF CHAPTER

Putting It Into Practice Questions & Answers

1. You are working with the Interdisciplinary Team in the nutrition care process for a client who needs additional nourishment to reach a desired weight goal. In spite of being served the nourishment three times a day, she has not gained the desired weight. Upon inquiry, you find that she doesn't like the nourishment. What steps would you take to help resolve this concern?

   A. *1. Verify that she has indeed been served the nourishments either by visiting with the client if she is cognitive or by observing the service of the nourishments.*

   2. If she has been served the nourishment and is not consuming them, visit with the client to make sure she understands why she is receiving them. Try to determine what exactly she doesn't like about the nourishment. (e.g. if it is the taste, texture, temperature, mouthfeel)

   3. Offer her a different type of nourishment such as a popsicle instead of something to drink or pudding with the meal.

   4. Follow up to make sure she is consuming the alternative.

2. An audit of your nourishment delivery systems shows that nourishments are being delivered to the floors/wings but clients are not receiving them. What are some steps you should take to address this concern?

   A. *1. Investigate where the service process is breaking down. (e.g. Is it a timing issue, a staff issue, a storage space issue?)*

   2. If needed, seek the help of members of your Interdisciplinary Team such as the Director of Nursing to help resolve the issue.

   3. Once a solution has been implemented, follow up to make sure it is working.

Implement Continuous Quality Improvement Procedures for Foodservice Department

Overview and Objectives

Quality of products and services is the aim of virtually every organization. Quality is adherence to standards, processes, and outcomes. In this chapter you will discover why a Certified Dietary Manager needs to take a proactive approach towards managing quality, and you will identify techniques for verifying quality.

After completing this chapter, you should be able to:

- ✓ Define objectives and standards for foodservice
- ✓ Implement and monitor quality indicators
- ✓ Implement necessary procedural changes
- ✓ Interpret and report to designated persons
- ✓ Implement auditing tool to determine the effectiveness of quality indicators
- ✓ Implement approaches to facilitate client's compliance with nutritional therapy

The Quality Progression

Quality initiatives in healthcare have been around for decades. Avedis Donabedian's 1966 article described ways to evaluate the quality of healthcare. He proposed a broad definition of quality and three areas in which to measure it:

- ✓ "structure-the physical and staffing characteristics of caring for patients;
- ✓ process-the method of delivery;
- ✓ outcome-the results of care."

This system is still in use today although there is greater emphasis on process and outcomes.

In the past, measuring quality meant measuring whether you were meeting certain pre-set standards. For instance, you may have a pre-set standard that all hot food leaving the kitchen be a minimum of 150°F. Your measurement would be to take the temperature of a certain percentage of hot foods prior to leaving the kitchen. Today, while that is still important, the focus is on the outcome-how many clients are satisfied that their hot food is hot? And the focus is on the process—how do you know your clients are satisfied that the food is hot, what process do you use to measure their satisfaction, and how are you addressing their dissatisfaction. The pre-set standard of measuring the temperature of hot foods as it leaves the kitchen now becomes part of the process to achieve the outcome. In 2006, Centers for Medicare and Medicaid (CMS), revised F 520 surveyor Interpretive Guidance and put forth the following definitions:

- ✓ **"Quality Assessment"** is an evaluation of a process and/or outcomes of a process to determine if a defined standard of quality is being achieved.
- ✓ **"Quality Assurance"** is the organizational structure, processes, and procedures designed to ensure that care practices are consistently applied and the facility meets or exceeds an expected standard of quality. Quality assurance includes the implementation of principles of *continuous quality improvement (CQI).*
- ✓ **"Quality Improvement (QI)"** is an ongoing interdisciplinary process that is designed to improve the delivery of services and resident outcomes.

Glossary

Quality Assessment
The evaluation of processes and/or outcomes to determine if a defined standard of quality is being achieved

Quality Assurance
Sum total of structure, processes, and procedures designed to ensure that clients feel that both food and services are excellent and the facility meets or exceeds an expected standard of quality

Quality Improvement
The ongoing process to improve the delivery of food, services, and resident outcomes

Quality Standard
Your facility's definition of what constitutes quality for a product such as food or service

Outcome
End result of work

Quality Indicator
Measures of outcomes

PDCA
Cycle of process improvement: plan, do, check, act

Quality Assurance Processes

In healthcare, there have been many names for quality assurance processes. (e.g. CQI, QI, QA, PDCA, LEAN, QAPI) Today, healthcare is realizing that quality is an essential element of organizational strategy, not a single initiative. CMS calls it QAPI (Quality Assessment and Performance Improvement). Your facility probably has some type of quality initiative. Whatever your facility calls your quality initiative, it should have these characteristics:

- ✓ Focus on clients and what they need, rather than on employees or departments and what they do.
- ✓ Be a team approach that is cross departmental
- ✓ Use and evaluate the data
- ✓ Is proactive and continuous. You don't wait for a problem to occur; you continuously look at processes and ways to improve the processes.
- ✓ Contain a performance improvement segment.

Quality initiatives use some key terminology. One term is **outcome**. An outcome is the end result of work such as the results of client interactions Using the temperature of food example from above, the outcome of serving hot food is a satisfied client. In a healthcare environment, a health outcome describes the consequences of clinical interventions. For instance, if members of the healthcare team work together to improve a client's nutritional status, what happens to that client's nutritional status is the outcome of the clinical care plan. **Quality indicators (QIs)** are measures of outcomes. According to Centers for Medicare and Medicaid Services (CMS), an indicator is "a key clinical value or quality characteristic used to measure, over time, the performance, processes, and outcomes of an organization or some component of healthcare delivery." If we look at the temperature of food example again, the quality indicator would be that a certain percentage of clients are very satisfied with their foodservice. As you can see by this definition, indicators are designed to facilitate collection and analysis of data. They are objective and measurable. A general process for implementing QA in healthcare uses two acronyms: FOCUS and PDCA.

FOCUS means:

F—Find a process to improve

O—Organize to improve a process

C—Clarify what is known

U—Understand variation

S—Select a process improvement

Once you have selected a process to improve, the next acronym relates to the plan itself. **PDCA** means:

P— Plan: Decide what you will do to improve the process. Decide what information you will collect, and how you will measure outcomes.

D— Do: Make the improvements.

C— Check: Collect and review data, and evaluate how the plan is working.

A— Act: Act on what you have learned. If you have made a successful improvement, make sure it becomes part of your policies and procedures. If not, try an alternate plan.

The Institute for Healthcare Improvement (www.ihi.org) has developed a worksheet that can help you with the Plan, Do, Check/Study, Act for performance improvement. Their tool is shown in Figure 3.1. The Medicare Quality Improvement Community (MedQIC) Web site is "a free on-line resource for quality improvement interventions and associated tools, toolkits, presentations, and links to other resources." The Website is funded by CMS to provide a site to share resources based on the CMS scope of work.

Establishing Standards and Quality Processes

Measuring quality really means assuring that your operation is meeting certain standards. These standards become the backbone of your quality processes. A **quality standard** is your facility's definition of what constitutes quality for a product (such as food) or a service. A single product or service may have a list of standards you aim to meet. For example, a quality standard for steak tenderloin might stipulate that the steak will be tender, the temperature will be 145°F or higher, and the food will be neatly presented on a plate, with a garnish.

A quality standard for cafeteria checkout might stipulate that the customer will be able to check out within three minutes, the transaction will be accurate, and the customer will receive a receipt. A quality standard for nutritional assessment might specify that an assessment will be completed within three days of admission to the facility. The same standard might also specify what types of information will be included in the assessment.

For food production, some operations use photographs to show how products should look upon completion. Along with photos, specific standards may be listed. These standards may include both qualitative specifications and food safety or Hazard Analysis Critical Control Point (HACCP) specifications.

Figure 3.1 PDSA Worksheet for Testing Change

Aim: (overall goal you wish to achieve)

Every goal will require multiple smaller tests of change

Describe your first (or next) test of change	Person responsible	When to be done	Where to be done

Plan:

List the tasks needed to set up this test of change	Person responsible	When to be done	Where to be done

Predict what will happen when the test is carried out	Measures to determine if prediction succeeds

Do: Describe what actually happened when you ran the test.

Study: Describe the measured results and how they compared to the predictions.

Act: Describe what modifications to the plan will be made for the next cycle from what you learned.

Source: Institute for Healthcare Improvement

It is not always necessary or even worthwhile to write a quality standard for everything your operation does. However, through ongoing communications with both clients and superiors, it is practical to target specific products and/or services for which to specify standards. Standards themselves may need to be revisited and revised periodically.

Once quality standards exist, you can evaluate and monitor quality. Standards also provide support to the process of training employees. In other words, every time you train an employee about what to do, you can also train the employee about what the results of the work should be. This sets up a clear expectation and provides essential direction.

Developing Foodservice Quality Control Processes

Effective quality control requires a proactive approach. In other words, rather than waiting for a complaint or a set of poor survey results to surface, a quality-oriented Certified Dietary Manager monitors and improves quality continuously.

Quality management stems from operating objectives and relates to all other aspects of the operation, including things like:

✓ Service and delivery systems
✓ Menu development
✓ Purchasing specifications
✓ Standardized recipe development
✓ Food production
✓ Scheduling of employees and tasks
✓ Employee performance standards
✓ Employee training.

Figure 3.2 illustrates the broad picture of how quality management fits into a manager's responsibilities.

In Step 1, foodservice department objectives are established. These must be in harmony with the broad purposes of the operation. In Step 2, strategies to attain objectives must be planned. In Step 3, specific operating procedures must be developed. Procedures may relate to product specifications, standardized recipes, equipment specifications, schedules, delivery procedures, and much more. Developing good initial procedures requires knowledge of foodservice operations as well as good judgment.

Figure 3.2 **Quality Management Overview**

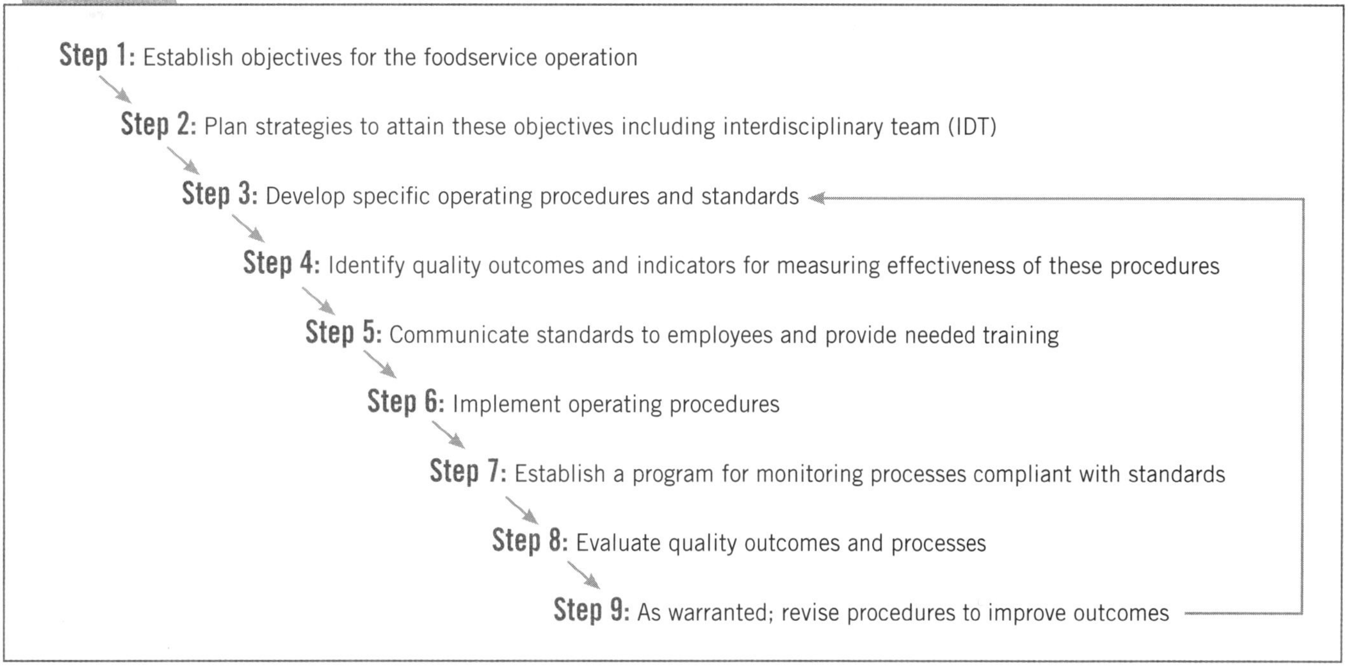

Step 1: Establish objectives for the foodservice operation
↘
Step 2: Plan strategies to attain these objectives including interdisciplinary team (IDT)
↘
Step 3: Develop specific operating procedures and standards ←
↘
Step 4: Identify quality outcomes and indicators for measuring effectiveness of these procedures
↘
Step 5: Communicate standards to employees and provide needed training
↘
Step 6: Implement operating procedures
↘
Step 7: Establish a program for monitoring processes compliant with standards
↘
Step 8: Evaluate quality outcomes and processes
↘
Step 9: As warranted; revise procedures to improve outcomes (→ back to Step 3)

In Step 4, quality standards are developed. It is helpful to clarify these before beginning a new procedure. Objectively, these standards help you define how you will know whether a procedure is effective. They give you a way to begin measuring effectiveness immediately.

Essential to the success of any quality management program is the involvement of employees. In Step 5, employees become aware of specific outcomes that you as a team need to achieve. By knowing what these outcomes are, employees can more readily help with tweaking and adjustment down the line. In addition, training at this point is critical.

After specific operating procedures have been developed, they must be implemented (Step 6). In Step 7, the Certified Dietary Manager begins to evaluate the effectiveness of foodservice services. Types of questions that will help in this evaluation include:

- ✓ How do quality results compare with the standards established?
- ✓ Did a procedure produce any unintentional or unexpected results? If so, which of these is acceptable/not acceptable?
- ✓ Where results do not meet quality standards, what is the cause (or causes)?
- ✓ What interventions will address these causes?
- ✓ Is the procedure itself sound, or does it need to be revised?

Following evaluation, a Certified Dietary Manager needs to assess any revisions or interventions that may be in order. Any intervention or procedural revision should be evaluated again. Sometimes, several rounds of interventions or revision are required to achieve intended results. In addition, involvement of employees and team-oriented quality efforts are typically most effective in raising quality of services or products.

With this big picture in mind, let's examine some of the tools a manager can use to gather information related to quality standards. These include taste panels, test trays, temperature and quality, satisfaction surveys, plate waste studies, performance standards and checklists or self audits. Performance standards will be addressed in Chapter 6.

Taste Panels

A taste panel can help determine whether a product meets the given standards. It can also help you achieve an outcome of client satisfaction with food. The people on the panel should have knowledge about food standards and the ability to distinguish flavors. When practical, it may also be appropriate to include a few actual clients in a taste panel. For example, a dining services committee composed of clients in an assisted living community may be an excellent source of panelists.

In a formal taste panel, participants rate each product using a score sheet, such as the one shown in Figure 3.3. The score sheet notes taste, odor, flavor, color, texture, and appearance of the sample product.

Figure 3.3 Product Score Sheet

Name N.S. (Person on Taste Panel) Date ______ Name of Product ______

		Extremely Poor	Very Poor	Poor	Between Poor & Fair	Fair	Between Fair & Good	Good	Very Good	Extremely Good
Taste	Sweet								✓	
	Salty									
	Bitter									
	Sour									
Odor								✓		
Flavor									✓	
Color										✓
Texture								✓		
Appearance									✓	

The tastes, such as sweet, salty, bitter, and sour, along with the smell of a food, contribute to how people experience flavor. Taste sensitivity decreases with age, increasing the need for seasoning for elderly clients.

Color is also important. Many foods have characteristic colors closely identified with certain highly acceptable qualities. For example, the desired color of an apple is the color present when the fruit is at its peak of maturity. If the color is darkened or faded, the fruit is not perceived as being high in quality. Color sometimes does not reflect quality, as in the example of oranges. They may be mature in flavor but still be green in color. Thus, color is often a subjective—but very important—evaluation.

Texture is judged by the food item's characteristic texture, which may be stringy, smooth, crisp, mushy, tough, tender, or hard. Appearance refers to the exterior, interior, and portion size in a bowl or on a plate. Factors to consider include a characteristic and/or regular shape, unbroken pieces, correct portion size, proper moistness level, and good color. Is the interior appealing in terms of texture and color? Does the portion look attractive? Does it fit the container in which it is to be served?

Figure 3.4 outlines suggested quality standards for common food products. Realize that evaluation of a product is somewhat subjective, and will reflect individual tastes and preferences. The information or feedback received through a

Figure 3.4 Suggested Quality Standards for Common Food Products

Product	Indicators of Quality
Yeast Bread	Golden brown color, symmetrical, uniform shape, rounded top, good volume, free of tunnels, moist, elastic crumb, nutlike flavor
Muffins	Golden brown color, well shaped with slightly rounded top, moist crumb, light and tender, good flavor, bumpy crust (smooth crust for cake-style muffins), free of tunnels, moist, elastic crumb, nutlike flavor
Cake	Golden brown color (except chocolate cake), smooth surface, slightly rounded top, high volume, fine grain, light but not crumbly, soft/moist texture, tender crumb, delicate sweet and well-blended flavor
Cookies	Uniform shape and color, good flavor, crisp or chewy texture (depending on type of cookie)
Pastry	Golden brown color, blistery surface, uniform and attractive edges, fits pan well, flaky or mealy texture, cuts easily, pleasant/bland flavor
Cream of Vegetable Soup	Thin white sauce base with off-white color; smooth texture that coats a spoon lightly, well blended flavor Vegetables should be finely chopped but have a shape.
Scalloped Potatoes	Potato slices uniform in size; potatoes are tender yet firm; has creamy white sauce; finely chopped onions cling to the potatoes; mild potato flavor with delicate flavor of sauce
Pasta	Cooked al denté, uniformly moist and tender to the bite, not sticky, mild starchy flavor
Oatmeal	Grains are tender, consistency is soft and forms a soft mass in the bowl; not gummy or sticky

Adapted in part from Molt, M. Food for Fifty, 13th ed. Pearson Education, Inc., 2011.

taste panel, however, is very valuable. A manager can use taste panel feedback to tweak and adjust quality of individual food products.

Several tips can help with managing food product quality. Both training programs and use of standardized recipes help an operation to produce food that is consistently high in quality. It's a good idea to interact with employees during food production, and to involve them in the evaluation process. To achieve food quality, several things must happen:

- ✓ An expectation (standard) must be established and communicated to employees.
- ✓ Employees need to be provided with products or ingredients consistent with the quality standard.
- ✓ Employees must receive proper operational support to make quality possible. This means you furnish the proper tools and equipment for the job, and schedule employees in such a way that necessary procedures and time frames are feasible.
- ✓ Before being served, the final product must be checked for quality. Work with employees if the product does not meet the standard. An effective exchange allows employees to bring problems and questions to your attention, and allows you as a manager to provide coaching for improvement.

Putting It Into Practice: 1

You observe that the muffins made for the evening meal are peaked and dark brown in color. These do not meet your quality standards. What are the steps you should take to correct this problem?

(Check your answer at the end of this chapter)

Client reactions to the final product should be shared with employees. When the product receives praise, do not hesitate to pass this recognition on to the staff members who produced the food item. Information about a product that has been overcooked or over-seasoned should also be shared. Discuss whether the equipment is at fault, the recipe is a problem, or human error played a part in the unacceptable product.

Test Trays

Periodically, it is a good practice to prepare a test tray as a way of evaluating tray service and the quality of foods as handled through a tray assembly system. Test trays can help you achieve an outcome such as client satisfaction with food. A test tray is one assembled as part of the usual process, specifically for the purpose of quality evaluation. Some managers create a test tray by inserting a "dummy" tray card or tray ticket into the stack for tray assembly. For a realistic measure, a manager often does not identify this to tray employees as a test.

One strategy in preparing test trays is to make one that will test the outer limits of quality, or the worst case that may be occurring in the process. To evaluate the outer limits of quality, some managers position a test tray as one that will be created late in the tray assembly process, and/or one traveling the greatest distance for delivery.

Give this tray of food the same treatment as other trays receive. Deliver it to the service area, and evaluate the tray. You can compare the tray to standards, asking questions such as:

- ✓ Are hot foods served at or above 135°F?
- ✓ Are cold foods served at or below 41°F?
- ✓ Are colors bright?
- ✓ Are items on the tray in the correct locations?
- ✓ Are products served accurately (according to diet order)?
- ✓ Is food palatable and enjoyable?

If "no" was the answer to any one of the questions, you can research the causes and make corrections.

Temperature and Quality

Note that temperature plays a role in quality, too, even aside from food safety issues. Temperature affects texture of some foods, and it even affects flavor. Keep in mind that smell contributes to taste. A hot food that has cooled off may give off less aroma and prove less flavorful. This may be one explanation why seniors rate temperature over flavor in defining food quality. A cold food that has warmed up can lose something, too, as with warm soda pop.

Temperature and food quality are issues throughout holding and service. For example, frozen sweet peas placed in boiling water or steamed to an internal temperature of 200°F for $1^1/_2$ minutes will be hot and tasty. They will have a dark green color and be slightly crunchy. Frozen sweet peas held on a 212°F steam table for 30 minutes will look pale green and be mushy in texture. This is one reason for batch cooking vegetables and other products that are sensitive to the holding process.

Always check the temperature of the food during preparation. Do not transfer hot food to the trayline if the product is below standard. Also check the temperature of food just before serving. Take the temperature again midway through service.

Another aspect of temperature management is the balance between food safety guidelines and food preparation guidelines. In efforts to comply with food safety requirements, employees sometimes overcook foods by bringing them to temperatures that are too high, or cooking for excessive periods of time, or both.

An example is a burger. To meet FDA Food Code recommendations, it must reach 155°F. To be safe, a standard practice is to overshoot the mark, and cook to a higher temperature. However, if the temperature goes much beyond 165°F, the burger may begin to become dry and unappealing. This is a delicate balance that requires careful planning and management. Some operations establish both minimum and maximum temperatures for certain products, especially for meats.

Satisfaction Surveys/Process Improvement

Identifying individual clients food preferences should be a continual process, and a component of clinical nutritional care in a healthcare facility. Beyond the individual care plan information or tray cards generated for healthcare clients, a manager needs to monitor trends in preferences and food acceptance. In other words, as a manager, one role is to be continually alert to the big picture. For example, if a high number of clients request a substitution for meatloaf at lunch, this may be a clue that the meatloaf suffers a quality issue, or that the menu item itself is not a good choice for this group. Chapter 4 provides an in-depth discussion of food acceptance surveys.

Plate Waste Studies

A plate waste study can also provide valuable information about food acceptance. Figure 3.5 illustrates a format for collecting plate waste information. In this process, you review soiled trays before breaking them down, and tabulate wasted or uneaten food. To make this information meaningful, it's important to randomly select a good proportion of soiled trays at any single meal. The benefit from conducting a plate waste study is the overall information you receive about specific food products. One example was a plate waste study where shrimp was served. Many plates contained wasted shrimp. Further investigation showed that too many shrimp were being served so the serving size was changed.

Putting It Into Practice: 2

The test tray came back with the hot foods at 120°F. This is a concern because of client satisfaction and food safety. What are the steps you should take to correct this problem?

(Check your answer at the end of this chapter)

If a product is repeatedly refused, you may re-assess its quality, make adjustments, and re-check its acceptance in another plate waste study. Or, you may take it off the menu. You can also use this method to document the intake of specific clients you are monitoring through the nutrition care process. This would help you achieve an outcome for a specific client who needs to gain weight.

Checklists and Self-Audits

To ensure ongoing compliance with standards and regulations, a Certified Dietary Manager can use checklists and self-audits. An audit is a systematic, documented method of evaluating an operation in comparison with established standards. When you perform a self-audit, your own operation (rather than

surveyors from the outside) is conducting the audit as an internal quality management activity.

By formalizing the audit process with a tool such as a checklist or self-audit, you can ensure that you are reviewing every practice that contributes to quality processes in your operation. You do not have to wonder whether you've observed everything you should. The audit reminds you, point by point.

In a self-audit, you can identify exceptions or problems, and then create an immediate plan to correct them. The benefit of performing a self-audit is that you can proactively identify problem areas and correct them without waiting for a surveyor to point them out.

By establishing a scheduled routine for self-audits, you can assure ongoing compliance. In fact, the best preparation for a survey—whether by a health department, The Joint Commission (TJC), or a Centers for Medicare and Medicaid Services (CMS) survey team—is simply to comply with standards all the time. One example is the set of quality standards in Figure 3.4.

To create a self-audit tool, you can use the following steps:

1. Review all the standards with which you need to comply, along with your internal quality standards, and list criteria for quality and compliance. When you have multiple standards, such as some from CMS, some from the health department, and some from your own facility, your job as a manager is to consolidate them into one list.
2. Translate each standard into clear, specific, measurable/observable inspection criteria that identify what you need to see to know that the criteria have been met. It is not enough to say: The dining room will be pleasant. Instead, list the factors that make the dining room pleasant, such as adequate lighting, cleanliness, minimal noise, attractive table settings, etc. By doing this, you develop a tool that leaves nothing to judgment or imagination. Your criteria can be applied consistently, with clear expectations.

Putting It Into Practice: 3

As you observe plate waste, you notice that many plates are returning with the green beans uneaten. What is the first step you should take to correct this problem?

(Check your answer at the end of this chapter)

Figure 3.5 Plate Waste Information

In the second column, tally the number of people who refused the product; use the third column to show how many plates came back with half the product, and the fourth column for empty plates.

Cycle Menu: Week 1, Day 3, Meal 3	Plate Full of Product	Half the Food Consumed	Empty Plate
Soup	III	𝍸	𝍸 𝍸 II
Juice			
Salad	I	II	𝍸 𝍸 𝍸 II
Entree	II	𝍸 I	𝍸 𝍸 II
Vegetable	𝍸 II	𝍸 IIII	III
Dessert	I	II	𝍸 𝍸 𝍸 II

3. Group these inspection criteria by logical or functional area to create several different audits. For example, you may develop a meal service audit, a food production audit, a food sanitation audit, a safety audit, a clinical care audit, and perhaps a few others. Ultimately, each tool you create should be clear-cut and easy to use. It should not be so long that no one wants to complete it!

See Figure 3.6 for an example of a self-audit tool.

A Certified Dietary Manager typically delegates some auditing responsibilities to work teams. For example, an audit of the dining room service can include a supervisor and/or a few employees in this service area. Any time you place the audit into the hands of employees, you also empower them to manage quality within their own realms of responsibility. You also give them the message that you expect them to work together to make quality a reality. An audit tool can also be a very effective training tool for new employees, and an aid for reviewing required procedures with experienced staff members.

In conducting a self-audit, the assigned person should review the criteria, use a checkmark or other system to indicate whether the criteria are met, and add a plan of correction if warranted. Often, a problem can be corrected on the spot, and this is ideal. The employee who completes an audit should also date and sign the document, acknowledge responsibility and accountability, and return the form to the supervisor or manager.

Even when audits are conducted by others in your department, it is important to review every completed audit document. Sometimes an audit will reveal chronic problems with procedures, training, equipment, or other issues that a manager needs to address. Ultimately, the manager is responsible for compliance with all established standards. Also, the manager should maintain completed audit documents for future reference and for surveyors who may request to see them.

In all, an ongoing self-audit procedure is an essential tool for managing quality. To ensure that audits occur, it is a good idea to create a schedule for audits and assign responsibility on a calendar. Then, monitor to assure that audits are completed on a timely and thorough basis and problems are addressed.

The Role of Expectation/Outcomes

Outcomes and expectations are related. As a facility, when you determine your outcomes, you should also be looking at what your clients are expecting. Then, your outcomes are written to meet those expectations. Your outcomes are the results of your client interactions either with you and your department or your foodservice department.

To understand how clients perceive and rank quality, it's critical to understand the role of expectations. Part of evaluation of taste and quality boils down to whether a food matches what a client expects. Individually, we each have an idea of what a food should be like, and these ideas vary among all of us. Being different or putting a new twist on a traditional product is sometimes effective, but only if it is communicated in advance, so that the client will not be unhappily surprised. Often, quality becomes a gauge of whether the food a client receives is the food he expected. In any facility, this factor merits special atten-

Figure 3.6 **Meal Service Self-Audit Tool**

Dining and Foodservice Audit	Yes	Sometimes	No	Correction Plan
1. Food complaints from residents, family, and others are routinely investigated.				
2. Results of food complaint investigations are appropriately documented.				
3. Dining room(s) has/have comfortable sound levels.				
4. Dining room(s) has/have adequate illumination.				
5. Dining room(s) has/have appropriate furnishings to meet resident needs and quality of life.				
6. Dining room(s) has/have adequate ventilation.				
7. Dining room(s) is/are absent of inappropriate odors.				
8. Dining room(s) has/have sufficient space.				
9. Resident rooms (where residents eat meals) have comfortable sound levels.				
10. Resident rooms (where residents eat meals) have adequate illumination.				
11. Resident rooms (where residents eat meals) have appropriate furnishings to meet meal service needs and quality of life.				
12. Resident rooms (where residents eat meals) have adequate ventilation.				
13. Resident rooms (where residents eat meals) are absent of inappropriate odors.				
14. Resident rooms (where residents eat meals) have sufficient space.				
15. Tables are adjusted to accommodate wheelchairs where meals are served.				
16. Appropriate hygiene is provided prior to meals.				
17. Resident eyeglasses, dentures, and/or hearing aids are in place prior to meals.				
18. Resident chairs, wheelchairs, gerichairs, etc., are at an appropriate distance from tables or tray tables.				
19. Assistive devices/utensils are identified in care plans.				
20. Assistive devices/utensils are provided and used as planned.				
21. Dishware and flatware is appropriate for each resident.				
22. Single-use disposable diningware is not used except in an emergency.				
23. Each resident has an appropriate place setting including water (except those with fluid restrictions).				
24. Meals are attractive (color, shape, presentation).				
25. Meals are palatable.				

(Continued)

Figure 3.6 **Meal Service Self-Audit Tool** *(Continued)*

Dining and Foodservice Audit	Yes	Sometimes	No	Correction Plan
26. Meals are at appropriate temperatures.				
27. Meals are served within 30 minutes of scheduled meal time.				
28. Substitutes are offered to residents as needed.				
29. Substitutes arrive within 15 minutes of request from resident.				
30. Diet cards list food preferences.				
31. Food preferences are honored.				
32. Correct portion sizes are served according to the menu.				
33. Condiment requests are honored.				
34. Residents are promptly assisted with eating.				
35. Appropriate verbal cuing is provided at meal times.				
36. Residents at the same table are served concurrently.				
37. Resident concerns regarding taste, temperature, quality, quantity, and appearance are addressed promptly and appropriately.				
38. Mechanically altered diets are prepared appropriately (ground, NDD).				
39. Resident refusals of food items are addressed to determine reason(s) for refusal.				
40. Food placement, color, and textures address resident needs or deficits.				
41. Test tray sent to furthest unit is palatable and at correct temperatures.				
42. Medication pass does not interfere with quality of meal service.				
43. Pain medications are given prior to meals so that meals can be eaten in comfort.				
44. Foods served are not routinely or unnecessarily used as vehicle to administer medications.				
45. Meal intakes for food items are monitored accurately and in a timely manner.				
46. Intakes for fluids are monitored accurately and in a timely manner.				
47. Plates are returned to kitchen with 75 percent or more of meals consumed.				
48. Foodservice staff are prepared to discuss dietary services with surveyor (staff assignments, meal monitoring procedures).				
49. Resident care plans regarding meals, feeding, dietary needs are followed at meal service.				

Note: This tool provides some audit criteria based on CMS standards, but is not comprehensive. Please consult your current standards to ensure all applicable criteria are met.

tion. A recent poll of restaurant customers found the #1 reason for dissatisfaction was not receiving food as ordered or expected.

In serving clients who have given up some control of their own meals, it's especially important to evaluate expectations and plate accuracy. Tray assembly service systems require attention to how meal choices are gathered and honored. The move to restaurant service and room service models have improved client satisfaction results.

In surveys, sometimes clients will comment that meals are not "accurate." This affects your outcome of a client satisfaction. When this occurs, carefully evaluate what this means. Possible sources of a comment such as this include:

- ✓ The client did not complete a selective menu.
- ✓ The client completed a selective menu, but did not understand which meal it indicated.
- ✓ The client selected foods from a menu or by placing a phone call, and clinical staff had to adjust selections to meet a diet order.
- ✓ The client has experienced a change in diet order that affected food choices on the tray.
- ✓ The client asked the nurse for a specific food, and the request was not passed on to the foodservice department.
- ✓ The client asked for foods that are not available ("write-ins").
- ✓ A clinical staff person has not taken food preferences for a client, or has not communicated them to tray assembly employee.
- ✓ An error was made in processing orders, tray tickets, or plates.
- ✓ An error was made in tray assembly.
- ✓ A food shortage occurred, and the manager had to make a substitution.
- ✓ A tray was properly assembled according to client's order, and food was removed during transit or delivery.

Clearly, many factors contribute to a perception of accuracy. A tremendous amount of communication is involved as well. When concerns about tray/plate accuracy arise, a manager should track the meal service process and identify the breakdown. Feedback in this area can also help to pinpoint areas that require stronger communications.

Consider this example: You learn that clients rated meal accuracy poorly for a certain meal. In tracking the service, you note that a macaroni and cheese was substituted for scalloped potato casserole. Two questions should come to mind:

- ✓ How did this occur, and what steps can be taken to prevent this in the future? A solution may be as simple as revising the forecast figures for this product.
- ✓ Was the substitution explained to clients? If it wasn't, then from a client's perspective, the switch was a mistake. Although substitutions are not desirable in meal service, they are occasionally unavoidable. Some operations keep small substitution cards on hand, and place these on trays when a substitution has to occur. This at least tells clients that the foodservice department recognizes the change and that it was not an error. A substitution card

may say something like: "Sorry! The item you requested was not available today, and we had to make a substitution. For further assistance with your meal service, please call extension 404." Outcome measurement helps bring the focus of all you do back to the client.

External Standards for Quality

Some standards begin with sources external to your operation. In fact, both governmental and private associations may be involved in the evaluation of foodservices—and thus, with the establishment of standards. For example, to support a healthcare facility with maintaining accreditation, you will need to assure that the foodservice operation meets standards established by The Joint Commission (TJC). If your facility receives Medicare reimbursement for services, you may also be subject to certain standards enforced by the Centers for Medicare and Medicaid Services (CMS).

In addition, you may be responsible for complying with specific standards for state and local agencies, as well as with sanitation standards as enforced by a state and/or local health department.

External standards form a backdrop for quality management in many healthcare organizations. In a correctional facility, there may be other sets of standards affecting the foodservice operation. For example, federal law stipulates religious freedom for inmates, and this carries through to honoring food choices related to religious convictions. State departments of corrections may also apply certain standards.

In a public school setting, standards for menu planning and program management come from the USDA for schools participating in the National School Lunch Program and seeking reimbursements and commodity foods.

Before examining an internal quality management process, let's take a closer look at some of the external sources of standards that influence a healthcare foodservice department.

The Joint Commission

There are several for-profit agencies that offer voluntary accreditation according to their established standards of care. They are not be confused with the requirements of a state license or for the requirement to certify for federal funds. The most well known is The Joint Commissions (TJC), formerly the Joint Commission on Accreditation of Healthcare Organizations (JCAHO). Originally, The Joint Commission only accredited hospitals but it has moved into other healthcare facilities such as long-term care. In the past, CMS approved the authority for The Joint Commission, accreditation programs. As of July 2010, The Joint Commission's hospital accreditation program will be subject to Centers for Medicare & Medicaid (CMS) requirements for accrediting organizations. According to the Joint Commission, their mission is: To *continuously improve healthcare for the public, in collaboration with other stakeholders, by evaluating healthcare organizations and inspiring them to excel in providing safe and effective care of the highest quality and value.* The Joint Commission has established standards that each facility is measured against.

To comply with TJC standards, it is essential to review the current standards with others in your own organization. Check those labeled as pertaining to nutritional services, and then review those labeled under other categories, too, as many standards are somewhat universal throughout the organization. For example, one standard will explain how to verify staff credentials and assure that they are up-to-date. Another will address disaster planning, which is a facility-wide function.

Next, clarify any standards that are unclear. Your own standards, in-house experts, a consulting dietitian, and colleagues may be sources of information.

Governmental Agencies and CMS

The National Social Security Act mandates that facilities participating in Medicare and Medicaid programs meet minimum health and safety standards. Medicare is a federal insurance program with payment for services made by the federal government through intermediaries. Medicaid is a state program that provides medical services to people receiving public assistance under the Social Security program (and to other needy persons as well). The requirements pertain to hospitals, skilled nursing facilities, and a wide range of other providers and suppliers of health services.

The Medicare program is administered by CMS, which is an agency of the U.S. Department of Health and Human Services. States may also establish additional requirements under the Medicaid program. Typically, the federal government sets minimum standards; states may develop more specific standards, and those that provide the greatest degree of control will apply.

An agency is designated in each state to carry out the requirements of the Social Security Act. Among other requirements is the need to visit facilities to assure that minimum standards are met and to complete various records.

While state-level officials are generally responsible for conducting on-site surveys for Medicare and Medicaid requirements, the federal government has several responsibilities:

- ✓ Review survey and certification reports submitted by state agencies
- ✓ Evaluate fiscal, administrative, and procedural aspects of its agreements with the states
- ✓ Conduct some on-site surveys of Medicare and Medicaid facilities
- ✓ Review and approve state budgets and expense reports dealing with survey/certification activities.

The Survey Process

Both TJC and CMS use surveys as part of their accreditation or enforcement effort. CMS contracts with state agencies for surveys of healthcare facilities. As part of its enforcement effort, CMS and its contracted state agencies conduct on-site surveys of healthcare facilities. Each time a team of surveyors arrives to evaluate compliance of a healthcare facility with CMS regulations, all managers become involved. A survey is typically unannounced, and may occur on any day of the week. A standard long-term care (LTC) survey is designed to review compliance with CMS regulations, including all the detail of the various F-Tags. A new survey process for long-term care was beta-tested in six states. It is called the CMS Quality Indicator Survey or QIS. National implementation of the QIS is progressing state-by-state as resources are available to conduct training of state and federal surveyors. The QIS process provides for the review of larger samples of clients based on the Minimum Data Set (MDS), observations, interviews, and clinical record reviews.

A Certified Dietary Manager is involved in many quality management issues. Interdisciplinary effort is a strong focus of quality management and CMS regulations. Thus, neither surveyors nor administrators divide up CMS regulations and hand a section to each manager. The manager is often the most accessible person during a survey and you need to understand the regulations, your facility's quality assessment process, and how your data supports your performance improvement.

Each state agency designated to administer the Medicare and Medicaid programs has several duties, which, taken together, are referred to as the certification process. Since the standards used will change, they are not included in this text.

These basic standards may be combined into an overall facility requirement. While the foodservice department needs to have job descriptions, orientation, on-the-job training, and continuing education available through cooperation with all departments within the facility, the state agency is responsible for the following:

- ✓ Identify as many qualified providers and suppliers of health services as possible. There must be eligible facilities on a state-wide basis.
- ✓ Conduct investigations and fact-finding surveys to determine how well participating facilities comply with requirements. Often this investigation is done in conjunction with the state's own licensure and other regulatory programs.
- ✓ Complete certification, re-certification, and periodic follow-up reports dealing with whether facilities are qualified to participate in programs. The states can take final action only on facilities participating in the Medicaid program but must make recommendations to the federal government about facilities participating in Medicare programs.
- ✓ Provide consultative services to providers and suppliers and to those seeking eligibility for the program in order to help them maintain required standards and qualify for participation.

As a Certified Dietary Manager, it is your responsibility to be very familiar with the rules and regulations established in the state for the type of facility where you work. It is also your responsibility to work collaboratively and coop-

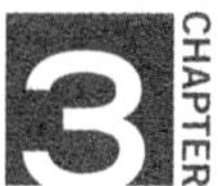

eratively with the Inerdisciplinary Team (IDT). In general terms, the manager must provide a nutritionally adequate diet. The diet should supply the nutrients for the age group being served.

The modified diets ordered by the doctor should be followed using the guidelines set forth in the diet manual approved at the facility. The manager may make suggestions for diet changes in the medical record, but the individual who has ultimate responsibility to issue an order should be carefully considered; in some states and/or facilities, this choice may be dictated by licensure laws and/or policies of the facility.

In addition, the minimum time allowed between the last meal in the evening to the first meal in the morning may be specified in requirements (e.g. 14 hours between the evening meal/snack and breakfast). A facility that participates in Medicare must also meet the conditions established by the federal government. Discuss these conditions with the administrator in order to understand the role that foodservices plays in meeting the requirements.

There is a close relationship among the certification process, state license requirements, programs for professional accreditation (such as TJC), and medical assistance standards. Typically, the relationships among these standards require close coordination and information exchange. For example, healthcare facilities cannot qualify for Medicare assistance unless they have first been licensed by the state. Standards used by TJC generally meet many of the standards issued by the federal government. Thus, the facility is not faced with sets of conflicting standards which make compliance with any defined standards impossible. The guidelines, recommendations, standards, and interpretations of each regulatory agency and professional association interface to provide guidelines for managing healthcare facilities.

It is important to be up-to-date with a set of current requirements. CMS regulations change continuously. Unlike TJC, there may be variations in standards administration from one state to another, so your own state must be used as a source of information. To verify the standards for which you are responsible, work with your own administrator or IDT, and ask for copies of the standards. Also be aware that the CMS website (www.cms.gov) provides information and clarification. One of its features allows users to request clarification about specific standards, and to review questions and answers from others. An entire section specifically addresses the foodservice department.

CMS standards address many basic requirements, such as the need to establish menus, to assure that required nutrients are provided, and to assure that food is palatable and safe. They also emphasize honoring the needs of individual clients, and providing substitutions or alternates when requested. In addition, they stipulate a maximum time that may elapse from dinner to breakfast. They address staffing, dining room environment, and more. Like TJC standards, the CMS survey protocol includes a section about foodservice, as well as information in other sections that is pertinent to foodservice.

What are some steps you can take to help prepare your staff for a state survey?

(Check your answer at the end of this chapter)

For example, clients' rights and the right to refuse care apply to dietary choices and the right to refuse nutritional support. Confidentiality procedures relate to everyone handling client information, which of course includes foodservice staff. Standards relating to infection control have cross-over implications for sanitation and food safety in a foodservice operation. A number of standards relating to nutritional status, hydration, and feeding assistance (if required) are truly interdepartmental issues.

For example, in honoring a diet order for thick liquids, both nursing and foodservice staff need to work together to assure this is carried through. In tracking weight changes or malnutrition, staff must also work together closely to monitor progress and implement therapeutic plans.

In a long-term care environment, it is easy to understand that clients' clinical needs may change over time. So, CMS documentation requirements stipulate a schedule for assessing clients. For example, an admission assessment must be completed within a resident's first five days in the facility. Another assessment is required at approximately a two-week point, and then approximately monthly afterwards. Any major clinical change also signals the need for an assessment.

While all of this activity serves to ensure critical reimbursements to an institution, it also has an interesting bearing on quality management. A protocol for assessment serves as a type of quality management tool, and a way of ensuring that services are (dynamically) geared towards what each resident needs. Clinical assessments are a very client-specific, proactive quality management tool.

CMS also uses quality indicators for tracking and benchmarking care. Quality indicators highlight issues relating to clinical care. Several quality indicators are very specific to nutritional care, as implemented by the healthcare team. For more information about quality indicators and CMS standards for clinical nutritional care and documentation, please consult *Nutrition and Medical Nutrition Therapy* (ANFP, 2012) or the CMS website. As a Certified Dietary Manager, you can weave this into your routine quality management procedures, and evaluate this information as you would any other quality data.

The Centers for Medicare & Medicaid Services (CMS) initiated a new fivestar quality rating system for nursing homes in December 2008 that resembles the "star" rating system that measures quality in hotel chains. Clarity and public awareness is what CMS is hoping to provide from this initiative. Giving consumers a recognizable scale to search for quality elder care is what prompted the creation of the five-star quality ratings. The ratings are based on three separate categories:

1) Health Inspections

2) Quality Measures

3) Staffing Levels

Each category is assigned from one to five stars, with one star being the lowest rating and five stars the highest. CMS includes this statement when describing the rating's merits. *"Nursing homes with five stars are considered to have above average quality compared to other nursing homes in that state. Nursing homes*

Putting It Into Practice: 5

When the surveyors arrive at your facility, what should you do?

(Check your answer at the end of this chapter)

with one star have quality much below the average in that state (but the nursing home still meets Medicare's minimum Requirements)."

Legal Implications

Surveyors look at what you do for quality assurance and at how you are using the data for performance improvement. CMS has language in both the hospital and long-term care regulations that facilities must:

- ✓ Develop, implement, and maintain an effective, ongoing, facility-wide, data-driven quality assessment and performance improvement program
- ✓ Involve all departments and services
- ✓ Focus on indicators related to improved health outcomes.

At the time of a survey, a Certified Dietary Manager may be asked to provide documentation and information pertinent to the survey. Surveyors will focus on quality indicators. They will review medical records and interview clients. Part of the survey may include a detailed tour of foodservice areas. A manager should accompany a surveyor and cooperate fully. When the survey concludes, the survey team will state any deficiencies noted and reference F-Tag numbers. A deficiency is a finding that the facility is not in compliance with CMS Guidelines. The facility is cited and instructed to correct the deficiency. Deficiencies are categorized by the level of risk/harm that may occur. If a problem is identified, the manager and other members of the interdisciplinary team need to follow up promptly and effectively to correct them. If deficiencies are not corrected within a reasonable amount of time, the facility may be shut down. In all, a Certified Dietary Manager plays a critical role in assuring that quality of foodservice meets the needs of clients, and that the end results of care are excellent.

END OF CHAPTER

Putting It Into Practice Questions & Answers

1. You observe that the muffins made for the evening meal are peaked and dark brown in color. These do not meet your quality standards. What are the steps you should take to correct this problem?

   A. *1. Remove the muffins from service and substitute with a comparable product.*
   2. Speak privately with the cook to determine what happened (e.g. was it the recipe, was he too busy, etc.)
   3. If it is the recipe, adjust the recipe for the future use

2. The test tray came back with the hot foods at 120°F. This is a concern because of client satisfaction and food safety. What are the steps you should take to correct this problem?

   A. *1. Check to make sure that the food temperature prior to leaving the kitchen met your department standard for that product. (e.g. vegetables, 135°F, meat, 155°F etc.)*
   2. If the food was up to temperature at the beginning, look at the how the foods are kept hot during transport and make sure the equipment was working. (heated cart, plate warmers, etc.)
   3. Investigate how long the food sat at the end point before the tray temperatures were taken.
   4. Use the FOCUS and PDCA to identify and improve.
   5. Document your processes, your actions to improve the outcomes and processes, and the results of your follow-up.

3. As you observe plate waste, you notice that many plates are returning with the green beans uneaten. What is the first step you should take to correct this problem?

   A. *1. Taste the beans yourself.*
   2. Interview the clients to determine why they didn't eat them.
   3. Document your actions.

4. What are some steps you can take to help prepare your staff for a state survey?

   A. *1. Involve your staff to determine outcomes and quality indicators for your department.*
   2. Make sure that orientation to your quality processes is part of new employee orientation.
   3. Use a portion of each inservice to focus on quality initiatives (e.g. focus on an outcome, the processes used to achieve the outcome, the quality indicators, AND what data are collected and used to support the indicators).
   4. Use mock surveys regularly with one of your staff acting as the surveyor.

5. When the surveyors arrive at your facility, what should you do?

   A. *1. First and foremost, cooperate willingly.*
   2. Contact your Registered Dietitian if he/she is not onsite.
   3. Provide any documentation for which you are asked.
   4. Provide a tour of foodservice if requested.
   5. Address any deficiencies immediately.
   6. Document what you have done to address any deficiencies.

CHAPTER 4

Evaluate Food Acceptance Survey

Overview and Objectives

What role food plays in your facility and even what role your department plays is defined by your clients. Use the information in this chapter to examine how clients' needs influence your own foodservice operation. You will identify techniques for gathering meaningful data about your clients and their needs. A successful foodservice department knows who their clients are and routinely surveys each group. You will make recommendations and changes based on your survey results.

After completing this chapter, you should be able to:

✓ Identify client food preferences and food problems
✓ Identify data needs for judging food preferences
✓ Develop and conduct food acceptance surveys
✓ Analyze data and make recommendations/changes

Who Are Your Clients?

A client is someone who buys your goods or receives your services. In the foodservice environment, your goods are generally meals or foods. Your services are delivery of food through one mechanism or another. If you were asked to describe your clients, what would you say? If you started describing the hospital patients or nursing home clients, you would be partially correct. They are a very important part of your clientele. Another part of your clientele is the staff that work and eat at your facility. If you prepare meals for members of the community, such as "meals on wheels," they are also your clients. Do you prepare meals for family members on special occasions? Are there other groups you serve that aren't mentioned here? Everyone you provide meal service to is considered a client. Each of them has different needs and different expectations. Your clients may be called patient, clients, residents, students, inmates, or employees. For purposes of this textbook all of these will be called clients. A successful foodservice department knows who their clients are and routinely surveys each group.

Most operations have a list of client groups, not just one. Along with primary clients, who may comprise the largest group of people you serve, there are others. In a school, for example, you are likely to be serving teachers and employees as well as students. In a hospital, you may be serving employees, physicians, visitors, and even the community at large. Figure 4.1 lists examples of additional client groups you may serve in various foodservice settings.

Why Are Clients Important?

In a non-commercial environment, clients are almost always named in the mission statement. Regardless of the specifics, it is clear that the facility exists to take care of its clients. This alone dictates the need for a clear focus on clients in foodservice.

To plan a foodservice operation, you will find yourself asking key questions, such as:

✓ How many meals should we serve?

✓ What time should we serve meals?

✓ What type of service should we offer?

✓ What types of foods should we include (or exclude)?

✓ Where will we serve people?

✓ What will the presentation and environment look like?

✓ How will we accommodate unique client needs and preferences?

Needless to say, there are many more questions like these. In fact, a multitude of options controlling nearly every aspect of menu and service is available to any foodservice operation. So, much boils down to decision making. To make these decisions, you need to consider your clients. Ultimately, what constitutes

Figure 4.1 Additional Client Groups: Examples

Public School Teachers Other employees Visitors Consultants and inspectors Professional groups (meetings, seminars) **Rehabilitation Center** Potential residents and families Employees Physicians Community members Consultants and inspectors Sales representatives Professional groups (meetings, seminars) **Correctional Facility** Guards and other employees Consultants and inspectors Sales representatives	**Hospital** Visitors Employees Physicians Community members Students (in training) Consultants and inspectors Sales representatives Outpatients Professional groups (meetings, seminars) **Child Day Care Center** Teachers Other employees **Business Dining** Consultants and inspectors Visitors and guests Clients and prospective clients Professional groups (meetings, seminars) Children enrolled in on-site day care	**Skilled Nursing Facility** Potential residents and families Employees Physicians Community members Consultants and inspectors Sales representatives Professional groups (meetings, seminars) **University** Faculty members Other employees Visitors and guests Prospective students and families Sports teams Consultants and inspectors Sales representatives Professional groups (meetings, seminars) Attendees of conferences

a good decision for one group of clients may not be a good decision for another. The bottom line has to be that the sum total of your decisions creates a foodservice operation that gives your own clients exactly what they need, the way they need it, and when they need it. In other words, it's really your clients who define the answers to your questions. They do not tell you how you will accomplish your job, but they do tell you what the results of your work will need to be.

Often, the challenge a Certified Dietary Manager faces is how to satisfy clients' needs, while also addressing many additional constraints, which may include budgetary limitations and requirements from external courses such as laws, regulations, and accreditation standards. Non-commercial foodservice operations perform a continuous balancing act to work within all established limits, using resources most effectively to meet the needs of clients.

Managers in non-commercial foodservice are quickly abandoning the traditional regard for their clients as a captive audience. Successful players in the field, including successful foodservice contract companies, have adopted a new outlook. They consider it a privilege to serve clients, and recognize an ongoing need to provide food and services that meet clients' needs and expectations. Central to this outlook are two dimensions: inward looking and outward looking. Inward looking means self-examination by looking at satisfaction and image, participation rate, and client loyalty.

Inward Looking

Satisfaction and image. In some situations, the element of choice works a bit differently. In a hospital or a skilled nursing facility, for example, the clients may not have the option of eating somewhere else. However, their satisfaction is still critical to the operation. In these environments, competition jumps to the next level. The hospital meal service may not be competing with the doughnut shop next door. However, the hospital itself may very well be competing with the hospital a few miles away. How will clients choose which hospital to use? Choices may hinge on previous experiences in the hospital, impressions of the hospital, and reputation within the community. So, competition is between hospitals, rather than between foodservice operations.

For a skilled nursing facility, a similar model applies. Among other things, a potential client and her family selecting a facility will evaluate the quality of the environment and care they can expect from each option. Foodservice is a major contributor to the image a facility builds, to community perceptions of quality of care, and ultimately—to the decision-making process of potential clients of a facility.

In healthcare, physicians themselves also become clients in many respects. A physician brings business to the facility, and often has the choice of selecting one facility or another. Hospitals today recognize the value of providing a full range of high-quality supportive services to physicians, encouraging them to bring their clients to the facility.

In prisons, satisfaction takes on yet a different aspect. An inmate most certainly has no choice of one facility over another. Yet satisfaction looms as a critical

During your weekly inservice meeting, some of your staff complain about all the additional work involved with a new room service menu. What would you tell them to help them accept the changes?

(Check your answer at the end of this chapter)

issue in ensuring smooth operations. Richard B. Dansdill, a Certified Dietary Manager with Fremont Correctional Facility, Canon City, Colorado, notes, "If you study correctional history, you will learn that a large number of the serious riots in correctional facilities started with problems in foodservice." (Dietary Manager, June 2000) In other words, know what your client needs are and then work to satisfy them. It sounds simple; it is anything but simple. Once you have identified your clients and their needs, you can continue to improve satisfaction and image by adopting and implementing standards. For instance, the *Disney Institute* recommends adopting service standards such as, "safety, courtesy, efficiency, and show."

Participation Rate. Participation rate refers to the proportion of a potential client group that patronizes non-commercial foodservice. In an assisted living community, the question would be: What percentage use the on-site restaurant? If 70 of 100 use the restaurant, the participation rate is 70 percent. If you are in a hospital and are serving employees, you may be concerned with participation rate for lunch in the hospital cafeteria. If half of employees eat in the cafeteria, you have a participation rate of 50 percent. Participation rate is very important in the school foodservice market, where a key impetus is to encourage more students to use school meal services. This also ties into satisfaction and image. In universities, the drive is often to encourage students to use the campus dining plan.

Higher rates of participation in non-commercial foodservice can have significant impact on operational revenues. With certain costs being fixed—such as the cost of operating a kitchen and the cost of paying managers—an operation can often achieve greater economy of scale through increased participation. In turn, this can bring about an improved financial bottom line. In some facilities, participation rate is also important for meeting other aspects of the mission. For example, a public school that strives to meet children's nutritional needs would also want to boost participation rates in order to assure sound nutrition for the students.

Client Loyalty. If a foodservice operation does a successful job of appealing to clients' needs, it can gain a following. Just like a "favorite restaurant," the operation develops a sense of loyalty from clients. They want to continue enjoying the services of the operation. They want to choose this operation over an alternative. They want to keep coming back. Loyalty is very valuable to any business, and non-commercial foodservice is no exception. Loyalty means repeat patronage, and a certain level of security in ongoing revenues to the operation.

As you can see, competing in the marketplace, bolstering satisfaction and image, boosting participation rates, and developing loyalty all feed into the mission and objectives of many facilities. Success in each of these areas requires a serious commitment to clients and their needs. Furthermore, success requires making the effort to get to know your own client groups, understand their needs, and respond to their preferences. The more effectively you do this, the more readily you can achieve a valid competitive edge in this evolving marketplace.

Unique Needs of Clients. What do your clients need? What do they like? Answers vary. This is because many factors affect clients' food-related needs, meal expectations, service needs, and even their ability to enjoy food. Clients' unique needs may relate to likes and dislikes, expectations and variety, choice, appetite, sense of taste, drug therapies, allergies and intolerances, cultural and ethnic influences, lifestyle, routines and timing, religious convictions, emotional overtones, and personal values about food and nutrition. In addition, further needs may be dictated by presentation and environment, disabilities, language and literacy, culinary trends, and health status. Beyond these factors, some clients have very specific foodservice needs and follow special diets (therapeutic diets). See Figure 4.2 for a closer look at these factors.

Outward Looking

Outward looking means looking outside your department and in some cases, even outside your facility such as your competition. It also includes your clients.

Competition. In many cases, non-commercial foodservice is competing side-by-side with other forms of commercial and retail operations. For example, employees of a large company can eat in the employee cafeteria or food court. Alternately, they can take advantage of the growing fast-food industry, and perhaps walk to the chicken franchise around the corner, or the doughnut shop next door. Or, they may pack their own lunch (brown bag). In another example, a college student may choose to eat in the dining hall, or order a pizza for delivery to his residence hall, or run to the local convenience store for a take-out submarine sandwich. A resident of an assisted living community who wishes to go out to eat may choose the community's on-site restaurant, or drive a mile to a different, privately-owned restaurant. A professional group holding a meeting in your facility may have the option of bringing in refreshments from a private catering service, or using yours; likewise with a fund-raising group holding a black-tie dinner.

There are many professional programs that can help you and your facility and/or department identify your client base and improve your service through knowing the needs of your clients. One such program is the *Disney Institute.* The *Disney Institute* defines "Guestology—knowing your guests (demographics) and understanding your Guests (psychographics)." Another program that helps you focus on your clients and their needs is the Diamond 4C's, a quality improvement program. To remain competitive today, your facility, and ultimately your department, need to define your customers/clients, their needs, and customized innovative methods to meet those needs. See *Management in the News* at the end of this chapter for the full article about implementing the Diamond 4C's program at your facility.

Learning About Your Clients

By now, it's clear that there is much to learn about your clients. Of course, client needs and expectations do not stay the same over time. So, an effective Certified Dietary Manager continues to monitor clients and obtain feedback and suggestions. Furthermore, it's important to realize that a manager needs to address diversity among clients. In fact, not all clients are the same as each other. One of the strategies used in foodservice planning is to look for ways to give everyone what they need.

Figure 4.2 Factors that Influence Client Dietary Needs

Factor	Description
Likes and Dislikes	The most powerful influence on food choices are personal preferences. Find out what they are for your clients.
Expectations	Your dining room and foodservice paint a picture that shapes the expectations of your clients. Do you have an elegant dining room? Are your signs scribbled or neatly lettered? Is your staff smiling during service? What picture are you painting?
Variety	You know the old saying, "Variety is the spice of life." Offering variety is especially essential in healthcare, school, and correctional foodservice.
Choice	Room service, selective menus, restaurant style service, self-service bars, coffee kiosks, and food courts all improve client satisfaction through increased choices.
Appetite	Your clients may be impacted by both physiological and emotional factors that may affect their appetite. Offering a variety of portion sizes will help to meet client needs.
Sense of Taste and Smell	Your client's sense of taste and smell greatly factor into their enjoyment of food. Know your client's condition and work with them to add additional herbs and spices.
Drug Therapies	Medications may impact taste and smell. Clients taking several medications may need as much as 12 times as much salt and three times as much sugar to achieve the same taste sensations.
Allergies and Intolerances	Lactose intolerance (the inability to digest milk sugar) and allergies (such as nuts or wheat) mean providing accurate identification of products that may contain allergens. Know the allergies and intolerances of your clients.
Cultural and Ethnic Influences	Cultural and ethnic foods, ingredients, and/or seasoning styles relate to familiarity and comfort. These play a part in clients' expectations and perceptions of meal services.
Lifestyle	People are busier today and often eat on the go. You may meet your client needs by offering take-out food, sack lunches, and even room service.
Religious Convictions	For any clients whose religious beliefs influence eating choices, it is essential to acknowledge those choices and offer suitable options. Chapter One of the *Nutrition and Medical Nutrition Therapy* textbook offers a full discussion of cultural, ethnic, and religious influences on menu options.
Personal Values	Both food choices and service concepts relate to clients' personal value systems. An example of this is vegetarianism or people who feel strongly about healthy eating. You will be expected to identify these needs and develop services and alternatives that accommodate them.
Language and Literacy	Language or literacy barriers may require you to evaluate carefully how best to communicate with clients, to relate menus, to offer services, and to gather requests and choices.

How can you learn more about your clients? There are many methods, both formal and informal. Figure 4.3 lists examples.

Client Satisfaction Survey. A client satisfaction survey provides an excellent means of learning more about clients. The results of a survey, examined carefully, can assist you in refining menu offerings, service mechanisms, and more. What is a satisfaction survey? A **satisfaction survey** is a series of questions designed to elicit feedback from clients in a systematic fashion. Among the considerations for implementing a survey are: the method you choose for offering the survey, the way you select clients to participate, and the actual questions you ask. Here is a closer look.

There are many methods for offering a survey. You may print a questionnaire and deliver it with meals. You may visit clients in person and ask them to answer a series of questions through a brief interview process. You may telephone

Glossary

Satisfaction Survey
A series of questions designed to elicit feedback from clients in a systematic fashion

Figure 4.3 **Ways to Learn About Clients**

Informal Methods	Formal Methods
• Be present during meal times and observe. • Talk to clients during meal times and ask friendly questions about the meal. • Talk to foodservice staff involved in serving and ask about feedback and requests they receive from clients. • Accept any complaint as valuable feedback and use it to evaluate needs. • Talk to related staff, such as wait staff, nurses, or other staff, and ask what they are noticing or hearing. • After a catered function, talk to the person(s) who requested the catering and ask how everything went. • Wear a name tag that identifies your role or title in the facility and make eye contact with people you see. This makes it easy for clients to approach you to give you feedback. • Talk to your peers in similar organizations and share observations about trends that are developing. • Read foodservice trade journals to learn more about trends and issues.	• Create a suggestion box for use by both clients and employees. Review suggestions carefully. • Provide a comment card on tables where clients dine. • Tabulate plate waste**.** This is the food that is left on a plate returned with soiled dishes. Systematically calculate what is left uneaten, and examine percentages of uneaten food for each menu item. Sometimes, uneaten food gives you a good measure of what clients did not enjoy. • Monitor menu mix and product sales. Sales figures often provide a good indicator of what menu items clients are enjoying. • Use technology to provide an interactive method for clients to provide feedback from tables or bedsides (in a healthcare facility). • In a healthcare setting, ask clinical staff to gather information about the needs of clients, to pass along relevant needs, and to help assure that individual needs are addressed. • Create an advisory committee or focus group comprised of clients and ask them to help provide feedback and suggestions. • Conduct formal satisfaction surveys. • Using a mix of clients, evaluate test trays for temperature and quality. • Use an outside source (e.g. Press Ganey). • Mystery Shoppers—individuals to act as guests/clients and then write a report on their experience.

clients to ask questions. You may send a mailing to past clients asking them to answer questions. You may offer a questionnaire on your foodservice website and invite clients to complete it. You may use other technology, such as a computer-based kiosk (free-standing station), or a handheld computer at tables.

Each method has advantages and disadvantages, and it's important to consider what method will be most effective for your own client group. For example, if you are planning to use printed materials, consider whether all your clients will be able to read them, and whether you are communicating in a language they know. If you are planning to use technology, evaluate clients' comfort level with the devices. In a university environment, for example, technology is frequently used to gather feedback from students. This is a natural fit for a population that uses computers and the Internet on a daily basis. However, among clients of an eldercare community, a smaller percentage of clients may feel comfortable interacting with technology.

A printed piece is easy to ignore. It is inconvenient, and may elicit responses only from those clients who have strong positive or negative feelings. In addition, it can leave out anyone who is unable to read and anyone who is not in strong enough physical condition to complete a form.

A personal interaction offers its own advantages. Clients are keenly aware of your interest in their satisfaction and may also feel free to tell you more. A disadvantage is that some clients worry about hurting the feelings of the survey taker and will therefore hesitate to express concerns.

In some situations, a broad-scale client survey mechanism may already be in place (such as using Press Ganey). Sometimes, the entire survey process is outsourced, or administered by an outside firm. Foodservice satisfaction may be one of several topics addressed on a broad-scale survey of satisfaction.

Putting It Into Practice: 2

What considerations should you include when planning a paper survey for clients in a long-term care facility?

(Check your answer at the end of this chapter)

Figure 4.4 Selection of Survey Participants

In Axl Assisted Living Community, there are seven residential buildings. Some residents do not receive any meal service to their living quarters. Others receive home-delivered meals on a daily basis. The community also operates an on-site cafe and a convenience store with take-out foods. In all, there are 500 residents in the community. The survey is going to be administered by telephone, and the Certified Dietary Manager has determined he has the resources (staffing) to complete 100 calls. How does the Certified Dietary Manager select clients to participate in the satisfaction survey?

In this case, there are several different services to evaluate: home-delivered meals, the on-site cafe, and the convenience store. The Certified Dietary Manager knows who uses home-delivered meals, but does not know who uses the other services. In addition, the Certified Dietary Manager has no way of knowing which residents (if any) do not use the cafe and the store. Thus, the most useful selection would simply be a random one from among all the buildings. This is likely to pull a representation of all client categories.

The Certified Dietary Manager goes through a complete roster of residents and highlights every fifth one for a phone call.

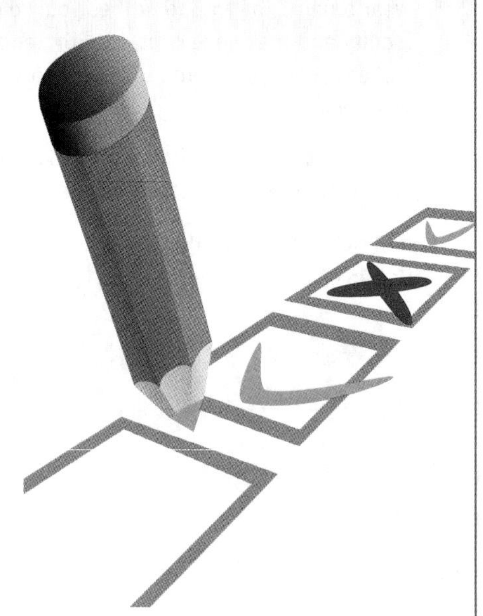

Figure 4.5 **Ways to Ask a Question**

Leading:

1. You like the food we deliver to you, don't you?
2. The food reaches you on time, doesn't it?
3. You use the convenience store, right?
4. You haven't had any problems with the service in the cafe, have you?

Neutral:

1. How do you feel about the food we deliver to you?
2. How is the timing of your deliveries?
3. How often do you use the convenience store?
4. How do you feel about the service at the cafe?

Who receives a survey can have tremendous bearing on the value of information gathered. Past clients may have different reactions than current clients. Clients who use your services may have different feelings than clients who do not participate. For example, in a business dining environment, you would not only wish to survey regular clients, you would also want to hear from employees who pack their own meals, or use other food establishments, in order to learn what it would take to attract them to your cafeteria.

The most effective selection method includes a cross-section of clients and potential clients (if relevant), This means you have a representative sample from all groups. You may select all your clients for a survey, or take a like percentage from each group you identify. Figure 4.4 provides an example of this process.

What types of questions should you ask in a survey to learn about your clients? And what kinds of choices should you provide for answers? What you ask can make a big difference in what you ultimately find out. For starters, each question should be a neutral question. This means the surveyor is not expecting a particular answer. The opposite of a neutral question is a leading question, in which the surveyor attempts to elicit a particular response, or seems to "lead" the participant to an answer. Figure 4.5 shows examples of leading and neutral questions.

In addition, there are several ways to allow a participant to answer a question. An **open-ended question** allows the participant to answer freely, saying whatever comes to mind. It cannot be answered with a "yes" or "no," or with a number. It invites free expression. In Figure 4.5, neutral questions 1, 2, and 4 are all open-ended questions. This type of question is especially valuable for learning more information than just what the question is asking. For example, when you ask, "How do you feel about the food we deliver to you?"—you may learn things that surprise you. You may receive answers such as:

✓ It's fabulous, and I could not live here without this service.

✓ I can't eat it because I'm on a low-salt diet, and you keep giving me salty foods.

Putting It Into Practice: 3

Your facility is interested in getting feedback about the menu selections in foodservice. Which formal method in Fig. 4.3 would be the best way to get a good cross section of opinions that would also provide specific information?

(Check your answer at the end of this chapter)

✓ The delivery person is so kind, he always sets up the table for me, too.

✓ The entrees are usually cold when I get them.

✓ The beef is too tough to chew.

✓ I know I signed up for this service, but I've never received a meal.

As you can see, there are so many possible responses that without an open-ended question, you could miss some feedback you really need to hear! Realistically, there is no way you could ask enough questions to cover all the bases and elicit each of these answers without an open-ended question.

On the other hand, a **closed question** also has value in a survey. A closed question is one with a limited number of specific answers. In Figure 4.5, leading question 3 is an example of a closed question. When you ask, "How often do you use the convenience store?"—you can provide choices for the answers, such as:

✓ Every day

✓ 2-5 times per week

✓ Less than once per week

✓ Never.

Answer choices can measure frequency, such as these. Alternately, they can be ratings. A common rating technique uses the **Likert Scale**, which is a system for allowing people to rate how they feel about something by choosing a word or a number. For example, a survey question that says, "Rate your satisfaction on a scale of 1 to 5" is using a Likert Scale. Some surveyors avoid numbers in a survey, because users may make errors in interpreting the numeric scale. Words are more clear. Figure 4.6 shows sample questions from a survey that uses the Likert Scale.

From closed questions with answers that rate frequency or a Likert Scale, you can develop specific figures that identify areas for action and measure trends. For example, you can calculate participation rates in use of the convenience store. Or, you can calculate how many clients feel their hot foods are hot enough

Glossary

Closed Question
A question with a limited number of answers such as one easily answered with yes or no

Open-Ended Question
Allows the participant to answer freely, saying whatever comes to mind

Likert Scale
A common rating technique that uses words or numbers

Figure 4.6 Survey Using a Likert Scale

1. How would you rate the offerings in the convenience store? (circle one)

excellent good average below average poor

2. How would you rate the quality of food in the cafe? (circle one)

excellent good average below average poor

when they arrive. If you ask the same closed questions again in a few months, you can measure the success of your interventions.

Another advantage to closed questions is that they are easier to ask than open-ended questions. Closed questions can be delivered on a survey form. Too many open-ended questions on a survey require participants to do a lot of writing, and some simply won't do it. Yet another advantage of closed questions is that they elicit answers that are easy to tabulate and summarize.

To learn about your clients, you really need to use both types of questions on a survey. If you use a survey that offers answers on the Likert Scale, for example, you may wish to include one open-ended question at the end, such as, "What other comments would you like to make about the foodservices?"

Let's consider those situations where you are interacting with clients, as opposed to delivering a formal survey. Here, your best tool is the open-ended question. For example, while walking through the cafe during lunch service, the Certified Dietary Manager of Axl Healthcare stops by tables and asks clients, "How is your service today?" or "How is your food?" or "What do you think about today's menu?"

As you can see, a Certified Dietary Manager who is focused on clients will use a variety of formal and informal techniques, as well as a mix of question types, in order to gather feedback and keep in touch with clients.

Evaluating Survey Results

As you gather information from formal and informal interactions, how can you summarize and evaluate it? As you receive answers to open-ended questions, the most important thing to do is listen and think about responses one by one. Follow through on anything that surprises you, and make your own observations. Next, you may also notice similarities among answers. If so, you can group answers and tally them. For example, if 11 people say that the convenience store closes too early in the day, you can tally this information and use it in your planning. If you are sharing answers with your boss or others in your department, you may also just make a list of responses so that reviewers can read them one by one.

How about closed questions? Here, you can tally answers to each question and calculate rates of responses. Figure 4.7 shows how to calculate percentage rates for responses to a closed survey question.

What do the results of the question in Figure 4.7 tell you? Overall, they tell you that you are doing a great job of offering items your clients want to see in the convenience store. They also tell you that a small proportion of your clients are looking for something they are not finding at the store. Hopefully, on this same survey, you solicited some comments with an open-ended question. You may want to look through these to see if anyone has named items they wish you would carry.

What follow-up should you do? You may want to work with employees staffing the convenience store and ask them what clients are looking for. You may request that they ask each client, "Are you finding everything you need?" You may even want to ask them to start making a list of items that clients ask for but do not find. You may decide to evaluate comments and lists, and you may select new items for the store to carry. Furthermore, after a period of time, you would want to re-survey clients to measure the effectiveness of actions you have taken.

Thoughtful interpretation of a survey can help you improve products and services, identify client needs, and even develop new concepts. As an ongoing process, you will likely use surveys to keep a pulse. A survey is not useful just for solving problems. It is valuable for preventing problem, and for assuring successful competition, good participation rates, and client loyalty. In addition, before you begin anything new, you may use surveys to better understand your market. This becomes a valuable basis for planning.

Figure 4.7 Calculating Percentages for a Survey Response

First ask: How many people responded to the survey?

Next, ask: How many people gave each answer to a question?

Then, for each possible response, divide the number of responses by the total number of people who responded to the survey. If you do this on a calculator, you can generally round your answer to two decimal places. If you remove the decimal, now you have a percentage.

Example: A sample survey given to clients of Axl Healthcare included the following question.

How would you rate the offerings in the convenience store? (circle one)

excellent good average below average poor

Your count says 65 people completed the survey.

On this question, 41 answered "excellent;" 12 answered "good;" 6 answered "average;" 4 answered "below average;" and 2 answered "poor."

Your summary shows:

Excellent	41÷ 65 = 0.6308	or about 63%
Good	12 ÷ 65 = 0.1846	or about 18%
Average	6 ÷ 65 = 0.0923	or about 9%
Below Average	4 ÷ 65 = 0.0615	or about 6%
Poor	2 ÷ 65 = 0.0308	or about 3%

Management in the News

The Diamond Approach to Quality Improvement in Food Service

by Linda S. Eck Mills, MBA, RD, LDN, FADA

Diamonds are a girl's best friend and are brilliant to behold. When you examine them you look at the 4 C's—Clarity, Cut, Color, and Carat. So what does a diamond have to do with food service? Consider using the diamond approach to quality improvement and look at the Diamond 4C's™ of food service—Compliance, Courtesy, Cuisine, and Customization.

The Diamond 4C's are your "best friend" in the new Diamond Quality Improvement (DQI) model. Quality doesn't just happen, it's a strategic process. The purpose is to help you focus on the right problem, at the right time, and determine the right solution.

Compliance

Compliance looks at safety and regulatory compliance, core competencies, and is non-negotiable. It's all about providing a safe, clean, and efficient environment for patients, staff, and visitors. Look at employee hygiene, cleaning and sanitation, food handling, and facility maintenance.

Courtesy

Courtesy deals with customer satisfaction. Respect the emotions, abilities, and culture of those you serve, work with, and greet. This is where professionalism, flexibility, respect for customer needs, accessibility, and partnership all come together.

Care for individuals who reside in healthcare communities must meet two goals: maintain health and preserve quality of life. These goals can compete when it comes to delivery of nutrition care. Food must meet nutrition needs but also enhance quality of life.

Cuisine

Cuisine is providing wholesome and delicious foods to those we serve. Consider culinary expertise, cost effectiveness, variety, freshness, and nutrient analysis.

Customization

Customization involves creativity, innovation, and competitive opportunities. This methodology is a tool for improving quality in food service. It empowers foodservice leaders to develop clear strategies and "win-win" solutions for improving the operation with efficient use of time and resources.

Let's back up a minute and look at the FACE™ of the key foodservice delivery systems—Food, Associates/staff, Communication/technology, and Equipment/layout and design. These are the key resources in the department. You need to align the Diamond 4C's with FACE and keep polishing to make a "brilliant" department. But where do you start? Strategic planning embraces Juran's trilogy of quality—quality planning, quality improvement, and quality control.

(Continued...)

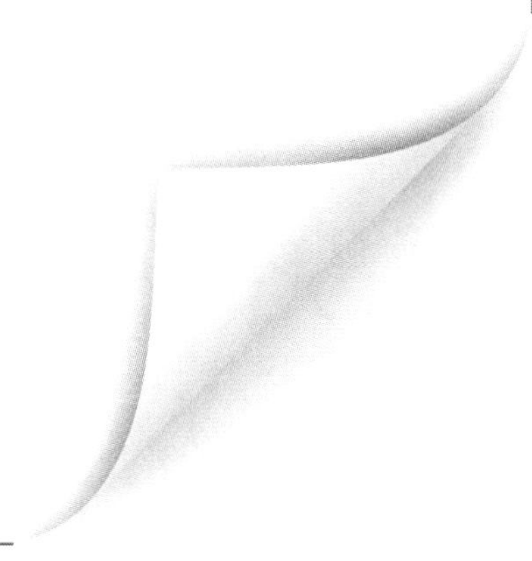

The Diamond Approach to Quality Improvement in Food Service *(Continued)*

Quality Planning

Quality planning includes developing mission/vision statements, assessing the voice of the customer, organizing all customer data, translating the voice of the customer into specific needs, and finally determining critical quality issues. Look at customer feedback, dissatisfaction, and evaluations. Seek to understand the customer by probing and discovering through interviews and focus groups. Then determine priorities for your operation.

Use the grid below for decision-making and prioritization. Remember that the priority matrix will help you prioritize your solutions.

Quality Improvement

In quality improvement the critical quality issues are categorized according to 4C's service standards. Innovations need to be planned to be successful. Map the critical quality issues into a success grid on the following page. Once the success grid is completed, decide what three or four things need to be done for the year. Develop the project team for each strategy before conducting a pilot.

DQI Dashboard for Decision-Making™

	Food	Associate/Staff	Communication/ Technology	Equipment/Layout
Compliance				
Courtesy				
Cuisine				
Customization				

Priority 1—Non-negotiable or Essential I **Priority 2**—Core business I **Priority 3**—Competitive opportunity

Sample Completed DQI Dashboard for Healthcare Segment Decision-Making

	Food	Associate/Staff	Communication/ Technology	Equipment/Layout
Compliance	1	1	1	1
Courtesy	3	2	3	3
Cuisine	2	3	3	2
Customization	3	3	3	3

NOTE: This grid is customized for the Healthcare segment. The DQI model can be modified for various other settings. Priority levels may shift depending on industry segment.

The Diamond Approach to Quality Improvement in Food Service *(Continued)*

Quality Control

Quality control is the final phase. There are two components—monitoring and sustaining changes. Quality control becomes your benchmarking. Conduct weekly team meetings to review and update the projects. Standardize new processes through staff education and training, update policies and procedures, validate output metrics and continue to monitor, and develop contingency plans for each new process.

This new quality control model gives you a how-to and win-win strategy to be successful. Hone in on the areas you need to focus on to meet the strategic goals to be unique and innovative. Go for the "WOW!" to make your department the best while striving for sustainable improvement in your operation.

Linda S. Eck Mills, MBA, RD, LDN, FADA is a professional speaker, career and life coach, and author of the book From Mundane to Ah Ha! Effective Training Objects. Mills directs the DMA Program at Lehigh Carbon Community College (Schnecksville, PA), and is a consulting dietitian. Contact her at Linda@dycomserv.com or www.dycomserv.com

Diamond 4C's Grid—Ideas for Innovation (Quality Improvement)

	Food	Associate/Staff	Communication/ Technology	Equipment/Layout
Compliance	Use a T-stick to temp thin meats	Glove2Go™, Cool Chef Head-band, Cool Chef Scarf	NAFEM data protocol, RFI tags (bar codes), Computer-ized HACCP	NSF/UL equipment
Courtesy	Guest paging by iPhone	Room service	Digital dining	Tea cart service between meals
Cuisine	Mini desserts, flatbreads	Presentation style	Nutrient analysis available to customer	Cost effectiveness
Customization	Partnership with suppliers	Staff training	Blogs	Equipment suites

REFERENCES

Source: "Polishing the Face of Healthcare Foodservice: The Diamond Approach" session presented by Sharon Cox and Crystal Duncan at the American Dietetic Association 2009 Food & Nutrition Conference & Expo.

END OF CHAPTER

Putting It Into Practice Questions & Answers

1. During your weekly inservice meeting, some of your staff complains about all the additional work involved with a new room service menu. What would you tell them to help them accept the changes?

   A. *You can talk about the fact that people are very mobile today and there is always competition waiting for your clients. Keeping your clients happy also means keeping jobs. Perhaps you can remind them of the mission of the facility with a client focus. Acknowledge their concerns by asking for their patience when trying something new. Change always takes a little longer at first.*

2. What considerations should you include when planning a paper survey for clients in a long-term care facility?

   A. *Keep it simple by providing multiple choice answers. Consider larger print. Offer them the survey while they are waiting for a meal and you can get better participation.*

3. Your facility is interested in getting feedback about the menu selections in foodservice. Which formal method in Figure 4.3 would be the best way to get a good cross section of opinions that would also provide specific information?

   A. *With a focus group, you can select a cross section of your clients. You meet with them together and can gather specific suggestions.*

Using Appropriate Resources to Modify Standard Menus to Suit Client Needs

Overview and Objectives

The menu is the starting point for many decisions involving purchasing, production, and service of food. You will examine the basics of menu planning and utilize diet manuals in modifying menus for your clients. You will identify standard food weights and measures. You will also review both your legal and moral responsibilities for providing nutritious food to your clients.

After completing this chapter, you should be able to:

- ✓ Identify appropriate nutrition tables/charts and diet manuals
- ✓ Use standard food weights, measures, and recipes correctly
- ✓ Utilize peer and supervisory resources available as needed
- ✓ Honor legal and moral responsibilities regarding diet needs
- ✓ Modify menus based on local non-commercial foodservice or societal factors

Types of Menus

There are three main types of menus: static, cycle, or special (aka single use) menu. It is possible for one facility to offer all three types of menu styles. The facility may also vary the number of choices within each type of menu. The number of choices might range from many with an *a la carte menu* to few choices, or none, such as one offered in a catered meal to physicians.

Cycle

In many facilities, clients enjoy service for ongoing periods of time. A client of a skilled nursing facility receives ongoing meal service for weeks, months, or even years; likewise with an employee eating in a business dining setting, or an inmate eating in a correctional facility, or a student on a college campus. For this reason, a Certified Dietary Manager needs to plan a method of providing variety for clients.

Certified Dietary Managers plan this variety by using a cycle menu. A **cycle menu** changes daily over a period of time—and then repeats itself, creating a cycle. Managers refer to the days of a cycle menu as "Day 1, Day 2," and so forth. Using a calendar, they match these planned days with actual dates.

The length of a cycle menu can be anything from a few days to as much as six weeks. The key is to make the cycle long enough to prevent clients from feeling

Glossary

Cycle Menu
Changes to a menu daily over a period of time or cycle such as three days or three weeks

Figure 5.1 **Sample Special (St. Patrick's Day) Menu for a Hospital Cafe**

Appetizers

- Baked Spinach Artichoke Dip with Pita Chips
- Bruschetta with Edamame Pesto

Entrees

- Corned Beef
- Irish Stew

Accompaniments

- Baked Cabbage with Bacon
- Boiled Potatoes and Carrots

Bread

- Irish Soda Bread with Raisins

Desserts

- Creme de Menthe Pie
- Chocolate Zucchini Cake

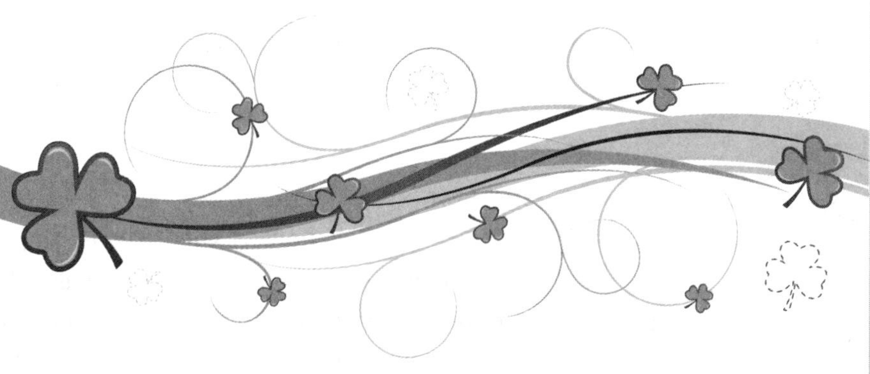

that meals are repetitive or too predictable. In hospitals, as average length-of-stay has decreased, so have the lengths of cycle menus. A decade ago, some hospitals used cycles as long as two or three weeks. Today, most hospitals have shortened their menus to a week, or even a few days. This is because many clients do not stay in the hospital long enough to experience repetition in a short cycle. In a skilled nursing facility, however, an extended cycle is very appropriate to minimize repetition while matching an extended length-of-stay.

Cycles are often defined in multiples of seven days, such as a one-week cycle, a two-week cycle, or a five-week cycle. Interestingly, some operations have chosen to break away from this concept. A cycle that is not developed in seven-day increments prevents day-of-the-week repetition. So, a three day cycle might present the "Day 1" offerings on Monday and Thursday one week, and on Sunday and Wednesday the next. This helps clients feel that a menu is not repetitive, even in a shortened cycle.

Putting It Into Practice: 1

Your hospital just implemented a room service menu. You still offer menus in the cafeteria that change every two weeks. What menu styles are you using?

(Check your answer at the end of this chapter)

Static

Another menu type, the restaurant style or room service menu does not change everyday. This is called a **static menu**. However, a Certified Dietary Manager may choose to rotate a few key items, such as entrees or chef's specials, over a cycle.

Special or Single Use

Sometimes there is a standard definition of a meal for service. This type of menu provides a complete meal at a fixed price. A complete meal might include an appetizer, a salad, an entree, a starch, a vegetable or fruit, a beverage, and possibly dessert. For example, a school lunch menu may offer a pre-defined list of foods that constitute a meal. Typically, these are planned in conjunction with USDA guidelines. A cafeteria may offer a pre-defined meal and label it as a **special** meal. Many times these special menus are used to help break the monotony of a cycle menu. See Figure 5.1 for an example.

A la Carte

An a la carte menu allows clients to select each item they desire for a meal. In a retail setting, each menu item is priced individually. This may be used in campus dining or in schools. It is also common in many cafeterias.

Menu Options

Besides different types of menus, there are also menu options for your clients. Two of the most common options in healthcare are selective and nonselective.

Selective Menus

A selective menu is the way to implement current federal regulations and, more importantly, enhance the quality of life and quality of care for your clients. A selective menu is one in which clients have the opportunity to make choices or selections in advance of meal service. For example, a selective menu usually offers at least two choices for an entrée and multiple choices for most items on the menu. Typically, a selective menu is distributed to clients in advance of the meal (about a day or half a day before service, depending on the system). Clients note their selections, which are retrieved and used in the kitchen as trays or meals are prepared. Computer-based selective menu systems may use handheld computers and/or telephone systems for entry of choices into an automated system. Figure 5.2 shows an actual selective menu with options for general, carbohydrate counting, clear liquid, and full liquid diets. Notice that the modifications for the carbohydrate counting diet are the numbers of 'carbs' found in specific menu items. That way, the client who knows how many 'carbs' they can have still has many choices. Menu options on a selective menu in a hospital should rotate daily for variety.

In healthcare facilities, or in any environment where the foodservice department is responsible for honoring therapeutic diets, it is standard practice to review menu choices before they are served. If clients make choices on a selective menu, a member of the foodservice staff then reviews these choices against a nutrition kardex card or computerized tray ticket.

Glossary

Static Menu
A fixed menu that doesn't change such as a room service menu

Special or Single Use Menu
A menu planned for service on a special day such as a Mother's Day Tea

Selective Menu
One in which clients have the opportunity to make choices or selections in advance of or immediately prior to meal service

Nonselective Menu
One in which clients do not have the opportunity to make choices for main dishes

Figure 5.2 Sample Selective Menu with Carbohydrate Count

Room Number: ______ Pt. Name: ____________________ Diet Order: ____________

DOB: ____________ Meal: **B L D** Time if advance: ____________ Total Carb Choices: ____________

Breakfast
- Scrambled eggs
- Egg beaters
- Pancake = **1**
- Waffle = **4**
- Bacon
- Sausage link

Cereals
- Oatmeal: ½ cup = **1**
- Malt O Meal: ½ cup = **1**
- Cream of Wheat: ½ cup = **1**
- Bran Flakes: 1 box = **1**
- Cherrios: 1 box = **1**
- Cornflakes: 1 box = **1**
- Frosted Flakes: 1 box = **1**
- Fruit Loops: 1 box = **2**
- Raisin Bran: 1 box = **2**
- Rice Krispies: 1 box = **1**

Fruits/Yogurt
- Apple = **1**
- Banana = **2**
- Orange Slices = **1**
- Fresh Fruit: ½ cup = **1**
- Applesauce: ½ cup = **1**
- Stewed Prunes: 4 = **1**
- Flavored Yogurt: 6 oz. = **2**

Bakery/Breads
- English Muffin: ½ = **1**
- Muffin: small = **2**; large = **4**
- White Toast: 1 slice = **1**
- Bagel: ½ = **2**
- Coffeecake: 1 piece = **6**
- Dinner Roll: 1 = **1**
- White Bread: 1 slice = **1**

Entrees
- Roast Turkey
- Baked Chicken
- Roast Beef
- Chef Salad = **1**
- Taco Salad: 1 pkg. = **1**
- Cafe Special (Noon M-F)
- Ham

Soups
- Chicken Noodle: 1 cup = **1**
- Tomato: 1 cup = **1**
- Cream of Broccoli: 1 cup = **1**
- Chili: 1 cup = **1**
- Crackers: 3 = **1**
- LS Tomato: 1 cup = **1**
- LS Chicken Noodle: 1 cup = **1**
- LS Vegetable: 1 cup = **1**
- LS Crackers: 3 = **1**

Sides
- Mashed Potatoes: ½ cup = **1**
- Baked Potato: ½ = **1**
- Rice: 1/3 cup = **1**
- Carrots or Peas: ½ cup = **1**
- Corn: ½ cup = **1**
- Green Beans: ½ cup = **0**
- Broccoli/Cauliflower: ½ cup = **0**
- Gravy: regular or large
- Baked Beans: ½ cup = **1.5**

Salads
- Tossed
- Dressing
- Coleslaw
- Cottage Cheese
- Potato Salad: ½ cup = **1**
- Pasta Salad: ½ cup = **1**

Sandwiches
- White, Whole Wheat, Bun*
- Hamburger
- Cheeseburger
- Sliced Meat
- Turkey, Ham, Chicken: 1/3 cup = **1**
- Grilled Cheese
- Grilled Chicken
- Ham and Cheese
- Ham (hot, cold)
- Grilled Ham & Cheese
- Tuna salad, Egg salad
- Ham salad

Each bread = **1, Bun = **2***

Desserts
- Angel food cake: 1 piece = **1**
- Pie: 1 piece = **3**
- Ice cream: ½ cup = **1**
- Sherbet: ½ cup = **2**
- Cake: 1 piece = **2**
- Cookies: 1 = **1**
- Vanilla Wafers: 5 = **1**
- Pudding: 1 = **2**

Beverages
- Coffee
- Decaf Coffee
- Black Tea
- Green Tea
- Decaf Tea
- Iced Tea
- Lemon Juice
- Crystal LIght
  - Lemonade
  - Raspberry

Milk/Juices
- 2%: 1 cup = **1**
- Skim 1 cup = **1**
- Chocolate: 1 cup = **2**
- Apple Juice: ½ cup = **1**
- Cranberry Juice: 1/3 cup = **1**
- Diet Cranberry Juice: 1 cup = **1**
- Grape Juice: 1/3 cup = **1**
- Orange Juice: ½ cup = **1**
- Tomato Juice: 6 oz. = **½**
- V8 Juice: 6 oz. = **½**
- Prune Juice: 1/3 cup = **1**
- Pineapple Juice: 1/3 cup = **1**
- Hot Chocolate = **1**
- SF Hot Chocolate = **½**

(Continued)

Figure 5.2 Sample Selective Menu with Carbohydrate Count *(Continued)*

Condiments*	Clear Liquids	Full Liquids
• Butter	• Apple Juice: ½ cup = **1**	• Any clear liquid items
• Margarine	• Cranberry Juice: 1/3 cup = **1**	• Orange Juice: ½ cup = **1**
• Cream Cheese	• Grape Juice: 1/3 cup = **1**	• Milk, White: 1 cup = **1**
• Light Cream Cheese	• Diet Cranberry Juice: 1 cup = **1**	• Milk, Chocolate 1 cup = **2**
• Sour Cream	• Beef Broth	• Hot Cereal: ½ cup = **1**
• Creamer	• Chicken Broth	• Cream Soup (strained)
• Non Dairy Creamer	• Plain Gelatin: 1 = **1**	• Pudding: ½ cup = **2**
• Salt	• Pop Treat: 1 = **2**	• Ice Cream: ½ cup = **1**
• Salt Substitute	• Crystal Light	• Sherbet: ½ cup = **2**
• Sugar: 3 = **1**	• Coffee/Tea	• Creamer
• Splenda, Equal, Sweet-N-Low	• Creamer Breeze: 8 oz - 54g = **3.5**	• V8 Juice: 6 oz = **½**
• Syrup: 1 = **1**		• Tomato Juice: 6 oz = **½**
• Diet Syrup		• Prune Juice: 1/3 cup = **1**
• Jelly: 1 = **1**		• Pineapple Juice: 1/3 cup = **1**
• Pepper		• Boost: 8 oz - 41g = **~ 3**
• Mrs. Dash		
• Catsup		
• Mustard		
• Mayonnaise		
• Peanut butter		
** Condiments are okay: salt, sugar, Equal, Splenda, Sweet-N-Low, syrup, diet syrup. NOT PEPPER*		

Source: Southwest Health Center, Platteville WI, 2010. Used with permission.

Common adjustments on selective menus that may need to be made are:

✓ Portion sizes of products that count as fluid, for a fluid-restricted diet

✓ Portion sizes of high-carbohydrate foods, for a consistent-carbohydrate diet

✓ Consistency of foods and liquids for specific dysphagia diets

✓ Special adjustments for diets with multiple restrictions

✓ Adjustments to incorporate a standing order such as the addition of a liquid nutritional supplement to meals.

What happens if the client does not request enough food on a selective menu? What if the client selects food that is not on his/her diet? Foodservice staff should be trained to address a client's diet when they drop off the menu. e.g. "Good morning Mrs. Smith; I know that you are on a sodium restricted diet and here are your menu selections for today." This helps remind the client of their diet and sets the stage for their menu choices. If they see that the client has not selected very much food, the staff might say, "Oh, Mrs. Smith, our roast chicken is very tender and moist today; may I add that to your selection?" If the client insists on selecting something that is not on their menu, such as bacon on a salt restricted diet, gently remind the client that their diet does not allow them to have bacon. Always treat the clients with respect and respond in such a way that they don't become defensive.

On a selective menu, there may also be items a client writes in as a special request. How this is handled depends on the facility policy. In general, healthcare facilities attempt to honor write-in requests as practical. Many facilities develop a standardized list of write-in options to provide greater choice for clients.

Nonselective Menus

A **nonselective menu** is one in which clients do not have the opportunity to make choices for main dishes. Instead, they receive a standard, predefined menu. This is more common in a group dining experience such as a nursing home or assisted living. Even with a nonselective menu, you can focus on the clients by following their individualized food preferences with appropriate substitutions. You may be able to work with the medical staff to implement more liberalized diets so that all clients receive the general diet except for texture modifications.

Figure 5.3 Food Substitutions*

Food Item	Substitute Choices	Vitamin A Content (per 1/2 cup serving)	Vitamin C Content (per 1/2 cup serving)
Dark Green Vegetables	• Asparagus, boiled • Broccoli, frozen, boiled • Brussels sprouts, frozen, boiled • Green beans, canned • Green peppers, boiled • Kale (use in soups) • Mixed vegetables, frozen • Pea pods, boiled • Peas, frozen and boiled • Romaine lettuce, 1 cup	• 50 µg • 50 µg • 36 µg • 129 µg • 13 µg • 260 µg • 195 µg • 43 µg • 84 µg • 163 µg	• 7 µg • 50 mg • 35 mg • 4 mg • 60 mg • 16 mg • 3 mg • 38 mg • 8 mg • 14 mg
Bright Orange Vegetables	• Carrots, sliced, boiled • Sweet potatoes, boiled and mashed • Winter squash, baked	• 671 µg • 1000 µg • 268 µg	• 2.8 mg • 21 mg • 10 mg
White Vegetables	• Cabbage, boiled • Celery • Parsnips • Rutabaga • Turnips • Wax Beans	• 11 µg • 13 µg • 0 • 0 • 0 • 7 µg	• 30 mg • 2 mg • 10 mg • 16 • 9 mg • 3 mg
Red Vegetables	• Beets • Tomatoes, fresh, diced	• 1 µg • 38 µg	• 3 mg • 11 mg

* *Note: Vegetables are often the foods that clients will have an aversion to. Remember that substitutions have to be equivalent in nutritional value so choose another vegetable (s) that is roughly equivalent to the content of the leader nutrients, vitamin A and vitamin C*

Figure 5.4 From Menu to Service: Simple Flow of Work in a Foodservice Operation

In a nonselective menu system, it is also important to review and modify standard menu choices to accommodate specific diet orders. If your facility has implemented a liberalized diet, there may be very few diet orders, other than texture modifications. You will still want to follow individual food preferences, which may mean substituting a food item. Menu substitutions must be of equal nutritional value. For instance, if someone doesn't like cabbage, the substitute should be a food that replaces the vitamin C, such as tomatoes. Since menus are planned to incorporate color, try to replace a food with a similar or additional color. Your facility should have a list of approved substitutes for your menu cycle. See Figure 5.3 for food substitution choices.

The Impact of a Menu

By now, it is clear that a menu is a strong force in achieving client satisfaction. It has been said that the menu drives everything else in the kitchen. It is also a means of communicating with clients—and even marketing your fare to clients. However, it's more than that. A menu governs a series of events that will follow in the foodservice workflow. Figure 5.4 identifies this process in a simplified format.

As you can see, specifics of the recipes, the products you need to carry in inventory, and the entire preparation process all hinge on what the menu says. In addition, your requirements for staffing, equipment, and even physical layout and design depend on the menu.

Ultimately, the financial performance of your operation rests heavily on your menu, too. What it costs to produce and serve meals impacts your expenses. What you sell in cafeterias and retail arenas impact your revenues. In short, the menu is a critical and dominant force in your operation. As such, it merits special attention and careful planning.

Menu Planning Considerations

This section covers: customer/client satisfaction, nutrition and other resources, government regulations, standard weights and measures, management considerations, and cultural preferences.

Customer/Client Satisfaction

The most important consideration in menu planning is satisfying your customers/clients. Chapter 4 addressed many ways and means of satisfying clients. Remember to include cultural factors, food habits, and especially food preferences when planning your menus.

For the noon meal, green beans are on the menu. Your substitute for green beans is broccoli. One of your clients does not like either choice. What should you do?

(Check your answer at the end of this chapter)

Small facilities sometimes use a menu developed by their corporate office or a third party. It will be essential to adapt this menu to the needs, wants, and regional preferences of your clients.

Nutrition and Other Resources

Nutrition considerations should also be a primary goal of menu planning. It is important to maintain adequate nutritional status, to the extent possible. There are a number of resources to help you including the Dietary Guidelines for Americans 2010, Choose MyPlate, facility diet manual, and Recommended Dietary Allowances (RDAs). Figure 5.5 lists a number of standards that might be used to evaluate the nutritional content of your menus.

Government Regulations

Government regulation is another type of resource that plays a major part in menu planning. These regulations govern the type and quantity of food served at a meal. The Centers for Medicare & Medicaid Services (CMS) is a branch of the U.S. Department of Health and Human Services. CMS is the federal agency that administers the Medicare program and monitors the Medicaid programs offered by each state. All healthcare facilities have mandatory state licensing requirements. The facility is held to the strictest regulatory requirements, either state or federal. It is important to know and follow local and state regulations. These guidelines are dynamic, meaning they change constantly. Work with your facility administrator to make sure you have the most recent CMS guidelines that impact menu planning.

If you work in a school system, you will be expected to follow the USDA School Meals Initiative for Healthy Children. Critical upgrades to this initiative were launched in January 2010. Work with your school administrator to make sure you have the latest guidelines.

Sanitation regulations also play a part in menu planning as they dictate the temperature to which foods must be cooked, how quickly they need to be cooled, and the appropriate storage time of cooked and raw foods. You can work with your local sanitarian to make sure you have the most current sanitation regulations.

Standard Weights and Measures

An essential part of menu planning is using standard food weights, measures, and recipes correctly. To plan a menu, you and your staff need to know how many servings in a full-size steam table pan, how many servings from a quart when using a disher/portion scoop, how many tablespoons in a cup, how many servings you can expect from a case of fresh broccoli, etc. One very helpful book that provides these charts for standard weights and measures is Food for Fifty by Mary Molt. This reference also contains many quantity recipes that may help you in revising menus to meet your facility/client needs. Because standard weights and measures are so important to the outcome of your foodservice, it will be discussed further in Chapters 21 and 22.

Figure 5.5 Nutritional Guides or Standards for Menu Planning

Name of Guide	Source
Dietary Guidelines for Americans 2010	Department of Health and Human Sercies and U.S. Department of Agriculture
Choose MyPlate	U.S. Department of Agriculture
Exchange Lists (for diabetes or renal disease)	American Diabetes Association, American Dietetic Association, National Kidney Foundation
National Dysphagia Diet	American Dietetic Association and the Dietetics in Physical Medicine and Rehabilitation Practice Group
Recommended Dietary Allowances	National Research Council and the Nutrition Concepts & Medical Nutrition Therapy textbook
Nutrient Standard Menu Planning (NSMP)	U.S. Department of Agriculture or Assisted NSMP for school meal programs
Facility Diet Manual	Sample diet manual can be found at www.dds.ca.gov/publications/docs/DDSDietManual.pdf

Management Considerations

Since the menu drives what you do in the kitchen, it also drives your production and food costs. Other management considerations are: delivery methods, timing and labor, equipment, and food availability.

Production, service, and delivery methods. Your menu needs to be coordinated with your type of service. For instance, if you are doing display cooking, a stir-fry would be a great menu item. However, for cafeteria service where food may be held on a steam table, stir-fried items may lose quality and prove a poor choice.

If you use rethermalization methods for trays that are pre-assembled and chilled, it's important to examine what products stand up well to this process. Sometimes thickness of foods and presence of liquids, gravies, or sauces, and other aspects of the menu products you specify can influence final quality achieved through various systems. Before adding items to a menu, you may need to test intended recipes through your own equipment and systems to find out how they work.

Budget and cost. Next to labor, food cost is the second largest expense for your department and maybe even for your facility. That means managing food cost is a very important part of your job. Many facilities determine their food cost per client per day and your budget is allocated based on that figure. Whether your menu uses foods from raw ingredients or pre-prepared foods, both will impact your budget and your menu planning process. You can use food-cost percentage to help you compare your food costs to overall sales. Further discussion of this and other budget controls is in Chapter 28.

Timing and labor. How long it takes to prepare each menu item is an important consideration. Some menu items are more time-intensive than others. If you include a menu item that requires intensive preparation, you may need to pair it with a convenience or low-prep item to balance resources. The production schedule dictated by the menu must be realistic.

In addition, you must realistically match your menu to the skills of employees responsible for producing the menu items. Culinary challenges presented to minimally trained employees can lead to increased food costs through the loss of food or time. On the other hand, a facility that has a trained chef can use this resource to incorporate sophisticated techniques and preparation while holding food costs down. Through focused training, a Certified Dietary Manager can broaden the skills of food production employees so as to incorporate specific menu items that require specialized techniques.

Your foodservice department management team can help with menu planning by using their respective skills. For instance, the Certified Dietary Manager may provide input into the menu from the perspective of managing production. An executive chef can provide expertise on food items and preparation techniques. The Registered Dietitian can provide specific nutrition and therapeutic diet guidelines.

Equipment. Menu items may require a broad variety of equipment. Consider each proposed menu item in terms of physical layout and equipment. You also will have to consider what equipment will be in use at each time throughout the day. If every menu item for a given meal requires the use of the oven, you may not have enough oven space. Storage equipment and transport/delivery requirements can be related concerns.

Availability of food. What ingredients are available for your menu may be impacted by where your facility is located. Consider a rural facility that is 100 miles from a metropolitan center. You won't be able to get an immediate delivery of a special menu item. Today, with the emphasis on purchasing locally, your menu may reflect the ingredients that are available in your geographic region, such as Idaho potatoes, Washington apples, or Wisconsin cranberries. Weather may also impact what menu items are available. If there is a freeze in Florida, oranges or orange juice might be available but at a price too high to pay for your department budget. The availability of many of your produce items may be affected by weather and you may have to adjust your menu accordingly.

How would you adjust the following menu so it doesn't overload the same equipment?

- Baked Chicken
- Scalloped Potatoes
- Green Bean Casserole
- Baked Apples

(Check your answer at the end of this chapter)

Cultural Considerations

Cultural heritage should be a consideration when planning menus. To understand this aspect of menu planning, try asking yourself some questions. What does turkey and dressing with cranberry sauce mean to you? Many people will answer: Thanksgiving. This food has become part of a cultural tradition. Now, think about a wedding celebration. What food will always be served? Most people will answer: a wedding cake. Or, in China, the answer may be: roasted pig. Now, try another question. What food has become a symbol of American heritage and pride? Many people will answer: apple pie. From these examples, you can see that we regard food choices as cultural symbols. The meaning of

these foods is much deeper than a sum of protein, carbohydrate, fat, vitamins, and minerals—the sheer nutritional values.

Many food choices arise from what we learn through our own cultural experiences. Holidays, festivals, and important events each have associated foods. In addition, daily food choices vary by culture. Traditional German cuisine, for example, is likely to include sausage, schnitzel, spaetzel, beer, and other specialties. Japanese cuisine includes sushi, tempura, and rice. Swedish cuisine may include pancakes, even at meals other than breakfast. Mexican cuisine includes staples such as tortillas, rice, and refried beans. Creole cuisine, popular in New Orleans, represents a synthesis of French cooking with locally available foods, and the influences of Caribbean and Spanish cultures.

As a land of immigrants, the U.S. enjoys multi-faceted cultural diversity. Our menu choices are as rich and complex as our population itself. See Figure 5.6 for cultural food influences. Here are more examples of cultural and ethnic food influences.

Hispanics/Latinos. The United States Census Bureau defines Hispanics as those who indicate their origin to be Mexican, Puerto Rican, Cuban, Central or South American (e.g., Dominican, Nicaraguan, Colombian) or other Hispanic origin. The largest of these is the Mexican-American population, which represents at least two-thirds of all Hispanics/Latinos. According to a national survey conducted by the U.S. Department of Agriculture, "Hispanics tend to eat more rice, but less pasta and ready-to-eat cereals than their non-Hispanic white counterparts. Hispanics are also likely to consume vegetables, especially tomatoes, although they have a slightly higher consumption of fruits. Compared to non-Hispanic whites, Hispanics are more than twice as likely to drink whole milk, but much less likely to drink low-fat or skim milk. Hispanics are also more likely to eat beef, but less likely to eat processed meats such as hot dogs, sausage, and luncheon meats." Legumes and corn in combination are a good source of protein and cheese is a frequent ingredient in foods.

East Indian Americans. Staples of the Indian diet include rice, beans, lentils, and bread. Rice is usually served steamed and mixed with flavorings. Indian breads include chapatis, round flatbread made of whole wheat flour; and naan, a bread that uses yeast. India's religious beliefs have also influenced the diet of Indians (e.g. Hindus believe that cows are sacred so they do not eat beef.) Chicken or lamb, in moderation, is augmented with vegetables, dried beans, lentils and split peas. Curry powder, a mixture of spices, is often used to flavor Indian foods. The heart of Indian cooking is the combination of spices that gives each dish its unique flavor. Indian cuisine has become increasingly popular during the first decade of the 21st Century with over 1200 Indian food products now available in the U.S.

Chinese Americans. Vegetables, rice and noodles, fruits, and foods made from soybeans (such as tofu and soy milk) are very important foods in the Chinese-American diet. Plain rice is served at all meals. Sometimes fried rice is served. Pork, poultry, and fish are popular and used in small amounts to flavor the rice. Foods are often seasoned with soy sauce, which is high in sodium.

Figure 5.6 Cultural Influences on Food Intake in the United States

Group	Grains	Vegetables	Fruits	Meat	Dairy
Hispanic/Latino	Tortillas (may be made with lard), rice	Cactus, cassava, chayote, jicama, peppers, pinto beans, tomatoes (salsa)	Avocado, bananas, guava, mango, papaya, plantain, citrus fruits	Chorizo (sausage and other processed meat), goat meat, tongue, pork	Goat cheese, goat milk, whole milk
Asian (China, Japan, Korea, Southeast Asia)	Rice noodles	Garlic, ginger, mung beans, sprouts, bamboo shoots, bok choy, cabbage, carrots	Mango, banana, citrus fruit, coconut, pineapple	Small amounts of meat especially fish; eggs, tofu	Soy milk
Middle Eastern	Couscous, tahini, pita bread, filo dough	Tomatoes, olives, lentils, hummus, grape leaves, eggplant	Dates, figs, citrus fruits	Small amounts of lamb, fish, chicken	Yogurt, feta cheese
East Indian	Rice, whole wheat flat bread (naan)	Red lentils, pigeon peas, legumes, curries	Coconut, watermelon, mango	Many East Indian people are vegetarian; some mutton chicken, fish	Milk, butter, yogurt

Please note that this is not meant to be an exact list of foods. All of these cultures have diets that vary from one region/country to another.

(Low-sodium versions can be purchased). Corn oil, sesame oil, and peanut oil are used. Tea is the main beverage and it is always enjoyed black—without sugar, cream, or milk. Cow's milk and dairy products are not used often. Fruits are important and few sweets are eaten.

Japanese Americans. Some people are surprised to learn that Japanese food is quite different in appearance and taste from Chinese food. While Chinese food is often stir-fried, Japanese food is often simmered, boiled, steamed, or broiled. Also, Japanese foods are not as highly seasoned as Chinese dishes. Sushi, a rice wrapped in seaweed has become a popular food choice in the U.S. in the past decade. Rice is the staple of many Japanese-American diets, along with a variety of noodles. As in Chinese cooking, soybean products, such as soy sauce, are important. Seafood is generally more popular than meat and poultry. Vegetables, such as watercress and carrots, are an important part of most meals. Tea is the most popular beverage, especially green tea, an excellent source of antioxidants.

Middle Eastern Americans. Foods of choice in a traditional Middle Eastern diet include yogurt, cheeses (such as feta and goat cheese), lamb, poultry, chick peas, lentils, lemons, eggplant, pine nuts, olives, and olive oil. A Greek specialty is baklava, a baked dessert made with nuts, honey, and filo dough. Common cooking styles are grilling, frying, and stewing.

As a new Certified Dietary Manager, you want your menu to address the cultural differences of your clients. What is the first step to implementing a cultural change movement in your facility?

(Check your answer at the end of this chapter)

Regional Trends

Part of the cultural heritage unique to the U.S. is the development of regional culinary trends. Often, these trends reflect a mix of native cultures, foods that are grown and harvested in the area, and ethnic traditions contributed by settlers and immigrants over time. For example, New England is known for maple syrup, Boston beans, brown bread, and cranberry muffins. Maine is recognized for lobster. Blueberries are important in New Jersey and in the Midwest, where many are grown. In Pennsylvania and parts of Ohio, the Pennsylvania Dutch heritage gives rise to scrapple (a loaf made from meat scraps, broth, and flour), homemade noodles, and shoofly (molasses) pie.

Vidalia onions are a hallmark of Georgia's cuisine and are the official state vegetable. Peanuts and peaches are also key crops in Georgia. Florida is known for key limes and key lime pie, coquina soup, and other specialties. Kuchen is the official state dessert in South Dakota. Most people associate Idaho with potatoes, and New Orleans with Creole cuisine, such as jambalaya, "dirty" rice, and gumbo. Barbecued meats and pickled okra have special significance in Texas. In the Southwest (Arizona, New Mexico, Oklahoma, Texas), Mexican-style foods such as burritos and tacos are popular. Garlic is so important in California that the town of Gilroy celebrates an annual garlic festival. In fact, food celebrations, such as strawberry harvest festivals, maple syrup festivals, and many others are key events in all parts of the country.

Religious Practices

Religious beliefs, along with religious customs and rituals, can exert strong influence on menu planning. Fasting is one practice that many religions observe. The length of time one fasts varies with his/her religion and can range from one day to a month. Some Muslims observe Ramadan, which lasts for one month and fasting occurs from sun up to sun down. Think about how this practice might affect Muslim clients in a long-term facility. Religious laws will also affect menu planning.

Menu Revision

In the foodservice industry, most experts agree that a menu should not become static. For both ongoing and occasional clients, periodic revisions are a necessity. Here are some events that might signal a need for menu revision:

Seasonal change. People actually choose different foods at different times of the year. Summer foods may include salads, chilled entrees, and produce in peak season. Winter foods (where winters are cold) may include more soups, stews, and seasonally available produce.

Trends and fashions. Ever-changing, the world of food experiences culinary innovations as well as trends. Keeping pace with these helps a facility compete in the industry. For instance: edamame was not well known 20 years ago; today it is a common restaurant menu option.

Client feedback. Client suggestions, along with information gathered through surveys, often begin to show patterns. A suggestion that arises repeatedly—or a complaint about a particular menu—can be triggers for revision.

Glossary

Kosher
Fit, proper or in agreement with religious law. Kosher meat means the animal has been slaughtered in a special way. Usually Kosher foods have been blessed by a rabbi.

Comfort Food
Any food that imparts a unique sense of emotional well-being such as chicken soup

Special requests. A Certified Dietary Manager may monitor items that clients request or add to their own menus. If a request appears repeatedly, it may be time to add the item to the menu or increase its frequency.

Sales records. If you are monitoring sales records or selection data for the menu, you may discover that certain items are proving unpopular. One of the jobs of a Certified Dietary Manager is to identify menu "duds" and replace them with products clients crave.

Quality issues. Similarly, a Certified Dietary Manager conducting routine quality checks may determine that a certain item is not holding up well on the menu. There may be a solution. Changing the procedure or the recipe, using different techniques or equipment, or training staff may make a difference. If not, the item may need to be replaced.

Changes in the physical facility. Remodeling, renovations, or reallocation of space in a facility may impose changes on the foodservice department. Perhaps the opportunity exists to build an expanded cafeteria. A Certified Dietary Manager may explore a food court concept and its related menu implications. Or, a facility may have an opportunity to build a group dining area, where buffet service is an option. The menu needs to change accordingly.

Service revisions. Sometimes a Certified Dietary Manager faces the need to develop new services, or serve new clients. In addition, mergers and acquisitions may present new requirements to serve remote facilities. Integrating service changes with existing schemes may provide cause for re-evaluation of the menu as a whole and all related coordination issues.

A proposed menu revision should undergo evaluation for any nutrient standards that apply, as well as for costs. In addition, any menu revision creates ripple effects through the operational flow. To implement a change, systematically examine and plan related revisions required in staffing, service and delivery, inventory and purchasing, and food production.

In all, you can see that a menu wields great impact in every foodservice operation. Designing a menu that meets your clients' needs and expectations and uses your resources effectively is an enormous amount of work. However, the rewards are well worth the effort.

Late Trays

In a healthcare setting, it is essential to have a system for providing meals to clients who have just been admitted, whose diet orders have changed, or who have missed a meal due to testing or special procedures. Trays delivered between meal times by individual request are called late trays. Particularly in an acute care environment, menu-related information can change quickly. In many situations, late trays are cumbersome and expensive to produce and deliver. Obtaining required adjustments just before tray assembly can sometimes reduce the volume of late trays. Many healthcare operations strive to reduce late tray requests through their meal system design, because late trays can significantly increase the operating expense of a foodservice department. Room service is an example of a service model that can virtually eliminate late trays, because all meals are provided on demand.

Menu Substitutions

Even with liberalization, another issue often arises in long-term care environments—the need for substitutions on the menu. A substitution is an item that is substituted for another by the individual request of the client when he does not like or refuses to eat the food being served. Centers for Medicare & Medicaid Services (CMS) regulations specify that requests for substitutions should be permitted and honored, as long as they are reasonable and achievable. A substitution must be of similar nutritive value. On a selective menu, some Certified Dietary Managers use the term menu *write-in* to describe the same idea. A client may write an item on the menu that was not part of the planned cycle.

Providing substitutions upon request is part of the concept of giving clients control over their care; meal choice is considered a client right. In addition, adjusting offerings to a client's requests helps to ensure optimal nutritional intake. In all, honoring substitution requests contributes to quality of life, especially for nursing facility clients. Review Figure 5.3 for an appropriate substitution list.

What should a Certified Dietary Manager do with a substitution request? The answer is: Honor it or provide an alternate choice. Obviously, some requests are not feasible. However, many options may exist. For a long-term client, a Certified Dietary Manager may be able to make special arrangements to accommodate a special request. Sound management and practical realities dictate that the substitution process be planned and organized as part of the menu.

One way to provide substitutions is simply to offer alternate choices on a menu or in the service setting itself. This eliminates many of the challenges of providing substitutions at the last minute. It is one reason that some long-term care facilities have changed to selective menus. On a selective menu, clients can choose their substitutions or alternates in advance of service, and kitchen staff can tally requirements in time for production.

Keeping in mind the goal of honoring client requests, a Certified Dietary Manager may also develop a list of write-in requests that can be accommodated in the kitchen. Then, the manager plans production of these items in conjunction with routine meal service, or is at least prepared to honor these requests efficiently. Some offerings on the write-in list may cross over with items prepared daily for another service area, such as a cafeteria. In essence, this write-in list becomes its own supplementary menu. Designated staff may refer to this menu in guiding clients towards practical substitutions.

Individual Menu Review—Honoring Legal and Moral Responsibilties

Every healthcare menu system must have a method for ensuring that every client receives a meal, even if selections have not been made. Clients who do not complete a selective menu receive a house diet or default selection. For a client whose preferences are known, a member of the clinical staff may complete a menu based on care plan or kardex information. This information may be tracked in a diet office software system.

Furthermore, every menu communications system must include control steps to ensure that foods planned for the individual menu meet the current diet order prescribed by the physician. Whether menus are selective or non-selective, spoken or paper-based, or implemented through trayline or buffet service, trained foodservice staff must assist with individual menu review before a client consumes the meal. Figure 5.7 lists some of the criteria for menu review.

While menu review can be labor-intensive, a Certified Dietary Manager can structure menu systems to minimize the labor. For example, diet office software can review menu choices to check for compliance with meal patterns, or totals for restricted nutrients (such as sodium, protein, or fluid). It can eliminate foods the client is allergic to, or automate routine additions. This process requires that foodservice staff maintain a computerized set of care plans or kardex information, which the software uses in menu review.

When a foodservice staff member needs to make adjustments to an individual menu, communicating with the client is important for several reasons:

- ✓ The client has a right to know why the menu has changed.
- ✓ If the client does not know the menu has been adjusted intentionally, the revisions may be perceived as an error.
- ✓ Menu review provides an opportunity for education about a modified diet. A foodservice staff member can use this opportunity to explain a meal pattern or other menu adjustment.
- ✓ Discussing adjustments opens a dialogue in which foodservice staff can learn more about the client's diet-related needs and preferences.

A client requests a menu item that is not allowed on their diet. What do you do?

(Check your answer at the end of this chapter)

Figure 5.7 Criteria for Individual Menu Review (Healthcare)

Before a client receives a tray and consumes a meal, trained foodservice staff must review individual menus and answer the following questions:

- Do the selections provide a well-balanced meal, or has the client selected choices from nearly all categories (e.g. entree, vegetable, starch choice, beverage, etc.)?
- Are appropriate condiments included (e.g. margarine for bread, dressing for salad, etc.)?
- If the client's diet order specifies combined modifications, such as sodium-restricted and carbohydrate-controlled, are selections compliant with all sets of restrictions?
- If texture modifications (e.g. mechanical soft diet or National Dysphagia Diet levels) are part of the diet order, does each menu selection comply with the order?
- If the client has a meal pattern or a carbohydrate count, how do the totals compare to the plan?
- Are portion sizes indicated on the menu appropriate for this particular diet order?
- If the client has a fluid restriction, how do the figures add up?
- If the client has requested a substitution, is the request honored?
- If the diet order or kardex lists specific foods to avoid (e.g. allergies or food intolerances), have these items been removed from the menu?
- If the diet order or kardex lists specific additions for meals (e.g. nutrition supplements), are these items included?

END OF CHAPTER

Putting It Into Practice Questions & Answers

1. Your hospital just implemented a room service menu. You still offer menus in the cafeteria that change every two weeks. What menu styles are you using?

   A. *Cycle menu in the cafeteria and static menu for the room service menu.*

2. For the noon meal, green beans are on the menu. Your substitute for green beans is broccoli. One of your clients does not like either choice. What should you do?

   A. *Your first duty is to honor the rights of the client while balancing what they want with the nutritional content of the substitute. Can you offer other choices that also provide a similar amount of vitamin A such as mixed vegetables, winter squash, or carrots?*

3. How would you adjust the following menu so it doesn't overload the same equipment?
   - Baked Chicken
   - Scalloped Potatoes
   - Green Bean Casserole
   - Baked Apples

   A. *There are too many items that require the use of the oven. In small facilities you may only have one traditional size oven. The recipe could be adjusted to:*
   - *Baked Chicken*
   - *Potato Salad*
   - *Steamed Green Beans*
   - *Baked Apples*

4. As a new Certified Dietary Manager, you want your menu to address the cultural differences of your customers. What is the first step to implementing a cultural change movement in your facility?

   A. *Talk to clients! What do they like/want? What would they do regarding food choices and meal times if they don't live in your facility?*

5. A client requests a menu item that is not allowed on their diet. What do you do?

   A. *First, meet with the client to review current diet restrictions. If they still insist on having the menu item, provide that item, if possible, or offer an alternative. Second, document each step you took in the process in the medical record.*

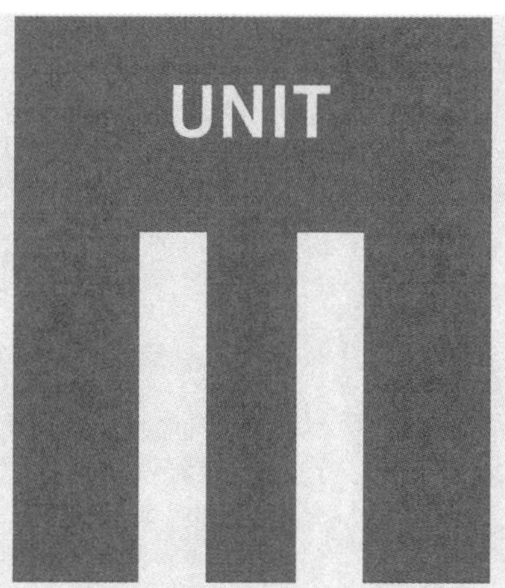

Hire & Supervise

There is a quote by an unknown author that says: *Love is blind but hiring shouldn't be!* The hiring decisions you make will be one of the most important decisions for your department. Once that employee is hired, employee development will also impact the success of your department. The more effort you put into hiring and employee development, the less time you will have to put into supervising that employee.

Develop and Maintain Employee Time Schedules and Assignments

Overview and Objectives

From pay period to pay period, you need to schedule employees to ensure that personnel are always available to do required work. Scheduling involves assessing both production and service, the volume of work or output, and how long it takes to fulfill assigned duties. You will also investigate the different types of schedules.

After completing this chapter, you should be able to:

- ✓ Prepare a time schedule
- ✓ Maintain time schedule chart/records
- ✓ Prepare absence/tardy reports for personnel files
- ✓ Identify overall staffing needs
- ✓ Calculate full time equivalents
- ✓ Identify and interpret daily tasks
- ✓ Determine capabilities and preferences of employees available
- ✓ Develop a work assignment chart
- ✓ Explain and coordinate work assignments

The work of your operation is defined through job analyses and job descriptions. Next, examine the sum total of the work to be completed on a given day in your operation. You develop schedules that match your needs for production and service, based on volume of work and deadlines, and then consider how long it takes to fulfill assigned duties. All of this information feeds into the process of scheduling employees.

Effective Scheduling

Well planned schedules are important for:

- ✓ Controlling your labor costs
- ✓ Ensuring that adequate labor resources are available at the right times and places to accomplish the work.

Essentially, you begin at the end with your scheduled service times and commitments, and then work backwards to determine what labor resources you will need when, in order to meet your commitments.

Piecing your requirements together simply requires thought and a bit of trial and error. Working with tasks and positions, you can devise job routines. Job routines tell *when* the work is done.

A job routine is an individual schedule for the work day within each position, and spells out the events of the work day in a format such as this:

6:00 AM	Punch in, ready to work
	Set up breakfast trayline for required items on Station 3
6:15 - 8:00 AM	Serve food on breakfast trayline
8:00 - 8:15 AM	Break
8:15 - 10:45 AM	Work in cold food production area portioning foods for lunch meal service
10:45 - 11:15 AM	Lunch break

The routine continues until the entire work day has been addressed. Developing an entire set of job routines helps you plan exactly how many people need to work on each day, and how to assign duties to them.

Your complete staffing plan and set of job routines may not be the same every day. In many foodservice operations, the volume of work and services declines on Saturdays and Sundays. For example, if you provide employee dining services, even in a seven-day-per-week healthcare facility, there may be fewer employees scheduled throughout the facility on a weekend. The volume of employee dining services you need to provide would be reduced. As a result, you may combine more work into single job routines, and you may need to schedule fewer employees. Holidays typically change the staffing requirements, too.

Your client count or census may also affect daily staffing needs. As client counts decrease, you may whittle down staffing accordingly. As they increase, you may need to increase staffing levels. The work performed in many positions of your operation should be adjusted in proportion to your volume. This is sound management and sound financial control.

Goals for Scheduling

Once you have determined how many people you need in each position for day-to-day operations, you can begin to write a schedule. This is a task that most managers complete about a week before each new pay period begins. A schedule identifies when each employee will work during that pay period, and to what position(s) that employee will be assigned.

When developing a schedule consider the following goals:

- ✓ Schedule staff to fit work needs
- ✓ Use creative scheduling plans
- ✓ Use the skill of your staff and each employee's schedule requests
- ✓ Use scheduling policies
- ✓ Plan ahead for special events

Schedule staff to fit work needs. It is generally not useful for all staff to begin and end shifts at the same time. They should be scheduled as the volume of

work requires. This is called **staggered scheduling**. For example, one dishwasher might be scheduled to begin work one hour before the evening meal period begins. This time may be used to clean up any remaining dishes from lunch and take care of production pots and pans for the dinner period. A second service employee might be brought in one-half hour before the time of service to perform other duties. Both employees will be ready for the evening rush period.

Other personnel would be scheduled through a process that provides the required number of staff for the volume of meals to be served at various hours. The first employee in will be the first employee to leave. Staggered ending times are also important to assure maximum employee efficiency.

Use creative scheduling plans. In foodservice operations, work flow may not be constant. There are times during the course of a day when a great deal must occur at once, such as just before and during meal service times. There are other times of the day that may not be as rushed. Employees should be scheduled accordingly. Staggered scheduling frequently reduces necessary labor hours, often reducing the need for full-time personnel.

Part-time staff can be hired to work short shifts, such as three, four, or five-hour shifts. Sometimes, a job is designed as a **split shift**, which is two short shifts in one day separated by a period of time off. Temporary employees can also be used. Many facilities maintain a list of people who don't want steady work, but who do like to work occasionally. If there is a special event, an employee illness, or other need for temporary assistance, these personnel can be very helpful.

Use the skills of your staff and each employee's schedule request. Consider personnel preferences whenever possible. You should have a mechanism for employees to use to communicate special scheduling needs in advance of the time you prepare the schedule. So, if Mary needs to be off on the first Tuesday of the pay period, she should let you know by completing a form. If Mark needs to leave by 2:00 PM to attend a wedding, he can request to work an early shift. If Juanita wishes to take a one-week vacation next month, she can let you know this, too.

Request forms may be used by personnel for indicating in advance those days/shifts when they wish to be off duty. You should honor these requests when possible.

You should also consider the skill sets of your staff. If you have an employee with a pleasing smile and personality, he or she might enjoy helping in the dining room or cafeteria with the clients.

Establish and use scheduling policies. Operation of a foodservice department typically requires staffing at times that many employees might not consider optimal work hours, such as very early in the morning, very late at night, on weekends, or on holidays. When employees work weekends, they often do not enjoy having two days off in a row. A day off might occur on a Tuesday one week, and on a Friday another week. In addition, the number of employees who can take days off or schedule vacation at any given time is limited. During peak vacation seasons, many employees may wish to take time off work. However, you cannot honor every request.

Glossary

Staggered Scheduling
Scheduling staff so they come in at different times instead of several coming in and leaving at the same time

Split Shift
Two short shifts separated by a period of time off in one day

To manage these kinds of situations, you want to have policies relating to working hours, rotation of shifts, rotation of scheduling for weekends, rotation of holiday assignments, and decision-making regarding requests for time off. If you don't have clear policies, then each decision becomes a random or arbitrary action, subject to the scrutiny of all employees. On occasion, the decisions made in preparation of a schedule can become a source of discontent among employees. If you don't have a consistent method for making decisions, employees may also feel that your scheduling practices are not fair and equitable.

So, the solution is simply to devise guidelines, make them known to all employees, and follow them consistently. Several factors may affect how you set policies. The first is employment law. There are limits to how many hours you will schedule each employee. Next, if your employees belong to a union, there may be stipulations in the union contract with which your policies must comply. If your facility as a whole has human resources policies that relate to scheduling, you must comply with these also. Beyond these constraints, you need to develop your own workable guidelines.

Here are examples of practices Certified Dietary Managers sometimes include in scheduling policies:

- ✓ Employees in _______ area are required to work weekends. The schedule is developed such that each employee works every other weekend.
- ✓ An employee who works the night shift on one day is not scheduled for the early morning shift the next day.
- ✓ For holiday scheduling, each employee completes a holiday request form, indicating a first, second, and third choice for holidays to be scheduled off duty. The manager takes these requests in sequence for each employee, honoring as many requests as possible.
- ✓ Requests for time off are granted on a first-come, first-served basis. If two requests are received on the same day and only one can be granted, the request is granted to the employee with the longest tenure.

Plan ahead for special events. You can use past schedules as a reference. Creating a schedule is a big job, so you do not want to re-invent the wheel every two weeks or so. Instead, you can retain past schedules and use them as a reference for developing new ones.

Creating the Schedule

Scheduling can be a time-consuming task. Managers may develop a standard scheduling form that has certain details filled in, such as the standard shifts, names of full-time employees, and the hours of operation.

When available, you can use software. Some facilities have computer programs for scheduling employees. A typical program allows you to enter special requests for each employee and to define your policies within the system. It generates a schedule based on all available information and allows you to review it and edit it if necessary.

Employee scheduling software may also allow you to establish desired staffing ratios that define the number of employees you will schedule based on meal or

Putting It Into Practice: 1

Two employees have submitted requests to have the same day off. Having both of them gone at the same time would pose a hardship to the department. What should you do?

(Check your answer at the end of this chapter)

client counts. You may also be able to run reports in advance to verify that your proposed schedule will meet the budget. Once your schedule information is set, you have several options: a master schedule, a daily schedule, an employee's personal schedule, and so forth. Please see Figure 6.1 and 6.2 for examples. Some systems allow you to search the employee records to identify available employees and contact information for use when you have unscheduled absences. Employee scheduling packages are available as part of a timeclock system and then integrate with timeclocks and payroll reporting.

Scheduling concerns for salaried (exempt) employees include:

✓ Consider personal preferences in schedules when possible.

✓ Determine what they should do (per the job description), and schedule them in a way that permits time to do the required tasks.

✓ Use job analysis information to develop staffing guides and routines.

✓ Promote cross-training so when unexpected absences occur, others can fill in.

Estimating Staffing Needs

Part of scheduling is estimating your staffing needs. How do you know how many staff you need for production, service, and sanitation? Production needs are established by the type of menu in your facility. A school may not need as many staff as a nursing home because of the difference in menu items produced. The number of wait staff or aids that you need is determined by the type of service you provide. If you have a full-service dining room, you may need more service staff than a facility that uses a trayline. Your sanitation staff will also depend upon how many meals are served in a day (dishwashing needs) and what maintenance tasks are completed by the facility's maintenance department. When using electronic scheduling, your software will allow you to add positions. See Figure 6.1 for an example.

Calculating total labor hours. This method requires you to look at each position or job analysis for production staff, service staff, sanitation staff, and management staff, as well as your hours of operation. For production staff, count the hours prior to any meal service time as production time. If you have a cafeteria, count the hours other than actual service time. For example, if you are a small hospital that also operates a cafeteria during the noon hour, you would count your production hours as shown in Figure 6.3. Repeat this example for service staff, sanitation staff, and management staff to determine the total hours needed.

Calculating FTEs. FTE stands for full-time equivalent. A full-time equivalent is the total number of hours worked over a period of time by one full-time employee. Most facilities use 40 hours in one week to equal one FTE. If one person works 8 hours per day, 5 days per week, 52 weeks per year, that person's work hours during the year total 2080 hours. This is one FTE per year.

If two people each work half-time at 20 hours per week, these two positions add up to one FTE. An FTE does not mean the number of employees in your operation. Instead, it is a conversion of labor hours to a standard unit.

Figure 6.1 Sample Screens to Add Positions (from Software)

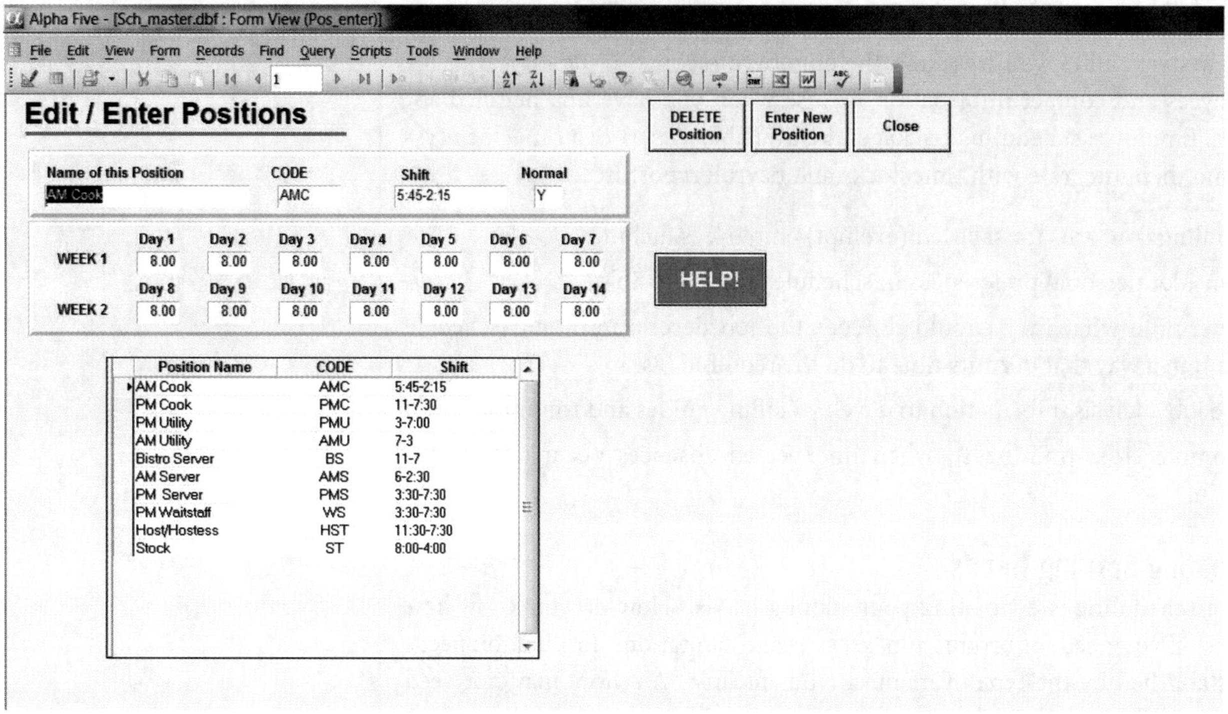

Alpha Five - [Sch_master.dbf : Form View (Pos_enter)]

File Edit View Form Records Find Query Scripts Tools Window Help

Edit / Enter Positions

DELETE Position | Enter New Position | Close

Name of this Position	CODE	Shift	Normal
AM Cook	AMC	5:45-2:15	Y

	Day 1	Day 2	Day 3	Day 4	Day 5	Day 6	Day 7
WEEK 1	8.00	8.00	8.00	8.00	8.00	8.00	8.00
	Day 8	Day 9	Day 10	Day 11	Day 12	Day 13	Day 14
WEEK 2	8.00	8.00	8.00	8.00	8.00	8.00	8.00

HELP!

Position Name	CODE	Shift
AM Cook	AMC	5:45-2:15
PM Cook	PMC	11-7:30
PM Utility	PMU	3-7:00
AM Utility	AMU	7-3
Bistro Server	BS	11-7
AM Server	AMS	6-2:30
PM Server	PMS	3:30-7:30
PM Waitstaff	WS	3:30-7:30
Host/Hostess	HST	11:30-7:30
Stock	ST	8:00-4:00

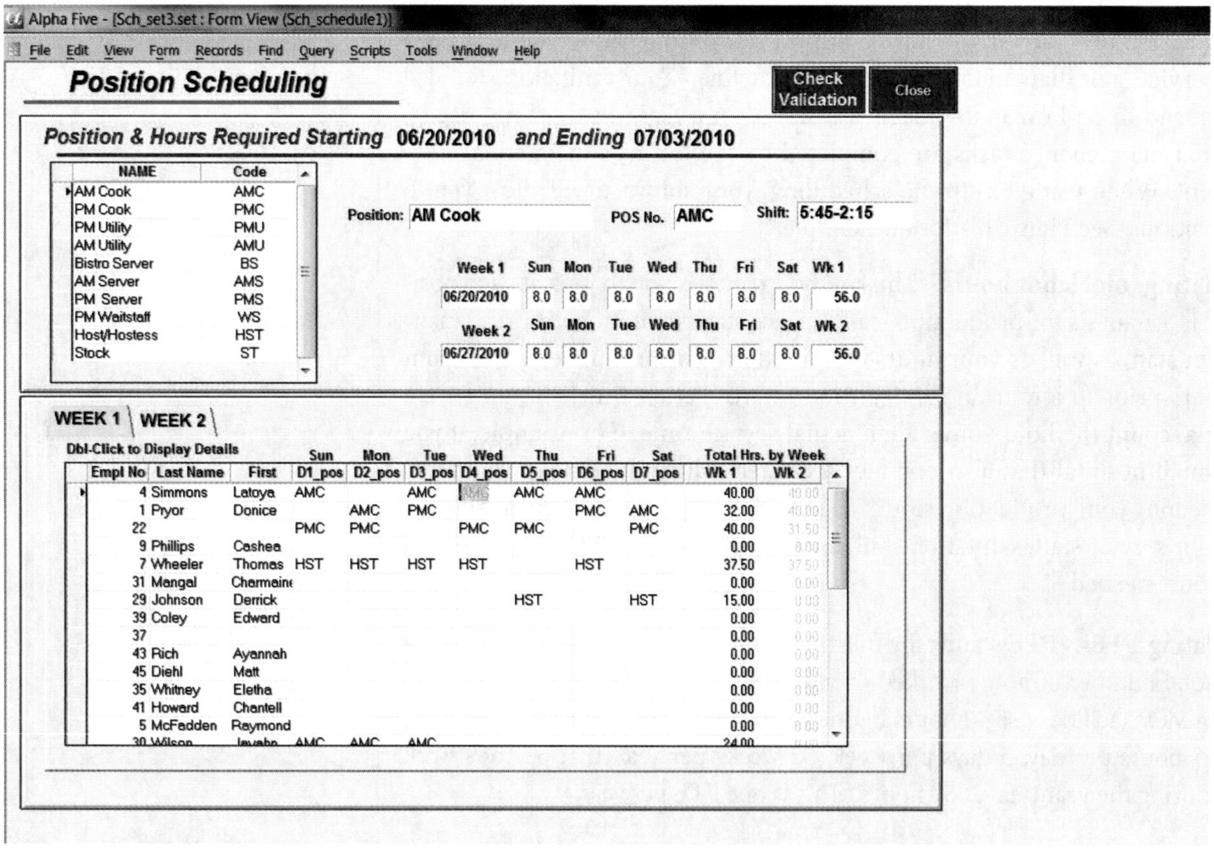

Alpha Five - [Sch_set3.set : Form View (Sch_schedule1)]

File Edit View Form Records Find Query Scripts Tools Window Help

Position Scheduling

Check Validation | Close

***Position & Hours Required Starting* 06/20/2010 *and Ending* 07/03/2010**

NAME	Code
AM Cook	AMC
PM Cook	PMC
PM Utility	PMU
AM Utility	AMU
Bistro Server	BS
AM Server	AMS
PM Server	PMS
PM Waitstaff	WS
Host/Hostess	HST
Stock	ST

Position: AM Cook POS No. AMC Shift: 5:45-2:15

Week 1	Sun	Mon	Tue	Wed	Thu	Fri	Sat	Wk 1
06/20/2010	8.0	8.0	8.0	8.0	8.0	8.0	8.0	56.0
Week 2	**Sun**	**Mon**	**Tue**	**Wed**	**Thu**	**Fri**	**Sat**	**Wk 2**
06/27/2010	8.0	8.0	8.0	8.0	8.0	8.0	8.0	56.0

WEEK 1 | WEEK 2

Dbl-Click to Display Details

			Sun	Mon	Tue	Wed	Thu	Fri	Sat	Total Hrs. by Week	
Empl No	Last Name	First	D1_pos	D2_pos	D3_pos	D4_pos	D5_pos	D6_pos	D7_pos	Wk 1	Wk 2
4	Simmons	Latoya	AMC		AMC	AMC	AMC	AMC		40.00	40.00
1	Pryor	Donice		AMC	PMC			PMC	AMC	32.00	40.00
22			PMC	PMC		PMC	PMC		PMC	40.00	31.50
9	Phillips	Cashea								0.00	0.00
7	Wheeler	Thomas	HST	HST	HST	HST		HST		37.50	37.50
31	Mangal	Charmaine								0.00	0.00
29	Johnson	Derrick					HST		HST	15.00	0.00
39	Coley	Edward								0.00	0.00
37										0.00	0.00
43	Rich	Ayannah								0.00	0.00
45	Diehl	Matt								0.00	0.00
35	Whitney	Eletha								0.00	0.00
41	Howard	Chantell								0.00	0.00
5	McFadden	Raymond								0.00	0.00
30	Wilson	Javahn	AMC	AMC	AMC					24.00	

Source: Dietary Manager by Brimstone Allon Enterprises. www.dietarymanagementsoftware.com

Figure 6.2 Sample Master Schedule and Individual Employee Schedule

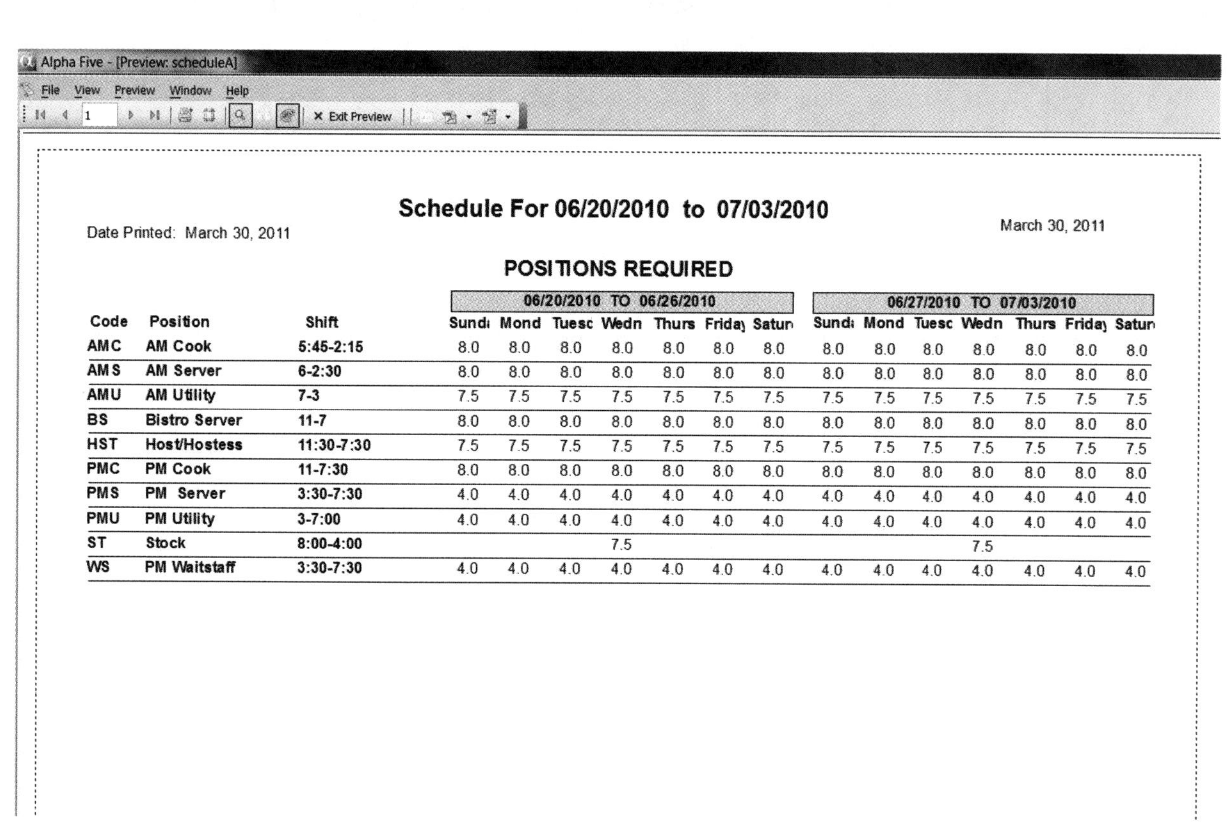

Alpha Five - [Preview: scheduleA]

Date Printed: March 30, 2011

Schedule For 06/20/2010 to 07/03/2010

March 30, 2011

POSITIONS REQUIRED

Code	Position	Shift	06/20/2010 TO 06/26/2010							06/27/2010 TO 07/03/2010						
			Sundi	Mond	Tuesc	Wedn	Thurs	Friday	Satur	Sundi	Mond	Tuesc	Wedn	Thurs	Friday	Satur
AMC	AM Cook	5:45-2:15	8.0	8.0	8.0	8.0	8.0	8.0	8.0	8.0	8.0	8.0	8.0	8.0	8.0	8.0
AMS	AM Server	6-2:30	8.0	8.0	8.0	8.0	8.0	8.0	8.0	8.0	8.0	8.0	8.0	8.0	8.0	8.0
AMU	AM Utility	7-3	7.5	7.5	7.5	7.5	7.5	7.5	7.5	7.5	7.5	7.5	7.5	7.5	7.5	7.5
BS	Bistro Server	11-7	8.0	8.0	8.0	8.0	8.0	8.0	8.0	8.0	8.0	8.0	8.0	8.0	8.0	8.0
HST	Host/Hostess	11:30-7:30	7.5	7.5	7.5	7.5	7.5	7.5	7.5	7.5	7.5	7.5	7.5	7.5	7.5	7.5
PMC	PM Cook	11-7:30	8.0	8.0	8.0	8.0	8.0	8.0	8.0	8.0	8.0	8.0	8.0	8.0	8.0	8.0
PMS	PM Server	3:30-7:30	4.0	4.0	4.0	4.0	4.0	4.0	4.0	4.0	4.0	4.0	4.0	4.0	4.0	4.0
PMU	PM Utility	3-7:00	4.0	4.0	4.0	4.0	4.0	4.0	4.0	4.0	4.0	4.0	4.0	4.0	4.0	4.0
ST	Stock	8:00-4:00				7.5							7.5			
WS	PM Waitstaff	3:30-7:30	4.0	4.0	4.0	4.0	4.0	4.0	4.0	4.0	4.0	4.0	4.0	4.0	4.0	4.0

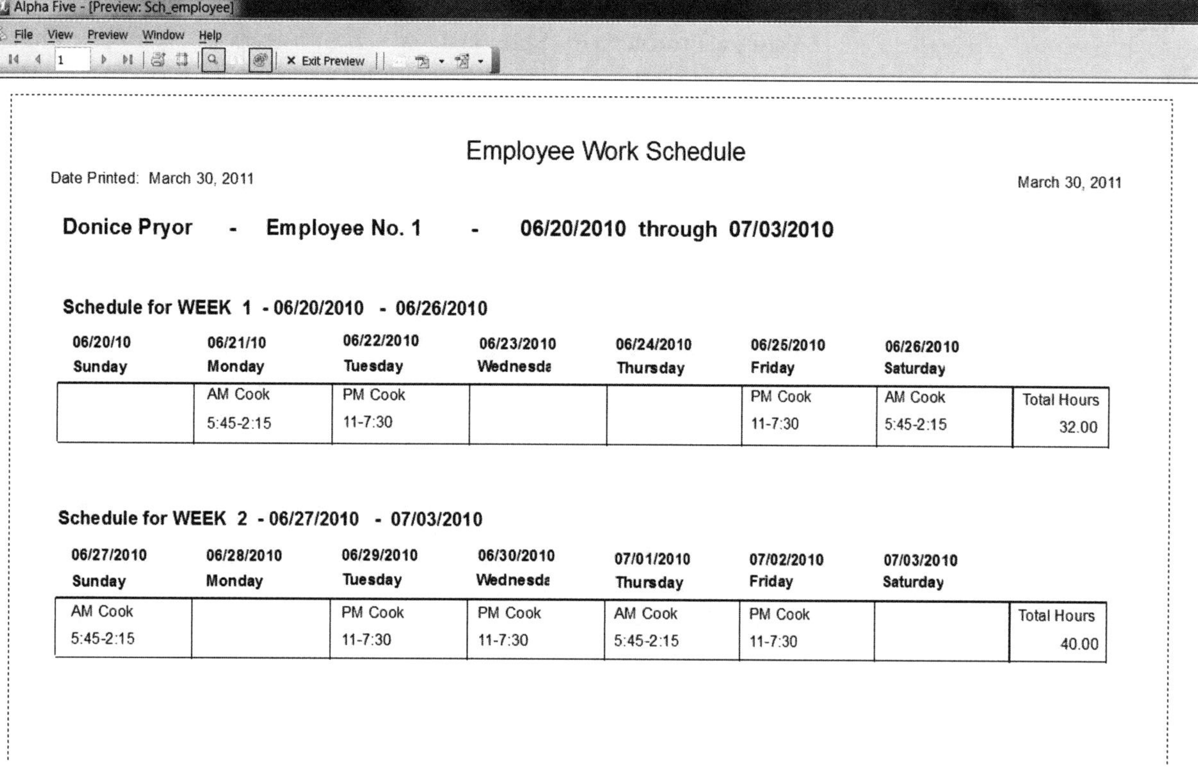

Alpha Five - [Preview: Sch_employee]

Employee Work Schedule

Date Printed: March 30, 2011

March 30, 2011

Donice Pryor - Employee No. 1 - 06/20/2010 through 07/03/2010

Schedule for WEEK 1 - 06/20/2010 - 06/26/2010

06/20/10 Sunday	06/21/10 Monday	06/22/2010 Tuesday	06/23/2010 Wednesda	06/24/2010 Thursday	06/25/2010 Friday	06/26/2010 Saturday	
	AM Cook 5:45-2:15	PM Cook 11-7:30			PM Cook 11-7:30	AM Cook 5:45-2:15	Total Hours 32.00

Schedule for WEEK 2 - 06/27/2010 - 07/03/2010

06/27/2010 Sunday	06/28/2010 Monday	06/29/2010 Tuesday	06/30/2010 Wednesda	07/01/2010 Thursday	07/02/2010 Friday	07/03/2010 Saturday	
AM Cook 5:45-2:15		PM Cook 11-7:30	PM Cook 11-7:30	AM Cook 5:45-2:15	PM Cook 11-7:30		Total Hours 40.00

Source: Dietary Manager by Brimstone Allon Enterprises. www.dietarymanagementsoftware.com

Figure 6.3 Foodservice Department Production Staff Hours (small hospital with cafeteria service)

	Labor Hours																	
Position	**Service**	**Prod**	**Sanit**	**5am**	**6am**	**7am**	**8am**	**9am**	**10am**	**11am**	**Noon**	**1pm**	**2pm**	**3pm**	**4pm**	**5pm**	**6pm**	**7pm**
Cook #1	3	5			Brfst. Prep	Brfst. Prep	Brfst. Serv		Lunch Prep	Lunch Serv	Lunch Serv							
Cook #2	3	5							Supper Prep	Cafe Set Up	Cafe Serv		Supper Prep	Supper Prep	Baking	Supper Serv		
D. Aid #1	6	1	1			Set Up	Cafe Serv		Lunch Prep	Set Up	Cafe Serv		Sanit					
D. Aid #2		4											Supper Prep	Supper Prep	Set Up	Supper Serv		
Dishwasher	1		3												Sanit	Supper Serv	Sanit	Sanit
Total Labor Hours	13	15	4															

Break Times

Glossary

FTE
Full-time equivalent or the number of standard hours for one full-time employee

Meals per Labor Hour
A productivity standard that is a calculation of the total meals divided by the total number of labor hours for a given time such as a week, month, or year (total meals ÷ total labor hours for a given time = meals per labor hour)

Minutes per Meal
A productivity standard that is a calculation of the total minutes in producing meals divided by the total meals served (total minutes to produce meals ÷ total meals served = minutes per meal)

Figure 6.4 shows some tips for calculating FTEs. You need to know how many FTEs are in your department in order to determine your productivity standard.

Using a Productivity Standard. Much of today's foodservice industry estimates their staffing needs using a productivity standard such as **meals per labor hour** or **minutes per meal**. If you know your meals per labor hour or minutes per meal, you can compare this figure to industry benchmarks. For instance, let's say you are a school foodservice and you have calculated your meals per labor hour to be 9.7. The industry standard is 13-15 meals per labor hour. This example means that your staff is not producing as many meals per labor hour as the benchmark. That could mean you are either overstaffed or you haven't calculated the total number of meals you are serving correctly. The Dietary Manager Professional Practice Standard for Estimating Staffing Needs can be found at the end of this chapter in the *Management in the News* section. Review this standard to determine your facility productivity standard. Once you have an accurate standard for your facility, you can compare your staffing to the benchmarks provided.

Types of Schedules

There are generally two types of employee schedules you would use to communicate to your staff: Master Schedule and a Shift Schedule.

Master Schedule. The master schedule is for the entire department and includes days on and off and vacations days for all employees. The master schedule may be developed for a week, two weeks, or even a month. It may also show the weekend rotations.

Figure 6.4 Calcuating FTEs

Example #1: Understanding One FTE	Example #3: Determining FTEs from annual labor hours
One person working full-time: 8 hours per day X 5 days per week X 52 weeks per year = 2080 hours per year = 1 FTE	You know your total number of labor hours for one year is 13,104. To determine FTEs: 13,104 total labor hours ÷ 2080 hours (1 FTE) = 6.3 FTEs
Example #2: Determining FTEs for part-time employees	**Example #4: Determining FTEs from monthly labor hours**
Four people working at 16 hours per week: 4 people X 16 hours per week X 52 weeks per year = 3328 hours per year To convert this to FTEs, divide the total number of hours per year by 2080: 3328 hours per year ÷ 2080 hours per one FTE = 1.6 FTEs	You know your total number of labor hours for one month is 3,600. Over one month, the number of hours incurred by one FTE is the annual figure divided by 12. So, an FTE value for one month is: 2080 hours ÷ 123 = 173.33 Now, to convert monthly labor hours into FTEs: 3,600 total labor hours per month ÷ 173.33 hours = 20.77 FTEs

Adapted from How to Calculate FTEs, Dietary Managers Association Website Resource Center, www.DMAonline.org/resource/main.html

Shift Schedule. The shift schedule shows the different shifts, when they begin and end, for different staff. For instance, using the small hospital example from Figure 6.3, a shift schedule for the cooks would look like the graph below. The shift schedule is useful when interviewing new employees to show them the options available.

Shift Schedule for Cooks

6 am 7 8 9 10 11 Noon 1 pm 2 3 4 5

Communicating the Schedule

Needless to say, a schedule works only if you communicate it clearly to all employees. Once the schedule has been developed, you should post it in a highly visible location for review by all employees. An employee can develop personal plans around the posted work schedule.

You want to make clear to each employee that it is his or her responsibility to review the schedule and comply with it. In addition, you need to make the schedule available far enough in advance that employees scheduled for a day or several days off before a new pay period begins have an opportunity to review the schedule. For example, you cannot post a schedule on Saturday if it takes effect on Monday, as many employees may not be at work, and they won't know

Putting It Into Practice: 2

What variables in a facility will affect scheduling in the foodservice department?

(Check your answer at the end of this chapter)

what their schedules are. Employees who are not at work during the time a new schedule is posted should be advised to call and confirm when they are scheduled to work again.

A schedule should be clear and specific. When two employees have the same first name, it's important to use a last name to avoid confusion. Naturally, each schedule should have its time period and dates identified very clearly, so that employees do not confuse the schedule for one pay period with that of another. Finally, a manager should keep an extra copy of the schedule in a secure location, in case the posted schedule disappears or becomes damaged.

Some managers write out individual schedules for each employee based on the master schedule. There are advantages and disadvantages to this practice. The advantage is that you are giving a written reference to the employee, who can take it home and use it to keep track of when to come in to work. The disadvantage is the possibility of error. If you write out these individual forms yourself and make an error in transcribing the details, you will have a problem. This is one place where software can be useful. Another approach is to provide a blank form for the individual schedule, and let each employee fill in his or her own from the master schedule. This places responsibility into the hands of each employee.

After use, schedules should be retained. You may need them for several purposes, such as reviewing and completing the records for payroll at the end of a pay period, reviewing past actions in order to enforce scheduling policies, and responding to inquires or complaints that may arise in the future.

Scheduling Adjustments

As with all things, the best laid plans can go awry. The most common scheduling challenge concerns employee tardiness and absence. When an employee is not able to come to work, you may need to contact someone else to perform the job. In a secure location accessible to managers, you need to have a master list of employees. Your list may also identify what jobs each employee is trained to do. When you need to cover a job, you may call other employees to see if they would be willing to come to work on short notice.

From here, you may have to adjust remaining days of the schedule for this pay period to avoid incurring overtime for the employee who has just punched in. Or, you may actually authorize overtime for this employee. How you handle this depends on your policies and your budget for overtime pay.

An alternative method of dealing with employee absence is the re-assignment of duties among existing staff. Sometimes, it is possible to divide the duties of an absent employee among staff members who are present. This requires careful planning, fairness, and tact.

To minimize the disruption and difficulty associated with finding coverage for jobs or re-working assignments, every facility develops and enforces some basic policies regarding unscheduled absences and tardiness. Most likely, these policies will come from the human resources department of your facility. For example, an attendance policy might specify that any full-time employee should

Putting It Into Practice: 3

You have the bi-weekly schedule posted but the facility census has dropped and you have to cut .5 FTE. How would you handle this issue?

(Check your answer at the end of this chapter)

not exceed a total of six occurrences of unscheduled absence or tardiness over a 12-month period. It may specify how far in advance a supervisor must be notified if an employee will be unable to come to work or will be late. It may specify that non-compliance with this policy is cause for corrective action.

A specific policy may also address the situation of *no-call, no-show.* In this situation, an employee does not come to work, and does not call to notify the manager. This is a serious situation that makes it especially difficult for a manager to direct and control the activities of the department. In some facilities, two occurrences of no-call, no-show may be considered cause for dismissal.

Reports and Documents

As a Certified Dietary Manager, you will most likely bear responsibility for ensuring that all documents and paperwork related to scheduling and payroll are maintained in a complete and accurate fashion. You may be required to initial timesheets and authorize any overtime. You will also need to check time records against the schedule to ensure there are no discrepancies.

Depending on the system used where you work, time records may be automated through an electronic timeclock. You may also receive computer-generated payroll reports. You should review these and ensure they are accurate. For instance you want to make sure employees are not punching the time clock for other employees if you are still using a time clock. If budget information is contained in these reports, you can check labor usage for each time period against your budget to verify that you are maintaining good control. For instance, you want to make sure employees are not punching the time clock for other employees, if you are still using a time clock.

Payroll reporting documents also include a summary of benefits paid out, such as sick time, vacation, or leave of absence. These, too, must be monitored. Within your own personnel record management system, you should also maintain accurate and timely records indicating when employees have come to work tardy and/or had unscheduled absences. Routine monitoring can help you provide timely feedback as required.

Controlling Overtime

What is overtime? Overtime refers to time worked in excess of the allowable amount beyond which laws require payment of one-and-one-half times the hourly rate for every hour worked. For example, applicable laws require the payment of time-and-a-half when more than 40 hours are worked within seven consecutive days. An employee paid $8 per hour and working for 44 hours would receive an overtime payment of $48 (4 hours overtime at $12 per hour) in addition to the 40 hours' worth of regular pay. Sometimes, an employee works more hours than scheduled on a single work day. Or, a manager asks an employee to work on an additional day not originally scheduled.

As you can see, overtime is very expensive and must be minimized to remain within budget. In some facilities, it may not be permitted at all. If overtime occurs frequently, you can look for factors that may be contri-buting to this situation.

Putting It Into Practice: 4

How much would you pay in overtime to someone who makes $11.35 per hour and he worked three additional hours?

(Check your answer at the end of this chapter)

These include:

- ✓ Ineffective or unrealistic scheduling
- ✓ Inaccurate estimation of the volume of work, or failure to adjust staffing according to an increase in volume
- ✓ Poor compliance with performance standards or poor work habits.

A Certified Dietary Manager can generally contain overtime through sound supervision. The key is to establish a policy of requiring advance authorization for overtime. An employee should check with the manager or supervisor, who must approve overtime. This gives the manager an opportunity to review why the need for overtime is arising and address any issues that require intervention. It also gives the manager a chance to use an alternate method of meeting the need, such as assigning another employee on a regular shift to pick up certain tasks.

Creative Staffing Ideas

In the continuous challenge to do more with less, Certified Dietary Managers are becoming quite creative in devising ways of providing essential human resources to the operation. One idea is to use cross-training, which means training one employee to perform more than one job. To a certain degree, **cross-training** is a given in foodservice operations. Most employees are trained for several positions. This gives the manager the flexibility to adjust staffing on a daily basis.

Branching out, some organizations even cross-train employees between departments. An employee of an environmental services or laundry department, for example, may also learn certain jobs in the foodservice department—and vice versa. Cross-trained employees then become part of a job pool, and can be assigned or re-assigned as needed into various work areas. This flexibility helps managers in all affected departments use human resources very efficiently.

Job sharing might be an idea that works in your community. With job sharing, you divide a full-time job into two or more shifts that are then shared by two or more part-time staff.

Another idea used frequently, particularly in healthcare facilities, is to establish a volunteer program. This is done on a facility-wide basis, and an individual is assigned to manage volunteer services. Volunteers are available from all walks of life, and many people who choose to volunteer have a deep commitment to others. The help of volunteers in a foodservice department is sometimes used to assist clients with menu selection, to transport items from one area to another, to perform certain clerical tasks, and much more.

Glossary

Job Sharing
Dividing a full-time position into two or more positions

Cross-training
Training an employee to do more than one job

Management in the News

Estimating Staffing Needs

by Susan Davis Allen, MS, RD, CHE

Professional Standards of Practice serve as a basis for quality dietetic practice for dietary managers. The Standard published here provides guidelines for CDMs to use when estimating staffing needs.

How often have you seen today's increasing healthcare costs result in a reduction of foodservice staff? As a Certified Dietary Manager, how do you justify your staffing needs?

The efficiency of a department can be evaluated and justified by knowing accurate costs related to meals per labor hour (or the minutes per meal). To accurately estimate labor costs, one must begin by determining the cost per meal. A simple method of doing that is dividing total food cost by the number of patient meals. Please see ANFP/DMA Practice Standard: Calculating Food Costs for more information on this subject. The standards that follow will help you accurately determine your cost for staffing, and meals per labor hour or minutes per meal. Once this is calculated, you can compare your department's efficiency against an industry standard.

Standard

The certified dietary manager (CDM) assures that staffing requirements are based on the department's output(meals/meal equivalents).

Criteria

1.1 Total meals/meal equivalents are data necessary prior to the determination of productivity standards.

1.2 Productivity standards are established for the facility; productivity standards can be either meals per labor hour or minutes per meal. (Directions for calculating are provided.)

1.3 The CDM calculates full-time equivalents (FTEs) for the department. (Directions for calculating are provided.)

1.4 The CDM determines staffing requirements based on the number of staff needed to produce the number of meals provided (Productivity Standards), FTEs, and the overtime needs. They take into consideration the type of meal service (tray vs. plate), the kitchen layout, the quality of the menu items (pre-prepared vs. "homemade"), and feedback from the foodservice staff. The CDM uses industry standard productivity levels as a benchmark for evaluating staffing needs.

1.5 The CDM estimates overtime needs based on the number of staff projected.

Assessment

1.1 The CDM prepares a monthly summary of productivity (meals per labor hour or minutes per meal).

1.2 The CDM shares the monthly report with the foodservice staff and administration for analysis and planning for future staffing needs.

1.3 The CDM uses feedback from the foodservice staff and administration in future staffing requirements in conjunction with data calculated using productivity standards.

Summing Up

This Practice Standard for Calculating Staffing Needs is a comprehensive tool to use frequently in the management of your department. We hope this information will lead you on the path to more efficient and effective operation of your foodservice department.

(Continued)

Estimating Staffing Needs *(Continued)*

How to Calculate Full-Time Equivalents (FTEs)		
Definitions	A federal standard for a full-time equivalent is the equivalent of an employee who works full time. It means counting all of the hours and determining how many full-time equivalents there are; it does not mean counting only those who work full time. Include all hours for foodservice employees, the certified dietary manager, and the consultant dietitian.	
An FTE =	• 8 hours/day or • 40 hours/week or	• 173.33 hours/month or • 2,080 hours/year
Monthly	• Total labor hours for the month: • Divided by total FTE hours per month: • Equals total FTE's for the month: (Total monthly hours divided by 173.33)	________ 173.33 = ________
Your Department's Labor Hours:		
Meals Per Labor Hour	Total meals/meal equivalents ÷ total labor hours = ________ meals per labor hour	*Example:* 13,800 meals/meal equivalents ÷ 1975 labor hours = 7 meals per labor hour.
Minutes Per Meal	Total number of labor minutes X 60 minutes ÷ total meals/meal equivalents = _ ________ minutes per meal	*Example:* (1975 labor hours X 60) = 118,500 ÷ 13,800 = 9 minutes per meal.
Labor Hours Per Meal	Total number of labor hours ÷ total meals/meal equivalents = ________ labor hours per meal	*Example:* 1,975 labor hours ÷ 13,800 meals/meal equivalents = .14 labor hours per meal.
Estimating Staffing Needs Using an Industry Productivity Level*		
Much research has gone into summarizing productivity levels. This reference* has determined the meals per labor hour for the following foodservice operations:		
• Quick-service restaurant . . . . . 9.5 • Fine dining restaurant. . . . . . . 1.4 • Family restaurant 4.8	• Cafeteria .5.5 • Acute Care Facility (hospital). 3.5	• Extended Care Facility . . . . .5.0 • School Foodservice. . . . 13-15.0
Check your calculations for determining your department's labor hours and meals per labor hour against this industry standard. If there is a significant difference, it is the responsibility of the CDM to evaluate this difference and justify the current staffing level, or make necessary adjustments.		

* *Gregoire, M. Foodservice Organizations, A Managerial and Systems Approach. Seventh Edition. Prentice Hall, 2010. pp. 450-451.*

REFERENCES

Allen, S.D. "Measuring Meal Production and Calculating Meal Equivalents." *Dietary Manager Magazine*, Jan. 2010. p. 25-28.

CD-HCF/DMA "Survival Skills for Nutrition Services." 2006. p. 95-98.

Palacio, J, Thies, M., Introduction to Foodservice, Eleventh edition. Pearson, Prentice Hall, 2009.

Gregoire, M. Foodservice Organizations, A Managerial and Systems Approach. Seventh edition. Prentice Hall, 2010. pp. 450-451.

END OF CHAPTER

Putting It Into Practice Questions & Answers

1. Two employees have submitted requests to have the same day off. Having both of them gone at the same time would pose a hardship to the department. What should you do?

   A. *First, ask them if either of them would be willing to change. Second, follow your facility policy, such as the person with the most seniority gets their request. If you work with a union, follow the union contract.*

2. What variables in a facility will affect scheduling in the foodservice department?

   A. *The type of service, the number of clients, the type of menu*

3. You have the bi-weekly schedule posted but the facility census has dropped and you have to cut .5 FTE. How would you handle this scheduling issue?

   A. *Meet with your staff to explain the situation and what you have to do. First, ask if anyone is willing to work less hours. Second, ask for suggestions from your staff. They may suggest everyone working 30 minutes less each day, for instance. If there are no agreeable suggestions, you may have to cut hours from one or two positions and other staff may have to take on added responsibilities. If you are a union facility, make sure you follow the union contract.*

4. How much would you pay in overtime for someone who earns $11.35 per hour and he worked three additional hours?

   A. *Overtime pay is 1.5 times the regular hourly rate. If the hourly rate is $11.35 and they worked three hours, the overtime pay would be: $11.35 x 3 x 1.5 or $51.075*

CHAPTER 7

Define Personnel Needs and Job Functions

Overview and Objectives

Planning for staffing involves anticipating the future, and what it will require in personnel. You need to use the tools of job descriptions and perform job analyses in order to best provide for staffing needs in your facility. You will also be expected to calculate FTEs and appreciate the impact of census on staffing and your department organization chart.

After completing this chapter, you should be able to:

✓ Conduct personnel needs analysis
✓ Conduct a task analysis
✓ Write a job analysis
✓ Write detailed job descriptions
✓ Prepare a departmental organizational chart

Personnel Needs Analysis

Staffing is one of the major functions of a Certified Dietary Manager and is defined as the selection of personnel to fulfill foodservice department needs. Completing a personnel needs analysis to determine staffing is done by reviewing staffing data and trends to determine your current and future hiring needs. In many foodservice departments with long-term staff, it will be especially important to consider future hiring needs. When conducting a personnel needs analysis there are several factors to consider, as indicated below.

Competencies or Skills Needed by Staff

An employee's skills and knowledge must match the requirements of the job. For example, an upscale catering service will require the expertise of someone trained in culinary arts. The job of serving clients in the dining room will require excellent service and people skills, along with an ability to work in an organized and efficient manner. It is important to identify what skills for each type of staff would be considered essential based on the type of facility you manage.

Strategic Plan

Most facilities today have some type of strategic plan in place that outlines the goals and objectives for the future. Your personnel needs analysis has to fit within that strategic plan. For instance, let's say one objective of your facility's strategic plan is to *expand community outreach*. One way to implement that would be to expand your cafeteria to serve community residents. That would impact your personnel needs analysis as your need for human resources/staffing would likely increase.

Budget

As you analyze your personnel needs, keep in mind that whatever staffing needs you determine will have to have a minimal impact on the budget. You may be able to justify staff additions with additional services that equal additional revenue. One way to minimize additional staff is by analyzing the tasks that each position performs. Many of the tasks may be performed by cross-trained staff from other departments, such as the environmental department who may also be able to assist with dining room service. Cross-training your staff can allow you to more efficiently use your labor budget.

Trends and Forecasting

Certified Dietary Managers should be flexible as staffing needs evolve. Today's fast-changing foodservices may foster personnel concerns you are not even aware of. Typically, a working team, comprised of human resource department representatives, top foodservice department staff, and other management staff within the department, is used. As you look at trends and forecasting future staffing needs, use the following data that your department or human resources department should have:

✓ Turnover rate
✓ Staffing levels
✓ Retirement eligibility.

If your human resource department does not calculate turnover rate, you can easily calculate that for your own department. Decide what length of time you want to consider. (For a long-term care facility, one year might be a good length of time; in a hospital where turnover is more common, you might use six months or even one month.) Determine the average number of employees over that time. Total the number of employees who left your employment during that time. Divide the number of employees who left by the average number of employees to determine your turnover rate.

January 1 – December 31 Average number of employees = 16
January 1 – December 31 Number who left employment = 2

2 ÷ 16 = .125 x 100 = 12.5% turnover rate
A 12.5% turnover rate is considered very low in comparison to the restaurant industry where turnover rate can be as high as 80%.

External Environment

There are many employment laws that affect your facility. The Certified Dietary Manager must make sure that all policies dealing with staffing/human resources are developed within the framework of the employment laws. If you have an HR (human resources) department, work with that department to develop goals and developmental programs for staff members who are new, in training,

Your department has 55 staff. If your turnover rate has been about 15%, your staffing level is 95%, and you know of four employees who will retire next year, forecast your hiring needs for next year.

(Check your answer at the end of this chapter)

or in career advancement modes. If you don't have an HR department, work with your administrator to make sure you are following the employment laws.

Another external influence on your staffing will be the CMS (Centers for Medicare and Medicaid Services) regulations. For instance, both state and federal regulations may address staffing in your department. An example of the regulations in the State of Texas reads as follows:

> *"The facility must employ a qualified dietitian either full-time, part-time, or on a consultant basis…*
>
> ***§19.1103 Sufficient Staffing***
>
> *The facility must employ sufficient dietary support personnel who are competent to carry out the functions of the dietary service."*

It will be very important to pay attention to these considerations as you analyze your personnel needs. The basic steps in personnel needs analysis are shown in Figure 7.1.

There are some external standards that have been published to provide guidelines for staffing. These were developed for the restaurant industry and with the movement toward more dining options in healthcare foodservice, they may be helpful when determining your staffing needs. Two of these are shown in Figures 7.2 (Staffing for Kitchen) and 7.3 (Staffing for the Dining Room).

Figure 7.1 **Steps in Personnel Needs Analysis**

Step 1: **Forecast future personnel needs**—The forecasting of future needs should be in harmony with the growth patterns and plans of the facility

Step 2: **Conduct inventory of current staff**—What are the skills, abilities, interests, and needs of currently employed staff members?

Step 3: **Assess staff planning needs**—Consider planned vacancies or changes

Step 4: **Develop internal training/education activities**—Depending upon your needs, retrain staff OR

Step 5: **Plan for new staff recruitments, selection, and training procedures**—Recruit, select and train new staff

Step 6: **Design program monitoring systems**—Develop a way to monitor your progress (how many staff were hired, trained, etc.?)

Step 7: **Control and evaluate planning system**—Evaluate how your analysis is working and make adjustments if necessary

In staffing, the bottom line is that planning for the future is the only effective way to ensure that the number of surprises will be minimal. No one can predict what will happen in the future. However, a great deal of your human resources requirement can, in fact, be predicted. By planning and taking appropriate action, you help to ensure that your operation will continue to function smoothly, now and in the future. A Certified Dietary Manager is perpetually thinking about these steps on a daily basis in order to meet ongoing staffing needs.

In contrast to the broad issue of staffing, a manager must also consider the finer detail involved in scheduling, or planning employees' specific activities and assignments from day-to-day.

Tools that help a manager with scheduling include a job analysis and a job description.

Figure 7.2 **Staffing Table for Kitchen**

Jobs to be Filled	For 0-49 Guests	For 50-99 Guests	For 100-175 Guests	For 175-Plus Guests
Chef	1	1	1	1
Cook	1	2	3	4
Salads-Pantry	1	2	2	3
Dishwasher	1	2	3	3
Potwasher	1	1	1	1
Cleaner	0	1	1	1
Storeroom Clerk	0	1	1	1
Baker	0	1	1	1

Source: Donald Lundberg. The Management of People in Hotels and Restaurants, *5/e © 1992. The McGraw-Hill Companies. All Rights Reserved. Reprinted by permission.*

Figure 7.3 **Staffing Table for Dining Room**

Jobs to be Filled	For 0-37 Guests	For 38-58 Guests	For 59-75 Guests	For 76-95 Guests	For 96-112 Guests	For 113-129 Guests	For 130-145 Guests	For 146-166 Guests	For 167-Plus Guests
Host/Hostess	1	1	1	1	1	1	1	1	1
Waiter/Waitress	2	3	4	5	6	7	8	9	10
Bus Person	1	2	2	3	3	3	3	4	5
Cocktail Server	1	1½	1½	2	2	2½	2½	2½	2½

Source: Donald Lundberg. The Management of People in Hotels and Restaurants, *5/e © 1992. The McGraw-Hill Companies. All Rights Reserved. Reprinted by permission.*

Job Analysis

What exactly is a job? The word job describes the tasks an employee is responsible and accountable for performing. Jobs have titles to help you refer to them. Titles are shown on organization charts, on schedules, and in descriptions of the jobs themselves. Jobs are not the same thing as individual people.

For example, you may have a job titled Morning Cashier. This is a position with a set of assigned responsibilities. One day, an employee named Mary may fill this position. The next day, a different employee, named Carlos, may fill it. The job title simply refers to the set of assigned work.

Tasks are the individual activities that, together, comprise a job. For example, the morning cashier job may involve tasks such as: setting up the cash register or point of sale system; counting the bank and verifying that it is accurate; checking out clients; and many others. The job of a trayline employee may involve tasks such as: transporting food and supplies to the trayline; portioning food; and cleaning the tray assembly line and work area after other tasks have been completed.

Tasks such as these are outlined in detail in a job description. A **job description** is very detailed. It tells exactly what the employee is responsible for doing. It tells to whom the employee reports. It defines the working hours of the job, and where the person works (such as dining room, receiving dock, trayline, dishroom, etc.) A job description also documents the qualifications a person must meet to be placed in this job, and the salary range for the position. It forms the basis for evaluating employees' performance.

How do you create a job description? You do this by first performing a **job analysis**. A job analysis is a breakdown of all the individual tasks involved by day. (The plural of job analysis is job analyses.)

Besides helping to develop a job description, a job analysis gives you more information. It serves as a tool for helping to identify what standard operating procedures you develop, what tools or equipment you provide, what orientation and training you offer, and what measurements or standards you develop in order to assure that an employee is performing effectively. It also helps to define the qualifications you will list on a job description. In turn, this helps to recruit individuals who are qualified to perform the job. It can also help to determine whether existing employees qualify for transfer or advancement into a different position.

A job analysis also becomes the basis for setting a rate of pay. Human resource professionals apply standard scoring systems and compensation surveys of peers to compare the tasks on this list with the tasks of job analyses in other institutions. They examine the level of responsibility involved in these tasks and the outcomes of the work. Based on this type of information, they can recommend a rate of pay that fits within standards for the industry.

Figure 7.4 shows a sample job analysis for a Hot Foods Cook. Notice that it divides the job of preparing food into individual tasks. A job analysis lists

Glossary

Job Analysis
An individual schedule, by day, for each staff position

Job Description
Detailed job list including hours and location of the job, qualifications and salary range

Figure 7.4 Sample Job Analysis

Position: Hot Foods Cook	
Task	**Frequency (No. times per day)**
Wash hands per established procedure	9
Withdraw ingredients from food stores and document on requisition forms	1
Use food production sheet and standardized recipes to measure ingredients per standard procedures	14
Complete food preparation of all assigned hot food items per standardized recipe instructions	14
Create pureed versions of assigned products per procedures	4
Complete HACCP records for food prepared	11
Arrange presentation and garnish food per recipe	14
Cover and label food products; take foods to hot holding area	2
Clean up work area	4
Complete pre-prep for next day	1
Complete leftover records after meal service	2
Discard or label and store leftovers per procedures	2

tasks specifically and concretely, but does not spell out procedures for doing the work. For example, if you are writing a job analysis for a receiving clerk, it is appropriate to list tasks such as: "Checks food deliveries against invoice" or "Rejects food deliveries that do not meet established standards for quality and sanitation." However, it is not useful to write tasks such as: "Uses good judgment," because this does not tell what the employee actually does.

Job Descriptions

Once you have completed a job analysis you can write a job description. Because a job description lists all of the tasks that comprise the job, it forms the basis for organizing work. Each facility is different, so, the job description for a cashier or trayline employee in one facility will not necessarily fit in another.

You should have a job description for each position in the foodservice operation. A sample job description appears in Figure 7.5. The exact format of a job description is usually set by your organization, and may include most or all of the following sections:

- ✓ Job title
- ✓ Section or department
- ✓ Supervisor's title
- ✓ Brief summary of basic responsibilities
- ✓ Description of duties
- ✓ Working conditions (e.g., heavy lifting involved)
- ✓ Employment qualifications or minimum job requirements
- ✓ Conditions of employment (e.g., health and drug screening)
- ✓ Wage scale
- ✓ Date developed or last revised.

Figure 7.5 Job Description: Certified Dietary Manager (Sample)

General Summary of Work: Responsible for the daily operations of foodservice department according to facility policy and procedures and federal/state regulations. Provides leadership and guidance to ensure that food quality, safety standards, and client expectations are satisfactorily met. Maintains records of department personnel, income and expenditures, food, supplies, inventory levels, and equipment.

Principle Tasks

Operations Management
- Recruit, interview, hire, train, coach, evaluate, reward, discipline, and when necessary, terminate employees
- Develop job descriptions and job duties for each level of foodservice personnel
- Develop work schedules to ensure adequate staff to cover each shift
- Create and monitor budgets for a cost-effective program
- Manage revenue generating services
- Use forecasts, food waste records, inventory and equipment records to plan the purchase of food, supplies and equipment
- Justify improvements in the department design and layout
- Work cooperatively with clients, facility staff, physicians, consultants, vendors, and other service providers

Foodservice Management
- Specify standards and procedures for preparing food
- Participate in menu planning including responding to client preferences, substitution lists, therapeutic diets, and industry trends
- Inspect meals and assure that standards for appearance, palatability, temperature, and servings times are met
- Manage the preparation and service of special nourishments and supplemental feedings
- Assure that foods are prepared according to production schedules, menus, and standardized recipes

Food Safety
- Assure safe receiving, storage, preparation, and service of food
- Protect food in all phases of preparation, holding, service, cooking, and transportation, using HACCP Guidelines
- Prepare cleaning schedules and maintain equipment to ensure food safety
- Ensure proper sanitation and safety practices of staff

Nutrition and Medical Nutrition Therapy
- Process new diet orders and diet changes; keeps diet cards updated
- Complete the assigned MDS section according to required timeline
- Determine client diet needs and develop appropriate dietary plans in cooperation with RD and in compliance with physicians' orders
- Review plan of care related to nutritional status; document concerns that can be resolved, improved or addressed to improve client's nutritional status and eating function
- Review, revise, and implement, in cooperation with the IDT, the client's nutrition assessment and plan of care
- Supports Registered Dietitian duties as needed

General Knowledge, Skills and Abilities

- Skill in motivating, coaching, and supervising foodservice personnel
- Intermediate computer skills
- Mathematical and numerical skills; mechanical aptitude helpful
- Has effective written and oral communication skills
- Demonstrated organizational skills
- Has current awareness of legislation and regulations influencing the practice of standards of care

Education Requirements

- Graduate of Dietary Manager's Course, 2-yr, or 4-yr foodservice program
- Successful completion of Certified Dietary Manager exam
- Two years' experience in foodservice management
- Prior experience in healthcare foodservice preferred

Physical Demands/Working Conditions

- Able to lift and carry in excess of 50 lbs.
- Able to withstand extreme temperatures, hot and cold
- Able to work long hours, including some evenings, weekends, holidays, as needed
- Able to interact positively with all ages of people

Job descriptions answer several questions, such as: What are the tasks an employee in this position must perform? Who supervises an employee in this position? What knowledge and skills must a candidate possess to qualify for this position? What is the pay scale for anyone who holds this position?

Job descriptions are also tools for managers, because they clarify who is responsible for what, e.g. who receives food deliveries—the foodservice supervisor or the cook. Occasionally, a manager may need to reference job descriptions with employees to clarify disagreements. Most managers use job descriptions as a communication tool to help define expectations of employees during job interviews, new employee orientation, and later in performance evaluation.

Job descriptions also indicate how each position relates to all other positions in the foodservice department. As such, they lay the foundation for the flow of communication, authority, and responsibility throughout the organization. They help a manager organize positions into work sections to form a basis for developing effective labor control systems.

You should maintain a reference of all job descriptions in your department. This may be on your computer network, as well as in a notebook. As jobs change, it is important to update job descriptions at least annually or as positions change. You should always have an organized, up-to-date reference to every position in your operation.

Note that many organizations complete a list of duties in a job description with this point: "Other duties as assigned." This addresses the fact that some flexibility is required. There may be one day when your department has an unexpected need to serve coffee and breakfast rolls to an ad hoc Board of Directors meeting in your building. To whom will you assign the work of providing this food? It may not fall under anyone's job description. There may be another day when two employees call you early in the morning and say they are unable to report to work. You may have to divide their responsibilities among other employees who are working today. These are just examples of why flexibility is important. From a management perspective, it is best to communicate your expectation of flexibility from the beginning with every employee. This minimizes surprises and possible resistance down the line.

Full-Time Equivalents (FTEs)

As part of the job of organizing work, a manager must coordinate job descriptions, staffing plans, and full-time equivalents (FTEs). FTEs, described in Chapter 6, are a way of measuring how many hours of work go into an overall labor budget. One person working full-time translates into one FTE. In analyzing sets of job analyses, creating job descriptions, and devising overall staffing plans that describe who will work when and for how long, a Certified Dietary Manager must ensure that the master plan matches the budget for FTEs.

Putting It Into Practice: 2

You have completed your forecasting for staffing needs and know that you need to add a new position of cashier to your staff. What is your next step?

(Check your answer at the end of this chapter)

An Organization Chart

As you write job descriptions for new employees you add them to your organization chart. An **organization chart** is a fundamental management tool that represents task groupings and responsibilities in a graphical formal. An organization chart shows the names of task groupings as departments or something similar. In a few words, it defines responsibilities.

Boxes representing groupings and/or positions (managers) are connected with solid lines. These lines signify responsibility, authority, and accountability. The chart shows lines of authority. In a traditional organization chart, authority flows from the top of the chart to the bottom. This tool does not tell everything. However, it provides a useful framework for organizing the work of an institution. An organization chart may show an entire facility, or a close-up view of a given area, such as a foodservice department. Figure 7.6 shows a sample organization chart for a hospital.

In this example, you can see the departments named in boxes. These include Admitting, Information Services, Human Resources, Medical Records, Quality Assurance, Public Relations, Audiology, Clinical Labs, and more. You can see that the hospital is organized into two main sections: administrative and medical. You can also see that there are three assistant administrators, who have responsibility for the operations of groups of departments. The Foodservice department falls under one of these assistant administrators.

Now, who reports to whom? Six people report to the hospital administrator: an administrative assistant, a secretary, three assistant administrators, and a director of finances. These relationships are illustrated by solid lines connecting the boxes. Does the secretary supervise anyone? No. There are no lines connecting the secretary to more boxes below. Does the department manager for Foodservice supervise anyone? Yes, but this chart shows only the major areas. Another, more detailed chart would show the divisions and relationships within the Foodservice Services department.

The flow of formal power may go through several hierarchies, or levels. An organization chart graphically illustrates a concept called **chain of command**, which means the flow of formal power through organizational lines. In any organization, chain of command has to be clearly defined. As you look through an organization chart, you should be able to trace the chain of command for any area from top to bottom, or from bottom to top. If you are in charge of the Foodservice department in this hospital, you know that your supervisor is the Assistant Administrator of Support Services. That person's supervisor is the Administrator. Furthermore, the Administrator reports to the Board of Trustees.

Another key management term is **delegation**. Delegation means passing authority downward through the organization. The ability to delegate is one of the essential features of a manager. The act of delegating recognizes that you do not do everything yourself, and that you cannot do everything yourself. For example, if you manage the Foodservice department, you know that you cannot cook all the food for all the meals. You delegate the authority

Glossary

Organization Chart
A graphical management tool that shows job relationships in a facility

Chain of Command
The flow of formal power through organizational lines

Delegation
Passing authority for tasks or assigning duties downward through the organization chart

Staff Position
Provides advisory or consulting support

Figure 7.6 Organization Chart for a Hospital

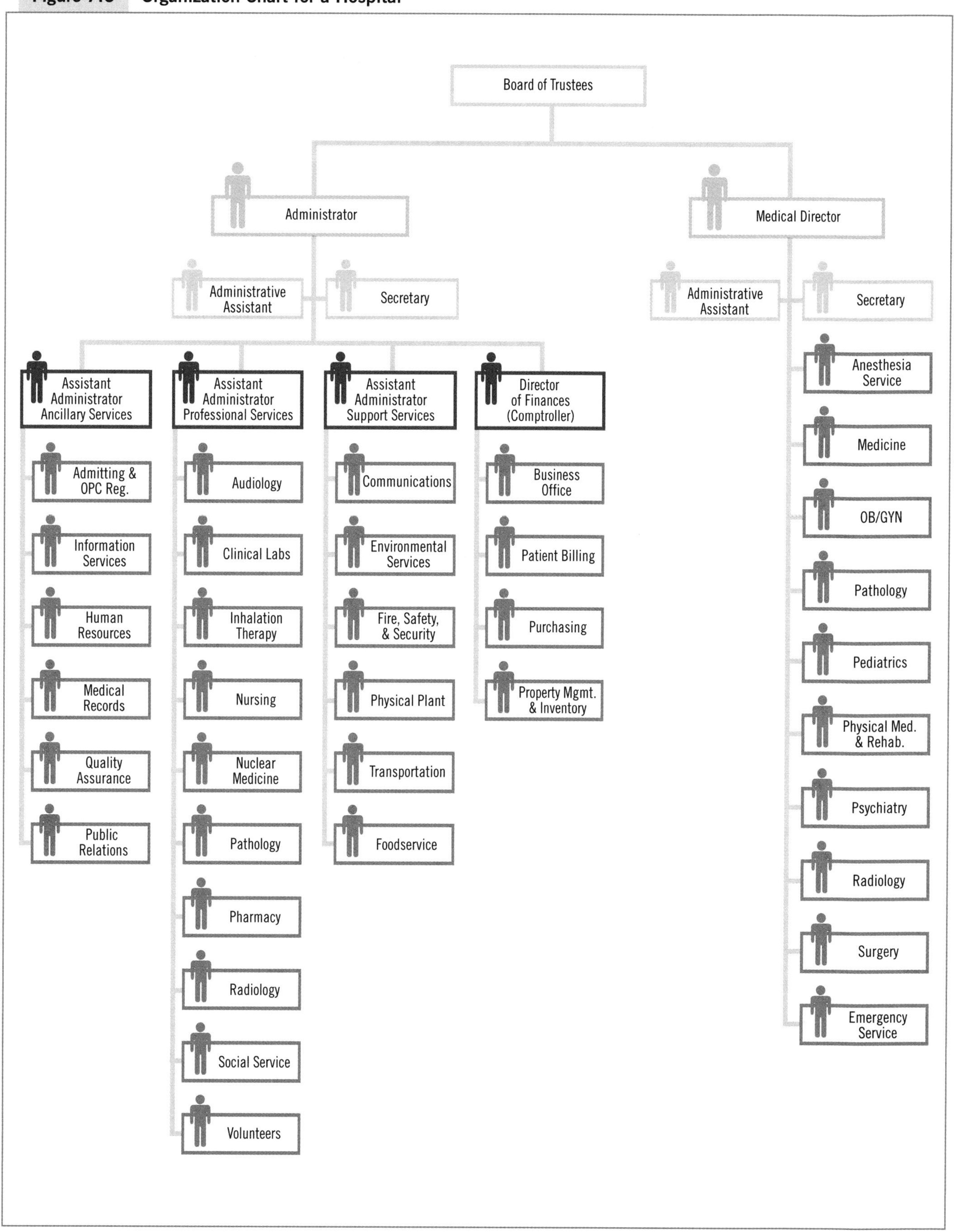

downward through the chain of command to a group of cooks. Along with the job, you delegate responsibility and accountability to the cooks.

So, the lines on the organization chart designate responsibility, authority, and accountability through the organization. You are responsible for Foodservice. You have the authority and formal power to make things happen in Foodservice. You are also accountable to the Assistant Administrator of Support Services for the work performed in Foodservice. Meanwhile, this Assistant Administrator is accountable to the Administrator for Foodservice, and so forth.

In any organization, people are expected to respect and follow the chain of command. In this hospital, it would be poor business etiquette (and possibly downright dangerous) for you to call the Administrator directly to discuss your new idea for the employee cafeteria or to complain about a problem you are having with the purchasing department. Instead, you should be discussing these matters with your own boss, the Assistant Administrator of Support Services. It is up to your boss to work through the next level up in the organization as needed.

You also notice in an organization chart that each person has only one boss. This is called unity of command, which means each person reports to only one superior. Management experts suggest that this is a sound idea. Multiple bosses could lead to conflicting command and a breakdown of functioning.

From the portion of the hospital's organization that is apparent on this chart, you may also notice that there is a limit to the number of lines flowing down from any one person. Realistically, one person can directly supervise only so many staff. What if the hospital administrator did not have the help of assistant administrators and a director of finances? Could one person effectively supervise these 26 departments? Of course, the answer is no. A consideration in organizing work is the ratio of managers to other employees.

Now, let's take a closer look at the finer picture, the organization of a foodservice department. Figure 7.7 shows a sample of a foodservice department for a retirement community serving about 365 people.

In this example, you can see that the person in charge of foodservice reports directly to the administrator of the organization. Furthermore, the foodservice operations are split into two main areas, which represent two main purposes. First, there is a Food Services section. This group clearly purchases and produces food for the residents of the retirement community. There are several levels of supervision, and there is an established chain of command.

Secondly, there is a Nutrition Services section. This section addresses the nutritional needs of residents (beyond food itself). Notice that within this area, there is also a Consultant Dietitian who reports to the Director of Foodservice, but does not directly supervise anyone at all. This type of relationship is sometimes called a staff relationship. A **staff position** provides advisory or consulting support to a manager who is in the chain of command. This person is not a supervisor and is not in the chain of command, but provides valuable expertise that the manager needs. In this example, the Consultant

Putting It Into Practice: 3

Using Figure 7.7 Sample Organization Chart for Retirement Community, if the PM Cook is unable to work his shift and the head cook is on vacation, who should he call to report his absence?

(Check your answer at the end of this chapter)

Figure 7.7 Sample Organization Chart for Retirement Community

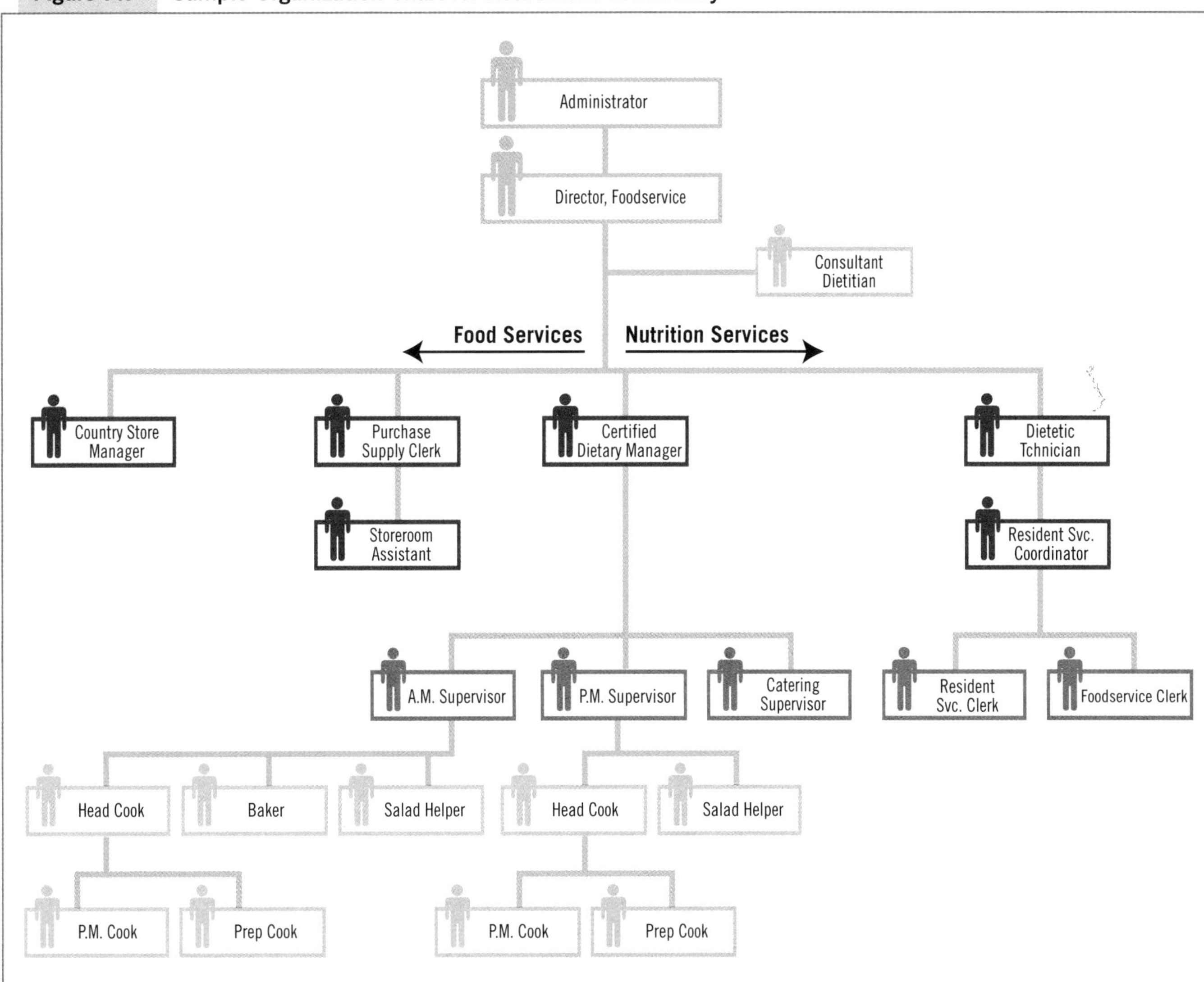

Dietitian provides expertise in nutrition to assist with the tasks of evaluating the individual needs of residents. Typically, a consultant dietitian in this setting may assist with planning menus to assure needs are met, and with planning, monitoring, and reviewing the nutritional care of individual residents. A staff position may be filled by an outside consultant, or even by an employee of the organization. The important point is that someone in a staff position supports a manager.

Additional examples of organization charts appear in Figures 7.8 and 7.9.

For the hospital foodservice department in Figure 7.8, there is a nutrition services section, although it does not use this name. Much like the retirement community, this healthcare organization delivers clinical nutritional services in addition to foodservice. Here, though, there is no staff position. Dietitians delivering this service report to the Director, Foodservice. This difference probably reflects the scope of service. Often, an acute care environment requires a high level of nutrition expertise applied intensively, within faster

Figure 7.8 **Sample Organization Chart for Small Hospital Dietary Services (200 Beds)**

Director, Food Services
Dietitians: Therapeutic, Clinical & Outpatient
Certified Dietary Manager
Cafeteria Supervisor
Food Production Manager
Foodservice Staff
Cooks
Foodservice Staff

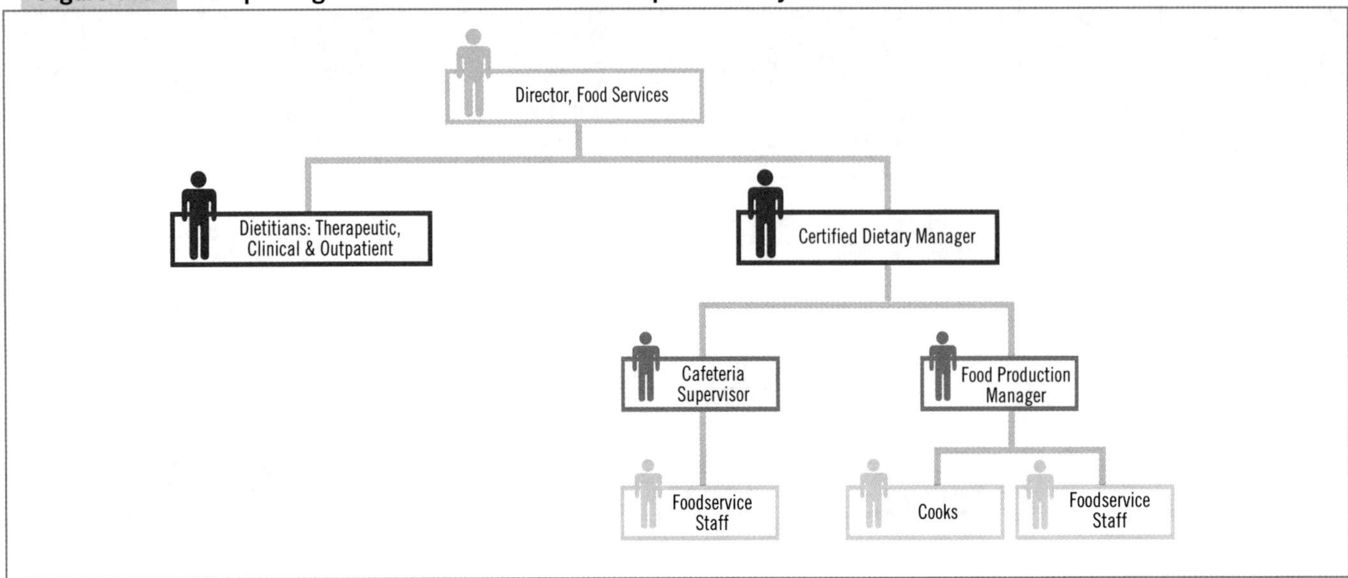

Figure 7.9 **Sample Organization Chart for Large University Foodservice***

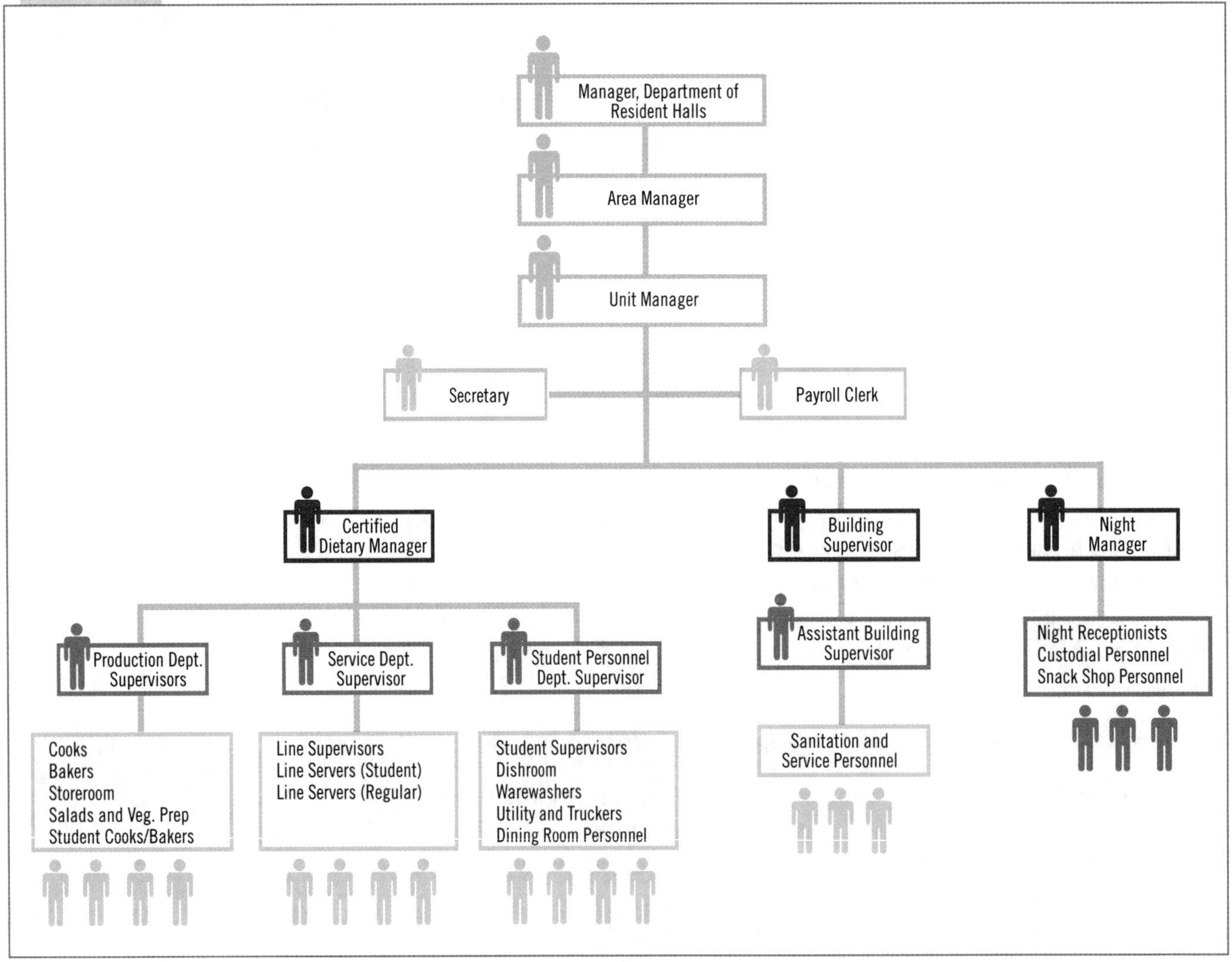

Manager, Department of Resident Halls
Area Manager
Unit Manager
Secretary
Payroll Clerk
Certified Dietary Manager
Building Supervisor
Night Manager
Production Dept. Supervisors
Service Dept. Supervisor
Student Personnel Dept. Supervisor
Assistant Building Supervisor
Night Receptionists
Custodial Personnel
Snack Shop Personnel
Cooks
Bakers
Storeroom
Salads and Veg. Prep
Student Cooks/Bakers
Line Supervisors
Line Servers (Student)
Line Servers (Regular)
Student Supervisors
Dishroom
Warewashers
Utility and Truckers
Dining Room Personnel
Sanitation and Service Personnel

** Approximately 40,000 students enrolled.*
Adapted from an organizational chart utilized by the Department of Resident Halls, Michigan State University.

turnaround requirements. This is because a client in an acute care setting typically stays for a short time, and has healthcare needs that may change significantly from day-to-day.

The structure of the university foodservice in Figure 7.9 is fairly different from that of the previous example. Clearly, the organization chart has been developed differently to reflect the purposes and tasks of this university foodservice operation. Notice that foodservices fall in with a cluster of activities that relate to residence halls. Why is foodservice bundled with sanitation employees and a building supervisor? In this environment, all of these functions relate closely to a single purpose of providing housing for students. You might also imagine that employees throughout this chart will need to coordinate their efforts, interact with each other, and work as a team to fulfill the purposes of the residence halls department. A manager shown at the top of this chart bears responsibility for assuring that the sum total of tasks related to housing are accomplished.

Some healthcare facilities are utilizing a circular organization chart. While it is more difficult to represent distinct reporting relationships, it encourages the integration of all employees on the chart and can be useful for representing team-based organizations. See Figure 7.10 for an example.

Notice that organization charts for foodservice operations bear many similari-

Figure 7.10 Circular Organizational Chart

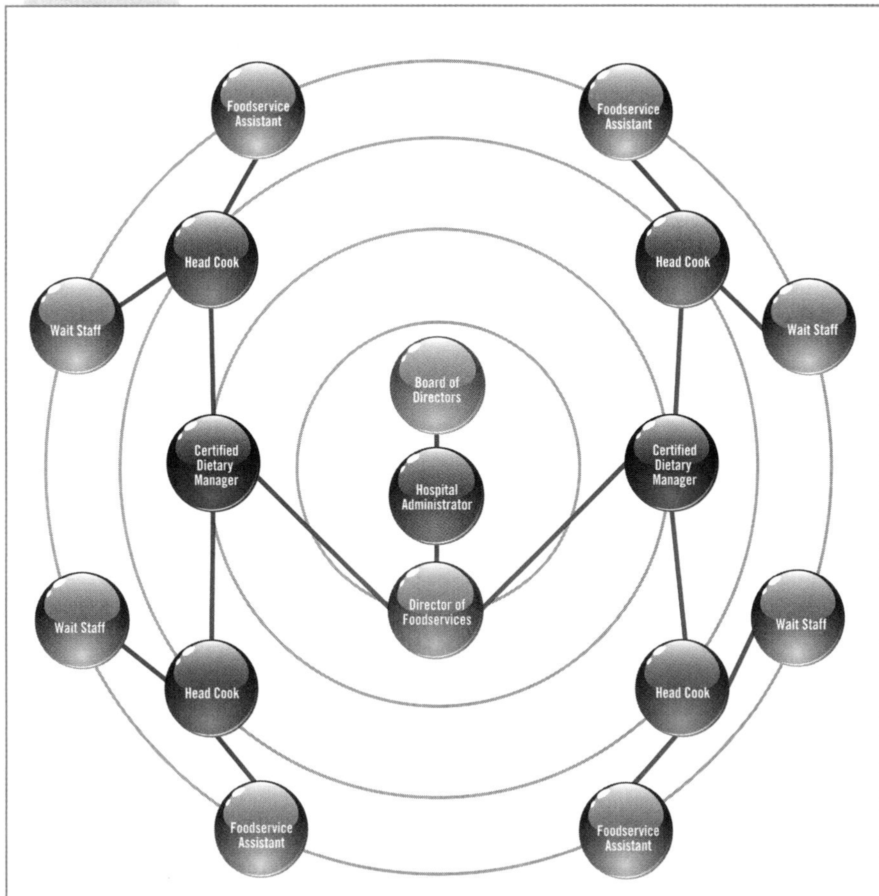

ties with each other. This is because many basic tasks of a foodservice operation are universal. Someone needs to plan a menu, order food, manage inventory, prepare food, and manage delivery of service. In a small organization, one person may have responsibility for many functions. In a larger operation, individual managers may have a more specialized role. However, in each of these examples, you can see that organization follows a logical task list that varies from one facility to another. It bundles related tasks. It pulls together similar resources and skills. It defines the responsibility, accountability, authority, legal power, and chain of command.

END OF CHAPTER

Putting It Into Practice Questions & Answers

1. Your department has 55 staff. If your turnover rate has been about 15%, your staffing level is 95%, and you know of four employees who will retire next year, forecast your hiring needs for next year.

   A. *If your turnover rate is 15% of 55 that is a minimum of 8 people you will have to replace this year. If your goal is to be staffed at 100% and you are at 95% then you would want to add 2.75 positions (5%). Finally you know that you will lose four employees through retirements. So, your hiring needs for next year would be 14.75 positions (8 + 2.75 + 4).*

2. You have completed your forecasting for staffing needs and know that you need to add a new position of cashier to your staff. What is your next step?

   A. *Completing a job analysis for the new position and then writing a job description.*

3. Using Figure 7.7 Sample Organization Chart for Retirement Community, if the PM Cook is unable to work his shift and the head cook is on vacation, who should he call to report his absence?

   A. *Looking at the organizational chart, the PM Cook reports directly to the Head Cook. Since the Head Cook is gone, he should contact the PM Supervisor who is the next in line up the chain of command.*

Interview and Select Employees

Overview and Objectives

Because of the high employee turnover rates, effective recruitment and interviewing becomes an important staffing tool. After initial recruitment efforts you can predict how well candidates will perform through a structured interview process. In this chapter, you will review employment laws, interview, and hiring techniques.

After completing this chapter, you should be able to:

✓ Identify fair employment laws and practices
✓ Develop interview procedures for a department
✓ Explain department procedures and policies to applicants
✓ Decide on applicants and record data
✓ Document selection procedures and policies

Before establishing policies and practices related to human resources management, it is important to be aware of certain constraints imposed by sources external to your organization. These take the form of federal and state employment laws that affect what a manager can and cannot do. In this chapter, we will explore several federal regulations. State regulations vary by location, so it is important to investigate these in your own state. In addition, the human resources department and/or legal counsel of your own facility can serve as an excellent resource for understanding your obligations with regard to personnel management.

Federal Equal Employment Opportunity (EEO) Laws

The U.S. Equal Employment Opportunity Commission (**EEOC**) provides the oversight and coordination of all federal equal employment opportunity regulations, practices, and policies. Figure 8.1 shows some of the important employment legislation that has been passed making it illegal to discriminate in hiring based on a person's race, color, religion, sex, national origin, age, disability, or pregnancy. The U.S. Equal Employment Opportunity Commission (EEOC) does not enforce the protections that prohibit discrimination and harassment based on sexual orientation, status as a parent, marital status and political affiliation. However, other federal agencies and many states and municipalities do. An organization may be held liable for the discriminatory acts of its employees

Glossary

EEOC
Equal Employment Opportunity Commission provides the oversight for federal employment legislation

even if administrators were unaware of those acts. Not only do you as a Certified Dietary Manager need to be aware of the legislation contained in Figure 8.1, but your employees also have to realize that they are under a legal obligation not to discriminate as well. If you have a human resources department, work with them whenever you have employment tasks.

These laws apply to all facilities that employee 15 or more people. These laws prohibit discrimination practices that are associated with any aspect of employment, including:

✓ Hiring and firing
✓ Compensation, assignment, or classification of employees
✓ Transfer, promotion, layoff, or recall
✓ Job advertisements
✓ Recruitment
✓ Testing
✓ Use of company facilities
✓ Training and apprenticeship programs
✓ Fringe benefits

Figure 8.1 Federal Laws Affecting Employment Management

Act/Law	Description
1963 Equal Pay Act	Protects men and women who perform substantially equal work in the same establishment from sex-based wage discrimination.
1964 Civil Rights Act	Protects employment discrimination based on race, color, religion, sex, or national origin.
1967 Age Discrimination in Employment Act	Protects individuals who are 40 years of age or older.
1973 Rehabilitation Act	Prohibits discrimination against qualified individuals with disabilities who work in the federal government.
1990 Americans with Disabilities Act	Prohibits employment discrimination against qualified individuals with disabilities in the private sector, and in state and local governments.
1991 Civil Rights Act, amended	Provides monetary damages in cases of intentional employment discrimination; established glass ceiling.
1993 Family and Medical Leave Act (FMLA)	Provides up to 12 weeks leave, unpaid and job-protected, per year to an employee for birth or adoption; or to care for a spouse, parent, or child with a serious health condition.
1994 Uniformed Services Employment and Reemployment Act	Protects individuals who leave work to fulfill their military service obligation.
1996 Health Insurance Portability and Accountability Act (HIPAA)	Protects confidentiality of medical records and provides for transfer of medical coverage of existing illnesses to another employer's insurance plan.
1996 Illegal Immigration Reform and Immigrant Responsibility Act	Provides for severe restrictions on persons who remain in the United States longer than permitted by their visa and/or who violate their nonimmigrant status.
2008 Genetic Information Nondiscrimination Act (GINA)	Prohibits employment discrimination based on genetic information about an applicant, employee, or former employee.

Source: www.eeoc.gov/facts/quanda.html Accessed 3.17.2011

✓ Pay, retirement plans, and disability leave

✓ Other terms and conditions of employment

Discrimination is treatment or consideration based on class or category, rather than individual merit. In essence, discrimination puts people in categories based on personal factors, and treats everyone within a category the same. Since this treatment is based on ignorance of the individuality of employees, it can generate unjust managerial policies, decisions, and actions based on stereotypes and prejudices.

Discrimination includes practices where the effects may not have been intended, such as using human resource tests that have not been validated as a selection device. In addition, there are certain questions that may not be asked on an employment application or during an interview. Care in structuring questions included in application forms is important. Figure 8.2 summarizes what a potential employer may and may not ask of a job applicant.

Dress codes and standards for personal appearance also have discriminatory implications. The same general dress code standards apply to men and women; the standards must be reasonable, appropriate, and consistent.

For example, if a facility requires some employees to be clean-shaven in the Admissions Department, this requirement should probably be imposed on other service employees working, for example, in foodservice and gift shop areas. There must be consistency throughout the organization in the interpretation of what is appropriate for employees. Individual departments or managers must not be allowed to make contrary decisions or rules.

Religious discrimination must be avoided. Employees must be scheduled so their work requirements will not conflict with religious commitments/beliefs, and it is necessary to make whatever schedule and other adjustments are necessary to meet these special requests. An employee's personal appearance may reflect religious heritage (length of hair, for example) and human resource policies must accommodate these special circumstances.

Certified Dietary Managers must not discriminate on the basis of sex. For example, personnel specifications such as weight or height that discriminate based on gender are unlawful unless they reflect essential attributes required for performing the job. These essential attributes are called bona fide occupational qualifications (BFOQ). An example of a legitimate BFOQ might be that storeroom employees must be able to lift or move heavy boxes of canned goods. Since this task can be done by a female employee, you might have difficulty defending a discrimination charge filed by a woman if all of these positions were filled by men. Discriminating against pregnant women or refusing to hire women (or men) because of uniform, locker space, or other problems are examples of unlawful practices.

The Discrimination in Employment Act of 1967 was enacted to prohibit arbitrary discrimination based upon age. It applies to persons over the age of 40. Offering different fringe benefit packages to older employees, refusing to train or promote them, and mandating their retirement are all examples of illegal acts.

You are interviewing a prospective employee who is visibly limping. During the interview, your head cook asks, "Can you tell me what happened to your leg?" Is this a legal question? Why or why not?

(Check your answer at the end of this chapter)

Discrimination
Treatment or consideration based on class or category, rather than individual merit

Figure 8.2 **Pre-Employment Inquiry Guide**

Subject	Lawful Pre-Employment Inquiries	Unlawful Pre-Employment Inquiries
Name	• Applicant's full name • Have you ever worked for this company under a different name? • Is any additional information relative to a different name necessary to check work record? If yes, explain.	• Original name of an applicant whose name has been changed by court order or otherwise. • Applicant's maiden name.
Address or Duration of Residence	• How long a resident of this state or city?	
Birthplace		• Birthplace of applicant. • Birthplace of applicant's parents, spouse, or other close relatives. • Requirement that applicant submit birth certificate, naturalization or baptismal record.
Age	• Are you 18 years old or older?*	• How old are you? What is your date of birth?
Religion or Creed		• Inquiry into an applicant's religious denomination, religious affiliations, church, parish, pastor, or religious holidays observed. • An applicant may not be told "This is a Catholic (Protestant or Jewish) organization."
Race or Color		• Complexion or color of skin.
Photograph		• Requirement that an applicant for employment affix a photograph to an employment application form. • Request an applicant, at his or her option, to submit a photograph. • Requirement for photograph after interview but before hiring.
Height		• Inquiry regarding applicant's height
Weight		• Inquiry regarding applicant's weight
Marital Status		• Requirement that an applicant provide any information regarding marital status or children. • Are you single or married? Do you have any children? Is your spouse employed? What is your spouse's name?
Sex		• Mr., Miss or Mrs., or inquiry regarding sex. • Inquiry as to the ability to reproduce or advocacy of any form of birth control.

** This question may be asked only for the purpose of determining whether applicants are of legal age for employment.*

(Continued)

Figure 8.2 Pre-Employment Inquiry Guide *(Continued)*

Subject	Lawful Pre-Employment Inquiries	Unlawful Pre-Employment Inquiries
Health	• Do you have any impairments (physical, mental, or medical) which would interfere with your ability to do the job for which you have applied? • Inquiry into contagious or communicable diseases which may endanger others. • If there are any positions for which you should not be considered or job duties you cannot perform because of a physical or mental handicap, please explain.	• Inquiries regarding an applicant's physical or mental condition (which are not directly related to the requirements of a specific job and which are used as a factor in making employment decisions in a way which is contrary to the provisions or purposes of the Civil Rights Act). • Requirements that women be given pelvic examinations.
Citizenship	• Are you a citizen of the United States? • If not a citizen of the United States, do you intend to become a citizen of the United States? • If you are not a United States citizen, have you the legal right to remain permanently in the United States? Do you intend to remain permanently in the United States?	• Of what country are you a citizen? • Whether an applicant is naturalized or a native-born citizen; the date when the applicant acquired citizenship. • Requirement that an applicant produce naturalization papers or first papers. • Whether applicant's parents or spouse are naturalized or native born citizens of the United States; the date when parent or spouse acquired citizenship.
Natural Origin	• Inquiry into languages applicant speaks and writes fluently.	• Inquiry into applicant's (a) lineage; (b) ancestry; (c) national origin; (d) descent; (e) parentage, or nationality. • Nationality of applicant's parents or spouse. • What is your mother tongue? • Inquiry into how applicant acquired ability to read, write, or speak a foreign language
Education	• Inquiry into the academic, vocational, or professional education of an applicant and the public and private schools attended.	
Experience	• Inquiry into work experience. • Inquiry into countries applicant has visited.	
Arrests	• Have you ever been convicted of a crime? If so, when, where, and nature of offense? • Are there any felony charges pending against you?	• Inquiry regarding arrests. Have you ever been arrested?
Relatives	• Names of applicant's relatives, other than a spouse, already employed by this company.	• Address of any relative of applicant, other than address (within the United States) of applicant's father and mother, husband or wife and minor dependent children.

(Continued)

Figure 8.2 Pre-Employment Inquiry Guide *(Continued)*

Subject	Lawful Pre-Employment Inquiries	Unlawful Pre-Employment Inquiries
Notify in Case of Emergency	• Name and address of person to be notified in case of accident or emergency.	• Name and address of nearest relative to be notified in case of accident or emergency.
Military Experience	• Inquiry into an applicant's military experience in the Armed Forces of the United States or in a State Militia. • Inquiry into applicant's service in a particular branch of United States Army, Navy, etc.	• Inquiry into an applicant's general military experience.
Organizations	• Inquiry into the organizations of which an applicant is a member excluding organizations, which by name or character indicate the race, color, religion, national origin, or ancestry of members.	• List all clubs, societies and lodges to which you belong.
Transportation	• Do you have reliable transportation to get to work by 7:00 am?	• Do you own a car?
References	• Who suggested that you apply for a position here?	

Source: State of Michigan, Michigan Department of Civil Rights, Lansing, Mich.

Federal Privacy Act

Federal and state laws also protect employees against invasion of their privacy. The Federal Privacy Act covers employee records, locker and personal inspections, background investigations, and other matters. Normally, employees are entitled to a reasonable expectation of privacy and, if this is denied, legal liability can result.

Americans with Disabilities Act (ADA)

The Americans With Disabilities Act (ADA), passed in 1990, requires covered organizations to take steps to accommodate disabled persons, including employees, and to employ qualified disabled job applicants.

The law's definition of **disability** is important: "A physical or mental impairment that substantially limits one or more major life activities of such individuals; a record of such an impairment; or being regarded as having such an impairment." This definition includes persons with a wide range of disabling conditions such as blindness, hearing impairments, arthritis, heart conditions, emphysema, shortness of stature, amputation, and others.

Regulations state that organizations must make "reasonable accommodations" as long as doing so does not create an "undue burden." Issues such as costs, financial resources of the facility, and its relationship, if any, with a parent corporation are all taken into account as these and related issues are assessed.

Glossary

Disability
"A physical or mental impairment that substantially limits one or more major life activities of such individuals; a record of such an impairment; or being regarded as having such an impairment"

Generally, public accommodations must remove architectural barriers in existing facilities if such removal is "readily achievable" (easily accomplishable and able to be carried out without too much difficulty or expense). Each public accommodation must evaluate its facilities and determine what can be done. If a problem exists, the organization typically must provide goods, services, facilities, and accommodations through alternative methods.

In regard to the facility itself, there are several priorities:

✓ The first priority is actual access to the public accommodation (doorways, entrance ramps, etc.).

✓ The second priority is access to goods and services. (For example, do all disabled visitors have access to the cafeteria?)

✓ The third priority is access to restroom facilities.

✓ The fourth priority is access to any other services, goods, or facilities offered by the organization.

A wide range of regulations apply when there is new construction or alteration to existing facilities. Likewise, enforcement provisions include opportunities for victims of discrimination to go to court.

Most healthcare facilities have been designed to accommodate persons with disabilities and, in fact, exist to provide health services for them. However, healthcare facilities may be confronted with the same types of issues as other organizations relative to the employment of persons with disabilities.

Figure 8.3 reviews major concerns that must be addressed in the personnel policies and procedures of most employers.

Figure 8.3 Americans with Disabilities Act Requirements Fact Sheet: Employment

- Employers may not discriminate against an individual with a disability in hiring or promotion if the person is otherwise qualified for the job.
- Employers can ask about one's ability to perform a job, but cannot inquire if someone has a disability or subject a person to tests that tend to screen out people with disabilities.
- Employers will need to provide "reasonable accommodation" to individuals with disabilities. This includes steps such as job restructuring and modification of equipment.
- Employers do not need to provide accommodations that impose an "undue hardship" on business operations.
- All employers with 15 or more employees must comply.

Sexual Harassment

Today, sexual harassment in the workplace receives significant attention and is one of the most frequent reasons for employee litigation (lawsuits). In March 1980, the EEOC issued specific guidelines dealing with sexual harassment. Sexual harassment is a violation of Title VII. Simply stated, in order for conduct to be considered sexual harassment, the conduct must: (1) be sexual in nature, and (2) be unwelcome. Sexual harassment may be physical, verbal (including suggestive comments), or visual (for example, displaying pornographic photographs).

While the laws and their interpretations may vary, some principles are well established. The Certified Dietary Manager and/or employer will probably be held liable for sexual harassment if an employee is deprived of a tangible job benefit (e.g., promotion) because of a refusal to provide sexual favors. If an employee's work environment is negatively affected (in the employee's opinion) by the sexual harassment of a supervisor or co-worker, and if the employer knows or should have known of this conduct and does not take immediate action, the employer will probably be held liable. The manager and the facility could also be found liable for the harassment of employees by clients or their guests if unwanted activities occurred, facility personnel were aware of them, and immediate corrective actions were not taken.

A facility must exercise reasonable care to prevent sexual harassment. In the event a manager is informed that an employee is being sexually harassed, the EEOC Guidelines on Discrimination Because of Sex indicate that the following steps should be taken:

1. Notify your own superior.
2. Investigate the situation according to your organization's policy.
3. Seek legal advice before further action is taken.
4. Confront the accused party, and get the accused party's side of the story.
5. Take any necessary disciplinary action(s).

To deal effectively with the issue of sexual harassment:

✓ Managers should be familiar with the policy. This policy should include disciplinary guidelines for both the individual who is guilty and guidelines for harassers who retaliate against those who report them. The policy should include a formal complaint procedure for employees to use if they think they have been victims of sexual harassment, with provisions for immediate investigation and prompt disciplinary action when appropriate.

✓ Employees should be educated on how to recognize sexual harassment, how to report it when it occurs, and the steps that will be taken if an employee is guilty of sexual harassment. All cases of possible sexual harassment must be investigated according to this policy set by management.

✓ Follow-up needs to be provided after all instances of sexual harassment. Victims must be contacted and witnesses need to be asked if the sexual harassment has indeed stopped and no retaliation is taking place.

Your male cook has a habit of calling the females with whom he works "honey." Is this a violation of the sexual harassment law?

(Check your answer at the end of this chapter)

Fair Labor Standards Act (FLSA)

The Fair Labor Standards Act (FLSA) addresses the idea that an employee deserves to be paid fairly. It defines:

✓ Minimum wage

✓ A 40-hour work week

✓ Requirements for overtime

✓ Restrictions on child labor.

Individual states also have provisions relating to these ideas, so what is legally acceptable does vary from state to state. The FLSA specifically includes state and local hospitals, as well as educational institutions. Among other things, the law requires that employees exceeding a 40-hour work week receive overtime pay.

The overtime pay requirement does not apply to an **exempt employee**. An exempt employee is on salary (as opposed to receiving an hourly wage). An exempt employee does not receive overtime compensation. In a facility where employees belong to a union, an exempt employee may have a broader definition. Employees who meet the following criteria can be exempt from the overtime provisions of the Wage and Hour Law as executives:

- ✓ They supervise two or more other employees
- ✓ Their salary is the minimum amount determined by the Wage and Hour Division (which changes periodically)
- ✓ They have the power to hire and fire, or their recommendations must carry significant weight
- ✓ Their primary duty is management. They can't do non-exempt work more than 40 percent of the time in any given work week. Generally, they can't do the work of the people they supervise
- ✓ They are able to exercise discretionary powers and set policies on the job.

Often only the department manager can set policies within that department, and all others follow those policies. If so, only one person in a department is usually considered exempt as an executive. However, the Wage and Hour Division has been interpreting this rule to allow an assistant manager who is working on an entirely different shift from the manager to be exempt if the other requirements are met.

Workers Compensation

The concept of workers compensation is to limit liability of the employer if an employee becomes injured on the job. It also provides income to an employee who is unable to work due to injury on the job. The federal government has laid the groundwork for workers compensation through the Federal Employment Compensation Act (FECA), which is administered by state governments. Each state has its own policies and legislation and administers the program.

Family and Medical Leave Act (FMLA)

This legislation, enacted in 1993, requires employers to provide at least 12 weeks of leave to a qualified employee who has specific family or medical reasons to request time off. This time may be paid or unpaid, according to the employer's policy. The law requires that this leave be available once during a one-year period.

During the leave, the employee should still be eligible for health insurance benefits (even though the employee may pay for these benefits). Upon returning to work, the employee should be reinstated into his or her previous position.

Glossary

Exempt Employee
An employee who is salaried and does not qualify for overtime compensation

Putting It Into Practice: 3

Your head cook, who supervises the pm cook and the assistant cook, receives an hourly wage. She recently put in extra hours to help prepare for a special meal. Is she entitled to overtime pay?

(Check your answer at the end of this chapter)

The types of situations that qualify for family and medical leave include:

✓ Birth of a child

✓ Adoption of a child

✓ Serious health condition of employee's spouse, parent, or child

✓ Serious illness experienced by the employee.

The law applies to small businesses with 15 or more employees and to all public agencies and schools. The law can also protect an individual employee who is unable to work because of a personal health condition. This has created a bit of legal confusion, because the legislation overlaps with the ADA. For example, cancer is considered both cause for medical leave and a disability. So, an employer might need to grant a 12-week leave to an employee with cancer according to the FMLA, and then grant additional leave or other accommodations afterwards to comply with the ADA. Rulings and statutes are evolving to address issues such as these.

Federal Unemployment Tax Act (FUTA)

Another form of protection provided by law is the financial protection awarded to employees in the case that they should become unemployed through no fault of their own. The law providing this protection is the Federal Unemployment Tax Act (FUTA). FUTA provides a right to unemployment compensation to protect the income of former employees while they seek new employment. It does not apply to an employee who was terminated through a disciplinary process.

For example, if a facility determines that it needs to eliminate a set of jobs, the employees who lose their jobs may be eligible to receive unemployment compensation. How much and for how long depends on a number of factors. State entities are involved in administering the legislation, and employers pay a tax to help provide funding for this program.

These are some examples of employment regulations, but this section does not present an exhaustive list. For information about federal employment regulations, you can visit the U.S. Department of Labor website Compliance Assistance section (www.dol.gov/compliance) to review regulations by name or topic. Furthermore, your own human resources department is the best authority on all the employment laws (federal and state) that may affect your actions as a manager. As you review your own organization's human resources policies and procedures, you will also find that these reflect the standards with which you must comply.

Selecting Employees

Selecting employees involves several steps: recruitment, screening, checking references, interviewing, and making a hiring decision. Some facilities may use their human resources department to coordinate the selection process. Either way, it will be important to have standardized procedures for each of these steps as they are covered by the EEOC. The government provides free guidelines for the selection process entitled, *Uniform Guidelines on Employee*

Selection Procedures located at this URL: http://www.uniformguidelines.com/. If you do not have an HR department, be sure and consult these guidelines including the questions and answers found on the Website.

The Recruitment Process

The recruitment process helps to build a pool of applicants for open jobs. As the Certified Dietary Manager, you will need to decide if you are going to recruit from within your facility or search outside the facility. Your human resources department can help you decide based on the job available and availability of employees. If you decide to recruit from outside your facility, your human resources department can help you find the best sources for obtaining employees, such as newspapers or online job posting services.

After initial recruitment efforts, a manager is faced with the task of trying to predict how well candidates will perform if they are selected as employees. Much of this occurs through a structured selection and interview process.

The Screening Process

Most businesses use a screening process to select the applicants to be interviewed. Screening means comparing each applicant's qualifications to the job description. To be protected by the EEOC and follow the Uniform Guidelines for Employee Selection, you should have a screening committee that compares each applicant in the same way to the job description. Some facilities have an outline of the job description that is used for each applicant, such as shown in Figure 8.4. Using the same template with each applicant helps to reduce discrimination. If you have too many applicants, you might use both the paper screening process and a screening interview to obtain additional information as to which applicants should be considered further.

Figure 8.4 Screening Template for Foodservice Employees

Qualifications	Education	Experience					Other
		Sanitation	Record Keeping	Food Protection	Nutrition	Customer/ Client Service	
Applicant #1							
Applicant #2							

Figure 8.5 Frequently Asked Interview Questions

- Why did you choose to interview with our organization?
- Describe your ideal job.
- What can you offer us?
- What skills have you developed?
- What did you enjoy most about your last employment?
- What did you enjoy least about your last employment?
- Have you ever quit a job? Why?
- Why should we hire you rather than another candidate?
- What do you consider to be your greatest strengths?
- Would you be successful working on a team?
- What do you know about our organization?
- Have you worked under deadline pressure? When?
- How do you feel about working in a structured environment?
- How do you feel about working overtime?
- How did you get along with your former co-workers?
- What are your expectations for rate of pay?
- Tell me about yourself.
- Do you have any computer experience?
- Would you be willing to take a drug test?
- How does your past experience apply to this position?
- How does this job match your interests?
- What skills do you have which will help in this job?
- What are your main strengths for this job?
- What major weaknesses will need to be overcome for you to do this job adequately?
- Will you have any problems getting to work?
- What other information can you provide which will help me to understand your capabilities for this work?
- What questions do you have about the job?
- When would you be able to begin work?

The Interview Process

Much information about job applicants can be gained from application forms, reference checks, selection tests, and medical exams.

✓ Reference Checks—If you don't have a human resources department, use a standard form for all candidates that asks for: dates of employment, reporting relationship, reason for leaving.

✓ Selection Tests—Each applicant should take a selection test.

✓ Medical Exams—The American with Disabilities Act requires that this be directly related to employment and cannot be required until employment is offered.

However, this is not enough for determining whether an applicant will be suitable for a job. One or more pre-employment job interviews are also essential to match a candidate with a job vacancy.

Why is it a good idea to have an advance checklist prepared for interviewing multiple candidates?

(Check your answer at the end of this chapter)

A Certified Dietary Manager and/or immediate supervisor who is not involved in this preliminary interview should be involved in an interview with the applicant before the final selection decision is made. The purpose of an interview is to assess the abilities, attitudes, and compatibility of the applicant for the position. It is very important that the immediate supervisor be involved in the applicant selection process. Figure 8.5 identifies some basic questions that may be useful during an interview.

An interview is really a planned conversation. Each party needs to obtain information from the other; an interview provides a format for this

Figure 8.6 Interviewing Tips

- Respect a candidate's feelings and self-esteem at all times. Strive to put the candidate at ease.
- Begin with a pleasant, professional introduction and appropriate light conversation.
- Remember that to the candidate, you are the organization.
- Don't give excessive encouragement verbally or nonverbally at any point.
- Examine candidate evidence in areas of past performance and achievement, as well as work philosophies and beliefs.
- Use verbal rejoinders to trigger additional response in crucial areas, such as "Tell me more...," "Give me another example," etc.
- Use nonverbal reminders, such as nodding, facial gestures, etc. to maintain a steady flow of information.
- Take notes as needed and in a natural sequence. Don't make a final appraisal of notes until the interview is concluded.
- If you don't see a desired characteristic, ask for it specifically. If it is still not apparent, score the applicant accordingly.
- Make yourself thoroughly knowledgeable about the candidate prior to the interview and use that knowledge throughout the meeting.
- Portray the available position adequately and accurately; question candidate to determine specific qualifications.
- Have a set questioning process prepared prior to the interview; seek specific data to match against the job description.
- Don't wander into EEOC-sensitive information unless you are seeking BFOQ—Bona Fide Occupational Qualifications. Avoid areas such as age, race, marital status, and any other sensitive areas unless information is volunteered by candidate.
- Let the candidate do the majority of the talking.
- Listen attentively, accurately, and actively.
- Postpone all final judgments until after the interview.
- Interrupt the candidate only when necessary, and then with tact and brevity.
- Ask candidate for permission to take notes, or merely inform candidate you will do so.
- Control excessive applicant rambling by introducing the next question or a rejoinder.
- Ensure the candidate answers a question at hand completely before moving on to another area.

communication. Generally, an interviewer works from a pre-determined list of questions in order to assure fairness in assessing candidates. However, the best interview process puts a candidate at ease and allows the candidate to open up and tell more. Figure 8.6 provides additional interviewing tips.

When you interview a prospective employee, you are indirectly setting the tone for the relationship that may follow if that individual is hired by your organization. The interview can ultimately be construed as a legally binding description of both the job opportunity and your company's own value system (or lack of it).

Types of Interview Questions. There are three basic types of interview questions: directive, non-directive, and situational. Directive interview questions are specific questions formulated in advance and asked in a checklist fashion. Questions asked should solicit important information.

Examples of directive interview questions include:

✓ What did you do in your last job?

✓ Why did you leave your last position?

Directive interview questions solicit facts and do not seek opinions. All topics of directive questions should directly impact on how well the applicant can perform the job. Any other questions may be in violation of EEOC or other laws. When directive interview questions are used, it is important that the job applicant be given time to ask questions and that the interviewer provide basic information about the job. Generally, the interviewer can record responses to questions as they are given.

The second type of interview question is non-directive. While questions are also planned and perhaps written down in advance, they are less structured and more non-directive so that the interviewee can provide creative responses. Examples of non-directive questions include:

- ✓ Why do you think you'll like this job?
- ✓ What elements do you consider important when you consider a new position?

Many interviewers like to use responses to non-directive questions as springboards for additional questions formulated on-the-fly. With this approach, the interviewer can go on in depth to learn more about the applicant. Applicants who are encouraged to speak on their own will usually provide much more information than they will in response to closed-ended, yes-or-no questions.

Use of situational interview questions is an excellent way to further evaluate how well a candidate will fit in with the department. These questions ask a candidate to describe a type of situation and related decisions and/or actions. Here are some examples of situational questions:

- ✓ Tell me about a time when you knew a co-worker was not following work procedures. What happened, and what did you do?
- ✓ Describe a personal conflict that you had with a co-worker. What happened, and how did you respond?
- ✓ If you knew someone was stealing, what would you do?
- ✓ Can you think of a time when you disagreed with a company policy? Tell me what you decided to do.
- ✓ If you saw an unsafe situation, what would you do?

During an interview, a Certified Dietary Manager can combine directive, non-directive, and situational questions to help build an understanding of the candidate's suitability for a job. To encourage the applicant to tell you as much as possible, avoid leading questions. Leading questions can also influence a candidate's response and interfere with your receiving valid information. Here are some examples of leading questions to avoid:

- ✓ "You would like to work here, wouldn't you?" or
- ✓ "You wouldn't argue with a client, would you?"

Preparing for and Conducting an Interview

Needless to say, there is much more to an interview than just asking questions. The interviewer must properly prepare for it. A private environment free from interruptions is best. Set a beginning time, and stick to it. Read over the application form and any other information available about the applicant. Provide enough time so that information can be solicited without the need to rush. Review the checklist of questions you plan to ask and be sure that all questions are relevant to the selection decision.

Some basic principles help develop good interview techniques. It is essential to put the applicant at ease. Candidates are likely to be nervous, so some friendly, opening conversation can be helpful in developing the rapport necessary for a good interview. A friendly handshake, a hospitable greeting, and perhaps a cup of coffee are always good ways to start.

Once the interview begins, ask simple questions first. Be aware of the time and don't allow yourself to feel rushed. Listen to what is being said. While this seems obvious, an interviewer sometimes listens with a bias or is thinking about other things and the real message of the candidate is lost. When the interviewee is speaking, concentrate rather than thinking ahead. Ask permission to take notes so that you can remember important things the candidate tells you. It is best to take notes on a separate sheet of paper and not on the resume or application. However, refrain from focusing on note-taking. Often, a few words will do, and you may make additional notes after the interview has ended. Strive to maintain excellent eye contact and observe the candidate's nonverbal behavior. Listen open-mindedly. Like a good journalist, you do not need to present your opinions about the candidate's comments. Your opinions may sway what the applicant tells you. It is more important to encourage expression, and listen to what the candidate says.

Recognize that the candidate is probably very eager to learn about the position and the facility. A rule of thumb is to listen for about 75 percent of the interview, and talk for about 25 percent. Most of your information about the facility can wait until the late stage of the interview. Again, relating the details of your philosophy and standards may influence an applicant to simply tell you what he thinks you want to hear.

Follow-up after the interview is necessary. If you are not working with an human resources department and are certain at the conclusion of the interview that the applicant will not be considered further, let him or her know. Perhaps there is another vacant position for which the interviewee will be eligible. Put yourself in the interviewee's place. Wouldn't you like to know about the interview results as soon as possible?

If you believe the applicant is qualified but want to interview others, it is fair to tell the interviewee that also. Name a time by which you will relate your selection decision. Adhere to the schedule, or apprise the interviewee of any changes in the timetable. If you believe the interviewee is qualified and you have no other applicants to consider, you may inform the interviewee that a job will be offered. Regardless of the outcome of the interview, let the interviewee know how you feel.

If you are working with a human resources department, each interview team member may be asked to rank the candidates based on the selection criteria.

The human resources department will follow up with the candidate after the interview.

Now let's look at some additional pointers:

- ✓ Watch for the halo effect, which means hiring people who are just like you. An effective manager recognizes the value of building a team with complementary skills.
- ✓ Take your time. If you are not prepared for an interview or feel pressure to make a decision immediately, you are likely to obtain incorrect or incomplete information about the applicant.
- ✓ Follow legal guidelines, such as EEOC and other applicable laws throughout the process.
- ✓ Use reasonable standards for comparison. For example, if you compare an applicant with another employee with many years of experience, perhaps no applicant will seem acceptable. Instead, compare the job applicant's skills with the job specification.
- ✓ Be upbeat about your organization, but refrain from making false promises or unrealistic commitments. Always tell the truth and let the applicant make decisions based upon a fair and reasonable expectation.
- ✓ Tell the applicant everything he or she should know to make a decision.
- ✓ Leave the applicant with a positive impression of your organization. Even if you will not be offering a job, the applicant is likely to be a member of the community, and your actions may have a public relations impact.
- ✓ Thank the candidate for meeting with you.

The Hiring Decision

To make a selection decision, review your notes from interviews and weigh them carefully. In certain cases, you may have picked up some "red flags" indicating a candidate may not be able to take direction, or work with others, or perform in a reliable manner. You will probably want to remove these candidates from your list.

At the same time, you may have a list of candidates who seem to be well qualified and whom you predict will fit in well with your job requirements. Who should be offered the position? Typically, this decision is made by reviewing applicant information; considering the relevance of training, experience, and education; assessing how well the candidate is likely to work with others on the team; and making a prediction of how likely the candidate is to become a successful long-term employee. Checking references at this point may provide additional decision information.

Sometimes, you may feel that you simply have not found a qualified candidate for an open job. While you may feel pressure to fill a job, it is usually worth waiting to make a solid match. Bringing in the "wrong" person may seem easy and expedient for the moment, but it is likely to create more work down the line. In fact, if the candidate does not work out, you will find yourself again at the point of recruiting. A better approach is to be able to say "no" when you need to, and immediately increase your recruitment efforts to find more candidates.

All information developed from the recruitment and selection process should be maintained on file in the new employee's personnel records. Sometimes reasons applicants were not selected may also be important. Documentation of applicant information is very important and must be emphasized as permanent files are developed.

END OF CHAPTER

Putting It Into Practice Questions & Answers

1. You are interviewing a prospective employee who is visibly limping. During the interview, your head cook asks, " Can you tell me what happened to your leg?" Is this a legal question? Why or why not?

   A. *No, this is not a legal question. You may not ask job applicants about the existence, nature, or severity of a disability. You may ask only about their ability to perform job functions. A job offer may be considered on the results of a medical examination, but only if the examination is required for all entering employees in the same job category.*

2. Your male cook has a habit of calling the females with whom he works "honey." Is this a violation of the sexual harassment law?

   A. *It could be if your employees feel uncomfortable when he calls them "honey." The law says as the manager you have to be aware of sexual harassment concerns, even if no one comes to you to complain. You should ask your female employees how they feel about the male cook calling them "honey." You or your HR department should also talk to your male cook and provide him with information about what is included in the sexual harassment law.*

3. Your head cook, who supervises the pm cook and the assistant cook, receives an hourly wage. She recently put in extra hours to help prepare for a special meal. Is she entitled to overtime pay?

   A. *What is your policy for requiring advance authorization for overtime? Did you authorize the time or was she acting on her own? Does she do this on a regular basis and then expect overtime? Has she worked more than 40 hours within seven days? These are questions that need to be answered first. If you have no advance authorization for overtime and she worked more than 40 hours within seven days, she is entitled to overtime pay.*

4. Why is it a good idea to have an advance checklist prepared for interviewing multiple candidates?

   A. *An advance checklist of questions assures that each candidate will be asked the same questions and treated equally during the interview process. The checklist should contain directive, non-directive, and situational questions.*

CHAPTER 9

Manage Department Personnel

Overview and Objectives

A large part of the Certified Dietary Manager's job is that of leading people. To manage people effectively, one must give feedback to employees and know how to conduct a performance review. This chapter helps the manager explore how to conduct a performance review.

After completing this chapter, you should be able to:

✓ Maintain personnel records in proper form

✓ Identify personnel management laws and practices

✓ Identify promotion/termination criteria

✓ Utilize a performance evaluation

✓ Justify personnel decisions including documentation for promotion and termination

✓ Follow disciplinary procedures to correct a problem

Recruitment, selection, and hiring all take considerable time and effort. Keeping your new and experienced employees also requires thought, effort, and management strategies. Please note that most of the information presented in this chapter is governed by state and federal laws. Since those laws were covered in Chapter 8, refer to them as you read through this chapter.

Employee Recognition

Many studies have been conducted to determine why employees leave their place of employment. Managers frequently believe it is because the employees want higher pay. In reality, it is because employees want recognition for what they do and they want to feel appreciated. There are three management strategies that will help you keep your employees:

✓ Treat your employees like your clients—with respect and dignity

✓ Provide an atmosphere of trust and support

✓ Reward your employees for a good job and deal fairly with those who don't.

Treat Your Employees Like Your Clients

One of the main reasons your clients leave is because you aren't meeting their needs. The same can be said for your employees; they most often leave because you aren't meeting their needs. Once you understand that your employees need to be treated with respect and dignity, you can show that by:

✓ Treating each employee fairly, regardless of the type of decisions you have to make.

✓ Demonstrating your integrity by doing what you say you are going to do.

✓ Providing regular feedback to each employee. Communicate to each employee what is required of them, what the rewards are, and how they are doing. Remember that communication goes two ways so make sure you ask them for feedback about what is required of them, what the rewards are, and how they think they are doing.

Provide an Atmosphere of Trust and Support

Communication is also the key to providing an atmosphere of trust and support. Communicate to your employees what your thoughts are about the direction of the department. Develop a consistent habit of communicating with each employee, in person. Getting to know your employee's lives outside of work by listening to them will show them you care and support them. Establish a relationship of trust and respect both outside the workplace and inside. Keep your relationship friendly and always professional.

Reward Your Employees for a Good Job

Rewarding your employees for a good job doesn't mean waiting until performance evaluation time. When you 'catch them in the act of doing a good job,' let them know it right then. One manager carried bite-sized candy bars with her and anytime she caught an employee doing a good job, she would toss them a candy bar. Rewards don't have to be monetary; in fact in today's economy, it probably won't be. Employees will appreciate a personal note from you. Ask during a staff meeting, "What went well this week?" then acknowledge the successes. There are many resources you can access to get ideas about rewarding your employees. See the *Management in the News* section at the end of this chapter for other examples. Don't forget to ask your employees how they want to be rewarded!

The Association of Nutrition & Foodservice Professionals (ANFP) promotes Pride in Food Service Week in early February. This can be an opportunity to call attention to the contribution foodservice employees make to the facility.

Along with rewarding your employees is treating each person fairly. There will be some employees you like better than others and that should not interfere with fair treatment for all employees. For example, if you have to lay off some staff due to a declining census, make sure the layoff decisions are based on the job duties, not the employee. Treating each person fairly also means taking the responsibility to address those who aren't carrying their load. When you don't address this, you are penalizing your good performers.

Employee Satisfaction Surveys

One way to gather feedback from your staff is through formal or informal employee satisfaction surveys. Some facilities have satisfaction surveys for the staff of the entire facility. If employees have an opportunity to express their feelings and beliefs about their job, they may be more satisfied with their job.

You have two employees who are interested in a new position you are creating to implement a culture change in your facility. One employee is pregnant and you know she will miss an important time in the training for this position but she is better qualified than the other applicant. Who should you choose for this position and why?

(Check your answer at the end of this chapter)

Satisfied staff usually means satisfied clients. Figure 9.1 shows a sample informal employee satisfaction survey.

Employee Turnover

Employee turnover is all too common in many foodservice operations. Some employees leave the job for explainable reasons such as relocation, graduation, and retirement. Often, turnover results in significant expense for a foodservice operation. This expense takes the form of:

- ✓ Managerial time required to recruit, interview, and select new employees
- ✓ Advertising expenses related to recruitment
- ✓ Managerial time required to orient and train new employees
- ✓ Temporary set-backs in productivity and/or quality during transitional phases
- ✓ The stress of adjustment for existing staff.

Clearly, a wise Certified Dietary Manager strives to retain valuable employees in order to minimize the burden and expense of ongoing recruitment. Why do employees leave? Several factors can contribute to turnover. These include:

- ✓ Lack of opportunities for professional growth and development
- ✓ Lack of effective supervision
- ✓ Inadequate levels of trust between the employee and the supervisor
- ✓ Lack of participative opportunities
- ✓ Perceived inequality regarding how employees are treated
- ✓ Poor compensation, such as wages and/or benefits
- ✓ Lack of rewards
- ✓ Competitive offers elsewhere
- ✓ Personal reasons.

Surprisingly, when surveyed about what makes them want to stay on the job, many employees rate pay as relatively unimportant. Some employees in the service industry stay because of the rewards of working with others and serving people. In addition, the opportunity to achieve self-fulfillment and satisfaction can be strong factors in retention. Good relationships with peers, supervisors, and even clients—along with a positive work climate—also rank very high.

One approach that is very helpful in retention is participative management. This can take many forms but the basic idea is to involve employees in the facility. Empowerment provides a form of participative management. Employee teams assigned to develop improvements, standards, procedures, or systems can be another form of participative management. These actions contribute to self-fulfillment.

Exit Interview

When an employee does leave, it is important to conduct an exit interview. An **exit interview** is an interview with an employee who is leaving the organization. Depending on organizational policy, it may be conducted for employees who voluntarily leave, or for all departing employees, including those who are terminated. It may be conducted by you as the Certified Dietary Manager, or by a designated member of the human resources staff.

Glossary

Exit Interview
An interview with an employee who is leaving the organization

Figure 9.1 Job Satisfaction Survey for Employees

Please note that answers to this survey are anonymous and confidential, and participation is voluntary. If you choose to complete the survey, it is due on (enter date here). We plan to use the results to improve job satisfaction and address any problems deemed necessary. When formulating your responses, please answer honestly and thoroughly. Thank you for your time!

Sincerely,
The Management Team

1. How satisfied are you with the overall management of the department?
   a. Very satisfied
   b. Mostly satisfied
   c. Mostly unsatisfied
   d. Very unsatisfied

Comments:

2. Are you provided with the tools and materials necessary to complete your job duties?
   a. Yes
   b. Sometimes
   c. No

Comments:

3. Are you encouraged to share your thoughts, ideas, and feelings about the department?
   a. Yes
   b. Sometimes
   c. No

Comments:

4. Do you believe that employees of the department are treated equally and that the management team does not demonstrate favoritism?
   a. Yes
   b. Sometimes
   c. No

Comments:

5. Do the job duties that you complete on a regular basis (not including special events or during emergencies) match the job description that you were provided with when you were hired?
   a. Yes
   b. Sometimes
   c. No

Comments:

6. Are you valued as a person by management?
   a. Yes
   b. Sometimes
   c. No

Comments:

7. Does management encourage teamwork?
   a. Yes
   b. Sometimes
   c. No

Comments:

8. Are meetings held appropriately (when needed, in a timely and organized manner, etc)?
   a. Yes
   b. Sometimes
   c. No

Comments:

9. Is management willing to make changes and improvements to the department when necessary?
   a. Yes
   b. Sometimes
   c. No

Comments:

10. Do you feel hopeful about the future of the department?
    a. Yes
    b. Sometimes
    c. No

Comments:

Additional Comments and Suggestions:

Review Date 3/09 **G-0969**

Source: RD411.com, used with permission.

An exit interview often provides valuable information which the organization can use to improve employee retention. Sometimes, an exit interview yields surprises, and it becomes apparent that without this process, managers may never have learned something they really needed to know! Questions that may be asked during an exit interview appear in Figure 9.2.

Figure 9.2 Sample Questions for an Exit Interview

- Why are you leaving the organization?*
- What did you enjoy most about working here?
- What did you enjoy least about working here?
- How would you describe your relationship with your supervisor?
- How would you describe the working environment?
- Is there anything that would have changed your decision to leave?*

** Omit these questions if the employee is not leaving voluntarily.*

As a matter of policy, information gathered through exit interviews should be routinely reviewed and assessed by human resources staff. You should also review this information and seek to learn everything you can from it to refine your approach to improving retention.

Performance Review

As part of the ongoing responsibility to provide feedback to employees, a Certified Dietary Manager must comply with organizational policies and procedures for **performance review**, a formal evaluation of an employee's work on the job. At times, a manager must also take corrective action to help improve performance. Both of these are documented activities and the documents become part of an employee's personnel file.

When a particular employee continues to have performance problems, a manager must decide how to intervene. Unfortunately, termination occasionally becomes the only solution. On the flip side of the coin, when employee performance meets or exceeds established standards, the manager is charged with providing recognition to encourage excellent performance.

Purpose of a Performance Review

A structured and scheduled component of nearly every organization, a performance review or performance appraisal or evaluation is a formal, structured meeting between employee and supervisor that encourages an exchange about the individual employee's performance on the job.

A performance review does several things:

✓ Ensures that the supervisor talks with the employee about performance, and provides extensive feedback.

✓ Identifies needs for improvement and growth.

✓ Serves as a formal basis for wage increases related to performance.

✓ Provides an opportunity for an employee to set personal work objectives that relate to the departmental objectives.

Performance Review
A formal, structured meeting between employee and supervisor about the individual employee's performance

- ✓ Provides an opportunity for the employee to raise needs related to the work, and for the manager to help.
- ✓ Provides documentation for the employee's personnel record.
- ✓ May be used to help evaluate eligibility for promotion.

How often a performance review occurs is generally dictated by the policy of a facility. For example, one facility may conduct performance reviews for every employee at three months of employment, six months of employment, and annually thereafter. The review is documented on a form that is standardized for the facility, signed by both employee and supervisor, and retained as part of the personnel file.

Employee performance review programs can benefit the employee, the Certified Dietary Manager, and the organization itself. For example, a manager who recognizes individual staff members through a formal review process may obtain ideas from employees about how work procedures can be improved. As strengths and weaknesses of each employee are identified, the employee and manager together can develop action plans to improve performance.

The groundwork for motivation can be laid during a performance review, too. This occurs when employees understand that the Certified Dietary Manager is concerned about them and is interested in learning about their needs. Coaching, counseling, training, orientation, and many other ongoing programs can be strengthened as the result of information learned during performance appraisal.

It also becomes easier to justify job actions, such as demotions and transfers, when formalized evaluation sessions have been completed and documented. If the Certified Dietary Manager can show that performance is consistently inadequate and, if the employee has agreed that a problem exists and that improvements will be made, failure to make these improvements may provide justification for actions that are taken.

Performance evaluation can help improve the relationship between the Certified Dietary Manager and employee. An effective manager asks for feedback during a review, and sometimes learns more about how to lead and motivate employees through this process. As the manager and employees work together as partners in the performance review process, a relationship can be built which helps each gain mutual understanding and respect.

Performance standards are an essential point of reference during a performance review. The process should account for how the quality and quantity of an employee's work compares with the performance standards that have already been established for the job.

Types of Performance Review

There are several basic types of performance reviews. Some of the options include a review that uses absolute standards, an open-ended summary, and an objectives-based evaluation.

Absolute Standards Performance Review. In this type of performance review, work performance of an individual staff member is considered as a stand-alone function, without comparison to others. One popular example of the absolute standard type of performance review is the critical incident method. Using this technique, the Certified Dietary Manager keeps a log of incidents that represent both effective and ineffective job performance. The log is then used to measure employee performance. The manager simply lists any activity observed on the job that he or she judges to be critical to job performance, and compares the observations with established performance standards. This way, an employee is receiving both reinforcement and coaching about observed behaviors.

Certain events are called "critical" because they illustrate the key behaviors that define (or violate) standards for performance. For example, a Certified Dietary Manager observes an employee arguing with a client. The manager may record this as a critical incident because it represents failure to meet a performance standard about providing friendly service. In another event, the same employee may check and record food temperatures of hot and cold foods before service with 100 percent accuracy. This may relate to another performance standard about documenting food temperatures accurately before serving trays. The manager may record this, too, as a critical incident on the performance review form.

In today's electronic world, a Certified Dietary Manager may have an electronic file for each employee. An efficient way to record a critical incident is to send yourself a brief e-mail with the details that provide the date and information regarding the incident. When you have time, move the e-mail into the employee's file.

Another type of absolute standards review is a checklist developed by the supervisor or the facility. The evaluation lists important performance items and provides a numeric rating scale. The supervisor selects a number to rate the performance of the employee related to each item. A sample checklist evaluation is shown in Figure 9.3.

Another example of the absolute standards approach is a forced-choice plan, which requires a Certified Dietary Manager to select a statement judged most accurate in describing how an employee performs on the job. A sample is shown in Figure 9.4. The manager first lists factors judged important to successful job performance in the left-hand column, then he or she must indicate how the work performance of the employee meets each of the criteria. In some facilities, both the employee and the manager mark separate forms and then compare their answers during the performance review.

Open-Ended Summary Performance Review. A review based on free text allows the supervisor to note strengths and weaknesses of the employee's performance, and to indicate suggestions and support for improvement. A sample appears in Figure 9.5.

(Continued on page 147)

Figure 9.3 Checklist Performance Review Form

Supervisory Evaluation

Name of Supervisor ____________ Department ____________ Date ________

Circle one for each item: *Scale: 7 = the highest level of performance*

ADMINISTRATION

Knows and utilizes proper forms and procedures	7 6 5 4 3 2 1
Meets deadlines	7 6 5 4 3 2 1
Organizes personal workload	7 6 5 4 3 2 1
Organizes work of those supervised	7 6 5 4 3 2 1
Apprises immediate superior of all current developments	7 6 5 4 3 2 1

Explain where improvement is needed:

____

LEADERSHIP

Sets goals and objectives for self	7 6 5 4 3 2 1
Sets goals and objectives for employees supervised	7 6 5 4 3 2 1
Meets goals and objectives for self	7 6 5 4 3 2 1
Helps employees meet goals and objectives	7 6 5 4 3 2 1
Supports employees supervised	7 6 5 4 3 2 1
Supports policies and procedures	7 6 5 4 3 2 1
Helps develop employee potential for advancement	7 6 5 4 3 2 1

Explain where improvement is needed:

____

MOTIVATION

Displays high propensity to accomplish and achieve	7 6 5 4 3 2 1
Supports goals of hospital	7 6 5 4 3 2 1
Functions as part of a team	7 6 5 4 3 2 1
Attempts to help others understand the importance of their work	7 6 5 4 3 2 1
Urges others to excel	7 6 5 4 3 2 1
Gives competent professional image	7 6 5 4 3 2 1

Explain where improvement is needed:

____

SUPERVISION

Gives continuous orientation and on-the-job training to employees supervised	7 6 5 4 3 2 1
Explains orders whenever possible	7 6 5 4 3 2 1
Answers questions fully or obtains answers for employees supervised	7 6 5 4 3 2 1
Administers and supports proper policy	7 6 5 4 3 2 1
Listens to and attempts to correct employee complaints	7 6 5 4 3 2 1
Holds periodic meetings with employees to pass on information	7 6 5 4 3 2 1
Provides effective feedback to employees	7 6 5 4 3 2 1

Explain where improvement is needed:

____

COMMENTS—Describe the supervisor specifically in terms of the following:

Technical competence: ________________________________

Creative ability: ________________________________

Motivation and drive: ________________________________

Human relations: ________________________________

Overall performance: ________________________________

Additional comments: ________________________________

Signature and title of individual completing evaluation: ________________________________

Signature of supervisor being evaluated: ________________________________

Supervisor's comments: ________________________________

Figure 9.4 **Forced-Choice Review Form**

Employee Name________________________ Job Title________________________

Dept. Name ____________________ No. ________ For Period ______________ through ______________

Reason for Evaluation: end of probation ○ wage increase ○ annual evaluation ○ termination ○ transfer ○ promotion ○ Other:

The purpose of this evaluation is to aid employees and their supervisors in determining the employee's strong points and shortcomings, if any, on the job. Asterisked (*) entries must be justified in the remarks section. All pre-written statements may be modified by adding or deleting words. Use additional paper if needed and indicate the total number of pages for this evaluation at the bottom of this page.

QUALITY					
The accuracy or completeness of each unit of work or assigned task. Don't confuse with Quantity.	* Superior, virtually every procedure is accomplished error-free. [ ]	Above average, each procedure is above standards normally expected. [ ]	Does job completely and thoroughly. [ ]	Sometimes inadequate, usually meets minimum standards. [ ]	* Careless, needs constant supervision and follow up. [ ]
QUANTITY					
Volume of work produced in terms of assigned units or tasks.	* Top producer, exceptionally fast. [ ]	Very fast employee, produces more than expected. [ ]	Completes assignments on time. [ ]	Marginal producer, sometimes falls behind. [ ]	* Needs prodding, consistently produces less than is expected. [ ]
INITIATIVE					
Desire to perform the job properly. Adherence to rules and regulations.	* Top producer, exceptionally fast. [ ]	Completes work and seeks additional tasks. [ ]	* Meets the requirements of the job. [ ]	Marginal producer, sometimes fails behind. [ ]	* Lacks initiative, seems to be lazy and/or uninterested. [ ]
PERSONAL GROOMING					
Personal hygiene, grooming, use of makeup, appropriateness of dress.	* Exceptionally well groomed, demonstrates good taste in dress. [ ]	Better than average appearance. [ ]	Meets requirements of the job. [ ]	* Frequently careless in appearance. [ ]	* Wears inappropriate clothing, disregards departmental standards. [ ]
ATTENDANCE					
Punctuality, absenteeism, tardiness.	Always dependable and on time. [ ]	Above average, seldom absent or tardy. [ ]	Demonstrates responsibility toward job requirements. Occasionally absent or tardy. [ ]	Needs improvement; is tardy or absent several times per month. [ ]	* Chronically absent or late. [ ]
DEPENDABILITY					
Judgment demonstrated in conserving confidential information, performing on the job, following instructions.	* Demonstrates exceptional judgment, learns quickly, needs little supervision. [ ]	Efficient, demonstrates discretion, good professional attitude. [ ]	Usually reliable, carries out instructions with normal supervision. [ ]	Inconsistent, requires follow-up and/or monitoring. [ ]	* Violates policy, fails to follow instructions. [ ]
RELATIONSHIP WITH OTHERS					
Patients, co-workers, public. General courtesies and attitudes.	Goes out of way to promote good will. [ ]	Gets along well with others, good attitude. [ ]	Satisfactory relationship with others, generally adapts to persons and situations, pleasant. [ ]	* Defensive, sometimes rigid to change, not always cooperative [ ]	* Antagonistic toward others, inconsiderate. [ ]

Date of Evaluation______________ Evaluator (print)________________________ Page 1 of ________ (total # of pages)

Evaluator's (supervisor's) remarks: ________________________________

Evaluator's Signature ________________________

Employee's remarks; ________________________________

Employee's signature________________________

Note: The employee's signature in no way shows that he or she agrees with this evaluation. It merely indicates that the employee has seen the evaluation and understands the contents.

Figure 9.5 **Open-Ended Performance Review Form**

Employee's Name: ______________ Assignment: ______________ Date: ________

List areas of strength:

List areas of weakness:

List help provided:

List disciplinary action if no improvement is shown:

General comments:

Comments by employee:

Signature of employee: ______________________________ Date: ________

Signature of evaluator: ______________________________ Date: ________

Objectives-Based Performance Review. This is developed with input from both the Certified Dietary Manager and the employee, and is based on individualized objectives. First, the two develop a mutually defined set of job-related objectives. Later, during a performance review session, the two assess how well these objectives have been met. They also develop a new set of objectives. This system is also called management by objectives.

Basic steps in an objectives-based evaluation plan include:

- ✓ The manager and employee set measurable behavioral objectives. The employee commits to attaining these objectives by the time of the next review.
- ✓ The employee is given assistance on the job through training, coaching, and/or other developmental activities.
- ✓ Employee and supervisor, separately, prepare a reflection on how each feels the employee met the objectives.
- ✓ At the time of the performance review, the actual level of performance is measured against the level defined by the objectives and they discuss the reflection.
- ✓ The supervisor and staff member work together to develop new objectives and plan strategies for attaining the objectives before the next performance review session.

You are the Certified Dietary Manager in a large county nursing home where the employees are long-term and are represented by a union. Currently, the performance review is done annually and now there are negotiations about completing the performance review every six months. As a member of the administrative team, what would you recommend and why?

(Check your answer at the end of this chapter)

Performance Review Process

The exact type of performance review form will likely depend on the facility. Using the form and method defined for your facility, you may need to customize your feedback somewhat for a foodservice employee. For example, if the standard form lists "quality of work" as a factor for evaluation, you should provide the indicators for performance standards for your own employees.

As with any feedback, a performance review should be very specific. The more an employee knows what the criteria are for evaluation, the more readily an employee can meet these criteria. Some Certified Dietary Managers provide a blank copy of the evaluation form to a new employee during orientation. This is a way to define expectations for the employee and make it clear what the employee needs to do to succeed.

Before conducting a review, you need to take the time to complete the form and give the review some thought. If multiple supervisors work with one employee, talk to each of them about the performance review, and obtain specific feedback and comments to include.

To conduct a performance review, set aside some time with the employee. Most Certified Dietary Managers schedule this in advance of the actual meeting. Find a time when both you and the employee will not feel rushed so that you can have a meaningful discussion. Then, set aside a private place to talk. A performance review should not be held in a high-traffic area, or in any place where others are likely to overhear the conversation. A performance review is a confidential exchange between you and the employee.

During a review, explain each item—what it is measuring, what standard is being used, and what specific observations you have made about the employee's performance. Throughout the review, give the employee time to react, respond, and ask questions. As with other types of feedback, a performance review gives the Certified Dietary Manager a time to listen to employees, and to learn how to remove obstacles on the job, provide training and support, and help the employee solve problems. You can also learn much more about an individual employee's motivational factors and needs. Let this be an exploration in which both of you walk away with greater understanding.

A performance review is often a time when an employee shares personal development needs in more detail. One employee may tell you that he would really like to learn a cook's position, or another may tell you she wants to learn how to work as a server. These aspirations are important; you should give them consideration. As the review concludes, you should have developed a simple plan for development on the job. It may include items such as additional training for the employee, practice of certain skills, and more.

Both the employee and the supervisor should sign and date the form. Signing the form indicates that the employee has received this feedback (not that the employee agrees with everything it says). A standard procedure allows an employee to note comments. If the employee disagrees with points in the evaluation, these should be discussed. The employee also may note this in the comments. If an employee refuses to sign the form, write "refused to sign," and date and initial the note.

Finally, the paperwork should follow the procedure defined for your facility to assure that a pay raise, if indicated, is processed, and that the form is filed in the employee's personnel record.

Several common pitfalls can occur during the employee performance review process. Some include:

- ✓ Surprising employees with negative feedback: If there has been an ongoing problem, the employee should know well before a performance review. The supervisor should be giving feedback on a regular basis so that there are not surprises. The same is true for positive feedback. Thus, an effective performance review becomes a summary of items that have already been discussed.
- ✓ Using reviews for corrective action only: Sometimes performance reviews are used only to reprimand employees rather than to assess where, if at all, employees can improve.
- ✓ Using ineffective review forms: If review forms do not correctly summarize factors important for effective job performance, the evaluation process will suffer. A Certified Dietary Manager should identify the specific, job-related criteria for review.
- ✓ Failing to use or keep up with performance reviews: Some managers may procrastinate due to busy schedules. Although it can be difficult to schedule time, a manager must give this process high priority. On occasion, an employee whose review has been postponed or overlooked begins to experience poor morale. If a pay raise may be associated with the review, the situation becomes compounded. The employee needs to know that performance is important to you.
- ✓ Comparing employees: The objective of performance reviews should be to compare employee performance with expected performance, not with that of other employees.
- ✓ Failing to use performance review information: Some managers may perform reviews—but then fail to make use of information gained, or neglect to follow through with commitments to support an employee's development. The best action is to follow through with plans and commitments.
- ✓ Failure to be thoroughly familiar with the union contract: If you work in a facility where employees are represented by a union, the contract will outline the performance review process. Make sure you know it and follow it.

Basic elements to include in the formalized employee review program are shown in Figure 9.6. Specific elements of the review process and related policies vary from one facility to another. You will need to familiarize yourself with procedures established for your own facility.

Figure 9.6 Elements for a Performance Review System

- Objectives for conducting performance reviews are defined.
- Performance standards are in place and have been communicated to employees.
- Employees are aware of the performance review process, criteria, and timetable from the time of initial employment.
- Employees have received relevant training.
- The schedule for completing performance reviews has been established and is being followed.
- The manager applies a consistent and fair review process to all employees.
- The manager provides objective, specific feedback during the review process, describing observed behaviors.
- The manager uses methods to solicit employee participation and comments during a review.
- The manager listens attentively.
- The manager and employee work together during a review to solve performance-related problems as appropriate.
- The manager seeks to resolve any misunderstandings and clarify expectations as needed during a review.
- The manager and employee agree upon areas for improvement and growth.
- If needed, the manager and employee create follow-up plans.
- The manager asks for the employee's commitment to achieving objectives.
- The manager completes required documentation and obtains the employee's signature as well. Documentation is placed in the personnel file.

Corrective Action

Corrective action is action taken by a supervisor to correct an employee performance problem. The goal is always to correct or improve performance. Despite how it sometimes may be viewed, corrective action is neither negative nor punitive. It is one of the basic tasks of management required to control the activities of the department.

As defined by the human resources policies of your facility, corrective action is generally a formal, documented process. A corrective action becomes part of an employee's personnel record. The form, like a performance review, is dated and signed by both supervisor and employee. Also, as in a performance review, the employee's signature represents acknowledgment that the employee has seen it, not that the employee agrees with the action. The corrective action form shows that an employee has been asked to make a specific behavioral change. In some organizations, this may be called a "written warning" or something similar. An example of a corrective action form appears in Figure 9.7.

As a Certified Dietary Manager, when you become aware of a performance problem, there are a few questions you should ask yourself right away. These are:

✓ Have you communicated expectations and performance standards?

✓ Have you provided the necessary training to support the employee's success?

✓ Have you already provided constructive feedback to the employee?

When the answers to these three questions are "YES," it is generally time to take corrective action.

Glossary

Corrective Action (Employee)
An action taken by a supervisor to correct an employee performance problem

Figure 9.7 **Sample Corrective Action Form**

Employee's Name: ______________________ Position: ______________________

Department: ______________________ Supervisor's Name: ______________________

○ Check if Violation of a Critical Rule ○ First Written Warning ○ Second Written Warning ○ Suspension Notice

Describe the performance to be corrected:

How to correct performance:

Follow-up plan and timetable:

Employee's comments:

Employee's signature (acknowledges receipt only) ______________________

Union representative's signature (if applicable) ______________________

Supervisor's signature ______________________ Date __________

Formal corrective action, which may also be called discipline, is a serious matter. In the extreme situation, it may provide documentation for eventual termination. Here are some examples of continued behavior that may require a formal, documented corrective action.

- ✓ Absenteeism/tardiness: An employee who is habitually late or absent may disrupt operations. Feedback regarding attendance should be based upon clearly established standards and policies that are uniformly administered. For example, a facility may have a policy that states an employee may not be absent or late to work more than six times in a 12-month period. In some facilities, an event of no-call, no-show (not calling in and not showing up for work) may be cause for immediate, formal corrective action.
- ✓ Violation of timeclock policies: Punching in too early, leaving early, not clocking out for lunch, or incurring unauthorized overtime can all be examples in this category.
- ✓ Repeated failure to meet work standards: If, following ongoing feedback and provision of all required support, an employee's performance falls significantly short of established standards, a supervisor may decide to take formal corrective action.

You have the opportunity to provide input into a new employee discipline process. What basic principles should be included in the new process?

(Check your answer at the end of this chapter)

✓ Violation of critical rules: Most facilities have defined a set of highly critical rules, the violation of which may be cause for immediate corrective action, suspension from work, or even termination. As a manager, you should become familiar with the policies in your own facility. In some facilities, any of the following might be considered cause for serious and immediate termination: theft, violation of confidentiality policies, sleeping on duty, violating safety rules or willfully endangering others, willful injury to another person (employee or client), or insubordination. **Insubordination** is a direct refusal to do what the supervisor asks.

Most facilities also have specific policies governing corrective action related to using drugs, drinking on duty, sexual harassment, possession of weapons on facility property, immoral, indecent conduct on duty, falsification of records, and punching someone else's time card. In some cases, such as drug use, a facility policy may define a series of steps for helping the employee address the problem, rather than dismissing the employee. An employee assistance program may be designed for this purpose. An **employee assistance program (EAP)** provides support to employees in solving personal problems that may be interfering with work. These may include drug use, alcohol abuse, family problems, and others. Some EAPs may provide assistance in identifying those who have or are at risk of alcohol and drug problems.

To take the appropriate course of action, a Certified Dietary Manager needs to know the facility's policy and the proper corrective action procedure. Particularly in serious situations, the manager needs to secure input from human resources and/or other managers. The manager needs to gather the facts and impose action only after a fair hearing of all sides from all persons involved. When practical, action should occur as soon as possible after a problem has occurred.

To prepare for a corrective action meeting with an employee, the Certified Dietary Manager should:

✓ Carefully investigate and gather facts.

✓ Prepare a corrective action document, writing out the description of the problem and steps for improvement. Write in factual, objective terms. (Avoid using "hearsay" or behavior described only by others.)

✓ Set aside a private time and location and ask the employee to meet.

✓ Explain to the employee why you are having this meeting, and explain that this is a corrective action that will become part of the employee's record.

✓ Explain the corrective action process and the policies related to it. For example, you should tell an employee that documentation of this meeting will become part of the personnel record. You should also outline the flow and timeframe of the corrective action process, as defined by the facility.

✓ State your objective, e.g., "I would like you to know that your performance is not acceptable, and I want to support you in correcting it immediately."

✓ Describe the performance problem to the employee. Be calm, objective, and matter-of-fact. Using the document as a reference, describe what you have observed.

Glossary

Insubordination
Direct refusal to do what the supervisor asks

Employee Assistance Program
Provides support to employees in solving personal problems such as drug and alcohol abuse, family problems, teamwork problems

- ✓ Firmly and clearly state why this behavior is not acceptable. Describe the established standard or policy that applies.
- ✓ Give a reason why this concerns you.
- ✓ Ask the employee for input. Ask why this behavior is happening.
- ✓ Ask the employee what he or she can do to correct this situation. As warranted, discuss with the employee and seek to problem-solve together.
- ✓ Agree on a plan of action, which may be very simple. If the plan requires action on your own part, be sure to follow through.
- ✓ Specifically ask for the employee's commitment in improving performance.
- ✓ Sign and ask the employee to sign the document and add comments, if desired. Provide a copy to the employee.
- ✓ File the document according to your policies and procedures.
- ✓ If you anticipate that the employee may disagree with your evaluation, meet with your supervisor first and review your evaluation plans. The supervisor may even support your evaluation by initialing it.

While Certified Dietary Managers may feel stressed and anxious about corrective action, it is helpful to keep in mind that performance comes from the employee. As a manager, you provide the proper direction and support. Ultimately, though, you do not control the employee's behavior. During a corrective action meeting, you can keep responsibility for action where it rightfully belongs—in the employee's realm. When you ask an employee, "What can you do to correct this situation?" you are asking the employee to accept responsibility and take action. Managers who do this find that this question removes a lot of pressure, and also builds a framework for successful performance improvement.

After taking corrective action, continue to be positive and upbeat in your interactions with the employee. Recognize that the employee may feel embarrassed or even angry. As follow-up, continue to observe performance. As soon as you see a corrected behavior, be sure to call it to the employee's attention and provide positive reinforcement. This helps an employee make a positive change in behavior.

Human resources policies and procedures should also specify a process for appealing a corrective action. In other words, if an employee feels the action is not justified, the employee can go to a union steward, a department or division head, or another person higher in the organization chart, as designated in the policy and procedure. See Figure 9.8 for basic prerequisites in a corrective action form.

Corrective action falls within the realm of **progressive discipline**, which is a series of defined steps a Certified Dietary Manager takes when an employee does not correct a performance problem after being given an opportunity to do so. The exact set of steps is defined by your human resources policies and procedures. Generally, each step in the progressive disciplinary process

Glossary

Progressive Discipline
A series of defined steps taken when an employee does not correct a performance problem

Figure 9.8 Basic Prerequisites for Effective Corrective Action

- Policies, rules, and procedures must be developed for all areas in the facility.
- Rules and policies must be explained to employees—and also provided in written form. For example, they can be included in employee handbooks and can be explained during orientation, training, and other activities.
- Policies, rules, and procedures must be reasonable, fair, and just from the perspective of both employees and the Certified Dietary Manager.
- Policies, rules, and procedures must be enforced in a consistent, fair, and honest manner. Thus, if one employee receives a formal written warning for missing three days of work during the past month, another employee who has the same attendance record should receive a written warning as well.
- Specific situations must be taken into account. The supervisor must determine whether observed problems were within or beyond the employee's control.
- The manager must use objective judgment.
- Supervisors must prepare for corrective action and make an effort to understand why the behavior is occurring and how the employee is motivated.
- Affected employees must be informed of any changes in policies, rules, and procedures before they are implemented.
- Corrective action programs should be administered objectively, without bias.
- The supervisor should not threaten, argue, and/or display anger.
- Corrective action should be done in private.
- A manager must keep corrective action a confidential exchange, and refrain from discussing it with other employees. (A manager may need to discuss the action confidentially with an immediate supervisor, a human resources staff member, or others who also commit to this confidentiality.)
- The corrective action should spell out exactly what the employee needs to do to improve behavior on the job. Both the manager and the employee must discuss this.
- A manager who is newly promoted or new to an organization needs to begin applying consistent performance standards from the start. Waiting and letting things slide becomes a set-up for poor success of corrective action in the future.

becomes more severe. For example, one progressive discipline policy might state the following:

Step 1: The first time a manager takes formal corrective action, it is documented, reviewed with the employee, signed, and placed in the personnel file as a "first written warning."

Step 2: If the problem continues, a second corrective action is taken and classified as a "second written warning."

Step 3: If the problem continues, the employee is suspended without pay (e.g. for three days).

Step 4: If the problem continues, the employee is terminated.

Your most experienced cashier arrives at work apparently drunk. What steps do you take to address this behavior?

(Check your answer at the end of this chapter)

Why Don't Employees Perform?

The toughest problem that sometimes arises is the situation in which an employee simply does not perform well. You ask an employee to comply with performance standards and it does not happen. You ask an employee to follow a specific procedure, but she does not. Why does this occur?

Needless to say, there is no easy answer to this troubling question. A Certified Dietary Manager needs to understand that certain aspects of employee performance are beyond immediate control. A good leader motivates and influences employees. However, excellent performance comes from within the employee. Some individuals are more able or ready to perform than others, even the day they start the job.

In research about client service issues, for example, experts have concluded that a portion of service skills can be trained. Yet another portion must come from the employee's unique personality. Thus, the advice is: hire someone who will do well. This advice probably extends to most employment situations. From the beginning, some individuals possess the drive and talent to perform well, given the proper, supportive environment. So, a Certified Dietary Manager should seek to identify these characteristics in the recruitment process.

Let's say you are past this stage. What can you do? Try running through a basic checklist with yourself. Perhaps you will notice a basic principle of supervision that you can tweak in your approach to the situation. In addition, you can use the advice of other managers whom you respect. Managers putting their heads together can share observations and ideas that help each other. Figure 9.9 identifies some questions you can ask to pinpoint any areas you may be able to target for action.

Termination

The questions listed in Figure 9.9 will not solve every problem. In the final analysis, a few situations may come to a dead end, where there is nothing further you can do as a Certified Dietary Manager to change the situation. First of all, it is important to know this, and to protect your own esteem as a manager. This can happen, and it does not mean you have failed in any way. Here are some examples of situations that may, not be resolvable:

✓ The employee's performance issue relates to an attitude that you are not able to influence.

✓ The employee simply lacks the ability to perform the job as defined, even with training.

Figure 9.9 What to Check When Employees Don't Perform Well

- Does the employee know what you expect? How can you be sure?
- Are your expectations and standards attainable? Measurable?
- Does the employee know how to do the work to the established standards of quality/quantity?
- Are there any obstacles to the employee's performance that relate to systems, procedures, resources, or interference? If so, identify them and intervene.
- What social relationships in the workplace may be affecting the employee's work? (For example, is the employee following an informal leader whose direction conflicts with yours?)
- Have you provided feedback to the employee? If so, how many times? How close to the event? How specific has your feedback been?
- Are you interacting with the employee on a fair and objective basis?
- What does the employee say is causing the problem you have identified?
- Is the employee capable of this particular job? If not, is there an alternate job in the organization that might be a better fit?
- What is the employee's attitude towards the job, and where is this attitude coming from? Can you influence it?
- Have you examined the employee's needs and sources of motivation?

If you reach a situation such as this one, you may have two options. If the employee is willing and motivated but simply not suited to the job, you may explore whether a transfer to a different position and/or different department may be a positive resolution.

If the employee is essentially unwilling to improve, termination may be the best course of action. Before terminating an employee, review the facts of the situation with your human resources staff and/or your superior, as defined by the policy where you work. Ensure that you have worked through the defined steps of a progressive disciplinary process with an employee, and are now at the point of termination.

Finally, you will need to meet with the employee to complete a termination. This does not have to be a hostile interaction. It is best to approach it matter-of-factly, reviewing the events that have led to this decision. If a union represents the employee, you may need to invite a union steward to this meeting. As with a formal corrective action, you may also need to invite another manager as a witness.

A termination must be documented according to established policies. Like other paperwork, it becomes part of the employee's record. In most situations in which a Certified Dietary Manager has been communicating with an employee, a termination should not be a surprise. However, it can generate anger. Assess the situation before beginning a termination meeting, and be prepared with assistance should it be required.

Most facilities define a probationary period for employees, such as three months. During a probationary period, unique policies may apply. An employee may be working on a "trial" basis, and termination during this time period may not require all steps outlined in progressive discipline.

Following a termination, some members of your workforce may feel distressed. You can explain that the employee is no longer with your organization. However, do not violate confidentiality by discussing the termination and the factors that led up to it. Many employees will understand the action through their own observations. Sometimes, termination of an employee who has been disruptive to the work of the team brings about an unexpected, positive shift in morale.

Labor Unions

It is not uncommon to work as a Certified Dietary Manager in an environment where foodservice staff belong to a labor union (an organization representing employees and designed to advance the needs and interests of its members). These needs and interests may relate to wages, benefits, working conditions, and other aspects of human resources management. Unionization provides certain advantages to employees. It also imposes certain requirements on the manager, who must comply with a union agreement.

There are differences between the goals of administrators and unions. Administrators strive to reduce labor costs and increase efficiency, to retain authority over the foodservice operation, and to maintain a non-union operation. In contrast, the union desires greater wages and benefits, improved working conditions for employees, and greater opportunities to bargain for the employees.

Impact of Unions

Once employees are represented by a union, the administration will need to follow all requirements agreed to in the contract. Each employee must be treated fairly and equally. Seniority, rather than other factors which might distinguish employees' qualifications and performance, may become a factor in matters affecting personnel-related decisions.

There can be advantages to unionization. The presence of a union prompts development and/or improvement of policies or procedures that affect relationships with employees, as well as ensuring that health and safety concerns are addressed.

Summary

A Certified Dietary Manager should be familiar with the provisions of any existing agreement between a union and the facility. Through effective management practices, a manager can often help a facility maintain a working environment that benefits employees and administration.

Legal Implications

If you work with a union contract that covers transfers, promotions, and discharges, you will have to make sure you read and follow your union contract when you are disciplining, transferring, or promoting your staff. Many of the government regulations from Chapter 8 also impact performance reviews such as the Civil Rights Act of 1991 and the Americans with Disabilities Act (ADA). If you are fortunate to have a human resource office, they can help you with the legal implications. If not, you need to be aware of the legislation that will impact your performance reviews.

Management in the News

25 Ways to Reward Employees (Without Spending a Dime)

by Dan Tynan

Your firm's employees work hard (well, most of them). And in a world where corporations like to boast about running "lean and mean," it may seem nearly impossible to compensate employees for doing good work without breaking the budget.

Related Articles

- 7 Things to Do on an Employee's First Day
- Employee Satisfaction Survey
- How Much is Your Employee Worth?
- The HR World Outsourcing Buyer's Guide

The good news? You don't have to. A January 2007 survey by staffing firm Accountemps found that "frequent recognition of accomplishments" was the top non-monetary compensation named by full- and part-time office workers, with "regular communication" coming in at No. 2. Both activities can make your staff more productive without shaving one millimeter off your bottom line.

We talked to management consultants, HR pros, career coaches, book authors and bosses from a range of industries to glean the 25 best ways to reward employees without breaking the bank. Here's their hard-earned advice.

1. **Flex those hours.** If there's one free reward that rises above the rest, it's flexible work schedules. Nearly every expert we contacted suggested flex time as a perk that offers the most gain with the least pain.

   "Give a little latitude in determining work schedules and to take time for family or personal issues (such as doctor's appointment and banking errands)," advised Richard Martin, president of Alcera Consulting Inc. "As long as the employee is deserving and doesn't abuse the privilege, this can go a long way to building trusting and mature relationships with key workers."
2. **Send a handwritten note.** Supervisors should ask top brass to write a personal note to employees who deserve recognition, advised Cindy Ventrice, author of "Make Their Day! Employee Recognition That Works." For example, AdvancedMD CEO Jim Pack handwrites his thank-you notes to employees on a $2 bill. "In three years of doing this, only one employee has asked if he could spend it," said company spokesman John Pilmer.
3. **Make work fun.** "During a business coaching engagement, I found employee morale to be way down," said Terri Levine, president of The Coaching Institute. "We created a weekly event to boost morale. One week we asked everyone to bring in a baby picture, post it on a wall, then pick which person matched each picture. Everyone was having fun and socializing while productivity went from 58 percent to 72 percent—all in the same week."
4. **Help them connect.** Introducing employees to key suppliers, customers or someone in senior management can help make an employee's career, says Ventrice— and it won't cost you a thing.
5. **Lose the shoes.** Kaerie Ray, an account executive with the Echo Media Group public relations firm, said implementing a "no-shoes policy" can make employees feel right at home with each other, which translates into increased productivity. (But she suggests keeping the footwear handy in case clients come in.) "It's great to be in an office where employees are more concerned about doing quality work than what shoes or jewelry they have on," she said. "We get so much done."

(Continued...)

25 Ways to Reward Employees (Without Spending a Dime) *(Continued)*

6. **Send them to the showers.** (As in parties, not lathering and rinsing.) "Every birth and wedding deserves a shower," said Ray. "Echo employees always leave early on shower days, and the food is on the house. No need to make up the time."
7. **Reward effort as well as success.** Even if their ideas sometimes fail, you want employees to keep producing them, said Alan Weiss, president of the Summit Consulting Group Inc. "When I consulted with the CEO of Calgon, we created an annual award for 'the best idea that didn't work' and presented a loving cup at the annual awards dinner. This stimulated innovation and positive behavior, not 'winning.'"
8. **Give them a free pass.** Levine suggests giving out a certain number of free days off to employees to use as they see fit. "Employees get a few of these a year and can use them as they like," she said. "They don't have to pretend to be sick. They can go to the beach, read a book, play with their kids ... it doesn't matter."
9. **Dole out cream and sugar.** During the busiest times of the year, executives at the Cigna Group push coffee carts around the office, serving drinks and refreshments to their colleagues, noted Steve Harrison, author of "The Manager's Book of Decencies: How Small Gestures Build Great Companies." As they serve, executives coach and encourage colleagues and hear about real consumer issues.
10. **Blow out the candles.** Cisco Systems Inc.'s CEO John Chambers hosts a monthly hour-long birthday breakfast for any employee with a birthday that month, says Harrison. "Employees are invited to ask him anything. They feel recognized, and he gains loyal employees who share their ideas."
11. **Spread the love.** Ask co-workers to write something they truly like or admire about an employee on a scrap of paper, then frame them along with a photograph of the employee, suggested David Russell, author of "Success With People – A Complete System for Effectively Managing People in Any Organization."
12. **Offer a swap.** Giving your best employees a chance to pick their own projects or trade tasks with a colleague empowers and rewards them at the same time, said Harrison.
13. **Applaud their efforts—literally.** If someone has done something really worthwhile, have your entire staff give them a standing ovation at the next meeting, suggested Sharlyn Lauby, president of HR consulting firm ITM Group Inc.
14. **Say it with flowers.** Professor Linda M. Lopeke, principal of SmartStartCoach.com, said she used to reward top employees by bringing in flowers from her garden and arranging them in a spectacular crystal vase on their desks. "Everybody knew what having the custody of the flowers meant," she said. "Surprisingly, even the men competed fiercely for custody of the flowers." In the winter, she'd substitute a showpiece display of floating glass fish.
15. **Walk it as you talk it.** The City of Dallas sponsored a walkathon where employees set goals for walking a certain number of steps each day, offering a free gym membership to those who walked the farthest. Not only did they get more fit, they turned their daily walks into traveling staff meetings, says city spokeswoman Danielle McCelland.

    "Group members were able to update one another on projects, solicit team input and improve their fitness," she said. "The organized program ended after three weeks, but the work group still holds their traveling staff meetings two months later."
16. **Pass the bucks.** Handing out monopoly money that can be redeemed for gifts and other goodies may not be strictly free, but it pays off handsomely in the long run. For example, associates at BankAtlantic can pass out "WOW! Bucks" to colleagues who've done something outstanding, said bank vice president Gregory Dalmotte. The bucks can eventually be traded in for real goods. "There's a clear correlation that words of encouragement have created associates who perform at a higher level," he says.

(Continued...)

25 Ways to Reward Employees (Without Spending a Dime) *(Continued)*

17. **Share the memories.** "My team created a scrapbook chronicling the impact I'd had on their company and gave it to me on my last day in the office," said Lopeke. "People who'd worked on my teams wrote testimonials and creative graphics highlighting some our team successes. It's the best gift I ever received in my 40-year career."
18. **Elect them to the Wall of Fame.** Several experts suggested setting aside a public space inside your firm and placing photos of employees who've accomplished something truly special, along with the details of what they did to earn their place on the wall.
19. **Create your own "Club Med."** Set aside a quiet space or unused office in your building where employees can meditate, chill out, nap, or otherwise re-center themselves, said John Putzier, author of "Get Weird! 101 Innovative Ways to Make Your Company a Great Place to Work."
20. **Stoke their passion.** "Great employees are not mercenaries," said Dr. Richard Chang, CEO of Richard Chang Associates Inc., a performance-improvement consultancy. "They don't just want to enjoy their work, they want to be passionate about it ... if you want your employees to feel valued and inspire their passion on your behalf, encourage them to make their own decisions. You can have systems in place to control the implementation of ideas, but you must be certain not to compromise the enthusiasm, creativity and hard work that make them possible in the first place."
21. **Give them a place to park it.** Reserve the best parking spot for employees who've done something truly worthwhile, said Lopeke. And if it's next to the CEO's Lexus so the employee can chat him or her up on the way into work, so much the better.
22. **Remember the spouses.** Independent management consultant Nan Amish recalled one time when she had 16 employees trapped in a hotel lobby on a Sunday night, waiting for the ballroom to open so they could set up a trade-show booth. "I bought flowers at a farmers market, a nice $6 bouquet of roses for each person," she said. "I told them to take them home to their significant others, apologizing for me taking them away from their families on a Sunday. The next day I got thank-yous from most of them. One wife sent a letter saying I could keep her husband until Friday."
23. **Publicize their successes.** "We like to publicly recognize employees so the whole company can share in their accomplishments," noted Scott Ragusa, president of contract businesses for staffing firm The Winter, Wyman Companies. "Each week, nominations for our quarterly 'Clutch' award are shared with the whole company. The Clutch nominations are a way to recognize our administrative and nonmanagerial professional staff members who have come through in the clutch in supporting their departments or the firm."
24. **Let them phone it in.** Telecommuting programs can relieve stress and make workers feel more appreciated, as well as more productive. "Reward the employee by starting with one day of telecommuting, then add additional days as performance heightens," suggested Brian Margarita, president of IT staffing firm TalentFuse Inc. "Having the option to cart the kids to soccer practice, visit the beach during the afternoon or cut out early to avoid traffic congestion is becoming more important than working an 80-hour week for a larger paycheck."
25. **Remember the secret words.** "The two most underused words in corporate America that get the highest ROI (return on investment) and ROT (return on your time) are the simple words 'thank you,'" noted Michael Guld, president of the Guld Resource Group author of "The Million Dollar Media Rep: How to Become a Television and Radio Sales Superstar."

While telling your employees you appreciate them should be obvious, added Amish, no one does it enough or is specific enough about what the employee did. "So when you share your appreciation, be specific about what you really liked, so they not only feel appreciated but can do it again."

Source: http://www.hrworld.com/features/25-employee-rewards, accessed 8/10/11

END OF CHAPTER

Putting It Into Practice Questions & Answers

1. You have two employees who are interested in a new position you are creating to implement a culture change in your facility. One employee is pregnant and you know she will miss an important time in the training for this position but she is better qualified the other applicant. Who should you choose for this position and why?

   A. *You should choose the applicant who is most qualified. Pregnancy is a protected status under the Civil Rights Law and you cannot discriminate against a pregnant employee.*

2. You are the Certified Dietary Manager in a large county nursing home where the employees are long-term and are represented by a union. Currently, the performance review is done annually and now there are negotiations about completing the performance review every six months. As a member of the administrative team, what would you recommend and why?

   A. *Recommend the performance reviews every six months. As you now know, employees want to be recognized for their work and they want feedback on their work. If you have performance reviews done bi-annually, that would give you an opportunity to recognize your employees twice as often. Since your employees have been there a long time, it might also provide a morale boost to receive feedback twice as often.*

3. You have the opportunity to provide input into a new employee discipline process. What basic principles should be included in the new process?

   A. *1. Policies, rules, and procedures are developed for all areas in the facility to achieve consistency (consistency is a key element).*

   2. Accurate job descriptions and job specifications are available and thoroughly explained to employees.

   3. Decide what steps should be involved (e.g. undocumented oral warning, documented oral warning, written reprimand, suspension, discharge).

   4. Is there a grievance procedure? Should one be established or modified?

4. Your most experienced cashier arrives at work apparently drunk. What steps do you take to address this behavior?

   A. *Observe the cashier if her behavior was reported to you by someone else. Replace the cashier with another staff person and ask to speak with the cashier privately. Ask the cashier if she can explain her observed behavior. Ask why this happened. Refer to your disciplinary policy for specific steps. Keep in mind that alcoholism is a disease and is protected by ADA. You may need to refer her to your EAP program for diagnosis and treatment.*

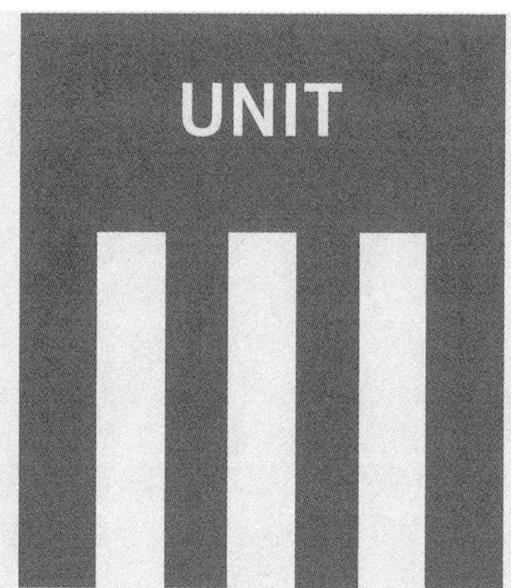

Develop Personnel and Communications

John Quincy Adams is quoted as saying, "If your actions inspire others to dream more, learn more, do more and become more, you are a leader." The ability to influence productivity in your department is a critical leadership skill. This chapter will help develop your leadership skills by focusing on improving productivity through employee training, assessing principles of work design, and communicating work plans, goals, and priorities.

Implement Required Changes in Foodservice Department

Overview and Objectives

A Certified Dietary Manager's job is to manage people to work in every part of the foodservice operation. Managing begins with planning - setting goals and objectives in order to measure progress, evaluate work, and set priorities. The best planning will not work unless the manager is able to motivate employees to help carry out the plan, and to direct and coach employees in their actions. In addition to supervising employees, providing direction, managing service issues, implementing change, and working with diversity throughout the organization, a manager must be able to communicate effectively.

After completing this chapter, you should be able to:

- ✓ Identify existing problems/needs
- ✓ Write memos presenting changes with justification
- ✓ Prepare plan of action to address problems/needs
- ✓ Communicate daily with staff
- ✓ Establish hygiene standards for personnel according to the FDA Food Code

Identify Existing Problems and Needs

The day-to-day activities of a Certified Dietary Manager are largely influenced by a bigger picture—a comparison of how you are doing compared to the department and the facility's goals and objectives. Goals and objectives are critical components of managerial planning and should help identify existing problems and needs. Goals and objectives can help measure progress, evaluate work, and set priorities.

For example, let's say you have a department goal to reduce food costs by 1 percent this year. An objective to meet that goal is to monitor inventory costs every week. This week you notice that inventory costs have gone up over the past few weeks. Now you have identified what may be a problem.

To begin to implement required changes in your department, it is important to have an understanding of goals and objectives.

Glossary

Goal
A statement that outlines an outcome or result

Objective
The steps to achieve the goal or the actions to get there

Goals Versus Objectives

Goals and objectives are closely related. Both describe purpose. However, a **goal** is a statement that outlines a broad direction or intention. An **objective** is a specific step that will help in accomplishing a goal. Here are some other comparisons:

- ✓ A goal is broad in focus while an objective is narrow.
- ✓ A goal is the aim. The objectives are how you get there.
- ✓ A goal may be abstract, but an objective is concrete and measurable.
- ✓ A goal is more long term, while an objective is short- to medium-term.
- ✓ A goal is the result we want; objectives are the actions to get there.

Many facilities create master plans for growth that may describe goals for the coming year, as well as goals for a five-year or even 10-year period. This kind of forward thinking helps to focus the direction a facility takes and keep it moving forward in a meaningful and effective manner. For example, a facility that operates skilled nursing facilities may establish a goal of expanding most of its units into senior living communities with assisted living and other services over a period of five years. Or, a school system may establish a goal of centralizing most of its services, including foodservice operations, over the coming two years.

Facilities set goals by looking into the future and predicting what will be necessary for success. Factors that may influence goal-setting including financial constraints, regulatory changes, staffing needs, challenges faced by the industry, new opportunities, a review of available and needed resources, and client feedback. Goals align with the vision and mission of the facility, helping to fulfill them.

Setting Objectives

Once broad goals have been established in any facility, a number of related objectives must be developed. Every branch, department, and individual plays a role in helping the facility achieve its objectives.

As a Certified Dietary Manager, you may play several key roles in managing objectives. First, you may participate in setting the objectives for the facility as a whole. In some facilities, a planning meeting involves all managers. In others, the process may be less direct. For example, your supervisor may ask you for ideas before a planning meeting takes place.

Whether or not your position is high in the organization chart, recognize that as a Certified Dietary Manager, you have key information and insights that can contribute to the formation of objectives. Stand back from your position and observe. Talk with peers to identify parallels in your facility. For example, while you have difficulty recruiting foodservice employees, you may learn that the manager of the environmental services department and the manager of the nursing department face the same issues. By taking in the bigger picture, you may be able to share thoughts that become meaningful in the planning process.

After objectives have been set, your job may be to help translate them for your own area. To do this, you must first understand the big picture clearly. Talk

Which of the following objectives would be appropriate for the goal: increase client satisfaction with foodservice. Explain why.

Objective #1: Survey the clients

Objective #2: Maintain cold temperatures on the salad bar

Objective #3: Hold an inservice on ways to improve client service by Feb. 16, 2012

(Check your answer at the end of this chapter)

with your supervisor and peers to clarify the intent. Then, think about how to extend these objectives and make them more specific. For example, if a goal is to improve client satisfaction, an objective may be to improve client satisfaction with meals.

Look for ways to make each objective clear and measurable. For example, a meal satisfaction objective may be measured with ratings or percent change. Here is a measurable objective: *Client ratings about the temperature of food will improve by at least 10% by December.* Criteria for goals and objectives are summarized in Figure 10.1.

Figure 10.1 Criteria for Goals and Objectives

SMART goals are:

S—Specific. Answer questions such as: What precisely will happen (describe the outcome)?

M—Meaningful. Answer questions such as: How does this relate to the mission?

A—Affordable. Answer questions such as: How can this be achieved with the resources available?

R—Reasonable. Answer questions such as: What makes this possible to achieve?

T—Timed. Answer questions such as: When will this be accomplished?

Effective Objectives are:

Specific: They describe what will be done, and by whom.

Challenging: They represent growth rather than status quo but are nevertheless practical.

Observable: They describe a change that you as a Certified Dietary Manager can objectively observe.

Measurable: They provide a form of a measure you can use to evaluate achievement.

Simple: They each cover one clear action item.

Plan of Action

As a Certified Dietary Manager, you can develop a plan, using your work teams as resources. In a plan of action, you tell how you will achieve the objective, or what steps you will take to accomplish it. There may be a series of steps associated with each objective. Figure 10.2 provides an example of a sample action plan.

To involve employees, you can assign them to special teams, with each team responsible for suggesting and later carrying out actions. Another approach is to hold meetings and use a brainstorming technique to identify options. As a group, you can then evaluate ideas, decide which you believe will be most successful, and finalize plans. You can assign tasks and responsibilities to employees. You can establish a timetable for action. See the *Management in the News* section at the end of this chapter for an example of a plan of action to implement Hazard Analysis & Critical Control Points (HACCP).

Figure 10.2 Sample Action Plan

Person Completing the Form____

Position____ Date____________________

Foodservice Department Goal: Computerize all cost-effective foodservice support functions by the year 2014.

Sample Objective: Certified Dietary Manager will present a recommendation for a cost-effective foodservice software solution to the vice president before January 1, 2014.

IMPLEMENTATION			EVALUATION	
What Needs to be Done?	**By Whom and When**	**What Resources**	**What is the evidence of Progress?**	**How and When will Evidence be Gathered**
Complete labor and service studies to determine opportunities for computerization by April	CDM by April, 2013	Time to complete labor and service studies	Labor and service studies are completed by April	CDM will compile studies and submit to VP
Complete a request for proposal (RFP) outlining at least three major computer support functions (e.g. inventory, scheduling, per client meal cost)	CDM by June 1, 2013	Assistance in preparing the RFP from Administrative Assistant; Cost of publishing RFP	RFP is published	Copies of RFP from the newspapers
Gather quotations for service from at least three competing software vendors	Administrative Assistant by August 15	Folder in which to keep quotes until the bid opening	Bid opening reveals all of the bids	Folder of bids is available to CDM and VP
Assemble a team of foodservice employees to review software options	CDM and appointed action team by September 30, 2013	Staff time to review the software option; Time for software vendors to demo software	Documentation of time spent reviewing options and viewing demos	CDM will document time
Check references of qualified software vendors	CDM or assigned action team member	Time to visit qualified software vendors	References are compiled	References are added to file folder of material by October 7, 2013
Evaluate all information and make a purchase recommendation with budget	CDM and action team by November 1, 2013	Time to evaluate all information; budget data from CDM	Recommendation is submitted to VP	By November 1, 2013

In virtually any facility when carrying out goals, objectives and a plan of action, change is going to occur. It may come from external sources as regulations and standards are revised, or it may come from within as a facility seeks to improve itself. It may come from personnel changes, or many other sources. A manager needs to be able to implement change, which naturally generates some resistance.

Change

Change is anything that requires revisions in the roles and routines of a workforce. Sometimes change is made voluntarily, as when employee groups generate ideas about performing work more effectively. At other times, change may be forced upon the department from higher levels in the facility or from external agencies, such as CMS, or TJC, or the local health department.

Change is really a continuing process, not an activity with a distinct start and finish. The facility in general and the foodservice department specifically are evolving at all times. In fact, experts in organizational behavior agree that change is a sign of a healthy, successful organization. An organization that is not able to change also is not able to adapt and excel. Change can generate excitement, commitment, and pride; but it must be managed in a way that helps employees feel positively about it.

All elements in the foodservice department and within the organization itself are closely related. Therefore, a change made in one area is likely to have an impact on other areas as well.

For change to be effective, the Certified Dietary Manager must first show employees why there is a need for change. It is important to be honest and provide the facts. Managers are more likely to implement change effectively when they have the respect of the employees.

Whenever possible, employees should be involved in the earliest planning phases of change. While foodservice employees may not have the option of rejecting change, they should have the option of participating in decisions about how to implement a change. Certified Dietary Managers can use participative management approaches to involve employees in planning. As employees are trained, coached, and counseled about changes being proposed, their involvement will, ideally, reduce their resistance to change. Typically, employee ownership and commitment will grow in direct relation to the amount of input they have into the entire process.

Mergers, acquisitions, new software, new foodservice equipment, remodeling, menu revisions, service system revisions, reorganization of parts of the organization, new regulations, budget cuts, census variations, new administrative staff and/or philosophies, and evolution of professional practice are all examples of forces for change.

Resistance to Change

Often it is difficult for Certified Dietary Managers to implement change. Why is this? It is human nature to be anxious and hesitant about changes and to resist change. Reasons for resisting change can include the following:

- ✓ Economic concerns: Sometimes changes have a negative economic impact upon employees.
- ✓ Inconvenience: Some changes will require employees to learn new operating procedures or become responsible for extra duties.
- ✓ Anxiety: Some changes make employees feel threatened by the unknown or insecure about their own work situations.
- ✓ Changing relationships: Some changes in the work environment can alter working relationships.
- ✓ Increased control by others: Some changes take away employees' independence. For example, more supervision may be a part of implementing new procedures.
- ✓ Mistrust in supervisors: Some changes generate a sense of mistrust or fear of what will happen next. This is particularly troublesome if employees and managers do not have sound working relationships to start with.
- ✓ Concerns about performance: Some changes generate fear of not doing a "good job" anymore. A very dedicated employee may, in particular, be troubled by change, as concerns loom about the ability to maintain excellent job performance with new tasks, new procedures, or new tools.

An organizational change, such as a move to a better office, can be warmly accepted, simply because it is seen to have obvious advantages. But not all changes fit into this category. Where changes create ambiguity and uncertainty, then resistance to change is likely to emerge. In essence, the resistance is not to change as such. Instead, it is to the personal loss (or possibility of personal loss) that people believe will accompany the change.

Change is easier to implement when you have developed a relationship of trust and respect with employees. In fact, some staff members may favor a change simply because they trust your judgment and believe in your leadership. Other staff members will need time to evaluate the proposed impacts of the change.

The relationship between the Certified Dietary Manager and employees evolves from a history of honesty, fair play, and a concern for the welfare of staff members. The manager must interact with employees as change is implemented, from the earliest point possible. The manager should:

- ✓ Share reasons for the change
- ✓ Solicit employees' input in planning, whenever possible
- ✓ Share the details of the change from employees' perspectives, e.g. how it will affect schedules, responsibilities, performance standards, procedures, and more
- ✓ Describe the anticipated results of the change

Your administrative team has just told you they want to open a new cafeteria. How would you introduce this to your staff?

(Check your answer at the end of this chapter)

✓ Explain how the change meets operational objectives of the foodservice team
✓ Explain what is expected of or needed from each employee during the change process
✓ Specifically request help and support in making the change succeed
✓ Describe what training will be provided (if appropriate)
✓ Allow employees to voice reactions and concerns openly and discuss them
✓ Accept the employees' feelings about the change
✓ Describe how the results of the change will be evaluated
✓ Answer questions
✓ Describe how each employee may seek help with solving any problems that may occur.

Involving employees in change begins long before it is implemented. Employees' views should be solicited from the time changes are first contemplated, through the process of actual decision-making. This begins with involving them in planning the goals, objectives and action plans. Employees can also provide help in generating alternatives, in conducting studies and tests, if applicable, and in developing the final procedures to be implemented. Certified Dietary Managers should also address any economic concerns employees may have. This can be done by communicating effectively and by analyzing the true impact of change on the employees.

It is best to use the tools of communication, participation, and negotiation to help employees accept change. If necessary, a manager may use authority as a tool in implementing change. It is helpful to involve both formal and informal employee groups and their leaders in the change process. Training programs are often necessary as changes are implemented. To help overcome resistance, employees need an opportunity to learn new procedures and gain confidence.

After change has been implemented, it must be evaluated. It is important to see whether the change has been beneficial and whether any additional changes are needed to further improve the effectiveness of the foodservice department. The Certified Dietary Manager should also assess whether there have been any unexpected spin-off effects of the change. Criteria for assessing the effectiveness of change goes back to the original reason for change. You can ask, "What was the objective of this change? How well has it been achieved?" Figure 10.3 provides a checklist for implementing change.

Diversity in the Workplace

According to the Bureau of Labor Statistics, (2010), at least 15.5 percent of the U.S. workforce is foreign-born. In certain states and in certain industries—such as foodservice—the proportion of foreign-born employees is higher. This alone tells us that the cultural backgrounds of foodservice employees can be very diverse. Beyond nationality, however, we can recognize that the U.S. society is a melting-pot in many different respects. People can come to the workforce of a foodservice department with many different languages or levels of literacy, customs, values, lifestyles, sexual preferences, religious convictions,

Figure 10.3 Checklist for Implementing Change

		YES	NO*
1.	Is change necessary?	○	○
2.	Do you completely understand—from your perspective as a supervisor—why the change is necessary—and what exactly it is supposed to do?	○	○
3.	Do you think about possible reasons why employees might resist the change—and develop effective counter arguments for these reasons?	○	○
4.	Do you use an individual counseling technique to discuss the change and its implications with each affected employee?	○	○
5.	Do you use a persuasive technique to discover employee perceptions of disadvantages—and to counter these with information which will help employees see advantages to change?	○	○
6.	Do you involve group leaders—both formal and informal—and request their help in gaining acceptance of change?	○	○
7.	Do you use a trial approach (test the proposed change and then modify it as necessary) rather than implement it on an "all or nothing" basis?	○	○
8.	Do you make sure that affected employees know what must be done differently before changes are implemented?	○	○
9.	Do you carefully supervise employees during the awkward transitional period when changes are being implemented?	○	○
10.	Do you provide carefully designed training experiences before changes are implemented?	○	○
11.	Do you develop indicators of effective change that measurably describe what the situation should be after the changes are made?	○	○
12.	Do you evaluate the results of the change based upon the extent to which indicators of effective change are seen in the work situation?	○	○
13.	Do you try to recognize any benefits that may result from employee resistance to change?	○	○
14.	Do you know how to generate a need for change?	○	○
15.	Do you have the respect of the employees who must change?	○	○
16.	Do you have a good track record for implementing change with few surprises for employees?	○	○
17.	Do you know what other changes are occurring in the organization at this time?	○	○
18.	Do you know the impact of the proposed change on other departments?	○	○
19.	Do you have necessary training programs already planned and in place?	○	○
20.	Do you know whether existing work flows will be improved as a result of the change?	○	○
21.	Do you know whether the situation requiring change is of continuing importance to the organization?	○	○
22.	Are all employees permitted, to the extent possible, to participate in all activities relating to the change?	○	○
23.	Do you know what you can and should do to increase pressure for change?	○	○
24.	Do you have all the information you need to make the change?	○	○

**If you answered No, revise your approach*

communications style, style of dress, problem-solving approaches, age, and much more.

Diversity is a term that describes the many ways in which people differ from each other, or the ways in which people are each unique. Diversity has multiple dimensions. A primary dimension is defined as one that is inborn and that exerts a profound and constant impact throughout a person's entire life or a substantial portion of it. Under this definition, primary dimensions include age, ethnicity, gender, physical abilities, or other qualities. Secondary dimensions are attributes that can be acquired, discarded, or modified. This category includes education, geographic location, income, marital status, religion, sexual orientation and work experience. Many organizations include both types of diversity in their definitions.

The very fact of diversity means that Certified Dietary Managers cannot assume all employees are the same. In 2011, for the first time, four generations are working together in the work place. Managers need to recognize and appreciate what is unique in every person on the team, including themselves. While this takes effort, it is very much worthwhile. Managing diversity is essential for promoting teamwork and accomplishing objectives. As a matter of fact, diversity is often the key resource that helps a work team meet its objectives. Why? Because each member of the team has something unique to contribute. Where one person cannot devise a workable solution to a problem, another can based on his or her own background. Diversity means having multiple perspectives and many points of view. This means a ready pool of ideas and approaches to any situation.

Every facility needs to have a clearly stated policy about diversity, which may say, for example, that your organization is committed to respecting the diversity of the work team. A policy may also explicitly prohibit derogatory comments about cultural groups. As a manager, you need to communicate this policy clearly, make it part of employee orientation, and enforce it.

When recruiting employees, be sure to consider how you go about it. Some recruitment avenues may in themselves lock out various groups. For example, you may consider recruiting through neighborhood newspapers or other venues to ensure that you are including members of your community in an equitable manner. Research data has shown that clients respond positively to faces that resemble their own. During an interview process, you want to ensure that you are not filtering the applicant's responses only through your own cultural backdrop. Instead, appreciate how individuals may be different and seek to hire people who represent the community in which your facility resides.

Within your department, it is not enough to examine only yourself and your own practices. As a Certified Dietary Manager, you need to observe behaviors within your work team, listen to employees, and express an interest in others. A manager can encourage employees to share their backgrounds through involvement in cultural theme days, for example.

Diversity
Describes the many ways in which people differ from each other

Consensus
General agreement within a group

When you need to resolve conflict among employees, look for possible underlying cultural differences, and try to facilitate understanding among employees. Be alert to differences in nonverbal behavior and how it is interpreted, which varies greatly among cultures.

Multicultural management does not mean that you must bend all rules. For example, if a male employee comes from a cultural background in which men do not accept orders from women—and the employee has a female supervisor—it is not your job to give the employee a male supervisor. Instead, you will need to work to generate a two-way cultural understanding. You may need to ask the employee more about his own culture, and then point out how gender roles vary. Ultimately, you will have to explain that certain job expectations are essential for your department to accomplish its mission, and ask for the employee's help in making departmental systems work. By recognizing the cultural difference, you can make the process much easier than it would be otherwise.

Today, many facilities offer diversity training to help Certified Dietary Managers uncover their own internal biases and teach skills for managing diversity. This can be a great resource. Mentoring is an effective tool to improve cross-generational working relationship. In all, a non-judgmental attitude of openness and acceptance can go a long way towards managing a diverse work team.

Disputes and Consensus

A work team is comprised of many individuals. Each has a unique cultural background, and a unique set of values. Through variations in interpreting communications, distinctions in cultural norms, and conflicts among personal values, disputes can sometimes arise. To maintain an effective work team, a manager needs to be alert to conflict situations and intervene in a timely manner to resolve disputes.

To be successful as a group, employees must be encouraged to share one critical value: respect for themselves and each other. The manager must model this respect. Based on a respectful relationship, many disputes and conflicts can be resolved. Often, the steps are as simple as hearing the issue from everyone's perspective, and helping everyone involved reach an understanding or consensus. A **consensus** is a general agreement within a group. It may not reflect the first choice of every individual member of the group. However, it reflects a plan that has been developed through some type of group process to represent the best, acceptable middle ground for everyone.

Two of your employees are having a loud disagreement in the kitchen during meal service. Your clients can hear them. What steps would you take to handle this situation?

(Check your answer at the end of this chapter)

A process such as this can help resolve conflicts between or among employees; conflicts between a union and an employer; conflicts that arise from the presence of a diverse workforce; and many other situations. The steps are as follows:

1. Base the process on respect, and do not let anything change this.
2. Recognize the importance of relationships among people, and protect these relationships.
3. Establish what the outcome of the process must be, such as a policy everyone will honor, or an agreement to which everyone will commit.

4. Discuss and clarify the issues, from multiple perspectives.
5. Assure that every member of the group participates.
6. Work creatively and fairly as a group to come up with solutions.
7. Select a solution that meets the defined needs of everyone involved as closely as possible. Apply a sense of fairness and balance during this process.
8. Ask each member of the group to commit to this solution.

So far in this chapter, we have discussed goals and objectives and managing change, diversity, and disputes. The underlying link to being successful with these activities is communication. How and what you communicate plays a major role in how effective your staff works together to achieve your department and facility's goals and objectives.

Communication

Communication is an exchange of information. Even when we do not say anything, we are still communicating by our actions. Most people talk; few people communicate. Lack of communication is the basis of most problems in life.

The communication process is complex. As a Certified Dietary Manager, you will be challenged to become an expert in the techniques of good communication, and apply your knowledge as you interact with administrators, physicians, clients, employees, and families. Miscommunication leads to dissatisfaction, misunderstanding, misinterpretation, and, in some cases, to anger and resentment. There are basic principles of communication that can help every manager be more effective.

Communications of all types share a few basic components. There is always a sender, a receiver, a message, and feedback. Figure 10.4 illustrates these elements.

If you are the sender, you have a message that you wish to transmit. You must think about the receiver's perspective as you put together the message. However, you are also influenced by your own perception of the message and the situation. Your perception is influenced by the skills, abilities, attitudes, and experiences that make up your background.

Figure 10.4 Elements of Basic Communication

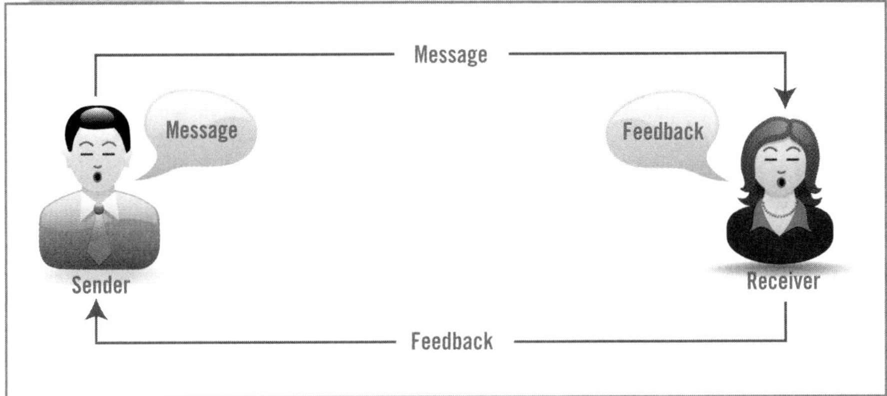

The message, verbal and/or nonverbal, is transmitted through formal and/or informal channels of communication. Examples of formal channels are meetings, memos, and rules. Informal communication channels include the grapevine, rumors, and general conversations. Finally, the message is received and the receiver attempts to understand it based upon his or her own perceptions.

Feedback is the reaction that the receiver has to the sender's message. Feedback lets you as a sender know how the message is being received. To be an effective communicator, you need to be alert to feedback, and be able to notice what a receiver is saying back to you. A receiver may be saying anything from: *I agree with you, to, I have no idea what you are talking about, to, I think your idea is off the wall!*

How do you read feedback? By listening and watching. Feedback may take many forms, including oral, written, e-mail, and body movements, such as a shrug of the shoulders. If you are able to read feedback and respond accordingly, you build trust, foster problem-solving, and enjoy effective communication.

Another aspect of communication is called interference. Sometimes, certain factors interfere with a flow of information between sender and receiver. Here are some examples of factors that can cause interference:

✓ Differences in perception: The sender must consider the receiver's perceptions and develop messages in a way which will make them more clearly understood.

✓ Lack of knowledge: The communication process cannot be effective when the sender and/or the receiver do not have adequate knowledge to understand each other. Imagine having a technical conversation with a rocket scientist. If you do not possess the same body of knowledge, you may have trouble understanding each other!

✓ Emotions: Sometimes emotions, either obvious or subconscious, can cause communication problems. Emotions can take first priority in people's minds, making it difficult to focus on a message. For example, a person who is very anxious may have difficulty processing and comprehending instructions. A person who is very angry may need to focus on the anger before being able to exchange information.

✓ Lack of interest: It is difficult to communicate effectively if the receiver and/or sender does not have an interest in the message being conveyed.

✓ Personality: Personality clashes between the receiver and sender can cause communication problems. For example, if you basically don't like someone, you may be less receptive to that person's message. Conversely, when sender and receiver have excellent rapport, they are likely to be able to communicate well.

✓ Appearance: Just as your personality and emotions may get in the way of effective communication, your appearance may detract from the effectiveness of communication. When we are upset about or pleased with another's appearance, it can have an impact on our acceptance of the message.

Putting It Into Practice: 4

You want to meet privately with an employee to listen to a concern. The noise from the kitchen is interfering. What should you do?

(Check your answer at the end of this chapter)

- ✓ Distractions: Noise, other conversation, temperature, physical discomfort, and other influences often make it difficult for communication to take place.
- ✓ Disorganization: If the sender or receiver is disorganized or uncertain about the exact message to be sent, communication problems arise.
- ✓ Language: There may be a lack of common understanding between parties when they do not speak the same language, or when the language used is not comfortable for one of the parties. In addition, use of particular words may cause problems. Slang, jargon, technical terms, or any unfamiliar vocabulary can prevent a message from getting through.
- ✓ Indirect access: Sometimes, the message goes through a number of parties before reaching the receiver. Particularly in a large facility, the message may be passed through a number of people before reaching the final receiver. Here, the opportunity for distortion is great. This is just like the familiar game, "Whisper Down the Alley." As players repeat a message to other players, the message becomes increasingly distorted.

To communicate well, keep in mind a few basic tips:

- ✓ Analyze the receiver: As a sender, consider the receiver's position. You may need to empathize, or understand how another person feels. You may need to recognize the receiver's concerns, interests, emotions, values, and much more. The best communications are geared towards the receiver.
- ✓ Use feedback: Watch and listen as you communicate. Sometimes, a nervous Certified Dietary Manager becomes consumed with the idea of speaking in public, or performing basic tasks, and forgets to focus on the receiver. In any live interaction, such as a conversation or a meeting, a receiver can guide you in your communication, and make the entire process much easier. The key is feedback.
- ✓ Make messages meaningful: It is important to consider the perceptions of the receiver as the message is developed. Would you give instructions to both a new and an experienced staff member in exactly the same manner? Of course not. You must think about the receiver as you formulate and send the message.
- ✓ Use face-to-face communications: Whenever possible, talk directly to others, so that you can assure your message is not distorted, and so that you can read feedback and respond accordingly.
- ✓ Communicate nonverbally: Your own nonverbal communication affects your message. In fact, the majority of what you communicate in person comes from your nonverbal language, rather than from your words. Be alert to the message you send with body language. At the same time, you can read the receiver's body language to obtain valuable feedback that you otherwise might not hear. Figure 10.5 lists a number of nonverbal clues. Note that cultural influences make a difference in interpretation of body language. For example, in an Asian culture, smiling may not always be comfortable, and use of gestures is minimized. A thumbs-up sign, considered very positive in North American culture, can be offensive to someone from Bangladesh where the same gesture is considered a gross insult. In a diverse workplace,

Figure 10.5 Nonverbal Communications

Using nonverbal communications can help you both send your message and understand feedback from the receiver.

Body Language	What it Means
Leaning slightly towards a person	I'm interested
Relaxed posture	I'm open to what you are saying
Eye contact	I think you are important
Nodding	I am listening
Pulling or touching ear	I want to listen to you
Looking away	I'm not interested
Touching nose	I don't like what you're saying
Rubbing nose and breaking eye contact	I'm lying
Touching cheek	I'm evaluating what you are saying
Hand over mouth	I disapprove, or I'm trying not to say anything
Hands clasped behind head	I'm arrogant
Tapping fingers	I'm feeling impatient
Fidgeting	I'm ready to go
Smile	I feel good about you and about myself
Clutching an object tightly	I'm nervous or afraid
Clasping hands behind back	I'm angry or frustrated
Crossed arms	I'm protecting myself
Open palms	I'm sincere and open
Looking at watch	I'm ready to end this conversation

take the time to learn more about the cultures of those with whom you communicate in order to use and understand nonverbal information.

- ✓ Respect personal space: For most North Americans, a distance of about 19" between people is comfortable. Moving in closer towards a person can create distress.
- ✓ Use clear language: Use words you know the receiver will understand. Sometimes, intentionally using complex vocabulary is a way of expressing arrogance and making a listener feel inferior. Recognize that specific words do not mean the same thing to everyone. Choose words carefully, and watch for responses. Clarify and re-state whenever necessary.
- ✓ Repeat the message: In both oral and written communications, a common method is to: tell the listener what you're going to tell him; tell him; tell him what you've told him. For any lengthy interchange, this routine can be helpful.
- ✓ Empathize: Seek to understand and respect the receiver's opinions, ideas, attitudes, and perceptions. Let the receiver know you understand by repeating key words or phrases back to him.
- ✓ Timing: Avoid distractions and find a person in a receptive mode.
- ✓ Consider the environment: It should be comfortable and impose minimal distractions.

- ✓ Listen: This is perhaps the most critical aspect of communication. Listening, both verbally and nonverbally, helps you ascertain feedback. In turn, this helps you refine your message and really get it through. It also helps you become a receiver, not just a sender. If you work as both a sender and a receiver, you make communication what it is really intended to be: a two-way process.

Flow of Communications in a Facility

In an facility, there is communication flowing in many directions. Some flows downwards, from your superiors to you, or from you to those you supervise. Some flows upwards, from you to your supervisor, or from subordinates to you. Some flows laterally, between and among peers.

Downward communication is frequently used in large facilities to convey policies, procedures, directives, objectives, and other information to subordinate personnel. It may be written or spoken. When a Certified Dietary Manager uses downward communication, it is often to give instructions, explain information or procedures, train employees, or communicate information that may have a bearing on employees' jobs. You should only use a bulletin board if it is kept current.

Downward communication is important. It may be the only contact subordinates have with upper management. As a result, administration must:

- ✓ Be honest, accurate, and factual, whether the information is good or bad news.
- ✓ Use words and phrases that subordinates can understand.
- ✓ Make the message specific; explain what effect it will have on the employee.

Downward communication usually follows the chain of command downward, meaning you would receive the information from your supervisor who received it from his/her director or from the CEO. Your job is to continue communicating down the chain of command with accurate, reliable, relevant information.

The Certified Dietary Manager is responsible for keeping a superior informed. Employees also will communicate ideas, requests, and opinions to their supervisor. **Upward communication** is usually reporting and questioning. In many facilities, upward communication is suppressed. Subordinates know the supervisor has the authority to fire, block promotions and salary increases, and give unpleasant assignments. So, a reluctance to communicate upward is common. The supervisor must find ways to work with subordinates to maintain face-to-face communication that is free-flowing, open, honest, and respectful of differences in opinions.

Effective Certified Dietary Managers help to invite this flow of communications by establishing an explicit open door policy. This policy says: *My door is always open. Come talk to me any time about anything.* Stating this to employees helps to ease reluctance. This policy can be challenging to honor, as a manager is very busy! If you establish this policy and an employee asks to speak with you at an inopportune time, it is fair to say: *I really want to hear what you*

The following are types of communication in the workplace. Label them as to the correct flow of communication (upward, downward, lateral):

1. Policy statement posted on the bulletin board
2. Suggestion box
3. E-mail to other department heads
4. Loudspeaker announcements
5. Focus group
6. Inservice

(Check your answer at the end of this chapter)

have to say. At the moment, there are some distractions. May we sit together at 4:00 so that I can give you my full attention?

If you have an open door policy, be sure to honor it. Nothing can be more disruptive to communication than to go back on your promise and violate trust.

Lateral communication among peers may involve discussions and meetings to solve problems and accomplish tasks that cross department or functional lines. This communication is critical in coordination, teamwork, and cooperation. Peers can be very effective at solving problems through discussion. Informally, lateral communication can also involve the channel called the grapevine or the rumor mill. This exists in all organizations.

The grapevine is a major communication tool in any organization, whether or not you recognize it. A savvy manager keeps in touch with the grapevine, where the most uninhibited communications take place among employees. It is not realistic or even wise to attempt to close off the grapevine and prevent communications among employees. However, a manager should be aware that the grapevine can lead to distortion of messages, communication of rumors, and other problems.

How do you prevent problems on the grapevine? The best answer is to communicate openly with all employees. For example, if employees have reason to guess that a change is coming—such as a layoff or a major system overhaul—give them information. When you don't, they have to guess. Guesses become rumors. Anxiety and ill feelings can snowball. What if you don't have all the information yourself? Then, simply be honest. Tell employees what you know, what you don't know, and when you expect to know more. Tell them that as you learn more, you will share information.

As possible, listen to the grapevine to gain insight into what employees think and feel. The grapevine may carry some factual information, but often it is half-truths and suspicions. The grapevine provides a channel for employees to express their fears, desires, and apprehensions. In most cases, the grapevine is unreliable, unconfirmed, and unauthorized. Certified Dietary Managers need to learn how to use the grapevine to their advantage and realize that it fills a need of the employees. Ignoring rumors can cause problems, as a rumor may have some elements of truth. When warranted, address a rumor directly with the group.

Downward Communication
Used to convey policies, procedures, directives, objectives and other information to subordinate personnel and follows the chain of command

Upward Communication
Used to communicate ideas, requests and opinions to supervisors

Lateral Communication
Occurs among peers and may involve discussion and meetings to solve problems and/or accomplish tasks

Persuasion Techniques

As a Certified Dietary Manager, you know you are the expert about certain matters in your facility. There are times when you need to obtain resources such as budget money or staffing. There are times when you need to request authorization to complete certain tasks you believe will accomplish defined objectives. There are times when you need to enlist the support of your supervisor, employees, and peers. In any of these situations, you are challenged to use the skills of persuasion.

Persuasion is an effort to influence and/or to change the beliefs, feelings, or attitudes of someone else. Persuasion strategies range from subtle suggestions to the use of force. Basic principles of persuasion a Certified Dietary Manager can use include the following:

✓ Establish credibility and trust. Often, it is part of a relationship that builds over time.

✓ Start by emphasizing common ground. For example, you may note that both you and your administrator are committed to improving client satisfaction ratings, containing the labor budget, or whatever objective is relevant. You may note values that you share or a situation you have both observed.

✓ Use concepts, examples, and analogies familiar to the listener's perspective and experiences.

✓ Speak positively and enthusiastically.

✓ Explain how the desired outcome will benefit the listener. This means translating the message into terms of "you."

✓ Repeat direct and indirect suggestions most critical to the point.

Effective Writing

Whether you enjoy writing or not, as a Certified Dietary Manager you can count on the periodic need to express yourself in writing. Your written communications may include business correspondence, memos, reports, policies and procedures, e-mail, posted notices, and more. When writing, always consider the reader. The message will be understood according to the receiver's perceptions and the ability to understand your words. Focus on the interests and perspective of the reader.

Compared with interpersonal communication, writing can be challenging because you do not have the opportunity to receive direct and immediate feedback that might help you refine your delivery. In a business environment, many of us feel compelled to use obscure words, stilted language, long sentences, and other techniques to impress the reader. In fact, the most effective business communications sound much like excellent oral delivery. They sound like a professional speaking to you face-to-face. There are a few cautions, though.

Written business communications should do a few things that are not always necessary in casual conversation, such as:

✓ Follow grammatical rules

✓ Use complete sentences

✓ Use proper terminology to describe things, rather than slang

✓ Present ideas in a logically organized flow.

Figure 10.6 lists some tips for effective writing in a business environment.

As you organize written documents, make sure the content flows in a logical manner. Present facts a reader needs to know before drawing a conclusion. Present steps in sequence. Provide a brief introduction at the beginning of a document, and a summary at the end. For a long document, include page numbers and a table of contents for easier reference. Use simple charts, graphs, or other appropriate images to illustrate information that is difficult to comprehend through words alone.

Figure 10.6 Effective Writing Tips

Be concise

Ineffective: It is necessary to implement a unique and innovative mechanism for acquiring and obtaining required supplies and accoutrements through the established food procurement system.

Improved: We would like to try a new method of purchasing.

Use business terminology

Ineffective: Let's rock.

Improved: We are eager to proceed.

Use "I" and "me" correctly

Ineffective: You and me need to discuss this.

Improved: You and I need to discuss this.

Ineffective: Perhaps she could share her thoughts with you and I.

Improved: Perhaps she could share her thoughts with you and me.

Avoid run-on sentences

Ineffective: We will evaluate this, you and I can meet next week.

Improved: We will evaluate this. Then, let's meet next week.

Be specific

Ineffective: Certain individuals have raised a number of complaints regarding temperatures of foods.

Improved: Last week, Mrs. Wiley said her mashed potatoes were too cold. Mr. Jones did, too.

Address people directly

Ineffective: One can see from this report that the foodservice department has improved client satisfaction scores.

Improved: As you can see, the foodservice department has improved client satisfaction scores.

Use simple words when possible

Ineffective: We would like to utilize the budgetary monies.

Improved: We would like to use budget funds.

After you write anything, take the time to read it through and proofread carefully. This is especially true of e-mail. It helps to leave the "to" line blank until you have proofed the entire message. Check for errors in spelling, punctuation, or grammar—all of which can create interference to your communication. Check whether the sentences are concise and clear. Check whether any thoughts may be vague or easily misunderstood. Often, it is easiest to proofread by reading a piece out loud.

Finally, if the content of a communication is likely to startle, surprise, or upset the receiver, consider using an interpersonal exchange instead. For example, you would not use e-mail to tell your supervisor that you have accepted a new job, or that the department is in crisis. If necessary, follow up a personal exchange with written communication.

Writing a Memo

A memo is a specific type of written business communication that is used frequently in most organizations. A memo is a brief document that provides a message about new information, such as a new procedure, or requests a reader to take an action, such as approving a plan or attending a meeting. To make a memo effective, you should direct it specifically to your reader(s), and spell out the action you are requesting.

A memo has five parts: a heading, an opening, a background, a brief discussion, and a summary. The heading includes these components: TO, FROM, DATE, and SUBJECT. The opening should state the purpose of the memo succinctly. The background gives the context of the information or request. A simple discussion section provides more detail about the plan or request. The

Figure 10.7 Sample Memo to Department Heads

TO:	All Department Managers	*Heading*
FROM:	Inez Timal, Director, Food & Nutrition Services	
DATE:	February 23, 20xx	
SUBJECT:	New Catering Request Form	
We would like you to be aware of a new form to be used for requesting catering services beginning on March 1.		*Opening*
Based on our experience processing requests, we have determined we can serve you better by collecting some additional information about your needs.		*Background*
The new catering request form, attached, includes spaces for you to indicate your preferred service style, as well as an ending time for your event. Your cooperation in providing this information will help us ensure that your event meets your expectations and ensure timely clean-up. In addition, the new form includes a space for you to indicate which budget account you would like to use for your catering charges. This will help us ensure that the accounting for your event is accurate.		*Discussion*
Thank you for your cooperation in using this new form. If you have any questions about the form or catering services, please contact me any time.		*Summary*

summary is a short statement that ties in with the opening, reminding the reader what should happen next. Figure 10.7 is an example of a memo in which these parts are labeled.

As a business communication, a memo should be well organized and concise. It should always leave the reader with a definite understanding of what to do next. As a Certified Dietary Manager, you should not use a memo to substitute for face-to-face communications or to make major requests that may require meetings, presentations, and discussion. However, you can use it to relate straightforward information. A typical memo does not exceed one or two pages. Sometimes, an attachment may be needed.

E-mail Etiquette

Much of today's business communication occurs through e-mail. Consider these simple rules if you communicate through e-mail.

- ✓ It is no different than writing a letter so use a greeting, a closing and sign your name.
- ✓ Always reread your e-mail before you send it to make sure there are no errors and the tone of your e-mail is friendly and professional.
- ✓ Do not over use emoticons and refrain from using 'texting' abbreviations.
- ✓ Refrain from sending an e-mail if you are angry; communicate in person.
- ✓ Respond in a timely manner or at least let the person know when you can respond. Timely is generally within 24 hours.

Business Etiquette

In any business communication, people expect to enjoy a few essential courtesies. These may include things like:

- ✓ Wearing your name badge so people know who you are
- ✓ Introducing yourself before addressing someone you do not know
- ✓ Returning telephone calls and responding to e-mail messages, unless they are from aggressive sales people with whom you are not doing business
- ✓ Looking at a person before speaking
- ✓ Talking in a calm tone of voice
- ✓ Allowing others to complete their thoughts before responding
- ✓ Respecting the chain of command in any organization
- ✓ Assuring that you are routing your communication to the right person, and copying those who should be copied on written correspondence.

Another element of business etiquette involves judgment about what to communicate and when to communicate it. This is particularly true in managing communications with your own superior. As you get started in a new job, clarify some basic expectations with your supervisor. You should know what the supervisor wants you to do. As you continue with your duties, be sure your supervisor is kept appropriately informed.

Through communication with your supervisor, you can establish a clear understanding about what and when to communicate—and avoid potential misunderstanding in the future. Often, simple attention to this agreement can prevent a broad range of difficulties. It can help you achieve the support you need from high levels in the organization, and can pave the way for a smooth relationship with your own superior.

Through attention to communication basics, a Certified Dietary Manager can implement required changes in the department.

A Case Study to Implement Personal Hygiene Standards According to the FDA Food Code

You may wonder why personal hygiene standards are included in this chapter? Training on personal hygiene standards are requirements you will be expected to implement.

As a new Certified Dietary Manager, you have noticed that staff members are too relaxed about personal hygiene standards. In discussions with your supervisor, you agree to add a goal and some objectives to help improve the personal hygiene standards over the next six months. You want to follow the FDA Food Code so your goal states: Foodservice employees will follow the FDA Food Code standards for washing arms, hands, and fingernails; as well as guidelines for jewelry and outer clothing.

Establishing the goal is the easy part; the hard part is putting the change into practice. Let's walk through your considerations as you try to implement required changes in your department.

The Problem

It will be very important for you to be familiar with what the FDA Food Code says about personal hygiene standards. See Figure 10.8 for the exact wording from the FDA Food Code. Underline the standards for which your staff members may need an update. For instance, are they washing their hands for 20 seconds and lathering with soap for at least 10-15 seconds? Are they using a nail brush to clean their fingernails? Do they know all the times they must wash their hands and where to wash? Are they using hand sanitizers and do they comply with the FDA Food Code? Are they following the guidelines for jewelry and outer clothing?

The Solution

Before the Change. Refer to the checklist for implementing change (Figure 10.3) and make sure you are following it. Before you actually implement the change, allow employees to give input and become part of the change. This might be through an inservice where you present the FDA Food Code and your concerns. That will decrease their resistance to the change.

Figure 10.8 FDA Food Code, 2009, pgs. 43-47

HANDS AND ARMS

2-301.11 Clean Condition.

FOOD EMPLOYEES shall keep their hands and exposed portions of their arms clean.[P]

2-301.12 Cleaning Procedure.

A. Except as specified in ¶ (D) of this section, FOOD EMPLOYEES shall clean their hands and exposed portions of their arms, including surrogate prosthetic devices for hands or arms for at least 20 seconds, using a cleaning compound in a HANDWASHING SINK that is equipped as specified under § 5-202.12 and Subpart 6-301.[P]

B. FOOD EMPLOYEES shall use the following cleaning procedure in the order stated to clean their hands and exposed portions of their arms, including surrogate prosthetic devices for hands and arms:

1. Rinse under clean, running warm water; [P]
2. Apply an amount of cleaning compound recommended by the cleaning compound manufacturer; [P]
3. Rub together vigorously for at least 10 to 15 seconds while:
   (a) Paying particular attention to removing soil from underneath the fingernails during the cleaning procedure,[P] and
   (b) Creating friction on the surfaces of the hands and arms or surrogate prosthetic devices for hands and arms, finger tips, and areas between the fingers; [P]
4. Thoroughly rinse under clean, running warm water;[P] and
5. Immediately follow the cleaning procedure with thorough drying using a method as specified under § 6-301.12.[P]

C. *To avoid recontaminating their hands or surrogate prosthetic devices, FOOD EMPLOYEES may use disposable paper towels or similar clean barriers when touching surfaces such as manually operated faucet handles on a HANDWASHING SINK or the handle of a restroom door.*

D. *If APPROVED and capable of removing the types of soils encountered in the FOOD operations involved, an automatic handwashing facility may be used by FOOD EMPLOYEES to clean their hands or surrogate prosthetic devices.*

2-301.13 Special Handwash Procedures.

Reserved.

Note: Requirements follwed by "P" indicate Priority items.

(Continued)

Figure 10.8 FDA Food Code *(Continued)*

2-301.14 When to Wash.

FOOD EMPLOYEES shall clean their hands and exposed portions of their arms as specified under § 2-301.12 immediately before engaging in FOOD preparation including working with exposed FOOD, clean EQUIPMENT and UTENSILS, and unwrapped SINGLE-SERVICE and SINGLE-USE ARTICLES[P] and:

A. After touching bare human body parts other than clean hands and clean, exposed portions of arms;[P]

B. After using the toilet room; [P]

C. After caring for or handling SERVICE ANIMALS or aquatic animals as specified in ¶ 2-403.11(B); [P]

D. Except as specified in ¶ 2-401.11(B), after coughing, sneezing, using a handkerchief or disposable tissue, using tobacco, eating, or drinking; [P]

E. After handling soiled EQUIPMENT or UTENSILS; [P]

F. During FOOD preparation, as often as necessary to remove soil and contamination and to prevent cross contamination when changing tasks; [P]

G. When switching between working with raw FOOD and working with READY-TO-EAT FOOD; [P]

H. Before donning gloves for working with FOOD; [P] and

I. After engaging in other activities that contaminate the hands. [P]

2-301.15 Where to Wash.

FOOD EMPLOYEES shall clean their hands in a HANDWASHING SINK or APPROVED automatic handwashing facility and may not clean their hands in a sink used for FOOD preparation or WAREWASHING, or in a service sink or a curbed cleaning facility used for the disposal of mop water and similar liquid waste.

2-301.16 Hand Antiseptics.

A. A hand antiseptic used as a topical application, a hand antiseptic solution used as a hand dip, or a hand antiseptic soap shall:
   1. Comply with one of the following:
      a. Be an APPROVED drug that is listed in the FDA publication **Approved Drug Products with Therapeutic Equivalence Evaluations** as an APPROVED drug based on safety and effectiveness; or
      b. Have active antimicrobial ingredients that are listed in the FDA monograph for OTC Health-Care Antiseptic Drug Products as an antiseptic handwash, and
   2. Comply with one of the following:
      a. Have components that are exempted from the requirement of being listed in federal FOOD ADDITIVE regulations as specified in 21 CFR 170.39 - Threshold of regulation for substances used in food-contact articles; or
      b. Comply with and be listed in:
         i. 21 CFR 178 - Indirect Food Additives: Adjuvants, Production Aids, and Sanitizers as regulated for use as a FOOD ADDITIVE with conditions of safe use, or
         ii. 21 CFR 182 - Substances Generally Recognized as Safe, 21 CFR 184 - Direct Food Substances Affirmed as Generally Recognized as Safe, or 21 CFR 186 - Indirect Food Substances Affirmed as Generally Recognized as Safe for use in contact with food, and
   3. Be applied only to hands that are cleaned as specified under § 2-301.12.

B. If a hand antiseptic or a hand antiseptic solution used as a hand dip does not meet the criteria specified under Subparagraph (A)(2) of this section, use shall be:
   1. Followed by thorough hand rinsing in clean water before hand contact with FOOD or by the use of gloves; or
   2. Limited to situations that involve no direct contact with FOOD by the bare hands.

C. A hand antiseptic solution used as a hand dip shall be maintained clean and at a strength equivalent to at least 100 MG/L chlorine.

Note: Requirements follwed by "P" indicate Priority items.

(Continued)

Figure 10.8 FDA Food Code *(Continued)*

FINGERNAILS

2-302.11 Maintenance.

A. FOOD EMPLOYEES shall keep their fingernails trimmed, filed, and maintained so the edges and surfaces are cleanable and not rough.

B. Unless wearing intact gloves in good repair, a FOOD EMPLOYEE may not wear fingernail polish or artificial fingernails when working with exposed FOOD.

JEWELRY

2-303.11 Prohibition.

Except for a *plain ring such as a wedding band*, while preparing FOOD, FOOD EMPLOYEES may not wear jewelry including medical information jewelry on their arms and hands.

OUTER CLOTHING

2-304.11 Clean Condition.

FOOD EMPLOYEES shall wear clean outer clothing to prevent contamination of FOOD, EQUIPMENT, UTENSILS, LINENS, and SINGLE SERVICE and SINGLE USE ARTICLES.

Communicate clearly that the change will happen and you want to know their concerns. Explain how this fits the facility's overall goals.

Remember that you have a diverse staff and that a multicultural approach involves increasing both your and others awareness, consciousness, and appreciation for diverse hygiene standards.

During the Change

Plan a training program in advance of your anticipated implementation. Maybe you want to hold a "kick off" event to help your employees focus on the changes. Throughout this process, communicate clearly, effectively, and often.

After the Change

Have frequent meetings to discuss employee concerns. Reward employees who put forth effort to make the change successful. Know that some people may be resistant. Investigating their complaints is part of successful communication. Encourage feedback; revisit and repeat changes throughout the six months.

Management in the News

Dietary Department General HACCP Plan

Rev: 05/14/11

by Michael Callahan, Director of Dietary Services and Executive Chef, Yukon-Kuskokwim Delta Regional Hospital

Food safety should be a critical component of any establishment that serves food to the public. As a food service department in a healthcare environment the standards of safety must by necessity be raised to an even higher level. Many of our customers are also patients in our hospital. Elders and other people with compromised health are at a much higher risk to the dangers of food-borne illness.

The spread of harmful pathogens (microorganisms) and the serious illnesses or death which may result from improper food handling are for the most part preventable. This plan has been developed from national and industry standard protocols for food safety in an effort to instruct the staff of the YKDRY Dietary department on the particular food safety issues in this establishment.

The items in this plan are not merely suggestions but must be held in strict compliance. However, with that stated it is each team member's responsibility to "test the plan." If in our day-to-day operations we find an item or procedure that needs to be added or revised, it is our duty to bring such observations to the team for review.

What is the YKHC HACCP Plan?

For YKHC purposes, a Hazard Analysis and Critical Control Points (HACCP) is a systematic preventive approach to food safety that addresses physical, chemical, and biological hazards as a means of preventing foodborne illnesses. HACCP is used in the food industry to identify potential food safety hazards, so that key actions, known as Critical Control Points (CCPs) can be taken to reduce or eliminate the risk of the hazards being realized. This system will be used at all stages of our dietary department food production and preparation processes from personal hygiene, the initial ordering of food, receiving, storage, prep, cooking, to the final service of food to our patients and customers.

The use of HACCP is a mandatory and critical part of the YKHC dietary department's daily standard operating procedure.

Guiding Principles

Along with the U.S. Food and Drug Administration (FDA), various professional organizations offer training and certification for food service professionals. This organization has chosen the "ServSafe" program developed by the National Restaurant Association as its prime source for food safety training and information. This kitchen will implement all current FDA guidelines as they are brought into common usage via ServSafe. Currently ServSafe is training and teaching to the 2005 FDA Food Code.

Personal Responsibilities

Training and Certification

All managers and cooks in this kitchen must maintain current food safety certification through ServSafe. If at the implementation of this plan a particular individual is not certified, that person has three months to obtain

(Continued...)

Dietary Department General HACCP Plan *(Continued)*

said training and certification. YKHC will provide training and testing opportunities. Each YKHC cook must either take advantage of the training opportunities offered through YKHC or find alternate means in order to adhere to this certification standard.

ServSafe certification is recommended for all dietary department employees for food safety and professional development. However, foodservice workers may substitute the "Alaska Food Worker Card" as evidence of knowledge of food safety principles.

Prior to beginning production all staff members are in clean kitchen uniforms. Clean kitchen apparel limits the risk of out side pathogens contaminating the end product during the manufacturing process.

Personal Health/Hygiene

It is the responsibility of each employee to report to their manager if they are experiencing any health symptoms that may impact food safety. These symptoms include: vomiting, diarrhea, sore throat, fever, and jaundice.

Hand Washing

Hand washing is our first line of defense in preventing food borne illnesses from occurring in our dining facility. YKHC dietary staff will not handle any food with out first washing hands and arms vigorously with hot soapy water for a minimum of 15 seconds, and then drying thoroughly. This hand washing criteria will be followed each time washing hands is required. Required hand washing moments include: exiting a restroom, before putting on gloves, after touching other objects such as door handles, hand carts, hair or other body parts, etc.

Gloves

Gloves must be worn while handling all **ready to eat foods** and serving foods for both our patients and on the cafeteria serving line. Remember that gloves need to be changed as often as you would wash your hands.

Uniforms and Hair Restraints

Street clothes pose a potential food safety risk. The dietary department provides hats, white chef coats and white shirts for food service staff. All workers are required to wear clean kitchen apparel, including hats each shift. Clean aprons are also provided. These must be worn and changed when soiled.

Cashiers are exempt from the "hat" portion of this requirement until a specified Front of House uniform can be specified and obtained.

Jewelry

For both safety and sanitation reasons food service staff are not permitted to wear any jewelry including watches, necklaces, rings, or earrings larger than simple studs. Facial jewelry, hoops, or studs etc. are prohibited as well.

YKHC Identified Hazard Analysis and Critical Control Points

Food Sourcing

Primarily a management responsibility; all food products including meat, fish, poultry and vegetables must be procured from reputable, licensed purveyors. In all cases proper documentation of all food purchases must be maintained for possible review for up to one year.

Food Receiving

- It is the responsibility of each food service worker in the YKHC dietary department to fully understand the safe temperatures that must be maintained for each product type.
- When receiving food, inspection must be made to insure that the food is delivered at the proper temperature, and that each item is free from contamination or damage. Shipping log must show that all un-frozen meat products have maintained a temperature below 40 degrees Fahrenheit.

(Continued...)

Dietary Department General HACCP Plan *(Continued)*

- Frozen food must received "frozen," (hard to the touch) and be inspected for evidence of thawing.
- Product packaging needs to be intact, boxes, bags and cans need to be free from damage. If a product is received at an improper temperature or inadequate condition, the product in question must be rejected.

Food Storage

Once the product is received take care to handle it properly storing dry goods in the proper store room and TCS foods (TCS foods are those foods that require temperature controls and monitoring) in the appropriate walk in. Make sure to log temps and time on individual logs to make sure each walk-in is at the correct temp for storing food safely.

- Throw away food that is expired past its expiration date, if food emits foul odor uncharacteristic of the food. Throw away food if it is contaminated by chemical or physical hazards. Throw away food that has growth of mold uncharacteristic of the food.
- Stacking Order: Always be aware of how food is stacked in each walk-in. Prepped or ready to eat food needs to be stored above meat & poultry. Poultry will always be stored below other foods.
- First in, first out: when receiving food or working with food from the walk-in refrigerators or freezers we must rotate stock so that we are using the oldest items first – This takes extra effort, but this added work will prevent us from utilizing expired food.
- It is the cooks responsibility to requisition frozen Meat, Poultry, and Fish a minimum of three days prior to date required.
- Label Meat & Poultry with the date placed in the defrost chiller. Throw away food that has been in the defrost chiller longer than seven (7) days.
- Also, label all pulled meat and other prepped food with the meal and date which it is to be used.

Safety and Sanitation

There is a difference between cleaning and sanitizing. In this facility we utilize a two-step cleaning and sanitizing process for all tables, counters, and equipment. The terms "clean" or cleaning" used herein always infer this dual process.

Our standard cleaning agent is "Orange Force" which is available in a spray bottle. Our sanitizing solution is a "MultiQuat" solution. Make sure you know both the safe handling procedures of each solution, and the location of the Material Safety Data Sheet (MSDS) book. The bottom line is to keep all food contact surfaces clean while not contaminating food with the cleaning solutions.

Use of MultiQuat sanitizer: We keep a large quantity of sanitizing spray bottles and pails on hand for daily usage. Sanitizing solution in buckets must be changed at the end of each meal/shift, buckets cleaned, and solution checked for proper concentration.

- Cutting boards: Always use clean, color coded cutting boards appropriate to each type of product you are preparing: red for beef, yellow for poultry, green for vegetables, etc. Signs are to be posted in the dietary department indicating proper colors for each product. Refer to these signs or ask your supervisor if you are in doubt.
- Knives must be cleaned and put away after each use. Always use a fresh, clean knife for each product type to avoid cross contamination.
- Counters must be cleaned and sanitized after each use and also after each meal/shift.
- Equipment—We have a variety of equipment that can be both dangerous and also have potential for causing food borne illness if not properly operated and or cleaned. It is the responsibility of the management to insure each worker is familiar with safe and sanitary operating procedures for each piece of kitchen equipment.
- NO kitchen worker will operate any piece of equipment without proper training and or authorization.

(Continued...)

Dietary Department General HACCP Plan *(Continued)*

Food Prep

- Work surfaces, sinks, cutting boards, knives, etc., must be clean and sanitized prior to using, and before changing food types
- Always utilize color-coded cutting boards appropriate for each food type.

Cooking Food

- All cooked foods prepared by this facility will be monitored to see that they meet the commonly accepted safe temperatures for each particular product. It is a requirement of continued employment that each cook know what these safe temperatures are. Signs are posted in the kitchen giving explicit instructions on temperature requirements for all foods we prepare.
- Batch logs will be maintained daily for each entrée that we prepare. This log indicates the entrée name, date, time, and temperature of the dish when it is removed from the stove or oven.
- Food must remain in the danger zone no longer than four hours. If food is allowed to remain in the danger zone longer than four hours it must be thrown out. Discard food if it has fallen on the floor, no three-second rule.
- When holding hot food for service you should check temp regularly to leave time for corrective action if necessary. Discard food if it has been through time/temp abuse. If you are not sure how the food has been handled throw it away. Using questionable food is not worth the risk of contaminating a patient, cafeteria customer or co-worker.

Hot Holding/Serving Lines

- Both time and temperature controls are utilized in this kitchen.
- Foods placed on each serving line must be maintained at an appropriate temperature to insure that the food stays out of the "Danger Zone." The generally accepted temperatures for Food Danger Zone are 41-140 degrees Fahrenheit. It will be our highest priority to minimize food exposure to the danger zone.
- Temperatures will be logged on all hot food placed on the serving lines. Food temperatures of items placed on the hot lines must be at or above the minimum safe level for each food type.
- All hot foods on the serving line must be held at 135f or above or discarded within two hours. Batch cooking is required so that foodstuffs are placed on the line incrementally, helping to eliminate potential time/temperature abuse and food waste.
- Until further notice the YKHC dietary department will no longer save any "leftover" from the serving line without the express permission and instructions from management. When authorized by management, food that is to be saved for future use must be tracked in writing indicating times and temperatures as required by commonly accepted industry practice.
- Food on serving lines must be portioned with an appropriate utensil. Examples: tongs, spoons, scoops, dishers, and spatulas
- Hands or fingers are not to be used to serve or plate food.

Sabotage

A very important aspect of food safety is insuring that foods remain free form deliberate contamination. In that vein it is important that no unescorted guests are permitted in the kitchen, refrigerators, freezers or other food storage locations.

Of special concern are former employees who may have a "grudge" or feel in some way "wronged." Under no circumstances will any former employees be allowed in the kitchen or food storage areas unaccompanied.

(Continued...)

Dietary Department General HACCP Plan *(Continued)*

It is also important that any vendors we choose or contract with have strict access controls over their food storage facilities.

Review of CCPs

CCPs in food production include: purchasing, receiving, storing, preparing, cooking, holding, serving, cooling and reheating. Time/temperature sensitive foods must be handled with the utmost care. Caution must be taken so as not to abuse the product by letting your product be exposed to extreme temperatures bringing it into a danger zone situation. Always cook food to the proper temp. When holding food, keep at 141 degrees or higher check every two hours to insure corrective action. Cool down production food to 70 degrees in two hours then down to 41 degrees or lower in four hours. When serving make sure plates, cups, platters, and utensils are clean, sanitized and free of chips or cracks. When reheating any food heat to 165 degrees for 15 seconds and then held at 141 degrees for no more than two hours. When storing food always use the first in first out method and throw out items past the expiration date.

Management Monitoring Procedures

It is the Manager's and shift leader's responsibility to monitor that daily checklists are being maintained, and making sure the kitchen is clean before and after each workday. Workstations and prep surfaces should be cleaned during slack time or every four hours, to prevent bacterial growth. Make sure to watch employee's wash hands early and often, as well as wearing gloves when appropriate.

Verify that the System Works

This HACCP plan is a work-in progress. We will review and make adjustments to the HACCP plan whenever changes are made to the menu or any aspect of the production process. HACCP plans identify not only food hazards but also other potential hazards of an establishment.

A major topic of our weekly staff meeting needs to address HACCP and review what is working or causing problems.

All employees must be aware of the importance the department HACCP plan in preventing pathogens from contaminating the food production process.

Every employee should have the conscience awareness of food-borne pathogens at all times.

Used with permission from Yukon-Kuskokwim Health Corporation (YKHC) Yukon-Kuskokwim Delta Regional Hospital (YKDRH)

END OF CHAPTER

Putting It Into Practice Questions & Answers

1. Which of the following objectives would be appropriate for the goal: increase client satisfaction with foodservice. Explain why.

   Objective #1. Survey the clients

   Objective #2. Maintain cold temperatures on the salad bar

   Objective #3. Hold an inservice on ways to improve client service by Feb. 16, 2012

   A. *The correct answer is #3 because it is measureable and observable. By adding a date, it is easily measureable. Holding an inservice will provide a written record that is also observable. Objective #1 might be observable but it isn't measureable. Objective #2 also isn't measureable.*

2. Your administrative team has just told you that they want you to open a new cafeteria. How would you introduce this to your staff?

   A. *Opening a new cafeteria is going to mean a big change. This is something that should be presented in person, to the entire staff. Review the "resistance to change" topics and try to prepare for those questions and concerns in advance. Also, it will be important to present this information as soon as possible.*

3. Two of your employees are having a loud disagreement in the kitchen during meal service. Your clients can hear them. What steps would you take to handle this situation?

   A. *If at all possible, remove them from the work area immediately and take them to your office or a private room. Explain your concern for the clients who may have been disrupted. If there is time to investigate the incident right then, ask questions about the cause and try to find the real source of the dispute. If there isn't time right then, invite them back to your office, one at a time, as soon as possible after the incident.*

4. You want to meet privately with an employee to listen to a concern. The noise from the kitchen is interfering. What should you do?

   A. *Move your meeting to a place where you can focus better on the person and hear the concern. This will show that you care about the person and the message the person is relating to you.*

5. The following are types of communication in the workplace. Label them as to the correct flow of communication (upward, downward, lateral):

   A. *1.* Policy statement posted on the bulletin board—*Downward communication*

   2. Suggestion box—*Upward communication*

   3. E-mail to other department heads—*Lateral communication*

   4. Loudspeaker announcements—*Downward communication*

   5. Focus group—*Upward communication as they are usually established to solicit specific feedback*

   6. Inservice—*This may depend upon the subject and the topic. If it is a mandatory inservice on sanitation, it is downward; if it is to discuss internal changes in the department it could be both lateral and upward.*

CHAPTER 11

Prepare, Plan and Conduct Department Meetings

Overview and Objectives

In every foodservice department, meetings are an important method of communicating. Successful meetings require communication before, during, and after the meeting.

After completing this chapter, you should be able to:

- ✓ Prepare and post meeting notice and agenda
- ✓ Plan meeting facilities and procedures
- ✓ Meet with key personnel to develop plans
- ✓ Follow proper procedures to conduct a meeting
- ✓ Write minutes of a meeting
- ✓ Plan follow-up actions resulting from the meeting

As a Certified Dietary Manager, you may need to hold meetings to introduce new procedures, evaluate quality information, recognize the work of the department, clarify policies, gather feedback, or present ongoing training. On an interdepartmental basis, you may need to hold or participate in meetings that help ensure organization-wide problem-solving, quality management, and/or systems revision.

A meeting is important because it brings groups of people together within work teams for structured communication. In this way, it can generate common understandings, stimulate creative problem-solving, and bring everyone onto the "same page" to promote teamwork.

Many Certified Dietary Managers face time pressures with their work teams and may have difficulty finding the available time and coordinating schedules to hold meetings. It is important to take the broad view, recognizing that time spent organizing, planning, and communicating in meetings can often improve productivity and effectiveness throughout the operation. The decision to call a meeting is a judgment call the manager must make. In addition, the manager has to use meeting time effectively, not allowing it to become a productivity drain, and keeping it on track.

When scheduling meetings, a manager may need to hold the same meeting, such as a training session, at several different times/days in order to reach all employee groups. Staggering meetings or meeting in small groups can be a good way to make space for a meeting without disrupting scheduled activities and commitments.

Types of Meetings

There are four typical types of meetings for which you may be responsible:

- ✓ Production meeting
- ✓ Training meeting such as an inservice
- ✓ Goal progress meeting—Are you meeting department goals?
- ✓ Teamwork meetings

Each of these meetings will have different guidelines, require different preparation, and will have a positive impact on your department. See Figure 11.1 for the details in conducting these meetings.

Techniques for Effective Meetings

Planning is essential for effective meetings. For example, the Certified Dietary Manager must identify the specific purpose of the meeting and gather any necessary background information. The group leader must also plan an agenda and a time limit for the meeting.

As you plan a meeting, consider who should attend, specific objectives for the discussion, and the best approach to involve group members in discussion.

- ✓ Select a time and day for the meeting that is most convenient for everyone.
- ✓ List the materials and equipment needed such as audio-visuals, handouts or equipment.
- ✓ Choose a place for the meeting that is quiet, comfortable, well lit, and large enough to provide ample space for all attendees.
- ✓ Notify all participants in advance.

How best to notify participants depends on your usual communications methods with the group involved. For example, if you are chair of your organization's safety committee and wish to announce a meeting of the committee, you will probably send a memo or an e-mail to each participant. However, if you are planning a training meeting for foodservice employees, you may find it more effective to post a prominent notice over the timeclock, or add a meeting notice to employees' paychecks.

When appropriate, distribute an agenda for the meeting to each member in advance. An **agenda** is a planned outline and timetable for what will happen during a meeting. It should also be reviewed verbally at the start of a meeting. A time limit should be established for each topic, but this limit should not be so rigid that it cannot be adjusted. The agenda serves as an outline for the meeting and can help you keep the meeting on track. In planning an agenda, be sure you are working with small, achievable objectives that can be accomplished within the established time-frame for a meeting.

Glossary

Agenda
Planned outline and timetable for a meeting; should include the meeting objective

Figure 11.1 Four Types of Meetings

<table>
<tr><th>Type of Meeting</th><th>Purpose of the Meeting</th><th>Preparation for Meeting</th></tr>
<tr><td>Daily Production Meeting</td><td>• Review the daily production, catering needs and assignments</td><td rowspan="2">• This is a quick, 15-minute daily meeting for production staff
• Held in the kitchen
• Everyone stands up to keep the meeting short
• Discuss any new recipes or efforts to make the production flow better and improve the client's experience.
• Review any problems or concerns from the day before</td></tr>
<tr><td>Weekly Production Meeting</td><td>• Weekly menu meetings with cooks; for catering to coordinate food production, delivery and pickup</td></tr>
<tr><td>Training Meeting</td><td>• Introduce new procedures and new equipment
• Review sanitation/safety regulations
• Develop new skills</td><td>• Prepare an agenda
• Hold at least bi-monthly
• Require staff attendance
• Ask someone to take minutes for documentation
• Limit the time to 30-45 minutes
• Bring in an outside trainer occasionally such as the local sanitarian
• Post notes from meetings in a prominent place</td></tr>
<tr><td>Goal Progress</td><td>• Review progress toward department goals. This could also be care planning meetings.</td><td>• Prepare an agenda
• Schedule at least quarterly
• Ask someone to record notes
• Provide data or charts that document your progress
• Analyze the results
• Identify areas for concern
• Develop a plan of action to correct areas of concern</td></tr>
<tr><td>Teamwork Meetings</td><td>• Discuss issues that may be cross-departmental, such as quality initiatives
• Work on department initiatives such as implementing HACCP.</td><td>• Prepare an agenda
• Schedule at least bi-monthly
• Expect team members to come prepared to participate
• Ask someone to record notes
• Give team members one minute to report on progress
• Limit the time to one hour
• Post notes from meetings in a prominent place
• Ask members of the group to take turns as the group leader/facilitator</td></tr>
</table>

At the beginning of the meeting, you should clearly state the objective(s) of the meeting and state your expected outcomes. You can also present all relevant tasks and encourage all attendees to participate actively in the meeting. Determining your meeting objective in advance sets the framework for an effective meeting. At the beginning of the meeting, it is helpful for the group leader to identify how each member will benefit from the meeting. If attendees do not know each other, introductions are very important. The leader should encourage a friendly team spirit and should discuss the meeting's importance. "Icebreaker" questions such as, " What is your favorite home-cooked meal?" are great for getting people involved.

As a group leader, you have several responsibilities as the meeting evolves. For example, you must guide the group to keep it on track, keep the discussion moving forward, and draw in unresponsive members of the group. You can ask the views and experiences of all attendees and ensure that one or a few speakers do not overpower the discussion.

If disagreement arises among group members, you should explore the reason for the disagreement and try to seek consensus. You should also make certain that all comments made by all attendees are understood by everyone. At times, you may need to re-state a viewpoint for a participant or clarify ideas. Summarizing progress and ensuring that time is spent effectively are also important as the meeting evolves. If necessary, identify the problem, goals and approaches.

As a group leader, you must watch the agenda as the meeting goes on, and take firm, polite action as required to conform to your timetable and objectives. Managing time during a meeting is easiest if you state the time allotted for each part of the meeting as it begins. For example, before discussing ideas for improving food temperatures on trayline, you can say: *We have 10 minutes for discussion on this. What are your ideas?* About eight minutes into the discussion, you can say: *We have two more minutes for discussion about this. Is there anyone who hasn't spoken yet who would like to offer an idea?* When necessary, you may have to close discussion and say something like: *Great! We have some good ides on this one. Now, we need to move on to our next agenda item.* If you find that one person is dominating the discussion, you may need to interrupt politely to give someone else an opportunity to contribute. For example, you may say: *Frank, thanks for giving us your thoughts on this. I am going to have to cut you off now so that we can hear from a few other people before our time runs out.*

At the end of the meeting, you should summarize the progress made. You should clarify the next actions to be taken, and see that everyone understands the action and their own tasks or assignments that may result from the meeting

When conducting a meeting, a leader often needs to generate discussion. To do this, you must first state the exact objective of the meeting at the outset. Stimulation occurs as you ask questions and explore ideas with the group. You also stimulate discussion by showing excitement and enthusiasm, by asking open-ended questions that allow people to present a broad range of ideas, and by thanking each person for speaking. On occasion, you may use a pre-meeting assignment to stimulate interest and discussion when the meeting actually

Your objective is to create a new system for receiving and storing food. What type of meeting would work best for this objective?

(Check your answer at the end of this chapter)

happens. For example, a meeting in which you will be exploring staffing adjustments might begin with a direction to attendees to consider this question: What is our greatest staffing challenge?

In a special technique called **brainstorming**, you ask participants to list ideas for solving a problem. To make this technique work, you need to establish firm ground rules. You explain that no idea is out of bounds, no idea is "good" or "bad," and discussion and judgment of ideas will be held until brainstorming is complete. This frees up participants to express thoughts. Even an idea that immediately proves ineffective can spark additional ideas. Unrestricted expression often allows everyone to think very freely, and can be a source of innovative solutions to problems. One idea that works very well is to use sticky notes during brainstorming and then group the similar notes together. This may assure that everyone contributes at least one idea.

During a meeting, each individual should be allowed to state opinions. As a group leader, you should make sure that all points made are considered objectively, and that ideas are examined fairly and openly. You also support members in meetings as you draw in non-contributing members and praise those who present their thoughts. When establishing ground rules for a meeting, you can make it clear that all ideas will be respected and that each attendee should participate.

As a group leader, you should observe participants and look for feedback, including nonverbal communication. Identify and resolve any resistance or conflicts that occur. If the discussion during a meeting brings out a conflict or a problem that is not part of the meeting's purpose, you can recognize it as important and set aside a separate time for it to be addressed. For example, during a meeting about trayline temperatures, imagine that one employee brings up the problem that there is never enough milk for trayline. You may say: *Thanks for bringing this up. This sounds like an important issue for us to review. Since it's not related to our objectives in this meeting, we will need to set aside time to focus on this separately. Would you please talk to me after the meeting and tell me more about your concern?* Sometimes, members of a group need special attention as a meeting evolves. Figure 11.2 indicates some basic strategies that can be used in troublesome situations.

Depending upon the type of meeting, you may want to consult with key personnel prior to the meeting to help plan the meeting. For instance, if your meeting is to review progress of department goals, you may want to meet with other interdisciplinary team leaders to collect information from them. You might also discuss with them any training needs others see that could be used during your training in-service meetings.

Glossary

Brainstorming
Asking all participants to suggest ideas for solving a problem

Figure 11.2 Strategies for Handling Group Problems

The Group Member Who:	Strategy to Use:
Wants to argue	Do not get involved. State/summarize the member's ideas and let the group decide upon their values.
Wants to help	Encourage the member to give ideas, especially when the discussion is veering off course.
Wants to discuss details	Acknowledge the member's points, but also remind member of the meeting's objective and the time limit that has been set.
Will not stop talking	Interrupt the group member tactfully and then ask a question to bring the participant back to the topic.
Is afraid to speak	Ask the group member easy questions, recognize earlier contributions, and make the person feel important.
Wants to be recognized	Recognize the individual and ask the person for unique solutions to the problems at hand.
Is not interested	Ask the group member how the discussion will impact him/her.
Acts superior	Recognize this person's ability and ask this person the most difficult and challenging questions.
Wants to show cleverness	Identify any trick questions and give them to the group for response.

Meeting Documentation

Documenting meetings is essential. A set of minutes, a summary of what has been discussed and decided, provides reference to everyone who has attended. Minutes can be used as reference for the next meeting on an ongoing project. They should include a summary of the action plan, assignments, and deadlines, as applicable. If appropriate, a recorder should be appointed to maintain a record of the meeting. This record should include at least:

✓ Name of meeting

✓ Date

✓ Time the meeting started and ended

✓ Name of the leader and recorder

✓ Names of those present

✓ Key points and discussion topics (brief)

✓ Action to take

✓ Who is responsible to take the action and related deadlines.

All participants should be provided a copy of the minutes. Corrections, if needed, should occur at the next meeting.

In meetings conducted for training purposes, documentation is important for proving that employees have received training. This documentation may be requested by inspectors and surveyors to verify that established standards are being met. A training meeting must include an attendance roster and a summary of the presentation.

Effective Speaking

Although we have been doing it since we were toddlers, each of us has more to learn about speaking. In a business environment, we have to speak with employees, supervisors, clients, team members, suppliers, and many more people routinely. Some spoken communications are one-on-one and informal. Others are group presentations and may be very formal.

A number of basic tips can help with speaking:

- ✓ Know what you are going to say and develop a plan or outline if you need it.
- ✓ Identify the most important points of the message and organize what you are going to say around these points.
- ✓ Deliver your most important point(s) first. This is when the receiver's attention is likely to be at its peak. It also helps the receiver focus on the remainder of your message.
- ✓ Concentrate on the listener. Speak to listeners' perspectives, and notice feedback.
- ✓ Speak enthusiastically. Your own interest and commitment to the importance of the message are contagious.
- ✓ Be prepared to back up the information you provide.
- ✓ Make eye contact.
- ✓ Share pride or compliments with employees when appropriate.
- ✓ Talk to uninterested employees after the meeting.

Figure 11.3 lists some of the traits and qualities that promote effective speaking.

Figure 11.3 Elements in Effective Speaking

• Confidence	• Friendliness	• Understanding	• Sensitivity
• Knowledge	• Objectivity	• Humility	• Charisma
• Organization	• Empathy	• Concern about Listener	• Concentration
• Pleasing Voice	• Open-Mindedness	• Responsiveness	• Spontaneity
• Concern	• Trustfulness	• Awareness of Situation	• Tact
• Control of Emotion	• Acceptable Appearance	• Humor	• Intelligence
• Language Command	• Honest	• Forcefulness	• Enthusiasm

Putting It Into Practice: 2

How would you handle an employee who seems uninterested in the meeting discussion?

(Check your answer at the end of this chapter)

In spoken communications, remember the value of silence and attention. Allow yourself to relax and listen to others. The truth is that most Certified Dietary Managers spend more time listening than they spend writing or speaking. A manager who is a good listener can obtain work-related information, be more effective in interpersonal relationships, and generate information necessary to make good decisions. There are several basic principles helpful in effective listening:

- ✓ Think about the central idea the speaker is trying to convey.
- ✓ Focus attention on what the speaker is saying, rather than on distracting factors.
- ✓ Listen objectively to what is being said, without trying to make an immediate judgment.

- ✓ Listen for more than facts. There may be a hidden agenda or a subtle message the speaker is hesitant to convey.
- ✓ Understand the speaker's basic ideas before discussing or disagreeing.
- ✓ Search for special meaning in the speaker's message. Some parts of the message are likely to be more important than others. On occasion, the really important message may be buried in the communication.
- ✓ Use feedback to express confusion or ask for clarification. Do not use "I" messages; emphasize "we" messages.

What about situations in which your spoken communication is a public presentation, or a more formal event? You may use presentations for a number of purposes, such as training or defending a budget or sharing information with colleagues, or asking for resources to implement a new idea.

In presentation, lecture alone can become boring. A wide variety of techniques make presentations more effective. These include:

- ✓ Demonstration: In this mode, you might show people how to do something. For example, you may demonstrate methods for garnishing plates, or taking an order for a meal. In training, practice should follow demonstration so that participants can adopt new skills.
- ✓ Discussion: This is a planned approach that uses group participation. For example, you may present basic information to a group and then permit the exchange of information through discussion. Stimulating questions, problems, or challenges help participants take ownership of the information and apply it meaningfully to themselves. This is also effective with small groups of 2 - 3 employees.
- ✓ Panel presentation: With this method, the Certified Dietary Manager may serve as a member of a small group. Frequently, panel members make a presentation, share discussion with each other, and then open up the floor for questions and further discussion from the audience. A panel presentation allows members of the audience to explore various aspects of the information, and consider various perspectives.
- ✓ Role playing: Role playing is a technique in which participants assume the role of someone else in a defined situation, and act it out. Role playing is often effective in training because it gives participants a chance to try and practice new skills in a safe environment.
- ✓ Case studies: A case study is a description of a specific situation, either real or imaginary. Events are reported without explanation, and attendees then use the experiences illustrated in the case as a basis for discussion. Certified Dietary Managers may use the case study approach to point out the need for additional space for preparation facilities, to discuss the need for a specific capital equipment item, or to help participants practice solving problems.

If you are giving a presentation, it is not unnatural to feel nervous in front of a group. This feeling can be managed, and practice and experience can make a big difference.

You are planning to implement a culture change in your facility. This will have a high impact on your department. When presenting this information, what presentation technique might be the most effective?

(Check your answer at the end of this chapter)

Presentation is often more effective if you:

- ✓ Organize your notes but refrain from reading a presentation word for word.
- ✓ Practice ahead of time so you will be comfortable with the material.
- ✓ Show up early and greet participants. Chat with them ahead of time to begin developing rapport and to learn about their interests in the subject matter.
- ✓ Make sure the room is comfortable and free of distractions.
- ✓ Check audio-visual equipment ahead of time and make sure it is working.
- ✓ If you are using slides, leave a colored page or interesting graphic or phrase on the screen as participants are entering the room. (Don't shock them with a white glare, or distract them with the content of your first "real" slide.)
- ✓ Make eye contact with the group.
- ✓ Check to make sure everyone can hear you, but refrain from blowing into a microphone.
- ✓ Use pauses to emphasize points.
- ✓ Vary your pace of speech and the inflection of your voice.
- ✓ Speak in a friendly, natural manner.
- ✓ Walk around the room as you speak, but don't pace.
- ✓ Surprise the audience to capture attention. This is a matter of personal style and professional propriety. Some presenters jump on desks, juggle balls to emphasize a point, or make other moves to keep the audience involved. Be sure that whatever techniques you choose are appropriate to the group and the setting.
- ✓ Use audio-visual aids to emphasize your points. Make sure the print is large enough to read.
- ✓ Use examples or stories to illustrate your points.
- ✓ Use appropriate humor in good taste.
- ✓ Use handouts when appropriate to reinforce content, but hold them until the end of the presentation. Otherwise, participants will read the handouts instead of listening to you.
- ✓ Keep the lights on.
- ✓ Show your enthusiasm for the subject.
- ✓ Be concise, and respect established timetables.
- ✓ Finish early so there is plenty of time for questions and discussion. The most meaningful communication often occurs during this phase of a presentation.
- ✓ When you take questions, repeat each question for the audience before answering it.

Audio-visual aids can help presentation. There are a few cautions, though. First of all, use aids to emphasize your points—not to present them. An effective slide, chart, or other aid contains few words, and may contain a picture or diagram that clarifies information. This is helpful because some people comprehend pictures more readily than words. This depends on individual learning style.

Let your visual aids support your content, but not distract from it. For example, a slide that contains animation with words flying across a page is likely to distract listeners' attention. Then, they won't be listening to you! A slide with too many words invites audience members to read instead of to hear.

Creative aids can be objects that you hold or pass among participants, recordings you play, or tools you use in a demonstration. In general, presenting your information through several media simultaneously enhances retention. People remember more of what they see and hear than what they hear alone. People remember the most when they also do or practice.

Meeting Follow-Up

If your meeting includes delegating staff members to accomplish a task after the meeting is over, it will be important to follow-up with those staff members before the next meeting. Depending on the task, it may be helpful to work with the staff members to develop a timeline to complete the tasks. Then, check with them to make sure they are following their timeline. Your role is to check progress and ensure that tasks are being completed.

Meeting follow-up also includes publishing meeting minutes. Some meeting experts have recommended that meeting minutes should be published and distributed within twenty-four hours of the meeting. That way, any errors are found and corrected in a timely manner rather than waiting weeks to review the proceedings.

END OF CHAPTER

Putting It Into Practice Questions & Answers

1. Your objective is to create a new system for receiving and storing food. What type of meeting would work best for this objective?

   A. *A teamwork meeting may be the best way to achieve this objective. It may take more than one meeting to accomplish this objective and you could divide your staff into small groups and assign them a task (such as creating a list of advantages or disadvantages to creating a new system).*

2. How would you handle an employee who seems disinterested in the meeting discussion?

   A. *Ask the staff member a specific question such as how the discussion might impact him/her or ask their opinion on the topic or meet with him/her after the meeting.*

3. You are planning to implement a culture change in your facility. This will have a high impact on your department. When presenting this information, what presentation technique might be the most effective?

   A. *Set up a panel discussion with other department supervisors, guests from other facilities that have implemented culture change, or even a state surveyor. Each of them could discuss the need for culture change from their perspective, why it is needed, and how it has been implemented in other facilities. This will allow staff members to hear other perspectives and provide them with valid reasons for accepting the culture change.*

CHAPTER 12

Meet Department Goals by Presenting Work Procedures and Plans

Overview and Objectives

Certified Dietary Managers are expected to meet department goals. You can best accomplish that by explaining to employees department resources, goals, responsibilities, and plans of action. This communication will be important in helping to motivate employees to accomplish department goals and objectives. Policy and procedures and performance standards represent an essential tool for presenting work procedures.

After completing this chapter, you should be able to:

- ✓ Explain department resources/equipment
- ✓ Utilize personnel organization and responsibilities chart
- ✓ Explain department responsibilities and liabilities
- ✓ Identify role responsibilities and performance standards
- ✓ Identify department tasks
- ✓ Review short-term and long-term goals for foodservice department
- ✓ Compare department goals against available resources
- ✓ Conduct staff discussion sessions to review organizational policies
- ✓ Follow standard sanitation and infectious disease control practices

Goals and Department Priorities

Chapter 10 introduced how a facility and foodservice department sets goals and objectives. Every successful organization conducts long-range and short-range planning on a regular basis, with the input of their managers. Goals outline the master plan for growth and the objectives outline the blueprint for achieving them. It is essential to have goals and objectives in order to know where and how your facility will grow. Goals and objectives represent the planning that must take place in any organization for it to be successful. A Certified Dietary Manager is involved in carrying out goals and objectives, as well as in translating them into specifics for the foodservice department. A foodservice department must also monitor progress towards goals and objectives and ensure that departmental activity follows the intended direction of the organization.

Meeting Goals and Priorities for Department

You have just come from your strategic planning meeting and know that you will have new and aggressive goals and priorities for your department for this next year. How do you meet those goals and also present work procedures and plans? Planning for your department has just begun. Planning means providing for the necessary resources to help you achieve your goals and then assigning staff members to the tasks you have identified.

As you begin this planning/implementation process, you must compare your goals and objectives to the resources you have available. For example, if your facility goal is to implement Culture Change, you will want to compare the objectives of the goal to your current staffing. That usually begins with a list of questions. Do you have enough staff to implement Culture Change? Can you justify additional staff? Will the Culture Change increase your food budget? Do you have the appropriate equipment to serve in the dining room? What other resources will you need to accomplish this goal? While you may not have all the answers to these questions, other Certified Dietary Managers can help you. In today's Web connected world, get connected to other Certified Dietary Managers through professional list serves such as the Association of Foodservice & Nutrition Personnel (AFNP) Online Member Community.

Once you have aligned your goals and resources, continue your planning by making a list of the tasks your department will have to accomplish to implement Culture Change. This task list will help determine what staff members should be assigned.

Finally, you can begin to meet department goals by presenting work procedures and plans. To accomplish this, the Certified Dietary Manager has to lead people. The best planning will not succeed unless the manager motivates employees to help carry out the plan, and directs and coaches employees in their actions.

Motivation

Motivation is an internal force that makes people do something in order to reach a goal. Motivation comes from inside a person. A Certified Dietary Manager cannot force motivation upon an employee, but can encourage or facilitate this internal process. A manager can provide job conditions that help employees to attain goals that have been developed internally. It becomes the mission of the manager, then, to match the employees' goals with those of the department.

Matching employee goals with those of the department begins during the interview. You can show them on the organizational chart where their position fits within the organization. Review the job description to make sure they understand the job expectations. Explain what resources the department has in terms of budget for both equipment and training. This information will help the potential employee decide if they are a good fit for your facility.

Managers must hire people capable of doing the jobs that are assigned to them. If employees are not capable of doing the jobs, no amount of training or motivational support will make them effective. Moreover, they must also be willing to do the job. They can have the ability to do the job, but if they don't really want to do it, they probably won't be effective. The third part of this interconnection is this: Employees can be willing to do the job and perfectly capable of doing the job, but if they are not shown how to do the job, they still may not be effective. On-the-job training is an effective motivator.

Once employees are capable, willing, and trained, the ongoing challenge is to figure out how to get them to do it, and do it graciously and consistently. It is important to understand why people do what they do, and to know what motivates them. Employees must have a reason for wanting to do what managers want them to do, and that comes from within them. To motivate employees, it is important to know them. The goal is to create a delicate set of conditions wherein they can meet their needs while doing what managers want them to do.

Theories of Motivation

Several theories of motivation address the question of why people do things. Some approaches take the stance that most people strive to reach their full potential. How far they have advanced toward reaching their full potential will determine what motivates them. The idea here is that if a manager knows where on this spectrum of *potential* employees are, the manager will know what motivates employees and can therefore provide the appropriate incentives.

There are many theories of motivation. The best-known theory in this arena is psychologist Abraham Maslow's hierarchy of needs. He states that individuals' specific needs drive behavior. Maslow's hierarchy of needs represents the order in which these needs become motivators of human behavior. These are illustrated in Figure 12.1.

Maslow says that the physiological needs of survival, such as food and water, come first. When these needs are being met, an individual moves from focusing on them to the next level of needs, involving security and safety, such as stability, protection, and freedom from fear and chaos. Next, social needs motivate behavior. These revolve around friendship, love, and the need to belong.

As each of these primary needs is met, the individual moves to a level of ego needs centered on self-esteem. One of them is the desire for self-esteem or self-respect, and for the freedom that provides such self-esteem. Pride and shame are essential motivators. Be sure to use compliments effectively. Another is the desire for the esteem of others, including status, fame, glory, dominance, recognition, attention, importance, dignity, and appreciation. The need for esteem gives rise in some people to the need for power as a way of commanding the esteem of others. Satisfaction of the need for self-esteem leads to feelings of self-confidence, strength, and worth. When these needs go unsatisfied, they produce feelings of inferiority, weakness, and helplessness.

It is important to recognize not everyone is motivated by the same thing. A Certified Dietary Manager can use these ideas to help an employee who has personal problems that relate to job security. The manager can emphasize pay rates, promotion opportunities, job security, and related aspects of the

Putting It Into Practice: 1

During an interview a potential employee explains that she left her previous job because there was no teamwork or camaraderie among the employees. What level of motivation does this clue you to?

(Check your answer at the end of this chapter)

Figure 12.1 Maslow's Hierarchy of Needs with Job Context Examples

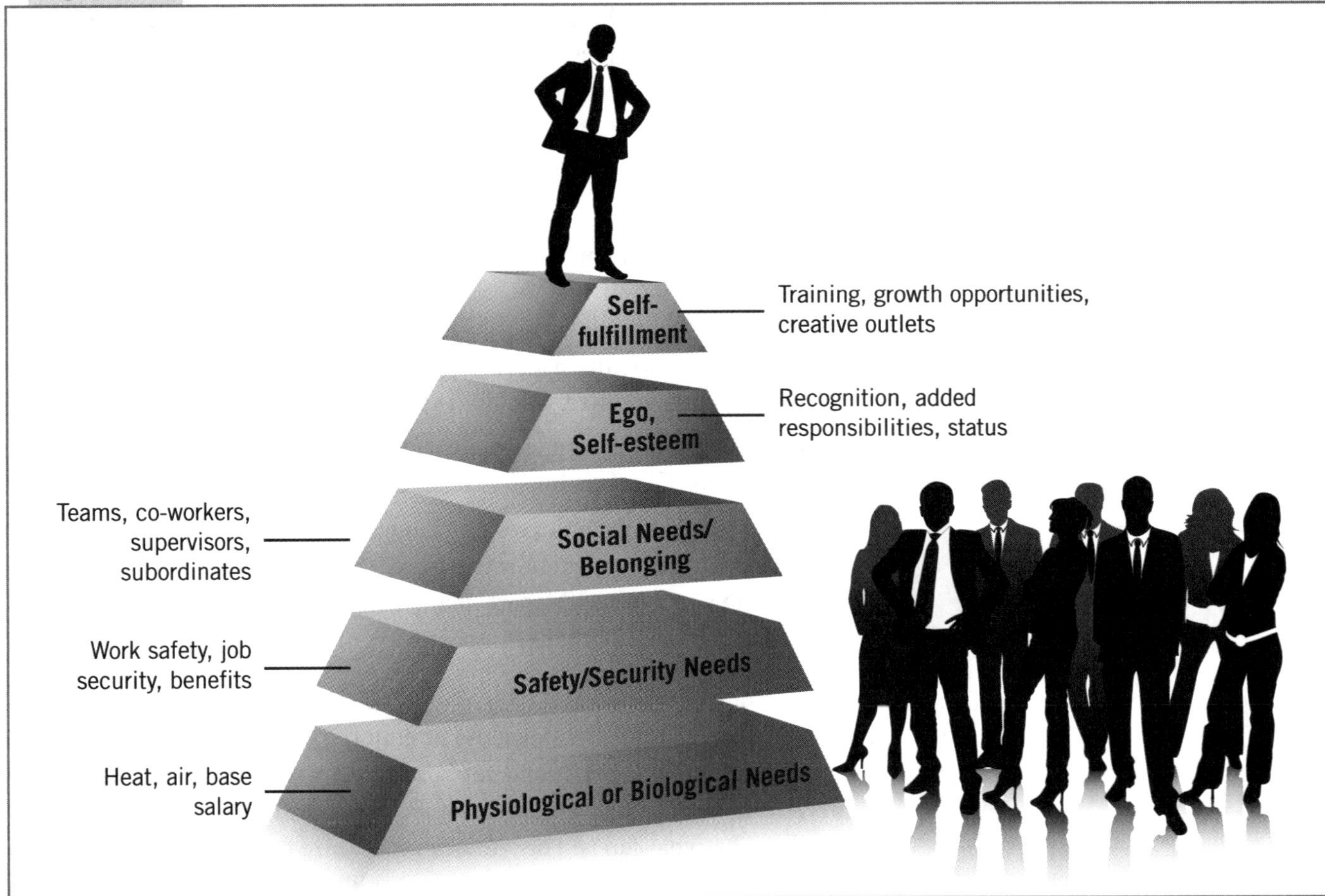

Source: Adapted Maslow, 1954

work to help the staff member see how a concern for physical needs might be met on the job. What if the manager believes a staff member is concerned about social needs? The manager might emphasize how these needs can be met through work-related activities. Creative supervisors can become aware of specific employee concerns and address them. For example, have an in-service on social diversity.

Employee needs can be met on the job in a variety of ways:

- ✓ Physiological Needs: rest breaks, pay checks, bonuses
- ✓ Safety/Security Needs: consistent application of work rules, policies, non-threatening environment, proper working equipment, effective safety management programs
- ✓ Social Needs: committee assignments, teamwork, friendship with fellow employees, sponsoring social activities such as bowling teams, employee picnics, newsletters
- ✓ Ego Needs: awards (e.g., weight-loss groups or employee of month), attendance at seminars, recognition
- ✓ Self-fulfillment Needs: training programs or tuition reimbursement; challenges on the job; involvement in planning of goals, objectives, and budgets; creative projects.

It is generally true that:

- ✓ The staff member who is interested in the work is more likely to have internal motivation, which will benefit the employee, the foodservice department, and the organization itself.
- ✓ The staff member who can identify with the organization and believe in it will be more willing to help the organization than will one motivated only by punishment and reward.
- ✓ Many employees do not consciously recognize their personal goals or needs, so motivation may be largely subconscious. Few people make an effort to analyze themselves objectively. The Certified Dietary Manager is challenged to recognize aspects of motivation that the employee may not even be able to verbalize.
- ✓ Money is not a primary and important motivator for many employees. In fact, money is often a maintenance factor, not a motivation factor.
- ✓ Competition among employees or groups of staff members within the same organization does not generally motivate. Therefore, many types of competition within a foodservice department (such as among service staff on different shifts) can have a negative impact.

From this information about motivation, you can see that as a Certified Dietary Manager, you need to pay close attention to what motivates employees. By providing for basic needs and supporting the need for self-fulfillment and achievement, you can help employees *want* to perform on the job. Based on the above theories, what can you do? You can recognize the needs of your employees. Then, you can meet these needs by providing fair compensation for work, opportunities for teamwork and socialization, training and challenges, and rewards. To motivate employees, you must communicate the objectives of your operation and involve each employee in fulfilling these objectives.

In addition, you can nurture a positive work climate, empower employees, build a team, give meaningful feedback, and provide recognition. Each of these strong motivators is discussed in remaining sections of this chapter.

Work Climate

Work climate refers to how it feels to work in a given environment. It is usually initiated by Certified Dietary Managers, and is often closely intertwined with the facility's philosophy. However, it is also greatly influenced at lower levels by the attitudes and actions of managers and supervisors.

A positive work climate supports employees in their needs for fulfillment and achievement. It maintains a positive, supportive environment for employees. Essentially, work climate becomes the state of mind employees have on the job.

The concept of work climate essentially states that how people feel about the job affects how they perform.

Interestingly, work climate affects client service, too. Employees who feel positive about their jobs tend to treat clients very positively, too. Employees who are unhappy on the job may tend to complain to clients, or perform their

work grudgingly. All of this affects customer/client service and the image of the department.

Some of the factors that tend to promote a positive work climate include:

- ✓ A role model of respect and support
- ✓ A belief in the value and talents of every individual in the organization
- ✓ Support for employees' needs, especially training and development
- ✓ A strong value for listening to others
- ✓ Managerial attention to problems that create stress among employees
- ✓ Encouragement of teamwork and enthusiasm
- ✓ A sense of calm, even when there are deadlines and time pressures
- ✓ Frequently expressed praise for the value of employees' accomplishments.
- ✓ Emphasize team work whenever possible.

Empowerment

Another idea that relates very closely to work climate is called empowerment. In contrast with old management theories that were highly autocratic, empowerment means that a Certified Dietary Manager gives the power to an employee to take action. Empowerment provides an opportunity for employees to achieve. As such, it is strongly motivating.

How does it work? Clearly, a manager cannot just say to employees, "Do whatever you want." So, a manager has to provide direction to this process. To empower employees, you can take several steps.

1. **Define the objectives very clearly:** Tell employees what the department is trying to achieve, and keep these objectives in the forefront by discussing them often.
2. **Clarify policies so that employees have a solid framework for decisions they will make on their own:** For example, if you have a policy of always providing a substitution for a client who is unhappy with the food, make sure employees know this and follow the policy.
3. **Define the limits:** Tell employees what situations you support them in handling on their own, and what situations you wish to become involved in. For example, you might empower employees to accept a complaint, but ask to become involved if a complaining client is becoming abusive or violent.
4. **Communicate and coach:** As employees take power into their own hands, be accessible to coach employees. Be willing to provide support at any time, and to discuss actions after the fact to help an employee develop a greater range of skills. Ask to be informed, at least after the fact, about information that is important to you as a manager.

Glossary

Empowerment
When management gives power to an employee to take action

Consider this example of using empowerment to achieve a department goal of improving customer/client service:

A waitstaff takes a complaint from a client in the dining room. The client says the roast beef was too tough. The waitstaff does not have to call a supervisor. He knows, through policy that you have established, that he has the power to do what he thinks will help the client feel satisfied. He immediately offers an alternative, which the client graciously accepts. He brings the client a new plate of food. He also passes along the concern about the roast beef to his supervisor and documents the substitute.

In checking further, the food production supervisor may bring the problem to the cook who prepared the beef, asking for help in solving the quality issue, and now empowering the cook as well.

Team Building

Yet another technique that is critical to the success of every foodservice operation is team building. A team approach recognizes that each employee is not working alone. Instead, all employees are working together to accomplish defined objectives. The parallel is a sports team. On a football team, the action of each player critically affects the bottom line—who wins the game. Players have to work together very cohesively, with superb coordination, in order to win.

Actually, the same ideas hold true in a foodservice department, as well as in a facility itself. The systems approach to management says that all the parts work together to accomplish the job. Serving a meal, for example, requires the coordinated efforts of people who purchase, receive, store, and withdraw food; people who prepare food; and people who serve food. When the meal is successful, it is successful because everyone on the team performed well and worked together. Even dishwashers need this recognition. Empathize by perceiving what it is like to do their job for 40 hours per week (i.e., key contributors to sanitation and safety, preventing foodborne illnesses).

When a sense of teamwork does not exist, efforts can become disjointed and the work flow within systems can deteriorate. The result is generally poor performance and poor quality. To encourage teamwork, you can take a number of actions:

- ✓ Communicate objectives. A football coach tells the team, "We are going to win!" As a Certified Dietary Manager, you tell the staff, "We are going to serve these clients the best food they have ever eaten!" or "We are going to re-define the meaning of excellent service." A common objective draws people together.
- ✓ Believe in your team. Your belief that the team can perform has a tremendous impact on what happens. Employees who are not sure what they *can* do will respond to your belief in their capabilities. Instilling confidence is a great motivator, too.
- ✓ Use enthusiasm. Your enthusiasm is contagious and is a key factor in getting the team truly excited about meeting objectives. It also contributes to a very positive work climate.

One of your department goals is to reduce food costs. What could you do to empower your chef to help in achieving this goal?

(Check your answer at the end of this chapter)

✓ Give team members roles and responsibilities. Make the contribution of each team member clear. This is done through job descriptions and performance standards.

✓ Use informal leaders. While a formal leader may have a position on the organization chart that defines authority over someone else, every organization also has informal leaders. An informal leader is one who, through personality factors, tends to gain the cooperation of others. Informal leaders can help support the objectives of the team and help support each "player."

✓ Provide the resources needed. To play football, the players need protective equipment, a ball, a field, and more. The coach makes sure all these resources are available. In a foodservice department, the Certified Dietary Manager needs to equip the employee team with everything they need to do their work and meet their objectives.

✓ Provide opportunities for fun. Letting off steam from a tiring day, enjoying an appropriate joke, or attending a departmental picnic are all examples of how members of a team can have fun together. When work is finished and employees are relaxing, more team building takes place.

✓ Resolve conflicts. Conflicts naturally arise among employees from time to time. An effective manager recognizes conflict, and works openly toward a resolution to keep the team together.

✓ Reward and recognize the team. As the team meets objectives, this should become cause for cheering, celebration, and public recognition. These actions reinforce the actions of the team, and provide fulfillment to each team member.

Through effective teamwork, a Certified Dietary Manager finds that a group accomplishes more, employees gain satisfaction, and systems function very well. Thus, a manager truly needs to function as a coach and build each employee's identity as part of the team.

One of the objectives for this chapter is to *Follow standard sanitation and infectious disease control practices.* That objective may seem out of place when we are discussing motivating employees to meet department goals. Sanitation and food safety are the responsibility of Certified Dietary Managers and motivating employees to implement food safety principles will be one of your more difficult tasks. Review the article in the *Management in the News* section at the end of this chapter for specific strategies in motivating staff to keep food safe.

Tools for Meeting Goals and Presenting Work Procedures and Plans

Meeting goals by presenting work procedures and plans takes motivation as well as tools. Three of those tools are the organization chart, performance standards, and policies and procedures.

Organization Chart

Note the word organization in organization chart. Remember in the first part of this chapter in planning, you created a list of tasks that will be required to accomplish your goals? As you group these tasks and decide which staff

members will be assigned to them, you are organizing. Use your organization chart to help you with this task. The organization chart illustrates your division of labor. The organization chart can you help you determine to which employee the tasks should be delegated.

Delegation is assigning tasks to the appropriate employee within your department. Delegation is one way to develop the potential of your employees. Remember, some employees might be motivated by the opportunity to take on added responsibility. As you delegate, consider the following:

✓ Tasks must be communicated clearly and effectively.

✓ Employees must be empowered with the authority to accomplish these tasks.

Another tool to assist you in presenting work procedures and plans are performance standards.

Performance Standards

To ensure that work is done well, you need to have a definition of what "well" means. This definition must be objective and very specific. It must allow you to measure quality in a definable manner.

One type of standard that serves as an essential management tool is a performance standard. **Performance standards** are specific statements describing the outcomes of the work performed. Here are some simple examples: A trayline employee is responsible for portioning food on trays. Performance standards specify what the task is, how it is to be done, and how well it has to be done.

✓ Items served match the list of food ordered, as specified on each tray ticket. (In this example, the what part is *items served*; the how is *match portions*; the how well is as *specified on each tray ticket.*)

✓ Food portions on tray match portions specified on each tray ticket. (In this example, the what is *food portions* on tray; the how is *match portions*; the how well is *specified on each tray ticket.*)

A performance standard for a food production job might specify that:

✓ Employee prepares food in accordance with standardized recipes.

✓ Employee prepares food in the quantity specified on the daily food production schedule.

✓ Employee delivers food to the service area by the time scheduled on the daily food production schedule.

✓ Endpoint cooking temperatures meet the standards specified on each recipe, and are accurately documented on the temperature log.

To develop meaningful performance standards, you should meet these three criteria:

✓ The standard must address the outcome in specific, clear, complete, and accurate terms. It should tell the employee exactly what you want. There should be nothing that is confusing or could be misunderstood.

✓ The standard must describe how well with measurable or observable behavior. "Good" and "well" are subjective terms, so you want to avoid them. The supervisor will use this standard to evaluate the employee's work performance, and the supervisor needs an objective standard to assure fairness.

Delegation
Passing authority for tasks or assigning duties downward through the organization chart

Performance Standard
Specific statements describing the outcomes of the work to be performed

✓ The standard should explain the "action" verb. For example, if the action verb is 'document,' the performance standard would require the employee to document.

An effective performance standard is within the physical and mental capabilities of the employees and is realistic in the working environment. If expectations are unrealistic, employees will be destined to fail in meeting them. If you discover that a certain standard is not being met on a consistent basis, you should re-examine the standard before proceeding with other interventions. Many Certified Dietary Managers involve employees in developing fair and realistic standards for their own work. Needless to say, each standard must adhere to company policies, company goals, and applicable legal and moral constraints.

While we all want performance to be perfect, we realize that this is not possible. So, it is not realistic to specify 100 percent compliance with every performance standard. What we can do, though, is specify a realistic and acceptable gauge of performance. Often, this gauge is expressed in terms of numbers. A number may express speed, quantity, or rate. For example, an accuracy rate is a number. Here is an example: Food is portioned accurately, as specified on each tray ticket, at a rate of 99 percent accuracy. Another time a number might measure rate of output, or productivity, such as: Employee accurately sets up the snack assembly station within a period of 15 minutes.

Developing Performance Standards. The steps for developing a performance standard are as follows:

Step 1: Using the organization chart, list all the job titles in the department. For example, your list may include Buffet Server, Receiving Clerk, Morning Cook, Afternoon Cook, Pot Washer, and others.

Step 2: Review the job descriptions for all of these positions and list the tasks or sets of tasks that comprise a single activity. For example, the tasks of "sanitizing pots" will require a performance standard, or, refer to your task list for meeting a goal.

Step 3: Write a performance standard for each task; seek employee input.

Step 4: Train employees.

Step 5: Evaluate performance (ongoing).

Performance Standards as a Communications Tool. In the process of interviewing employees, you will want to explain that your operation uses performance standards. This prepares a candidate for the commitment to quality that you will expect. You may choose to show a candidate a sample performance standard that relates to the position the candidate is applying for.

Training for employees follows from the job analysis, the job description and the performance standards. Whatever your procedures and standards specify must be included in both new employee orientation and ongoing employee training. For example, if you have developed a performance standard about documenting information for HACCP records, then your training must include the details of

Putting It Into Practice: 3

Your department goal is: Ensure the health and safety of our clients.

One objective is: Provide annual sanitation and safety training.

Write one performance standard for the objective that would tell the employee WHAT you want, HOW to do it, and HOW WELL it should be done.

(Check your answer at the end of this chapter)

how to do this (the procedure), as well as the description of how an employee will know it has been done effectively (the performance standard).

After an employee has been trained, you can evaluate the outcome of the work based on performance standards. Evaluation helps you take the next appropriate action to ensure performance standards are met. This action may be to reward an employee who is meeting standards, to provide more training, to revise the training program, or to discipline an employee.

After working through these steps, if you discover that employees are not meeting a standard, you need to determine why not. You may need to provide more or more effective training. Or, you may need to revise the performance standard to be more clear. When one particular employee is not meeting the standard but others are, this may be your clue that the employee needs coaching and direction, or even disciplinary action.

It can be easy just to assume that all employees know what you expect of them. However, this simply is not true. It would not be fair to evaluate employees based on unwritten rules or your own judgments about what constitutes "good work." Instead, you are spelling out expectations through performance standards. Every time you spell out an expectation to employees, you are increasing the likelihood that quality work will really occur!

Most of us respond very well to standards because they place us in control. We know how to tell whether we are doing what someone else expects us to do. As we meet standards, we can feel satisfied and confident about our own work. Managed effectively, performance standards can boost morale and pride and help meet department goals.

Another tool for meeting goals by presenting work procedures and plans are department policy and procedures.

Policies and Procedures

In every organization, a set of documents called policies and procedures serve as essential reference. A **policy** describes an organization's approach to a certain situation. A **procedure** details the steps in completing a task. The two are combined into a document called a "policy and procedure." For example, a policy and procedure about washing dishes may first state a policy that clean dishes are required for sanitation and for aesthetic reasons. Then, it would detail the steps involved in washing dishes.

Specific, documented policies and procedures may be required by third-party entities such as OSHA, CMS, TJC, your local health department, or others. Refer to Figure 12.2 for a sample policy and procedure on social networking.

For your own department, you should maintain a set of written policies and procedures. There are several reasons for this. They:

✓ Serve as reference for anyone unfamiliar with the policy or procedure associated with a task.

✓ Serve as a communication tool within the department when presenting procedural plans.

Glossary

Policy
Describes an organization's approach to a certain situation

Procedure
Details the steps in carrying out a policy

Figure 12.2 Sample Policy and Procedure: Social Networking

Policy Number: 684 Revised: 3/1/xx Approved by: ______________________

POLICY

[Facility Name} will be viewed by the public as a professional organization. This professional image extends to all types of media including but not limited to: blogs, social networking sites (e.g. Facebook, MySpace), professional networks (e.g. LinkedIn), photo sharing, video sharing, microblogging, podcasts.

PROCEDURE

1. Use your own personal e-mail when engaging in any social media or professional social networking such as LinkedIn.
2. If you choose to list your work affiliation in your personal profile such as on Facebook, then all posts to that network should be professional and respectful in nature. Your online presence reflects the facility.
3. If you choose to list your work affiliation in your personal profile, do not "friend" anyone that you do not personally know.
4. Refer to IT policies and procedures regarding using personal e-mail and social networking at work.
5. Keep client information confidential. Never use a client's information in any form of online media.
6. Personal blogs should have a disclosure statement so readers are aware that the content of the blog is personal.

- ✓ Serve as a communication tool for people external to the department.
- ✓ May be required by inspectors or surveyors examining your practices.
- ✓ Serve as reference for those who may succeed you.

To make policies and procedures easy to understand, present each one in a consistent, organized format. For example, one Certified Dietary Manager may maintain a notebook divided into sections with policies and procedures for:

- ✓ Departmental organization (including an organization chart)
- ✓ Menu planning
- ✓ Purchasing and inventory
- ✓ Food production
- ✓ Customer/Client service
- ✓ Special services and catering
- ✓ Clinical services
- ✓ Client rights
- ✓ HIPAA compliance and confidentiality
- ✓ Scheduling and staffing
- ✓ Personnel issues
- ✓ Emergency contact information
- ✓ Disaster management.

Each policy and procedure should have a clear identifier. Some facilities use both numbers and titles. Any time a procedure is changed, update the document. Maintain policies and procedures in a readily accessible format. In some organizations, these appear on the corporate intranet (computer network), which makes them accessible to everyone. In other organizations, notebooks are available in several locations throughout the department. Always keep a secure copy of documents in case they become damaged or get lost.

Depending on the structure of your organization, you may maintain sets of institution-wide policies and procedures for reference in your own area. At the same time, copies of some of your procedures may be maintained as reference in other areas. A procedure addressing how to order in-house catering services, for example, may be essential reference in other departments. If this is the case, make sure that as you revise procedures, you distribute new copies to those concerned.

How do you communicate new or revised procedures? While maintaining complete documentation is important, it is not the primary or the best means of communicating. As procedures change, think about everyone who may be affected. This includes employees in your own department, as well as in others. Practically, procedures do not change until people do things differently. The basic principles of communication and managing change apply to making new procedures take effect.

In designing policies and procedures and managing daily activity in a foodservice department, consider some of the guidelines you must follow and use them as tools. For example, your policies and procedures may need to support compliance with CMS regulations, OSHA requirements, health department code, and other standards. These often become useful tools that can help you decide what to address and include in your own documents. However, the precise methodology of meeting these guidelines will be up to you as a Certified Dietary Manager. You will need to base decisions on how systems function in your facility, the flow of work, the responsibility and accountability detailed in your organization chart, and other practical factors.

Most healthcare facilities use policies and procedures to describe how to carry out facility missions. However, standard operating procedures (SOP) are also used in other industries. Using job analysis and performance standards, you can develop standard operating procedures. A particular SOP may apply to several distinct job descriptions. For example, you may have four trayline positions with certain tasks that overlap. An SOP for portioning food on trays may apply to all.

Standard operating procedures support your quality and performance standards. They are tools for achieving one of the basic tasks of management. Like policies and procedures, all SOPs should be maintained in a notebook or manual for easy reference by all employees, and should be kept up-to-date as procedures change.

Policies and procedures, SOPs, and performance standards represent essential tools for managing the quality of work and should be used when presenting work procedures and plans.

Management in the News

Motivating Staff to Keep Food Safe

by Janell Meyer, MBA

All foodservice employees are responsible for ensuring the food served in their operation is safe. However, it is the responsibility of managers and supervisors to monitor and motivate employees to consistently handle food safety.

Making time for food safety is not easy, given the other daily pressures employees and managers experience. But food safety should not be taken lightly. The numbers speak for themselves. In 2000, the USDA Economic Research Service estimated the cost from more than three million cases of foodborne illnesses from five bacterial pathogens at $6.9 billion per year. These estimates included personal medical expenses, productivity losses, and costs of premature deaths. This does not include the cost to the operations that served the unsafe food. National Restaurant Association figures show that one foodborne illness outbreak can cost an operation thousands of dollars and even result in closure.

Safe food is food that has been handled correctly from "farm to fork," and is food that will not cause an illness in the person who consumes it. Foods that have not been handled correctly have the potential of making customers ill, especially those in high-risk populations: the elderly, infants and young children, pregnant women, and others who are ill or on medications that cause compromised immune systems.

As a foodservice operator, what are the keys to keeping food safe? Three safe food-handling practices stand out as the areas under which foodservice employees have control: preventing cross contamination, time and temperature controls, and good personal hygiene—including compliance with employee health policies. It is important for foodservice management to have standard operating procedures (SOPs) that address best practices when handling food. SOPs provide structure for an operation, and help to facilitate training and consistency in how food is handled.

Preventing Cross Contamination

By keeping raw and ready-to-eat food separate, and clean food contact surfaces away from soiled, your operation can prevent cross contamination. Cross contamination occurs when pathogens spread from an employee, work surface, or contaminated food to another food item or food contact surface. Employees should use separate equipment for different foods, prepare ready-to-eat foods before handling raw foods in the same prep area or establish different work zones, and clean and sanitize work surfaces, equipment, and utensils after each task. Cross contamination can happen at almost any stage of food handling. Vigilance is required for the entire flow of food—from the back door to the customer.

Avoiding Time and Temperature Abuse

Time and temperature abuse can also occur anywhere within the flow of food through the foodservice operation. Keeping cold foods cold (below 41°F) and hot foods hot (above 135°F) is a good start. Using calibrated thermometers to accurately check temperatures and then recording these temperatures at specified times in the

(Continued...)

Motivating Staff to Keep Food Safe *(Continued)*

food flow is an excellent standard operating procedure. This gives you the knowledge and documentation that cooked foods have reached the required safe end-point cooking temperature, leftovers have cooled and been reheated in the required time frame, and all food has been stored at safe temperature.

Ensuring Proper Personal Hygiene

Poor personal hygiene by food handlers is often the cause of foodborne illness outbreaks. A Centers for Disease Control and Prevention (CDC) January 2011 report estimates that 58 percent of foodborne illnesses are caused by norovirus. Often norovirus is transmitted to food through food handlers with poor hand hygiene. Food handlers' personal hygiene consists of: hand practices—including handwashing, glove use and bare-hand contact with ready-to-eat food; personal cleanliness; and clothing, including hair restraints and jewelry.

Besides having personal hygiene policies in place, training employees about these policies and monitoring them in your foodservice operation, it is important as a manager or supervisor to always model good personal hygiene habits. Handwashing is the most important part of personal hygiene. Encouraging and modeling proper handwashing procedures and frequency is a powerful managerial tool. This can demonstrate to employees that handwashing is critical.

Good personal hygiene is much more difficult when an employee is ill. Having a set policy that conforms to state regulation and encourages employees not to come to work ill is good practice. Having a back-up plan in place to cover for ill employees is also important.

I know the keys to good food safety practices, but how am I supposed to get all of that done? It starts with making food safety a priority in your operation. Consider the risks of not making it a priority. A foodborne illness can be a life-or-death situation for certain populations. How many people are you willing to make sick? Financially, is your operation capable of closing down for several days or weeks and dealing with possible lawsuits? Most institutions rely on their food services for all or most of their food needs. How will clientele be nourished if your operation is closed down during a foodborne illness outbreak investigation? Thoughtfully weighing these considerations and risks should bring even the most financially concerned top management to this realization: Food safety is a priority goal.

Plenty of challenges exist for managers and supervisors. They can get in the way of consistent safe food practices. The employee turnover rate in many operations makes it seem cost-prohibitive to offer thorough food safety training, let alone ongoing training. When you are able to offer training, is it in the best form for the employee to learn and put into practice? The current workforce is very diverse—culturally, educationally, and generationally. The "one size fits all" approach to food safety training is rarely effective for all employees.

If only you had the time and resources available to you to individualize your food safety training for each employee. Besides offering them the knowledge needed, what really motivates each employee to handle food safely? Are they motivated internally by such things as getting personal satisfaction from knowing they have done a good job, or by knowing they plan to eat the food, too, and don't want to get sick? Are they motivated by external forces like the supervisor telling them they have done a good job handwashing today or a manager giving them a Safe Food Employee of the Month award?

What motivates your employees to handle food safely? Knowing what motivates your employees and what they see as barriers to safe food handling can be very helpful when providing training, as well as monitoring needed to ensure the food served in your operation is safe. See the Staff Motivational Strategies chart provided with this article.

Employees are the "last line of defense" and can potentially prevent or cause a foodborne illness. Supervisors and managers can remove barriers and help motivate employees to follow safe food handling

(Continued...)

Motivating Staff to Keep Food Safe *(Continued)*

practices. By communicating consistent messages to employees, providing needed resources such as training, offering rewards and discipline if needed, supervisors and managers can motivate employees.

It's also important to recognize that some employees are motivated internally— it just makes them feel good to do their job well and this includes following safe food practices. Usually employees are both internally (self) motivated as well as motivated by external interactions. Managing with this understanding of your workforce can help operations consistently provide safe food.

Staff Motivational Strategies

If the Employee Says/Exhibits This...	Try...
"I never see any of the managers washing their hands."	Remembering you are a role model and sometimes the easiest way to motivate employees is by showing them how important food safety is to you through your actions.
"That's not what the other supervisor told me to do."	Making sure communication from various managers and supervisors is consistent. Employees find it difficult to interpret "mixed messages." SOPs can provide a written reference to ensure consistency.
"I can't take temperatures of the foods because I can never find a thermometer around here."	Providing needed resources to employees so they can successfully implement safe food practices.
"We've always done it this way and no one has ever gotten sick."	Reminding employees that most foodborne illnesses go unreported and encourage them to change their ways for the sake of the customers. Many times employees also eat the food, so keeping food safe for self-consumption may also serve as a motivator.
An employee does not wash his/her hands using the recommended procedure.	Coaching the employee on proper handwashing procedures, and place visual reminders near the handwashing sink. It is important not to let this slide by without comment. Other employees are watching. It will send the message that proper handwashing is not important.
An employee is observed consistently out of compliance with the standard operating procedure on personal hygiene.	Implementing the operation's disciplinary process. If there is not a written process, consider developed procedures. Consistent actions toward employees is important.
An employee consistently follows safe food practices to prevent cross contamination.	Providing verbal praise frequently. Written performance evaluations may also include evaluation of food safety practices. Consider a food safety recognition program for employees who consistently follow safe food practices.

Janell Meyer, MBA, is the grant coordinator for multiple USDA funded food safety research projects at Iowa State University, Ames, IA. She is a ServSafe® instructor and has worked in the foodservice industry for over 20 years. Contact her at jrcmeyer@iastate.edus.

Co-authoring this article is Susan Arendt, PhD, RD, and Catherine Strohbehn, PhD, RD, CPFS. Arendt is a faculty member at Iowa State University and serves as principle investigator on two USDA food safety research projects (see Resources sidebar for more information). Strohbehn is certified by the National Environmental Health Association as a professional in food safety. She is the 2010 recipient of the NSF International Food Safety Leadership Educator Award. Strohbehn serves as director of the Iowa State University Extension Food Safety Project, which provides online science-based information and resources to consumers and those in retail foodservices at: www.iowafoodsafety.orgs.

END OF CHAPTER

Putting It Into Practice Questions & Answers

1. During an interview a potential employee explains that she left her previous job because there was no teamwork or camaraderie among the employees. What level of motivation does this clue you to?

   A. *It sounds as if this person values co-workers, teamwork, and belonging. That would be the Social Needs level. In managing this person, help her to feel accepted; assign her to work with others in team situations.*

2. One of your department goals is to reduce food costs. What could you do to empower your chef to help in achieving this goal?

   A. *Allow the chef to substitute ingredients, if necessary, rather than purchase what is needed from a local store. (e.g. substituting tomato sauce for tomato chunks) Make sure the chef understands that recipes used for meeting special diets cannot be changed unless the nutrient value of the substitute is the same as the original ingredient.*

3. Your department goal is: Ensure the health and safety of our clients. One objective is: Provide annual sanitation and safety training. Write one performance standard for the objective that would tell the employee WHAT you want, HOW to do it, and HOW WELL it should be done.

   A. *Each staff member is certified in sanitation and participates in continuing education as measured by random testing and performance appraisals.*

CHAPTER 13

Teach Employees

Overview and Objectives

This unit of six chapters is all about Develop Personnel and Communications. A key part of developing personnel is training. As you train, you build the value of people in your facility, but you also promote motivation, positive morale, and superior performance. In training, you plan to achieve results and behaviors that align with your facility's needs and objectives.

After completing this chapter, you should be able to:

✓ Orient new employees to facility procedures

✓ Conduct/arrange in-service training

✓ Instruct employees on compliance with HIPAA guidelines

✓ Provide follow-up after orientation

✓ Ensure employees' compliance with safe food preparation practices

✓ Identify training resources and needs

✓ Develop and implement training programs

✓ Inspect all areas of department for sanitary conditions

Teaching employees involves training content, techniques, evaluation, and the trainers themselves. Training improves all aspects of the foodservice department. It is important to remember as you review this material that training is not a one-time event, it is a process.

Training Overview

Maslow's Hierarchy of Needs (Chapter 12) presents the idea that each of us has a need to grow and develop. Mastering new skills and realizing potential are tremendous motivators. Training can meet employees' basic needs and foster good morale. Training serves other purposes, too. For a facility, effective training can:

✓ Reduce the occurrence of injuries, accidents, and mistakes

✓ Improve quality of services and/or products

✓ Improve productivity

✓ Reduce turnover rate and recruitment expenses

✓ Bring about better management of resources, often with associated cost reductions

✓ Improve compliance with regulations and standards

✓ Support implementation of new procedures or techniques, new systems, or new equipment.

All foodservice employees, those new on the job and those with years of experience, can benefit from effective training programs. The TJC, OSHA, most state licensing laws, and many health department regulations require specific ongoing employee training programs, which may specify training in such topics as:

✓ Sanitation practices

✓ Employee illness reporting

✓ Safety and disaster preparedness

✓ Role in medical nutrition therapy

✓ Confidentiality

✓ Safe operation of equipment

✓ Injury/accident prevention and reporting

✓ Safe use of chemicals

✓ Risk management

✓ Sexual harassment

✓ Labor laws and employees' rights.

A number of regulations and standards stipulate that orientation and training must be provided to all employees from all shifts, and must be planned and conducted for all foodservice personnel. Check with members of your own facility to determine specific guidelines that apply to your own situation. As new procedures are implemented and new equipment is purchased, there is a need for ongoing inservice (on-the-job) training. Furthermore, tenured employees need periodic updates and refreshers, even for information they have learned in the past, to refresh motivation and reinforce work practices.

You should also document training. Documentation may be required by inspectors or surveyors, and it also helps you keep track of what you have done. One way to do this is to ask each attendee to sign an attendance sheet and file this along with the outline of the training session.

Developing and implementing effective training programs is not difficult, but it does require time to develop a plan and procedures to ensure that training is effective.

Steps in Training

Step 1: The first step in training is to determine the need—who and what should be offered.

Step 2: Determining training content is the second step in training. How do you determine what content to cover in training? By now, you may be formulating a list. To identify content, you can:

- ✓ Check standards that specify content
- ✓ Identify changes in your operation that require training
- ✓ Review quality studies and identify areas that require training for improvement
- ✓ Review operating objectives and select items that require training
- ✓ Talk with employees during performance reviews and ask them what they need and want to learn
- ✓ Observe operations and make your own notes of skills that need to be developed
- ✓ Check with colleagues for new ideas about training content.

As you define training content, try to focus on specifics. For example, a session about all aspects of safety may be too much. A session about using knives safely, and another session about lifting objects safely are likely to generate better outcomes.

Step 3: How do you begin planning your training session? Once you have decided on the training content, the third step is to decide on an objective/outcome of the training. To write an objective, start with thinking about what you want the employees to be able to do at the end of the training. This is the outcome of your training. If you have completed a task analysis for performance standards, these tasks can become your training objectives. A well written objective begins with an action verb and should fit the SMART principle:

- ✓ Specific
- ✓ Measureable
- ✓ Achievable
- ✓ Relevant
- ✓ Timely

Examples of SMART training objectives for foodservice employees are listed below:

- ✓ Use MSDS forms
- ✓ Use proper protective equipment when using chemicals in the kitchen
- ✓ Document food waste using appropriate forms
- ✓ Compute cost of menu items
- ✓ Demonstrate proper handwashing procedures
- ✓ Use proper portion control utensils
- ✓ Use proper cooling procedures

As you can see, these all begin with a verb and are outcomes of the training session.

Step 4: Once you have your objective, it's time to gather the materials you will need for teaching the objective. Your materials will depend upon your objectives. For example, if you are training on how to use MSDS forms, then having actual forms available will improve your training. Use proper portion control utensils will require having various portioning utensils and maybe some food items to practice portioning. You can use posters and reminder signs in your department to reinforce training content. Many training resources are available through trade and industry Websites.

Step 5: Decide where to hold the training. Does your facility have a conference room where you can be undisturbed and comfortable? Perhaps you will want to use the kitchen if you are going to be demonstrating equipment. Make sure to reserve any rooms you need ahead of time.

Step 6: Promote the training. Post the date, place, and time far enough ahead for every shift to see the information. If it is a facility-wide training, confirm that your staff has received the information.

Step 7: Conduct the training. See the section later in this chapter on training techniques.

Step 8: Evaluate the training. See the section later in this chapter on evaluating the training.

Who Should Train?

Can anyone train? The answer to this question is no—at least without training to become a good trainer. A trainer must have an ability to teach and be willing to commit the time necessary for training activities.

Since the person selected to train is critical to the ultimate success of the program, the characteristics of effective trainers must be applied to the selection of a trainer. Among the attributes of a good trainer are:

- ✓ An interest in training
- ✓ Extensive knowledge of the subject matter
- ✓ An ability to communicate effectively
- ✓ Strong interpersonal skills
- ✓ Patience
- ✓ A sense of humor
- ✓ Respect for trainees
- ✓ Confidence in the ability of others to learn
- ✓ An enthusiasm for the training assignment.

As with every other task on the job, a motivated individual can develop and refine training skills. As a Certified Dietary Manager, you can expect to deliver a great deal of training. At the same time, you can enlist the help of staff members who are showing excellent performance, a positive attitude, and motivation to

What types of training materials or resources would be useful when training employees on personal hygiene?

(Check your answer at the end of this chapter)

lead others. This provides recognition to qualified staff members and creates new opportunities for them. In addition, you may find that a staff member who is particularly skillful at a certain task is the best teacher.

Beyond the foodservice staff, there may be others in your facility and your community who can provide training about specific topics. For example, a social worker in your facility may be an excellent resource for providing a training session about dealing with angry clients, or a financial expert may be able to deliver a session about cost control. A local college or university may be able to provide training about almost any topic. A consulting dietitian may provide training about special diets or tube feedings, or many other topics. Vendors and others may also offer training.

When you delegate training to others, be sure he or she is aware of the objectives or outcomes you have set. Discuss the content, and suggest that you review an outline together before finalizing the program. If applicable, you may also wish to review handouts in advance and assure that they complement your own internal policies and procedures.

Training Techniques

Several principles of learning should be incorporated into training programs. First of all, trainees must have a desire to learn. There must be an internal motivating force that leads employees to desire additional job knowledge and/or new job-related skills. You cannot force employees to learn. Trainees must see the benefits in training and must recognize how their own wants, needs, and goals can be met through training. Sometimes, you can create the desire to learn by presenting a thought-provoking question, piece of information, or problem at the beginning of a training session. You can also relate the training to personal experiences and personal needs.

Foodservice employees want to take an active part in training activities. Everyone learns best by doing, not by passively reading or listening. The more staff members can be involved and active in training, the more effective training will be.

Training must focus on real-world problems which employees face and solve on the job. Trainees, then, must see how the training activities will apply directly to their own work. Perhaps the most important aspect of training adults is the idea of transfer of learning. This means relating the training content to the job, where participants carry it out in actual practice.

Furthermore, a trainee's prior experiences influence learning. This concept is especially important in group training, where each employee brings a different background to the training. Trainees learn at different rates and will react differently to specific training experiences. Each person has a unique and individual learning style. For this reason, most trainers use a variety of communication techniques in order to provide something for everyone.

People learn differently. For instance, some people are auditory learners (they learn by hearing the information). Some people are verbal learners (they learn

Putting It Into Practice: 2

You want to cover food safety and sanitation in a training session. With the topic of hand washing, how would you incorporate the three major learning styles (auditory, verbal, and kinesthetic)?

(Check your answer at the end of this chapter)

by reading). Many people learn by doing (this is known as kinesthetic learning). When your training techniques combine listening, reading, and doing, your trainees will learn more. You may need to determine the literacy level of your employees. If your employees have low reading skills, use more pictures in your training. When you have a diverse group of employees, language may also be a barrier.

What techniques can you use to train employees? Lectures, videotapes and DVDs are examples of one-way flow of information from the trainer to the trainees. Although these methods are inexpensive and require little preparation time, they require the learner to be passive. To use these aids effectively, you need to follow up with activities that help participants transfer the information, such as problem solving, hands-on practice, or role playing.

Computer-assisted instruction adopts the principles of programmed instruction and adds the power and flexibility associated with rapidly expanding computer technology. Today, many foodservice training programs are available through the Web or on CD-ROM. Well designed computer-based training uses two important learning principles—motivation and feedback. If access to computers is not possible, perhaps video/DVD training sessions can be made available during down time or breaks.

Another option is use of case studies that present a problem or situation. Trainees analyze and discuss the problem and devise a set of solutions. You may have them work in small groups.

A variation of this is a group activity in which participants have to carry out a task. As an example, Figure 13.1 presents a training aid for a fire safety inservice that sends employees through their own work areas to identify locations of various fire-protection devices.

Figure 13.1 Fire Safety Activity: Fighting Fire—Where Is It?

Write down the location of these items closest to your work area.
Smoke detector:
Heat detector:
Fire alarm box:
Silver (water) fire extinguisher for paper, cloth:
Red (carbon dioxide) fire extinguisher for grease, oil, flammable liquids, or electrical equipment:
Evacuation route:
Alternate evacuation route:

Source: F&N Training Paks. ©The Grossbauer Group. Used with permission

For any procedure requiring a series of steps, demonstration is a very useful technique. An effective demonstration breaks a task into clear steps, and walks trainees through the steps at a comfortable pace. Following a demonstration, each trainee needs to practice the procedure with feedback from the trainer. Then, the trainee should do it again. On the job, the trainee should repeat the process with intermittent feedback and support from the Certified Dietary Manager.

Types of Training

One type of training is called on-the-job training. This technique is common in many foodservice departments, because it is practical and easy to transfer. It involves simply teaching an employee how to do a job while the employee is on location and actually on-the-job (OJT).

To conduct on-the-job training, break down the job into parts, just as you would for a demonstration. In the training, address each part, and provide the procedures, performance standards, safety information, and all relevant components. Then, demonstrate, and allow the employee to practice.

Repetition is important both to make sure that the trainee knows how to do the work and to allow the employee to build confidence and speed. Coaching, an integral part of training, is also important while the trainee practices. The trainer can observe and make friendly suggestions about the work. The trainer should frequently compliment the trainee for performance that meets quality standards. The final step in on-the-job training is follow-up. After the training has been completed, the trainee should be able to do work without constant supervision. However, the trainer should continue to observe the trainee to assure that no problems arise. At this time, reinforcement and feedback become important. Figure 13.2 lists the steps for on-the-job training.

Inservice Training

Inservice training is professional development for your employees to help them develop or update specific skills. It takes place after the employee has started working. Inservice training should follow the training steps outlined earlier in this chapter. See Figure 13.3 for an inservice outline for a HIPAA presentation.

There are many topics that you can and should include in your inservice training. Some examples are:

- ✓ Coping with emergencies
- ✓ Dealing with difficult clients
- ✓ Professional and ethical expectations for foodservice employees
- ✓ Security and confidentiality (HIPAA guidelines)
- ✓ Client/Customer Service

As reinforcement for inservice training activities, provide employees with a handout or brochure that summarizes key points. A sample handout for a fire safety inservice appears in Figure 13.4.

Figure 13.2 Four Steps for On-The-Job Training

STEP 1: Prepare
Arrange work area: Arrange the work area to allow the trainer to stand next to the trainee; collect any needed tools; remove distractions if possible.
Put trainee at ease: Reduce the trainee's anxiety, assure him/her that you are there to help. Encourage the trainee to ask questions if he/she doesn't understand any directions.
STEP 2: Present
Demonstrate the job function: Show the trainee how to do the job function by actually doing it and allowing him/her to observe. If the trainee desires, he/she may take notes during this phase.
Explain key points: While demonstrating, explain key points to the trainee. Attempt to answer the questions: Who, What, When, Where, Why, and How.
Repeat the demonstration: The trainer again performs the task as the trainee observes. This reinforcement increases the likelihood that the trainee will retain the new information.
STEP 3: Practice
Let the trainee attempt parts of the job: Allow the trainee to practice part of the job. After he/she attempts to do part of the job, provide constructive feedback, coaching, and suggestions.
Let the trainee perform the entire job under observation: The trainer now provides feedback periodically rather than frequently and encourages the trainee to begin acting independently.
STEP 4: Follow Up
Conduct periodic progress checks: The trainer steps back and only spot checks the trainee's progress.
Allow the learner to work independently: At this point, the trainee has formally completed the training topic, but is encouraged to seek out the trainer if assistance is needed. Complete the training checklist.

New Employee Orientation

Another type of training is new employee orientation. The process of motivating employees and establishing expectations begins with an appropriate orientation. It is also your first opportunity to teach employees. Before new employees actually begin work, they should be oriented to both the facility and the department. Orientation is a planned, structured introduction to the workplace and the job. As a newcomer, an employee wants to fit in and perform well. By beginning your teaching with orientation, you are providing tools that make all of this possible. You are also establishing groundwork that will become a basis for the employees' relationships with you and others, and the basis for habits the employee will develop on the job. You will be providing information while this individual is in a highly receptive state.

Putting It Into Practice: 3

Write a SMART objective for New Employee Orientation, day one.

(Check your answer at the end of this chapter)

Just like any training program, an effective orientation program hinges on planning. Most Certified Dietary Managers develop content for orientation, and use it repeatedly and consistently for all employees in defined work areas. There may be specific components of an orientation program that apply only to certain jobs. For example, procedures about locating food supplies and following standardized recipes may be part of the orientation program for a cook, but not for waitstaff.

Figure 13.3 HIPAA and Privacy Staff Inservice

Use: Nutrition staff member to deliver this inservice to nurses, nursing assistants, and kitchen staff. Check with your facility to get a copies of the HIPAA form they use with patients for participants to review. Serve a healthy snack for participants.

Introduction: Every American, including those who work in hospitals, nursing homes, assisted living facilities, and medical offices is affected by the American Health Insurance Portability and Accountability Act that took effect in April 2003. Referred to as HIPAA, this Act provides patients with access to their medical records and more control over how their personal health information is used or disclosed. Health care providers are required by law to be HIPAA-compliant.

Quick reading to review the topic:

- Centers for Medicare and Medicaid Services. HIPAA Overview. Available at www.cms.hhs.gov/HIPAAGenInfo. Accessed May 1, 2006
- Medical Privacy-National Standards to Protect the Privacy of Personal Health Information. Available at www.hhs.gov/ocr/hipaa. Accessed May 1, 2006.

Objectives:

- Staff members will know how to define HIPAA.
- Staff members will understand the importance of HIPAA to the facility and to patients.

Outline:

I. What is HIPAA?
   a. Health Insurance Portability and Accountability Acct.
   b. This law gives patients rights to their medical information.
   c. This law protects patient's health information by limiting the way their information can be used by doctors, hospitals, nursing facilities, pharmacies, and other health care providers.
   d. Health care facilities must provide written notice to their patients about their rights to privacy.
   e. Patients can request that their communications with medical personal are private and that their information is not disclosed to anyone without their permission.
   f. Medical information about a patient cannot be used for advertising or marketing purposes.

II. Effect of HIPAA on medical facilities
   a. Each medical facility must have privacy procedures in place.
   b. Staff must be trained on these privacy procedures.
   c. Disciplinary action can result if private information is incorrectly transmitted by an employee.
   d. Employees must be careful not to release information about a patient.

III. Effect of HIPAA on facility staff
   a. Patient information is confidential and should not be shared with anyone, including staff who do not have access to facility medical records.
   b. Patients may request that their presence in a facility be kept private (for example, their name might not be posted on a listing of residents posted in a hallway).

Activity: Roll play. Select three employees to roll play the following situation (elderly woman, nursing assistant, and unit nurse):

Susie Q is a nursing assistant at a large city hospital. One afternoon she is approached by an elderly woman asking about the condition of her grandchild, who is housed on Susie's unit. How should Susie respond to the request for information?

Correct answer to the roll play:

Susie Q should ask the elderly woman to confirm her identity and refer her to the nurse on the unit. The unit nurse should check the child's chart to see who has access to her medical information. If the elderly woman is not listed as a contact person, the nurse should explain that she can't respond due to HIPAA and refer her to the responsible party listed on the child's medical record.

Source: RD411.com Used with permission

Figure 13.4 Sample Handout for Fire Safety Inservice

FIRE RESPONSE PROCEDURE	
RACE	PASS
R: REMOVE everyone from danger	P: PULL the pin
A: Turn on the ALARM	A: AIM at the base of the fire
C: CONFINE the fire	S: SQUEEZE the trigger and keep the extinguisher in an upright position
E: EXTINGUISH the fire if you can do it safely	S: SWEEP from side to side

It is helpful to use an orientation checklist to organize the content, to assure that everything is covered, and to develop documentation of the orientation. An example appears in Figure 13.5. Some facilities require two sets of initials next to each item on a checklist: the supervisor's initials to verify that this content has been covered, and the employee's initials as a way of accepting responsibility for having learned this content.

An additional scheduling consideration relates to the length of time for orientation. Realize that a new employee is virtually bombarded with information. It is not realistic to expect a new employee to learn everything in one sitting. If possible, a useful approach to this problem is to schedule orientation in small chunks. On the first day, you may cover some basic elements related to time-clock procedures, uniforms, and department layout. As follow-up on the next day, you may cover work procedures and routines. At yet another time, you may review safety policies. Working with content in segments gives the employee time to process new information and improves retention. An additional advantage of this approach is that as an employee begins working, familiarity grows. The employee develops a context in which to understand and store this new information. The employee may also develop questions and curiosities that enhance learning. When conducting an orientation, use the training steps outlined earlier in this chapter as your guide.

Sanitation and Safety Training

This is listed as a type of training because safety and sanitation training is a mandatory training. The final report of an FDA Ad Hoc Committee on Training stated that "80 percent of all foodborne illness can be traced to a procedural problem due to the actions of employees who either did not know or understand the value of using designated procedures to keep food from becoming contaminated." (McSwane, David, Nancy Rue, Richard Linton. *Essentials of Food Safety and Sanitation.* Upper Saddle River, NJ, Prentice Hall, 1998)

Certified Dietary Managers have an obligation to train every member of the foodservice team in food protection. In fact, the FDA 2009 Food Code stipulates that managers must train employees in such topics as:

✓ The risks of bare-hand contact with food
✓ When and where to wash hands
✓ How to wash hands
✓ How to maintain fingernails
✓ Prohibition of jewelry
✓ Basic hygiene.

How can you ensure employees' compliance with FDA food safety regulations?

(Check your answer at the end of this chapter)

The FDA 2009 Food Code also notes that managers must document sanitation training. Many managers document training with attendance sign-in sheets, along with a summary of each training meeting.

Training improves the likelihood of compliance with food handling policies and practices, reduces the need for constant supervision, and improves employee self-esteem and job satisfaction. Training for food safety should include topics

Figure 13.5 Orientation Checklist

Employee's Name: ______________________ Starting Date: ______________

Job Title: ______________________ Supervisor: ______________________

Topic	Date Discussed	Supervisor's Initials	Employee's Initials
Introduction to supervisor and co-workers			
Orientation to work areas			
Locker room location and use			
Dress code and uniforms			
Employee schedule			
Request for time off			
Attendance policy			
Timeclock procedures			
Meal and break policies			
Payroll procedures			
Overtime policy			
Handwashing requirements—when to wash hands			
Handwashing procedure			
Employee health policy and illness reporting			
Employee Health & Wellness (Health Risk Assessment)			
Safety rules			
Minimum Data Set (MDS) and chemical safety			
Fire safety procedures			
Confidentiality policies			
Personnel policies			
Critical rules			
Performance standards			
Performance review process			
Probationary period			
Progressive discipline policy			
Grievance procedures			
Job route for: (position)*			
Job route for: (position)*			
Job route for: (position)*			
Equipment operation for:*			
Equipment operation for:*			
Equipment operation for:*			
Policies and procedures for:*			
Policies and procedures for:*			
Policies and procedures for:*			
Policies and procedures for:*			
Temperature recording and logs			
Food requisition withdrawal form			
How to report concerns			
Departmental goals and objectives			
Sanitation program			
Quality management process			
Customer service initiative			
Disaster and emergency procedures			

**List all positions an employee may cover and equipment and procedures that apply.*

such as personal hygiene; restrictions and precautions for illness; why, when, and how to take temperatures; safe thawing and preparation practices; sanitation techniques; and all other food protection practices that relate to the employees' job responsibilities. Trainers should be carefully selected based on job knowledge and ability to facilitate learning. Training strategies appropriate for sanitation training include new employee orientation, on-the-job training, and group training (inservices). Each of these approaches is important for improving and maintaining the sanitation skills and knowledge of foodservice employees.

For instance, the on-the-job training program for a new dishwasher would focus on the proper steps in manual and automatic dishwashing. The new employee would learn how to perform these job tasks by working with an experienced employee. The instruction would be accomplished through observation and return demonstration by the new employee, while the experienced employee provides coaching and feedback.

The Certified Dietary Manager may require instructional materials to assist in providing food safety training to staff. A variety of resources are available from groups and organizations such as:

- ✓ Professional associations in the foodservice and hospitality industry
- ✓ State departments of public health
- ✓ Federal agencies such as the Food and Drug Administration, United States Department of Agriculture, and Centers for Disease Control and Prevention
- ✓ Cooperative Extension Programs
- ✓ Local colleges, universities, and technical schools
- ✓ Vendors and suppliers to the foodservice industry
- ✓ State and local health departments.

Many free posters, handouts, and interactive resources about food safety are available on reliable websites, such as those of the U.S. government and county extension agencies. Many are available in various languages, and some rely on graphics to support the message. These can be useful in training employees who speak English as a second language or have language barriers.

Evaluating Training

Remember that training is not an event but a process and a vital part of that process is evaluating the training. Two ways of evaluating training are measuring knowledge gains or satisfaction with a written evaluation, and by giving feedback.

Written Evaluation

Some standards applying to non-commercial foodservice operations specify that employees' knowledge should be measured both before and after training. So, some Certified Dietary Managers use a pre-test and a post-test to measure knowledge. A sample pre-test that doubles as a post-test appears in Figure 13.6. A test such as this does not measure transfer of learning, but it does tell you whether employees have grasped the prerequisite information.

As a matter of course, you should also ask employees to evaluate training sessions themselves. Find out whether participants felt the training was useful, what questions were left unanswered, and how participants rate their own confidence in being able to do something differently on the job. Ask them what they will do differently as a result of training. Ask them what else they would like to learn. A sample inservice training session evaluation appears in Figure 13.7.

The best way to assess your own training efforts is to work with your list of objectives and observe what employees are actually doing. If you see objectives being met, you can be sure you have succeeded in training. If you don't, you need to analyze further.

Giving Feedback

Feedback is information about what an employee is doing. It provides perspective, direction, and recognition. Each of us, investing energy into our work, needs to hear from someone that our work is important. Feedback serves this need and builds employees' self-esteem. It also lets trainees know how they are doing.

Now, you may wonder: Is all of this true only for positive feedback and praise? Of course, everyone enjoys receiving positive feedback, such as praise for a task well done. At the same time, though, feedback about something that did not go perfectly conveys a critical message. The critical message is: *Your work matters. What you do is important.* Interestingly enough, when all forms of feedback are handled well, all forms of feedback can boost an employee's self-esteem.

In any interaction with an employee, self-esteem is an ongoing consideration. Whether an interaction works or doesn't work often relates directly to how the Certified Dietary Manager handles the self-esteem issue. Whether an employee changes behavior as a result of feedback often relates to whether the manager respected and protected the employee's self-esteem.

To understand how critical feedback can be for both employees who are doing the job well and employees who need to refine their skills, consider this example: Marty is a cafeteria server. His manager tells him to be careful about portion control. Marty habitually over-portions food. No one ever says anything to him about it. After a while, Marty concludes that talk about portion control was just hype. He doesn't believe anybody cares at all. He has no reason to change his behavior.

Meanwhile, Tina, who works next to him, has been carefully portioning food for a long time. She observes that Marty is not portioning food correctly. After a while, as no intervention occurs, her morale begins to suffer. She feels that she has been working conscientiously, and no one is recognizing her efforts. Tina stops making an effort to honor portion control guidelines, and she starts doing what Marty is doing.

Both of these employees may have work performance problems related to lack of feedback. Neither is likely to feel a strong sense of satisfaction in the job. Of course, portion control in the department is going to suffer, too. This example

Feedback
Providing information to employees about how they are doing

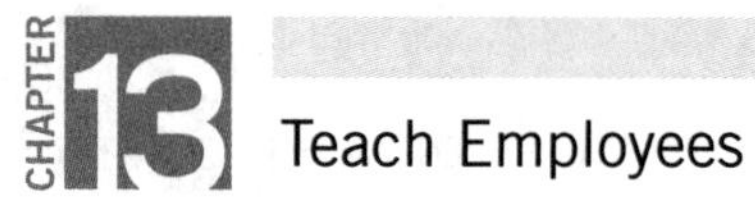

Figure 13.6 Sample Pre-Test/Post-Test (Measuring Knowledge Gain)

Name: ______________________________ Date: ______________

Department: ______________________________

1. **True or False:** HIPAA affects the nursing staff in a medical facility
2. What could happen to an employee who violates HIPAA and gives out confidential information?
   a. The employee could lose their job
   b. The patient could sue the facility
   c. Both of the above
   d. Neither of the above
3. HIPAA prevents facilities from using medical information without written permission for:
   a. Marketing
   b. Advertising
   c. Denial of health insurance
   d. A and B only
4. **True or False:** Each patient of a medical facility should have the opportunity to review written privacy procedures.
5. **True or False:** Staff at a doctor's office or medical facility should not reveal medical information to anyone without confirming their identity.

ANSWER KEY: 1. False 2. c. Both of the above 3. d. A and B only 4. True 5. True

Source: F&N Training Paks. ©The Grossbauer Group. Used with permission

Figure 13.7 Sample Inservice Evaluation Form (Measuring Satisfaction)

Inservice Session Title: ______________________________ Date: ______________

Please answer the following questions to help us improve our training programs.

1. Please rate how well this session relates to your own job:
   ○ excellent match ○ fair match ○ poor match
2. Was this material:
   ○ too complex ○ too simple ○ just right
3. Please rate the audio-visuals used:
   ○ excellent ○ fair ○ poor
4. Please rate the learning activities used:
   ○ excellent ○ fair ○ poor
5. Please rate the handouts used:
   ○ excellent ○ fair ○ poor
6. What did you like most about this training session?
7. What did you like least about this training session?
8. What topics would you like to see covered in future training?

illustrates that a manager needs to provide feedback, and that feedback ties in very closely with performance.

Some specific techniques can help a manager provide feedback effectively and honor each person's need for high self-esteem. These are discussed below.

Give feedback about good work. Many Certified Dietary Managers feel obligated to watch for employees' mistakes and "catch them when they're doing something wrong." Certainly, you do want to observe and correct problems. More importantly, though, you want to "catch" people doing things *right*—and tell them about it. Behavioral psychologists call this idea positive reinforcement. As a manager, you are likely to invest a lot less time and energy if you take this positive approach. Employees who are doing something well and hear about it are very likely to do it again. They know with certainty that this is the performance you want to see, and they feel confident about doing it again. One example is a manager, who, when observing employees doing something right, reached into her pocket and tossed them a miniature candy bar.

Make most feedback immediate. Another technique Certified Dietary Managers find helpful is to provide feedback on the spot as feasible. There are several reasons for this. One is that if an employee has been making a mistake and repeating it over time before he ever hears from you about it, he has already created a habit that must be broken. This is difficult. Another is that as an employee is doing the work, his attention is best focused on the task. Much later, he may not remember exactly what he did. (You may not remember in detail, either.) Immediacy gives the exchange the strongest impact.

Immediate feedback may not be appropriate if there is not enough time to discuss an issue that may become complex, or if the employee is in the presence of others who should not be privy to the exchange. For example, you would not want to tell an employee how to improve a service skill in front of a client or co-worker. You may need to wait in order to have some privacy for discussion.

Focus on behavior, not the person. Part of the way a Certified Dietary Manager preserves self-esteem when giving correction is by keeping the behavior separate from the person. So, express observations objectively. The observations are about what you see happening. Figure 13.8 illustrates some examples of this.

Figure 13.8 Examples of Feedback Statements

Focus on the Person		Focus on the Behavior*
You are really poor at managing portion sizes.	→	This product is coming out at 1/2 cup instead of 1/3 cup.
You just can't seem to put food away in the right places.	→	I'm seeing the canned pears on the shelf for cake mixes.
You aren't very friendly to clients.	→	I was watching for a smile during breakfast, and didn't see one.

** Each of these is a much more effective way to provide feedback.*

Follow with a reason and a question. When you are aiming to correct behavior, you can follow a simple feedback statement with two more parts: a reason and a question. This brings about an important set of communications.

First, the reason: Here, you are saying why it matters, e.g., *We need to meet these assigned portion sizes to control food costs and meet clients' nutritional needs. Or: Our departmental team has a goal of surprising people with our friendliness.* The reason reminds the employee that the work is important, and helps the employee keep the perspective of departmental and team objectives.

Next, the question: This helps you as a manager to listen. There may be something you don't know that has contributed to this behavior. There may be an obstacle in the way of the employee's doing the task as directed. If so, you want to find out. So, you ask: *Why did this happen? Or: How did this happen? Or: What do you think caused this?*

You are not asking in a threatening way, but in a genuinely curious manner. You are also not challenging the employee to devise a terrific excuse or rationalization. If you set the stage by being very matter-of-fact, you can help the employee respond matter-of-factly as well.

Listen. Feedback should be two-way. As a Certified Dietary Manager, you can learn a great deal from feedback that employees give to you. In particular, if you are stating a problem and a reason for its importance—and then asking about why it happened—now, you need to listen very carefully. You may learn something you really need to know. You may learn about another problem that caused this problem. Or, you may learn that an employee lacks resources or information that you can provide. Figure 13.9 gives an example of an exchange between manager and employee that uses the listening principle.

Figure 13.9 Listening: An Example

Chuck is a Certified Dietary Manager responsible for trayline operations. Mary is a trayline employee who places cold food items on the trays as they are assembled. Here are two versions of their conversation:

Version #1

Chuck: Mary, a little while ago, we ran three test trays. You didn't put any margarine on them. This is really serious. If the inspectors see this, we could be cited. You make sure it gets on the trays from now on, OK?

Mary: OK.

Version #2

Chuck: Mary, a little while ago, we ran three test trays. Each had margarine marked on the tray ticket, but I did not see any margarine on the trays. We are striving for 99.9% tray accuracy, so this concerns me. What do you think may have caused this?

Mary: When I set up the trayline, I couldn't find any margarine in the walk-in. I asked Fred in the stock area for some, and he said we were out. So, I couldn't put any on the trays.

In the first version of this conversation, Chuck, the manager, has taken the approach of simply telling the employee what to do. Chuck has not found out what really happened, nor has Chuck learned that he has an inventory management problem to address. So, most likely, Mary will walk away with ill feelings, and Chuck's problems will not go away. Why didn't Mary tell Chuck what the problem was? As the proverbial retort goes: He didn't ask!

In version #2 of this conversation, Chuck invited the employee to talk about what happened and why. Chuck had no idea what he would hear, but he decided it would be important to listen. Chuck learned about another problem that he can address. Now, he will have a conversation with Fred to determine whether/why the department is out of margarine. Depending on what he finds out, Chuck may even have another conversation with another employee responsible for purchasing. In any event, Chuck can now work with Mary to solve her problem. Mary is working with Chuck, too.

This is just one example of how a manager can gain important information by listening. Chuck can now identify that Mary's poor performance did not stem from a lack of motivation on Mary's part, or even a lack of knowledge. Mary simply didn't have what she needed to do the job correctly. This may also be an opportunity for Chuck to give Mary some direction about handling problems. Chuck may tell Mary that she may feel free to come to him right away for help in dealing with product shortages.

Give specific directions. When you are providing feedback to an employee, you may also need to give direction about refining behavior. This should be very specific. The more specific direction is, the easier it is for an employee to know exactly what to do—and then do it. Figure 13.10 gives examples of directions that are vague and directions that are specific.

Figure 13.10 **Directions: Be Specific**

Vague:	Specific:*
Make sure the dishmachine water is hot enough. →	Check the temperature gauge on the final rinse. If it is not in the range of 180-185°F, stop runinng dishes and notify a supervisor.
Give the best customer/client service you ~~can.~~ →	Smile, make eye contact, and say hello to every client as they enter the buffet area.
Keep the storeroom organized. →	Follow the labels, and place each item on the shelf bearing its label. If you run into any questions about where things belong, let me know.

** Each of these is a much more effective way to provide feedback.*

State directions in positive terms. As a simple rule of human communication, positive wording is easier to listen to and follow. Even when you have to tell an employee not to do something, there is always a positive way to phrase the direction. A positive direction focuses on what should happen.

If you are not sure how to change a direction into a positive phrase try these steps:

✓ Pretend you are writing a list of DO's and DON'Ts.

✓ First, write the DON'T.

✓ Then, write the same direction as a DO. Often, you can omit the word "do" and have a terrific direction.

Figure 13.11 contains some examples of this process.

Figure 13.11 Changing Negative Directions to Positive Directions

Don't:		Do:*
Don't put anything on the wrong shelf.	*Change to* →	Put everything on the shelf labeled for that product.
Don't argue with a client.	*Change to* →	Accept what the client says as his or her own expectation, and then strive to satisfy the client.
Don't miss anything on the tray ticket when you work your station.	*Change to* →	Place each item shown on the tray ticket for your station onto the tray.

** Each of these is a much more effective way to provide feedback.*

State feedback in terms of specific times, rather than always or never. A frustrated Certified Dietary Manager may at times be tempted to say something like: *You never put the dishes away right!* Actually, an employee can give better focus to your feedback if you confine the time to right now. You will get further by pointing out what you see now, without broadening the time frame to always or never.

Demonstrate and coach. In giving feedback to an employee and listening to responses, you may learn that an employee simply does not know how to do something. This is a training concern. Be sure to recognize this, and provide the training an employee needs to change behavior. Part of the training process is also to allow the employee to try it hands-on. As an employee practices, provide coaching to help the employee refine the behavior.

Communicate nonverbally. Experts suggest that the major part of the message a person hears from you does not come from your words at all. Instead, it comes from your nonverbal communication. Examples of nonverbal communication include your posture, your body position, your facial expression, your use of eye contact, and your tone of voice. To understand how it works, take the question mentioned above: *Why did this happen?*

Try asking this question with an angry tone, and then with a friendly tone. Now, talk with your classmate and try asking it with an angry tone while crossing your arms in front of you. Then, try asking it with a friendly tone while relaxing your arms at your sides. Now, let your classmate try the same with you. Ask each other what you have communicated to each other. Then, ask what gave this message. This is a good way to begin exploring nonverbal messages. You can also observe and practice your own nonverbal communications by working in front of a mirror. Finally, you can also observe how people react to your communications. If the results surprise you, think carefully about your voice and your body language.

Sometimes, Certified Dietary Managers look to training to solve all problems. It does not. When an employee performs poorly, most of us think the employee needs training. This may or may not be true. An employee may know how to do something, but fail to do it because of factors such as:

- ✓ Poor motivation
- ✓ Peer pressure
- ✓ Obstacles in the workplace
- ✓ Lack of resources (such as time or supplies)
- ✓ Malfunctioning equipment
- ✓ Poorly designed systems.

Whenever an employee's performance does not reflect the training you have provided, talk with the employee. Listen, and size up the need. Decide what interventions you can provide, and try them out.

END OF CHAPTER

Putting It Into Practice Questions & Answers

1. What types of training materials or resources would be useful when training employees on personal hygiene?

   A. *The local sanitarian, copies of the local sanitation regulations, statistics on foodborne illness from the Centers of Disease Control Website (http://www.cdc.gov/Features/dsFoodborneIllness/)*

2. You want to cover food safety and sanitation in a training session. With the topic of hand washing, how would you incorporate the three major learning styles (auditory, verbal, and kinesthetic)?

   A.
   - *Introduce the topic with information by explaining why hand washing is necessary. (Auditory)*
   - *Provide a handout/poster that shows the appropriate steps/procedure. (Verbal)*
   - *Ask employees to work in small groups to create a list of when hand washing is necessary when performing their job. (Verbal)*

3. Write a SMART objective for New Employee Orientation, day one.

   A.
   - *Employee will be able to locate timeclock and timecard and can name the person with whom they will be working in the kitchen.*
   - *Employee knows where to park and what equipment (clean apron) they will need to bring to work.*

   Note that these two examples are specific, measureable, achievable, relevant, and timely.

4. How can you ensure employees' compliance with FDA food safety regulations?

   A. *Offer training in short pieces (20 minutes or less). Provide demonstrations and allow employees to return the demonstration to you. Observe after the training and offer feedback to employees. Conduct periodic progress checks.*

CHAPTER 14

Justify Improvement in the Department Design and Layout

Overview and Objectives

One of the basic management functions is planning. Sometime during your tenure as a Certified Dietary Manager, you will have to plan a kitchen redesign. You will be expected to justify the department design and layout. This chapter helps you prepare for those tasks.

After completing this chapter, you should be able to:

- ✓ Define "work simplification" and "green" principles as they apply to the foodservice department
- ✓ Maintain records of suggestions and complaints received
- ✓ Conduct department improvement discussion session with staff
- ✓ Evaluate work flow, essential equipment relative to new department designs or construction
- ✓ Research concepts/products related to department facility design
- ✓ Prepare proposals, specifications for new construction or renovation in layout/design changes

Both design and equipment have an impact on a foodservice operation. Effective design and equipment choices allow you to fulfill your operational objectives related to the menu, customer/client service, quality, schedules, budget, and safety. Whether you are planning a new operation or evaluating changes to an existing operation, designing the physical layout is a critical step. In addition, any change to menus and service models can trigger a need to revise design, equipment, or both. Over time, equipment has to be replaced, and many considerations feed into the purchasing decisions.

In this chapter, you will learn basic concepts involved in foodservice design. You will also examine the process of specifying and purchasing foodservice equipment. You will have an opportunity to become familiar with a few common pieces of equipment. You will also learn how to plan and manage a preventive maintenance program and how to control equipment-related supply costs.

Physical Layout

The layout of a facility has a dramatic impact on the efficiency of foodservice operations. It can affect food quality and the ability to produce meals according to established timetables. It can also affect labor efficiency and staff scheduling. Several factors that affect the layout of the facility are:

The menu. As meals must be prepared for three or more meal periods and an extensive variety of items must be offered, there is an obvious need for storage and preparation space. The menu dictates the types of food products to be prepared, so it also indicates space and equipment requirements for equipment to accommodate inventory, pre-prep, preparation, holding, and service. For instance, if you deliver meals in carts, you have to have storage space for the carts.

Use of convenience foods. As the number and quantity of convenience items increases, the need for food production space and equipment decreases. Requirements for refrigerated and/or freezer storage space, though, may increase. Conversely, if many items are being made from scratch, on-site needs for preparation space and equipment increase.

Quantity of food to prepare. Equipment and work space must be sized to accommodate the number of meals being produced for on-site as well as off-site feeding and catering.

Production and service systems. Both production and service models influence the need for space and the use of space over time. In a decentralized system, much of the required work space and equipment shifts to decentralized units, such as serving pantries. In a centralized system, there is a much greater need for work space and equipment in the centralized location. In a cook-chill system, there may be greater opportunity to control scheduling of work, using space and labor time efficiently. Each system also dictates varying needs for storage. For example, a cook-chill system can require large refrigerated storage areas, along with blast chillers and rethermalization equipment. A decentralized service system dictates needs for refrigerated storage, transport equipment, and rethermalization units. Space for equipment and a layout that supports efficient work flow are essential.

Space. Space allocated for foodservice affects both the facility layout and the amount and type of equipment that can be considered. Based on the needs of a facility, compromises in space, design, and budget are common. Space constraints may drive decisions to choose space-efficient equipment options, and/or to choose single pieces of equipment that can perform multiple functions.

Funds. Budget funds allocated for equipment have an impact on plans. Foodservices sometimes need to compete with other departments for limited space and budgetary resources for remodeling and/or new building activities.

Design Principles

Preparation facilities must be designed to help ensure an efficient flow of products and efficient use of employees' time through each sequence in the food production/service cycle. The flow of work varies from one operation to another. As an example, products must be received and then stored in a designated area. Next, products must be issued for baking, meat, and/or vegetable preparation. Products must be cooked, prepared, distributed, and served. Supportive activities, including pot-washing and dishwashing, are also required. There is a relationship between serving and dining activities. In many facilities, intermediate steps of pre-portioning products on tray assembly lines make the workflow process even more complex. The flow of work among work areas should help to define layout. If you are moving to a room service model, the design of tray assembly lines may be very different or non-existent.

The menu is another factor to consider. Space, employees, equipment, and ingredients must be available to prepare each item required by the menu.

Typically, facilities are designed by considering workload requirements. Then, work centers are developed based on logical groupings of menu items and tasks. Generally, the layout of a foodservice area should enable a logical, economical flow of foods from receiving through storage, production, additional storage (if required), and service. It should support separation of clean, sanitized products from soiled products.

A physical design can be somewhat limiting. Sometimes after a design and layout have been established, other factors change. For example, in this operation, any of the following could occur:

- ✓ The bakers could become unionized, and the Certified Dietary Manager might determine it would be more economical to purchase many more convenience items for the bakery.
- ✓ A replacement oven may have different space requirements than the existing oven or different electrical service requirements.
- ✓ A new service may require the operation to double its production of salad and soup products.

These are just a few examples of how change can generate new challenges in physical design and equipment needs. When possible, a Certified Dietary Manager should look ahead and try to design facilities with some amount of flexibility, without incorporating unnecessary space or features. In selecting equipment, it is often possible to choose equipment that serves multiple uses for the greatest flexibility in responding to future needs and changes. For example, a convection oven/steamer can produce a variety of foods, applying a variety of cooking methods, such as steaming or roasting. It can be a versatile replacement for outdated equipment.

Factors to Consider

The task of designing a foodservice department is complex and should involve the team effort of a Certified Dietary Manager along with a project architect, foodservice design consultant, in-house engineering expert, and staff who use the equipment. Concerns that must be considered include:

Energy Efficiency. Over the lifetime of a piece of equipment, operating costs related to gas or electricity usage can be staggering. The foodservice department makes up a large percentage of a facility's energy bill. In 2001, an energy efficient program called Energy Star was launched to designate equipment that is highly efficient. An Energy Star rating meets the minimum efficiency criteria. Two research organizations, Foodservice Technology Center (FSTC), http://www.fishnick.com/saveenergy/rebates, and the Consortium for Energy

When considering design factors, how would your considerations for temperature and humidity be different for a kitchen versus a dining room?

(Check your answer at the end of this chapter)

Efficiency (CEE), http://www.cee1.org, also have energy efficiency equipment ratings. Their ratings are more stringent than the Energy Star. All commercial kitchen equipment will soon be manufactured with both energy and water efficiency. See the *Management in the News* section at the end of this chapter for Energy Star equipment examples and suggestions for how to find energy savings in your department.

You will be hearing much more about sustainable and "green" building in the near future. An emerging certification called LEED (Leadership in Energy and Environmental Design), developed by the U.S. Green Building Council, is encouraging building that is "designed and built using strategies aimed at improving performance across all the metrics that matter most. Some of these strategies are: energy savings, water efficiency, carbon dioxide emissions reduction, improved indoor environmental quality, and stewardship of resources and sensitivity to their impacts." Water efficiency is another aspect of "green" buildings. A number of facilities are looking at saving and reusing water. One example of water efficiency is a water-cooled ice machine. Other facilities are utilizing biotechnology. One university is using food scraps for bioenergy.

Even if you are not ready to purchase new equipment, you should have a plan in place that includes energy efficient equipment replacement recommendations. Perhaps your state or local utility has a rebate program. Or maybe you already know that when your freezer needs to be replaced you want a larger unit. If so, this should be included in your replacement plan with specifications for energy efficiency. As with any plan, it should be reviewed annually to make sure you have the latest information on efficient commercial kitchen equipment.

Ergonomic factors. Ergonomic factors influence the comfort, efficiency, and safety of a work environment, and are of great concern in foodservice. Designs that control physical fatigue and help prevent injury related to repetitive motion are important. These concerns are recognized as designers reduce distances employees must travel, adjust heights of work areas to fit the needs of employees, and develop comfortable (thickened) handles for small utensils. See Figure 14.1 for examples of ergonomic factors.

Noise. There can be a great deal of noise in food preparation areas. This can distract clients as well as employees, while creating stress. Use of soundproofing materials and the selection of less noisy equipment can help reduce these problems.

Lighting. Adequate lighting is critical for safety as well as for managing the quality of work of a foodservice department. Lighting is measured in foot candles. Lighting is another area where you can realize energy savings. Check out LED lighting for commercial freezers, for instance.

Temperature and humidity. Work in food preparation areas can be very hot. Concerns about temperature are appropriate as air conditioning needs are considered, and as cooking and cleaning equipment selection decisions are made.

Safety and sanitation. These concerns are important, and must meet all applicable local codes. Health regulations dictate cleanability of equipment;

temperature and humidity requirement for dry storage; lighting requirements; design and venting of heat, ventilation, and air conditioning systems, and much more.

Local construction codes. Building codes may stipulate many aspects of design. In some locales, special regulations apply to healthcare facilities.

Security. Security concerns are always a top priority in the design. For example, should storage areas be located close to the back door? No, because this may increase the opportunity for theft. Should receiving and preparation areas be under the view of the Certified Dietary Manager? Yes. Thus, an office design may use glass partitions that allow a manager to monitor operations from a desk. While the list of questions can continue, the point is that the control of food and materials during production and service is influenced by the amount of security built into the facility.

Design of Receiving and Storage Areas

Receiving areas should typically be as close as practical to storage areas. They should also be large enough to house incoming deliveries, so that employees can follow effective receiving practices. There must be space available for related equipment, such as scales and dollies.

To limit access by unauthorized persons, storerooms should be designed with walls that extend from the floor to the ceiling and with ceilings that cannot be entered from an adjoining room. Locked doors are usually required. If an ingredient room is used, it should be planned close to dry storage areas and close to food preparation areas.

Design of Food Preparation and Service Areas

In production areas, cooks sometimes need storage space for pre-preparation items. They may also need aisles to house supply carts. Furthermore, to organize work efficiently, they need counter space. They may also need space for small equipment, such as scales, slicers, and food processors.

For decentralized service in which products are heated or "finished" close to the point of service, consider what additional equipment and space requirements may exist.

In a cafeteria, it's important to structure a design that fits the service model. For example, a design for a straight-line service is much different from one used for a scramble service. In addition, it's important to consider client's entry and exit points, and to allow space for clients to move around comfortably while serving themselves, without getting in each others' way. If food items are to be prepared on an as-ordered basis, utility connections, ventilation systems, and space to house cook-to-order equipment in service areas must be considered. Equipment to hold hot and cold food items near the point of service will be needed. Sometimes cafeteria operations use a hot and/or cold food pass-through so that production staff can make items readily available for service without having to go into public foodservice areas. A pass-through is a connecting area between the kitchen and the service area.

You are considering a culture change and plan to move away from a trayline and implement restaurant service in the dining room. What design considerations do you need to consider when planning for this change?

(Check your answer at the end of this chapter)

Figure 14.1 **Examples of Ergonomic Factors**

Strains and Sprains

Ergonomic controls can help eliminate or limit exposure to musculoskeletal disorders (MSDs) in the workplace.

Potential Hazard: Repetitive movements may lead to strain and sprains. For example:

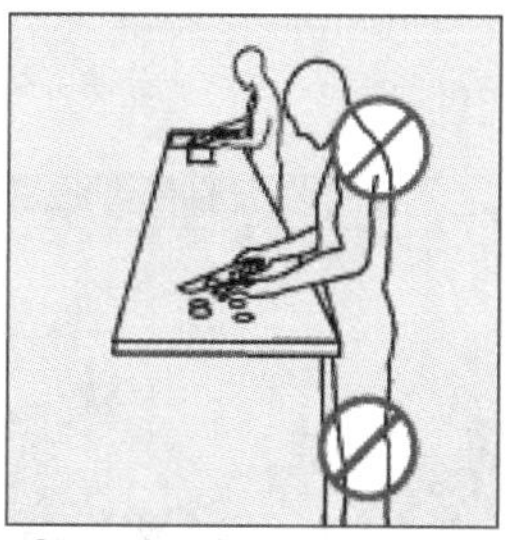
Chopping food preparation

- **Prolonged standing** and repetitive or prolonged motions such as reaching, lifting, and chopping while preparing food in food preparation areas. Static postures may occur as workers continuously stand in one position while chopping or preparing food, causing muscle fatigue and pooling of blood in the lower extremities. Awkward neck postures can lead to neck and strains and muscle stiffness if cooks are constantly tilting their heads downward to chop, dice, and mix food.
- **Reaching and lifting:** Frequent elevated extended reaches for supplies can cause back and shoulder injury resulting in muscle strain, or:
  > **Tendinitis:** Tendon inflammation occurring when a muscle or tendon is repeatedly tensed from overuse or unaccustomed use.
  > **Rotator Cuff Injuries:** The most common shoulder tendon disorder. Inflammation of the tendons of the rotator cuff of the shoulder, closely related to impingement syndrome. It can be caused by continuously working with the arms raised overhead, repeated throwing actions, or other repetitive movements of the arm.

Kitchen worker using elevated reach

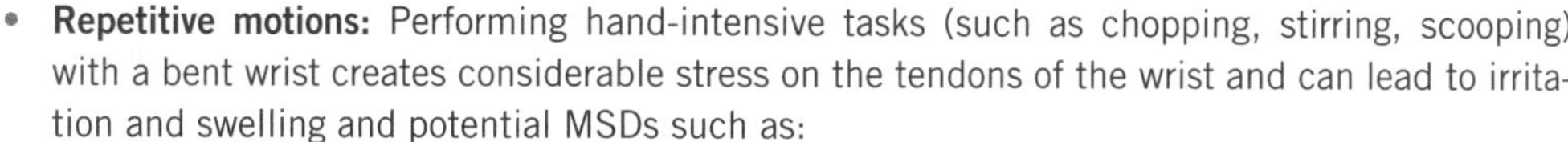
- **Repetitive motions:** Performing hand-intensive tasks (such as chopping, stirring, scooping) with a bent wrist creates considerable stress on the tendons of the wrist and can lead to irritation and swelling and potential MSDs such as:

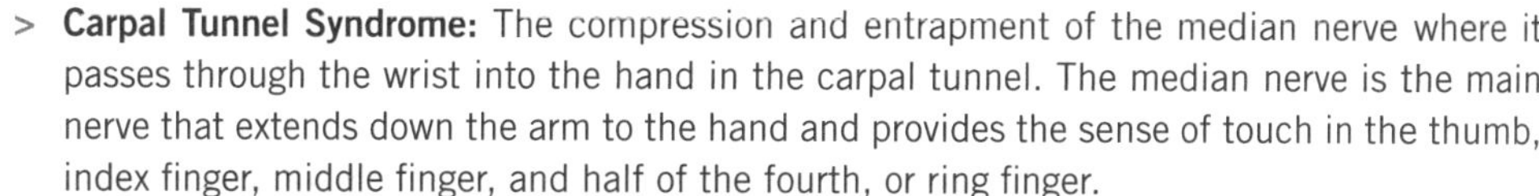
  > **Carpal Tunnel Syndrome:** The compression and entrapment of the median nerve where it passes through the wrist into the hand in the carpal tunnel. The median nerve is the main nerve that extends down the arm to the hand and provides the sense of touch in the thumb, index finger, middle finger, and half of the fourth, or ring finger.

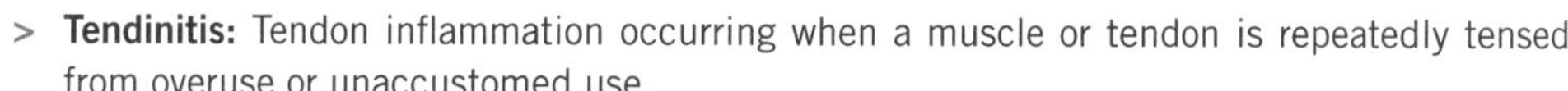
  > **Tendinitis:** Tendon inflammation occurring when a muscle or tendon is repeatedly tensed from overuse or unaccustomed use.

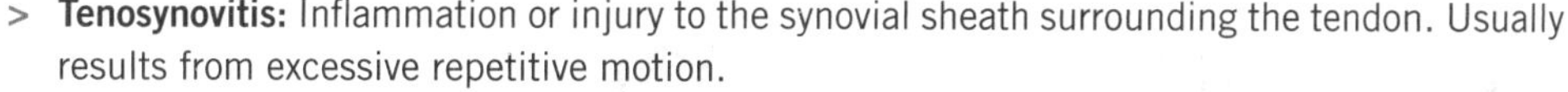
  > **Tenosynovitis:** Inflammation or injury to the synovial sheath surrounding the tendon. Usually results from excessive repetitive motion.

Kitchen worker

Young Worker Solutions

Employers have the primary responsibility for protecting the safety and health of their workers. Employees are responsible for following the safe work practices of their employers.

Reaching and lifting: Learn to lift properly and stay fit to help reduce the risk of injury from lifting.

- Lift with your knees, not your back.
- Lighten a heavy load that needs to be lifted or get help when lifting.
- Always make sure the load is balanced and even when lifting.
- Get help when lifting or pouring fluid out of heavy pots or use tilt containers to help minimize arm and back strain.

Don't lift heavy objects alone

Lift with a buddy

(Continued)

Figure 14.1 Examples of Ergonomic Factors *(Continued)*

Employer Solutions

Employers have the primary responsibility for protecting the safety and health of their workers. Employees are responsible for following the safe work practices of their employers.

Consider implementing recommended safe work practices, including: Assess work sites for ergonomic stressors and identify and address ways to decrease them. For example:

Box placed on side allows for less reaching

Prolonged Standing

- **Provide** stools or a foot rest bar at work stations. This provides workers an opportunity to shift weight from their feet while still maintaining reach and accessibility.
- **Provide** height-adjustable workspaces appropriate for the task being performed so that workers can keep elbows close to the body. For example, lower countertops, use height-adjustable countertops or stands, or provide work stands for employees.
- **Redesign** or reposition tasks to allow elbows to remain close to the body (for example, turn boxes over on their side to allow for easier access).
- **Avoid** awkward postures. For example, reposition tasks in front of workers rather than allowing them to reach above or behind to get supplies.

Repetitive Motions

- **Rotate** workers through repetitive tasks.
- **Use** mechanical aids for chopping, dicing, or mixing foods (such as food processors and mixers) rather than hand chopping or mixing.
- **Reduce** the amount of chopping tasks by purchasing ready-made salads, pre-sliced onions and vegetables, and other pre-prepared foods. This may be limited by budgetary considerations.
- **Restructure** jobs to reduce repeated motions, forceful hand exertions, and prolonged bending.
- **Select** ergonomically designed tools. For example:
  - > Use ergonomically designed kitchen scoops that allow the wrist to remain straight.
  - > Provide ergonomically designed knives that allow the wrist to remain straight.

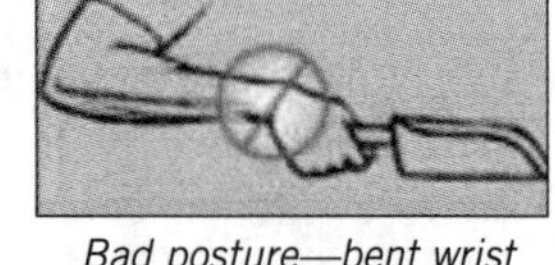

Bad posture—bent wrist

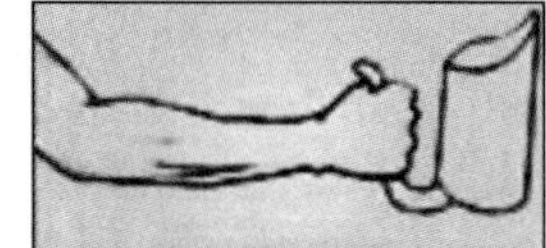

Better scoop—wrist remains straight during use

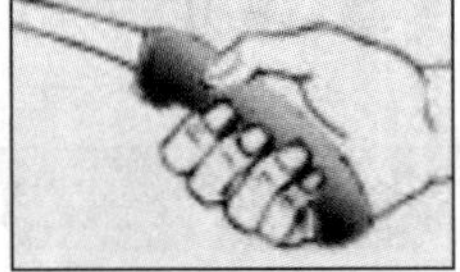

30-degree bend

45-degree bend

Pistol grip

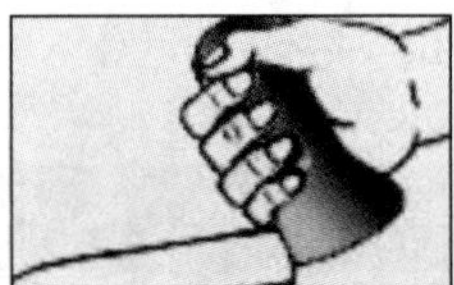

Upright handle

Strains and Sprains Potential Hazard

Workers who cook in restaurants are exposed to strains and sprains from prolonged standing and repetitive or prolonged reaching while cooking and turning food on a hot grill or stove surface.

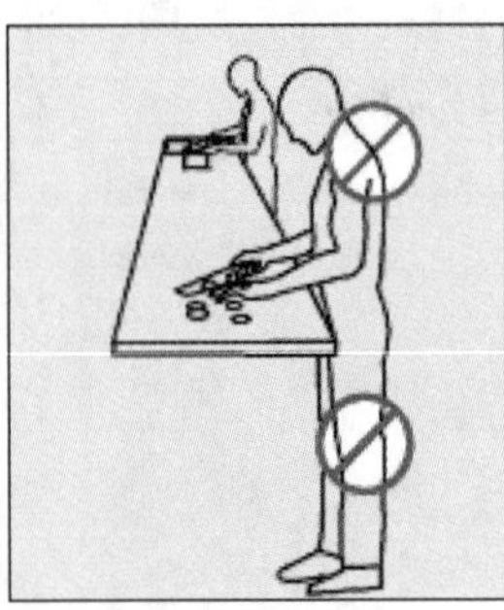

- Static postures may occur as cooks continuously stand in one position while cooking or preparing food, pooling of blood in the lower extremities, muscle fatigue, and pain.
- Prolonged standing on hard work surfaces such as concrete can create contact trauma and pain.
- Awkward neck postures can lead to neck strains and muscle stiffness if a cook constantly tilts the head downward or upward to cook food.
- Repeatedly lifting the arms or over-reaching can irritate the tendons or bursa of the shoulder, possibly to arm and shoulder strain.

(Continued)

Figure 14.1 Examples of Ergonomic Factors *(Continued)*

Young Worker Solutions

Employers have the primary responsibility for protecting the safety and health of their workers. Employees are responsible for following the safe work practices of their employers.

Identify strain and sprain hazards in your worksite and find ways to decrease them by applying ergonomic solutions. For example:

- **Avoid** static postures by continually changing your position. Use a foot rest bar or a low stool to help alter your posture by raising one foot and then the other.
- **Use** anti-fatigue mats, if available, on hard work surfaces. Anti-fatigue mats help contract and expand the muscles of the person standing on them, increasing blood-flow and reducing fatigue.
- **Wear** shoes with well-cushioned insteps and soles.
- **Minimize** reaching by organizing your work environment so that most cooking processes can be completed within easy reach and while keeping your elbows in close to your body.

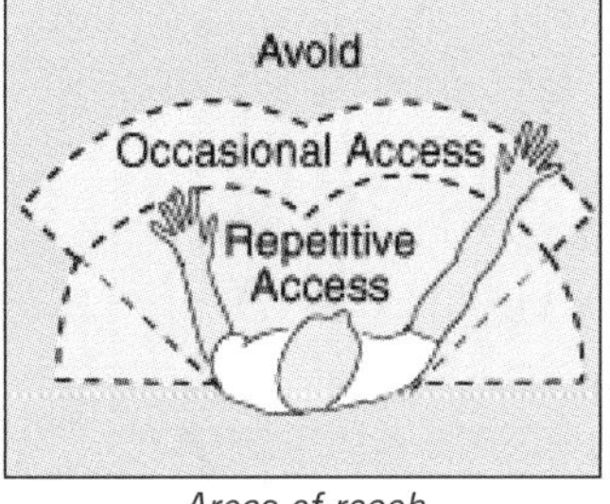

Areas of reach

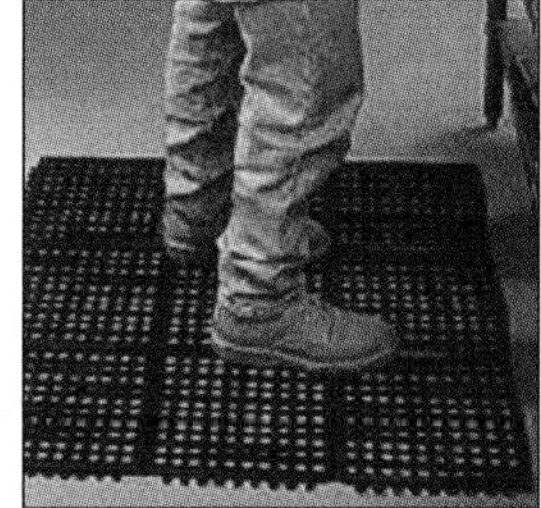
Anti-fatigue mat

Foot rest bar

Source: OSHA and Department of Labor Youth2Work program

If cafeteria operations are to collect cash, space for cashiers, point-of-sale equipment, and other necessary items must be included. Electrical and computer networking requirements are part of this planning component.

Dining area planners must consider not only the number of persons to be served at one time, but also the flow of soiled dishes back to dishwashing areas. Commonly, foodservice operations use a conveyor system to transport soiled dishes. Trash handling is another consideration here. It must be practical for the clients being served; it must comply with sanitation guidelines; and it must also be aesthetically comfortable.

Dining areas greatly influence clients' impressions of a foodservice establishment. The atmosphere of the facility itself, the cleanliness and condition of dining room furniture, fixtures and equipment, lighting, and a wide range of other concerns are important to these impressions. Planning a dining area requires consideration of questions such as:

✓ How many clients must be fed at one time?

✓ How much space should be allocated for each diner?

✓ Who else will be present (service staff, nursing staff, family, etc.), and how much additional space will be needed?

✓ What other activities besides dining services will occur in dining areas? (In many skilled nursing facilities, dining areas become multi-purpose rooms at other times of day.)

✓ What specialized equipment is needed to ensure client comfort?

✓ Will food be served in the dining area such as a salad bar or food cart?

Design of Other Foodservice Areas

In addition to food storage, production, assembly, serving, and dining areas, other spaces also merit planning. Consider the need for an office for Certified Dietary Managers and supervisors. What about space for dish and pot washing, holding of refuse until pickup, space for washing carts and shelving equipment, and so on? Where will cleaning and other chemicals be stored? What about space for refrigeration equipment for walk-in units? Where will mobile transport equipment be stored? Food prep areas have adequate handwashing and prep sinks available, according to local, state or federal codes.

Many healthcare facilities provide certain snacks from decentralized nourishment centers. The foodservice manager should lend expertise about how nourishments can be protected and held.

Space Allocation

The proportions of space used for receiving, storage, production, service, and clean-up can vary, depending on menus and service models. Figure 14.2 indicates the breakdown of space allocations for the traditional 6,000-square-foot kitchen. This is one that essentially cooks food and then serves it.

Figure 14.2 Space Allocation for a Traditional Kitchen

Subsystem	Space Allocation	
Receiving	120 sq. ft.	3.00%
Storage	1,120 sq. ft.	28.00%
Preparation	1,100 sq. ft.	27.50%
Cooking	470 sq. ft	11.75%
Serving	800 sq. ft.	20.00%
Clean-up	390 sq. ft.	9.75%
Subtotal	4,000 sq. ft.	100.00%
Fixed Space*	2,000 sq. ft.	
TOTAL	6,000 sq. ft	

** Includes janitorial storage, restrooms, lounge area, etc.*
Source: John B. Knight, PhD. Purdue University.

How might this allocation vary for other kitchens? A cook-chill kitchen would require much more refrigerated storage space. A kitchen relying intensively on convenience foods or a no-cook kitchen might require a great deal of storage space, but very little production space.

Design Principles and Employees

Your best source for getting input into redesigning or building a new kitchen will come from your current employees. They are the experts who use the equipment and the current kitchen design every day. They can provide you with suggestions about work flow and essential equipment relative to new department designs or construction. If you involve your employees with each

step of the redesign/design project, they will feel valued and you will have valuable information for your planning meetings.

Keep a record each time an employee complains about a piece of equipment or a design element in the kitchen. When you are ready for the redesign/design process, you will already have a head start on your needs. An easy way to document these complaints/suggestions is to have an e-mail file labeled Kitchen Design. Send yourself a quick e-mail each time an employee provides a suggestion or a complaint and then save the e-mail to your file. You will have instant documentation without the effort. Remember to include management needs such as wiring for computers.

Specifying and Purchasing Equipment

The Certified Dietary Manager occasionally needs to purchase capital foodservice equipment. **Capital equipment** is usually defined as expensive equipment with a long life. A capital investment is carried on the balance sheet of the facility. Exactly what qualifies as "expensive" is often defined by the facility. A common figure is $1500 or more.

In many facilities, a Certified Dietary Manager has direct purchasing authority for ongoing supplies and small purchases, but must seek approval to purchase capital equipment. So, the purchasing procedure may be different. A budget justification may be required. In addition, a manager may need to review plans and specifications with a maintenance or engineering expert to plan installation and to assure compliance with all relevant codes and regulations.

Because capital equipment does require significant investment and will become a part of the operation for a long time, purchasing decisions are very important. They merit careful research from energy use through repair history. The entire process requires significant lead time and advance planning because the consequences of new equipment will be around a long time after the purchase.

Before making a purchasing recommendation for capital items, follow these basic background procedures.

Step 1. Determine a need: The need may be defined by recurring problems, such as ongoing equipment breakdown that is not worth repair costs. Alternately, it may be defined by new production needs and service requirements, such as a decision to implement room service or start a catering program. Sometimes the need to replace capital equipment is driven by safety or sanitation concerns or "green" building initiatives.

Step 2. Consider the budget: Since the purchase of large equipment items will involve significant expense, these items generally must be included and approved in a capital budget separate from the department's operating budget.

Step 3. Investigate options: A Certified Dietary Manager may investigate options with a number of suppliers, or with a manufacturers' representative. Conduct a review with vendors, websites and peers to determine what is on the market. A starting point is any known requirements. From these, a Certified Dietary Manager can check available sources, compare features and specifications, and refine a needs list.

Step 4. Consult with others in the organization: A Certified Dietary Manager may need to consult the purchasing department for help in obtaining general information from equipment suppliers about potentially useful items, and help in developing final purchase specifications. Maintenance or engineering staff members responsible for managing the physical facility, code compliance, and utilities must also participate with department employees.

Step 5. Obtain price quotations: For very large purchases, a Certified Dietary Manager may use a process called **request for proposal (RFP)**. This is a formal document stating the requirements for the purchase. It is distributed to potential suppliers, each of whom indicates ability to meet each requirement, along with a price. Using an RFP for capital purchases is very similar to obtaining competitive bids for foods according to specifications. It assures that vendors are being evaluated objectively, and helps a Certified Dietary Manager make a purchasing decision. Price quotations must be very specific, indicating what is and is not covered by the purchase price, such as installation costs, training costs, service, service manuals, and maintenance. In some facilities, purchasing staff may be involved in requesting price quotations from suppliers, comparing quotations, and undertaking supplier negotiations.

Step 6. Prepare a budget justification: For any capital equipment, it is essential to justify the purchase. This is simply sound and responsible business practice. A Certified Dietary Manager needs to assure that the purchase is worth the investment. A **cost justification** or cost benefit analysis compares costs with benefits, so that decision-makers can determine value. The cost benefit analysis should contain an analysis of the:

- ✓ Energy efficiency
- ✓ Service and parts availability
- ✓ Ease of use

Figure 14.3 provides an example of an energy cost benefit analysis for a 24 cu. ft. refrigerator.

Glossary

Capital Equipment
Large equipment with a long life that usually costs over $1,500

Request For Proposal
Request for Proposal (RFP) is a written description of large dollar items that is then sent to suppliers to obtain a competitive bid

Cost Justification
Compares cost with benefits

Figure 14.3 Cost Benefit Analysis for a 24 cu. ft. Refrigerator/Cooler

Cost-Effectiveness Example (Reach-In, Solid Door Refrigerator, 24 cu. ft.)			
Performance	**Base Model**	**User Input**	**Energy Efficient Model**
Daily Energy Use	4.44 kWh	3.70kWh	3.09 kWh
Annual Energy Use	16321 kWh	13151 kWh	1127 kWh
Annual Energy Cost	$211	$176	$147
Lifetime Energy Cost	$2153	$1795	$1500
Lifetime Energy Cost Savings			$653
The Energy Efficient Model is cost-effective if its price is no more than $653 above the price of the Base Model.			

Source: http://www.fishnick.com/saveenergy/tools/calculators/ Used with permission.

Step 7. Make a decision: Again, this decision involves others in the facility. Ultimately, it is finalized in a purchase order or contract with the selected supplier.

In summary, for capital equipment purchases, a Certified Dietary Manager must be involved in:

- ✓ Determining the exact equipment needed
- ✓ Evaluating cost effectiveness and justifying equipment purchases to administrators
- ✓ Working with suppliers to determine specific equipment needs and specifications
- ✓ Analyzing information about alternative equipment items
- ✓ Developing economic analyses to determine which equipment should be purchased
- ✓ Determining compatibility with other equipment and impact on work flow
- ✓ Evaluating equipment safety and ease of use
- ✓ Evaluating sanitation design
- ✓ Determining equipment placement in the food preparation area
- ✓ Helping to develop purchase specifications
- ✓ Working with the supplier awarded the order to coordinate installation, training, and/or other activities
- ✓ Notifying administrators promptly about any problems that might require their attention.

Finding a Supplier for Equipment

To find a supplier, you can use any of the following resources.

Local equipment suppliers. A local supplier may be able to identify options and explain the differences among them. In some locales, there may be a showroom where you can examine actual equipment.

Trade shows. An industry trade show provides the opportunity to see and try equipment in person and discuss needs with a representative.

Trade magazines. Foodservice magazines offer ongoing coverage and advertising related to capital equipment. In addition, there are special (complimentary) magazines devoted solely to foodservice equipment. Some carry complete buyers guides or directories of sources, as well as informational articles about equipment designs and specifications.

The Internet. Major manufacturers of foodservice equipment offer considerable product information on websites. Many also offer contact information for a dealer or representative in your own area who may be able to help you. In addition, a number of foodservice equipment websites catalog products from various suppliers. Interactive tools may allow you to request specifications by fax, or retrieve them directly from the website.

Colleagues. It is also valuable to discuss equipment needs with colleagues, and obtain feedback and ideas about both specifications and products.

Selecting Foodservice Equipment

To make a decision about an equipment purchase, you can review a number of factors:

Suitability for intended use. Since a wide range of equipment products is available for almost any purpose, it is important to consider the suitability of each product. Equipment that is appropriate for the needs of one operation may not be suitable for another. Suitability issues include how well the equipment can perform the required job. They also include the volume of work a piece of equipment can handle, compared with your own productivity requirements. For example, for a pizza oven, you need to consider how many pizzas you will need to cook at a time to meet service requirements, and how long it will take to cook them. Specified equipment must accommodate the load, as well as any anticipated increases in volume. Some equipment is described in terms of a duty cycle, or how many operations it can perform within a specified period of time.

Ease of operation. Equipment should be as easy to use as possible, requiring minimal steps for operation, and providing a user-friendly design. To evaluate this, it's wise to test equipment, and involve employees who will be using it.

Durability and warranty. It is necessary to confirm that the product will stand up to its intended use. A warranty provides some indication of durability, as well as financial protection if the product cannot withstand use. Study a warranty carefully to determine any conditions that apply. Review what is and is not covered by the warranty, and whether service charges may apply.

Construction and safety. Closely aligned with durability is the integrity of the equipment's construction. Equipment must be easy to clean and safe to operate. Compliance with established standards for safety and sanitation are indicated by seals and certifications from various organizations, such as NSF and UL. See Figure 14.4 for a summary. Many pieces of foodservice equipment today are treated with antimicrobial protective compounds that discourage growth of bacteria and mold. These products are incorporated into construction materials and last the lifetime of the equipment.

Compatibility with existing equipment. It is important that equipment be compatible with existing systems. For example, trays being purchased must fit into existing carts, and attachments for electric mixers must fit existing equipment. As applicable, be sure equipment being purchased will fit into available space, integrate into existing structures and utility systems, move through existing doorways, and is compatible with existing wiring. Is equipment compatible with ADA regulations?

Assistance provided before and after purchase. Before a purchase, some suppliers provide design analysis, technical analysis, creative suggestions, and a plan for operational integration. After a purchase, suppliers may provide delivery, installation, on-site testing, demonstration, training, and maintenance. Evaluate and clarify tasks such as these. In cases where a supplier is not supplying these services, it is also important to determine how each will be accomplished, and what costs will be incurred.

Figure 14.4 Approval Agencies for Foodservice Equipment

National Sanitation Foundation (approval designated by the NSF seal): Provides standards for materials, design, construction, performance, cleanability, and foodservice sanitation.

Underwriters Laboratories (approval designed by the UL mark): Provides testing and certification to verify that electrical or gas equipment is safe to operate. Appliances are tested to ensure they comply with fire safety requirements and won't emit shock.

American Gas Association (AGA Certification): Provides safety testing services for gas appliances through the International Approval Service.

International Standards Organization (ISO): ISO standards address quality in manufacturing. Through compliance with established standards, a manufacturer can become ISO certified.

Agencies providing Energy information for Foodservice Equipment Energy Star®: Provides a listing of Energy Star commercial equipment. www.energystar.gov/products.

North American Association of Food Equipment Manufacturers (NAFEM): A trade organization that provides links to equipment companies. www.nafem.org

The Food Service Technology Center (FSTC): Provides fact sheets and other publications such as energy efficiency calculators on commercial equipment.

Federal Energy Management Program: Provides up-to-date information on energy efficient federal procurement, including the latest recommendations. http://www1.eere.energy.gov/femp/

Price. A detailed clarification of price incorporates the items above. In comparing prices from alternate suppliers, be sure you are comparing a bottom-line figure that reflects all associated costs.

Operating cost. This is different from price, but is critical in the evaluation of what a piece of equipment will cost. Operating costs include the cost of energy to use the equipment, as well as the cost of supplies. Some equipment uses proprietary, disposable supplies available only from the manufacturer. Pricing for such supplies must be evaluated carefully. To evaluate costs, it can be useful to project supply costs over a period of one year.

Service and reputation. As with food purchasing decisions, ultimate success with a purchase depends on a supplier's reliability in meeting commitments and the quality of service provided.

Types of Equipment. The menu you are serving, your style of service, and the number of meals served daily will have the greatest impact on the types of equipment you need. Figure 14.5 summarizes equipment options for preparing a variety of menu items. Each type of foodservice will need different equipment. Figure 14.6 outlines preparation equipment suitable for a school foodservice operation based on number of meals served daily. See Appendix B for a full listing and description of types of equipment.

Figure 14.5 Equipment and the Menu

		Ovens		Steam Equipment					Broilers	
	Ranges	Convec-tion	Cook & Hold	Steamers	Kettles	Braising Pans	Fryers	Griddles	Cheese-melters	Char-Broilers
Breakfast										
Eggs	•	•		•	•	•		•		
Pancakes	•					•		•		
Biscuits	•	•	•							
Bacon	•	•	•			•		•		
Hash Browns	•	•	•			•		•		
Appetizers										
Soups	•				•	•				
Pizza	•	•	•							
Shrimp	•	•		•	•	•	•	•	•	•
Fish	•	•		•	•	•	•	•	•	•
Scallop Gratin	•	•	•						•	
Potato Skins	•	•	•						•	
Entrees										
Steak	•	•				•		•	•	•
Roast Beef	•	•				•				
Whole Chicken	•	•	•		•	•				
Meatloaf	•	•	•			•				
Lamb	•	•			•			•	•	•
Veal	•	•			•	•		•	•	•
Burgers 4 oz.	•	•				•		•	•	•
Ribs	•	•	•	•	•	•				•
Chicken Parts	•	•	•	•	•	•	•	•		•
Shellfish	•	•		•	•	•	•	•	•	•
Salmon	•	•		•	•	•		•	•	•
Vegetables										
Grilled	•							•		•
Steamed	•		•	•	•	•				
Boiled	•				•	•				
In cream sauce	•	•			•	•				
Au Gratin	•	•	•						•	
Sautéed	•					•				
Sides										
Sauces	•				•	•				
Gratin Potatoes	•	•	•						•	
Baked Potatoes	•	•	•							
Mashed Potates	•	•	•	•	•	•				
Fries		•					•			
Rice	•		•	•	•	•				
Desserts & Bakery										
Breads	•	•								
Soufflés	•	•								
Pastries	•	•								
Cakes	•	•								
Creme Brulee	•	•	•						•	

Courtesy Vulcan-Hart. Reprinted with permission.

Figure 14.6 **Food Preparation Equipment for School Foodservice**

Preparation Equipment	Meals Prepared Per Day		
	<400	401-700	701-1000
Convection Ovens	(1) double	(2) double	(3) double
Tilting Braising Pans	(1) 23 or 30 gallon	(1) 23 or 30 gal & (1) 40 gal	(2) 40 gallon
Kettles	(1) 10 gallon	(1) 20 gallon	(1) 10 gal & (1) 20 gal
Steamers	(1) 2 compartment	(1) 2 compartment	(2) 2 compartment
Ranges	(1) 2-burner	(1) 2-burner	(1) 2-burner
Mixers	(1) 60 qt w/ 30 qt attachments	(1) 60 qt w/ 30 qt attachments	(1) 30 qt & (1) 60 qt
Slicers	(1) automatic	(1) automatic	(2) automatic
Food Processors	(1) tabletop	(1) tabletop	(1) tabletop
Heated Cabinets: Pass-thru or Reach-in	1 section	2 section	3 section
Refrigerators: Pass-thru or Reach-in	1 section	2 section	2 section

Source: Adapted from National Food Service Management Institute. University of Mississippi. Guidelines for Equipment to Healthy Meals. NFSMI-R-25-96. Used with permission.

Equipment Specifications

Any piece of equipment you choose for a foodservice department is available with alternatives and options. In preparing a capital budget or even making a small equipment purchase, you may need to develop an **equipment specification**. This is a detailed description of the product. In cases where you will ask multiple suppliers to quote equipment, as in an RFP, the specification is important for ensuring that you compare like features in a like manner while obtaining quotes. The specification nails down what you need and is essential for ensuring that what you purchase will meet your needs precisely.

To develop a specification, it helps to do some product research first so that you have an idea of what you can realistically expect. Next, answer questions about the product you will need, such as:

- ✓ What size or capacity is required?
- ✓ What time constraints must the product meet, e.g. cooking time for a particular product, number of dishes per hour, etc.?
- ✓ What construction materials do you want, e.g. stainless steel (___ gauge), glass, aluminum, antimicrobial treatment, etc.?
- ✓ What exterior finish do you want?
- ✓ For power equipment, do you need gas or electric, and to what specifications (e.g. 220 volt)?
- ✓ What motor do you need (e.g. ___ HP)?
- ✓ What technologies should equipment use, e.g. convection, conduction, pressureless steam, etc.?
- ✓ What water treatment systems or filtering systems do you require?
- ✓ What approvals do you require (UL, NSF, etc.)?

Glossary

Equipment Specification
A detailed description providing information needed to purchase a piece of equipment

- ✓ Where will this unit reside—floor model, countertop, under counter, etc.? Does it need legs or wheels?
- ✓ What space dimensions are available (specify length, width, depth, and height)?
- ✓ If the unit has doors that open, in what direction will they open, and what amount of space is available?
- ✓ What pan or tray sizes should this equipment use (if applicable)?
- ✓ What user features do you require, e.g. control panel features, manual or automatic functioning, multiple speed options, etc.?
- ✓ What special features do you need, e.g. HACCP data logging, programmable memory, optional accessories, etc.? (a range is typically sold with one oven rack or no oven rack—do you need more?)
- ✓ What features do you want to enhance cleanability, e.g. easy disassembly, self-cleaning options, etc.?
- ✓ What safety and ergonomic features do you require, such as auto shut-off when not in use, guards for sharp components, etc.?
- ✓ How will equipment be installed, and by whom?
- ✓ Where should utility connections be provided (back, side, etc.)?
- ✓ What are your warranty requirements (parts and/or service, for what period of time)?
- ✓ What energy-saving or energy efficiency requirements do you require (KW or BTU usage)?
- ✓ What training needs do you want to specify?

A sample equipment specification appears in Figure 14.7. You will also want to consult with suppliers for information, and with in-house engineering staff to be sure you are specifying power requirements and installation needs correctly. Once your specification is complete, you can provide it to suppliers and ask them for a quote. While you want to make a specification detailed enough to ensure your needs are met, leave some space for flexibility. In the final analysis, your specification should be realistic and attainable for a number of competing products in the marketplace.

Financing Capital Equipment Purchases

Financing may be a special concern, especially if adequate funds are not immediately available. In some situations, a facility may lease equipment. Leasing can also be a way to test feasibility of a new idea. For example, a facility desiring to test a satellite delivery program may use leased equipment for a short-term trial.

In another payment scenario, the supplier may finance the purchase. With a typical financing arrangement, an initial down payment is necessary at the time equipment is ordered to protect the supplier against costs incurred if the order is canceled. Another payment may be required at the time of delivery, and the remaining balance may be financed by the supplier at a defined interest rate. A Certified Dietary Manager needs to work closely with the business office to consider financing options.

Figure 14.7 Sample Specification—Convection Oven

Equipment Name:	Convection Oven, Floor model, Double Stack
Location:	Main kitchen, floor
Intended Use:	Hot food preparation for muffins, roasts, casseroles, potatoes, and similar products
Dimensions:	Must fit in area 5' x 5' x 5', maximum 70" in height
Power and Motor:	Gas, rear connection with auto shutoff valve; 44,000 BTU/hour; 115 volt electrical connection; ½ HP motor
Capacity:	10 10" x 26" pans with adjustable rack guides
Construction Details:	Stainless steel front, sides, and top; porcelain enamel on interior; glass windows on doors; wheels and casters
Other Features:	Auto-ignition, interior oven light; cook and hold cycle; minimum 5 programmable cooking settings
Approval:	UL listed, NSF seal, AGA certified, Energy Star
Warranty:	3 years parts and labor (minimum)
Delivery & Installation:	To be provided
Training:	On-site training required (one-time)

Sometimes suppliers offer special deals related to equipment in conjunction with food purchases. For example, a supplier of waffle batter may offer the specialized iron required to make waffles on a free-use basis for as long as the operation is purchasing the batter. This can be helpful with cash flow. However, it's important to evaluate a decision to bring in this equipment by all established criteria and to evaluate the overall costs of using the supplier's products.

When a capital budget is tight, another option is to purchase used equipment. This can be an alternative when funds are not available; when compatibility with other, older equipment is an issue; and/or when a facility does not need equipment that has a long life. Used equipment can become available as equipment suppliers receive trade-ins, as discontinued businesses hold auctions, as government agencies offer sales of surplus items, or as contracts expire on leased equipment and leasing companies sell the equipment. There are even used-equipment dealers in some large municipalities.

While availability may exist, there are, of course, some disadvantages to purchasing used equipment. Typically, used equipment does not include a warranty. The equipment may be sold on a cash-only basis. Responsibilities for moving and installing the equipment may rest with the buyer. The life expectancy of used equipment is typically shorter than that of new equipment, and used equipment may not have newer, preferred energy-saving design qualities. Maintenance requirements may be greater, compared with new equipment, and it is unlikely that competitive bids are possible. It may also be difficult to match required specifications with used equipment items that are available. It will be difficult to determine the severity of previous use, and the Certified Dietary Manager may need to deal with unfamiliar supplier sources and may have difficulty securing required service or parts.

When developing a specification for a commercial food processor, what information would you need to consider?

(Check your answer at the end of this chapter)

Equipment Maintenance

The best way to maintain equipment is through in-depth training on the use and upkeep of the piece of equipment. See Figure 14.8 for a list of common equipment training needs. Initial training on complex equipment is typically provided by the supplier. Training techniques used may include demonstrations, practice, or CDs. Some equipment bears clear labels with instructions and safety precautions. A Certified Dietary Manager may also create a simple cheat sheet or poster outlining operational steps.

Figure 14.8 Common Equipment Training Needs

- Overview—what this equipment is for
- How to turn equipment on and off
- Basic operational steps
- Safety precautions
- Protective equipment to use if required
- How to identify and use special attachments, and what each is for
- Procedures for cleaning and sanitizing
- Auto shut-off features
- Routine disassembly/reassembly (for cleaning)
- Procedures for cleaning and sanitizing (and what products to use)
- Food safety precautions (e.g. how to avoid cross-contamination when using a slicer)
- Use of self-cleaning features
- Use of programmable controls
- How to ensure adequate functioning
- Use of data logging, temperature monitoring, or related systems
- How to add consumable supplies
- Preventative maintenance
- Signs of trouble and reporting procedures

Maintain operating manuals and associated literature such as purchase price, vendor, and maintenance records in a well-organized equipment file, accessible to all who may need it.

All equipment requires basic care. A simple example is routine cleaning and sanitizing after use. On another level, many pieces of equipment require periodic preventative work to limit breakdowns and ensure maximum lifetime. Finally, equipment can experience breakdowns that require immediate repair.

Cleaning Schedule

Part of a Certified Dietary Manager's responsibility is to plan and manage all phases of maintenance. The first step is to define a cleaning schedule and assign tasks to employees. A cleaning schedule must flow from the production and service schedules, so that cleaning takes place when equipment is not in use, and cleaning and sanitation are completed before a cook needs to use equipment. To make a cleaning schedule effective, prepare a schedule, and make employees accountable. Most operations ask employees to sign off on cleaning tasks. On a daily basis, it's important to inspect this work and talk with employees about their responsibilities. Employees should also be encouraged to report any problems or concerns about equipment to the manager.

Specific cleaning procedures vary greatly from one piece of equipment to another, so it is important to develop procedures from manufacturers' instructions. As cleaning products are required, it is also important to name them specifically by product name for employees, rather than using generic terms.

Cleaning instructions should be readily available to assigned employees. Of course, cleaning should also be the subject of employee training and periodic review. An example of a cleaning procedure appears in Figure 14.9.

Figure 14.9 Sample Policy and Procedure: Equipment Cleaning

Department: Foodservice

Date: 10/20/05

Approval By: Joe Jones, Certified Dietary Manager

Subject or Title: Cleaning Electric Mixers

Policy: It is the policy of ABC Nursing Home that electric mixers be properly cleaned after each use according to the following procedure.

Procedure:

1. **Removable Parts:**
   a. Immediately after use, take bowls, beaters, and all removable parts to pot sink for washing and sanitizing according to manual pot-washing instructions.
   b. Fill both compartments of pail with warm water. To the wash compartment, add Cream Suds in the ratio of 2 oz. per gallon of water; to the rinse side, add Mikroklene in the ratio of 1 oz. per gallon. Use separate sponges for wash and rinse compartments.
   c. Rinse thoroughly with sponge dipped in sanitizing rinse solution and squeezed nearly dry. Dip and wring sponge frequently so all parts are sanitized.
   d. Allow removable parts to air dry on sanitary drying rack.
   e. Replace removable parts.
   f. Return cleaning equipment to proper storage.
2. **Stationary Parts:**
   a. Fill both compartments of pail with warm water. To the wash compartment, add Cream Suds in the ratio of 2 oz. per gallon of water; to the rinse side, add Mikroklene in the ratio of 1 oz. per gallon. Use separate sponges for wash and rinse compartments.
   b. Use sponge and detergent solution to thoroughly scrub all stationary parts of mixer. Pay particular attention to underside of head, corners, handles, and underneath rolled rims.
   c. Rinse thoroughly with sponge dipped in sanitizing rinse solution and squeezed nearly dry. Dip and wring sponge frequently so all parts are sanitized.
   d. Return cleaning equipment to proper storage.

Preventative Maintenance

Beyond cleaning, a Certified Dietary Manager should plan a preventative maintenance schedule for all equipment. **Preventative maintenance**, an organized routine of cleaning, inspecting, and maintaining equipment, is essential to ensure that:

✓ Equipment operates at maximum efficiency, often with savings in energy costs.

✓ Equipment works correctly.

✓ Equipment attains its maximum life expectancy.

✓ Unscheduled downtime is minimized.

Several basic steps can be used to develop preventative maintenance programs.

1. Identify and list all equipment in the foodservice facility that needs periodic inspection and maintenance. This includes equipment not only in the kitchen, but also in serving areas, clean-up areas, decentralized kitchens or pantries, and other areas.

Preventative Maintenance
An organized routine of cleaning, inspecting and maintaining equipment

2. Review maintenance requirements. Typically, this information is developed by the manufacturer and provided with the equipment at the time of purchase. You can incorporate manufacturer's recommendations about equipment maintenance into a preventative maintenance and repair log as illustrated in Figure 14.10. The log should identify routine maintenance functions and how often they need to be completed. This may include items such as oiling a motor or replacing a fluid. The form should also identify the equipment name, model, manufacturer, serial number, and purchase date. As routine maintenance and/or repairs are conducted, the log should document each activity.

3. Set up a schedule of preventative maintenance. Depending upon the equipment item, maintenance work may be necessary on a weekly, semi-annual, or other basis. Figure 14.11 illustrates a preventative maintenance schedule used for this purpose. This sample summarizes required preventative maintenance activities for a six-month period. Some operators track preventative maintenance activities through computerized systems—with a simple spreadsheet, or a software application designed expressly for equipment management.

4. Maintain complete documentation of all maintenance and repair activity. More than just paperwork, this documentation helps in identifying and justifying decisions to replace equipment. A piece of equipment whose repair overhead becomes excessive is often a candidate for replacement. With documentation, a Certified Dietary Manager can determine when replacement will be cost-effective.

Certain preventative maintenance tasks may require the work of individuals outside the foodservice department. For example, in-house engineering or maintenance staff may handle maintenance on a conveyor system, a small engine, or ventilation hoods and fans. Some facilities make use of maintenance or service contracts with suppliers. Under this plan, eligible suppliers bid on the facility's maintenance needs. Quotations may be based upon time and materials, which means the client pays for labor and supplies each time he or she orders repair service. Or, a contract may be structured to provide any needed services and parts for a set monthly fee. Arrangements such as these may apply to repairs as well as preventative maintenance, and often the two are bundled into a service agreement.

Regardless of the players involved, a Certified Dietary Manager bears responsibility for assuring that all preventative maintenance tasks are defined and tracked. In addition, it is important to assure that preventative maintenance meets manufacturers' recommendations, both to ensure effectiveness and to preserve the validity of any equipment warranty.

Over the past month a repair service has been called four times for your high-temp dishwasher that is 10 years old. What should you be documenting?

(Check your answer at the end of this chapter)

Figure 14.10 Equipment Maintenance and Repair Log

Service ____________________ Type Machine ________________ Equipment No. ______________

Location ____________________ Serial No. ________________ Model No. ______________

Make ____________________ Date Purchased ________________ Purchase Cost ______________

Preventative Maintenance Procedure

Function	Interval

Special Instructions

Specifications

Voltage	Drive
Amperage	Belts
Phase	Fuse
Pressure	Lubrication
Horsepower	Filter
RPM	Fluids

Spare Parts Required

Part	Mfr. Part No.	Hotel Stock No.	Quantity

Date	By	Work Performed	Hours	Material	Labor	Cost to Date

Figure 14.11 Preventative Maintenance Schedule

	Month:	January				February				March				April				May				June			
Equipment Item	Work Necessary Week:	1	2	3	4	1	2	3	4	1	2	3	4	1	2	3	4	1	2	3	4	1	2	3	4

Managing the Cost of Supplies

Chemical products are needed to clean dishes, pots and pans, and work areas. A wide range of products is available. Check with your supplier for ideas about available items and recommended uses, and use your supplier representative as a partner to help resolve cleaning and sanitation problems in the operation.

Cleaning supplies should be kept in non-food storage areas. As is true with other foodservice inventory, cleaning supplies must be properly controlled. Since these products are expensive, a formal issuing system similar to that used to control expensive food products may be in order. You may also decide to track usage of products. With a stable participation level, why would an increasing (or decreasing) amount of cleaning supplies be needed? Routinely ask and answer questions such as this.

Product selection also plays a role in supply cost management. Sometimes, a cost-benefit study is necessary to confirm which product is the most potentially useful. To undertake this study, first define what the product is to do. Then, ask suppliers for suggestions about and samples of products that they believe will be useful. Using the instructions provided by the manufacturer, test each product. Then objectively determine which meet your requirements.

From that group of products, next examine cost. For example, one gallon of a cleaning agent may cost $50 but clean twice as many square feet, compared with a less expensive product. Study is necessary to define the cost per square foot, rack of dishes, load of laundry, and so on, to make a fair comparison. This boils down to a usage cost, rather than a purchase price.

Another cost control consideration relates to how employees use products. Sometimes, employees are tempted to over-use cleaning products, in a belief that more is better. This not only costs money; it may also pose safety concerns. Training and ongoing supervision are in order. As applicable, also assure that the correct measuring or portioning devices are on hand to eliminate guesswork.

For certain equipment, supply usage is largely controlled by the equipment itself for self-cleaning. High-pressure cleaning systems with applicable chemicals are also used for cleaning many items. Monitoring supply usage can help you identify when there is a malfunction. Prompt service, in turn, can get supply usage under control.

The need for selecting a reputable supplier is just as important for the purchase of chemicals as it is for the purchase of food products, capital equipment items, and other purchases. The supplier must be honest, fair, and knowledgeable about the product needs of foodservices; must provide competitive pricing; must consistently meet the quality and quantity requirements of the facility; and must deliver the needed supplies in time.

Management in the News

ENERGY STAR®, a U.S. Environmental Protection Agency program, helps us all save money and protect our environment through energy-efficient products and practices. For more information, visit www.energystar.gov.

Look for the ENERGY STAR and Find Savings in Your Commercial Kitchen

Learn more at: www.energystar.gov/cfs

There are eight types of commercial food service (CFS) equipment that can earn EPA's ENERGY STAR. Qualified equipment models contribute to a cleaner environment by using less energy and less water than conventional CFS models. Since most commercial kitchen equipment lasts eight years or more, maximize your savings potential by choosing ENERGY STAR when replacing your appliances.

Compared to conventional CFS equipment, ENERGY STAR qualified equipment could save you the following over their lifetimes:

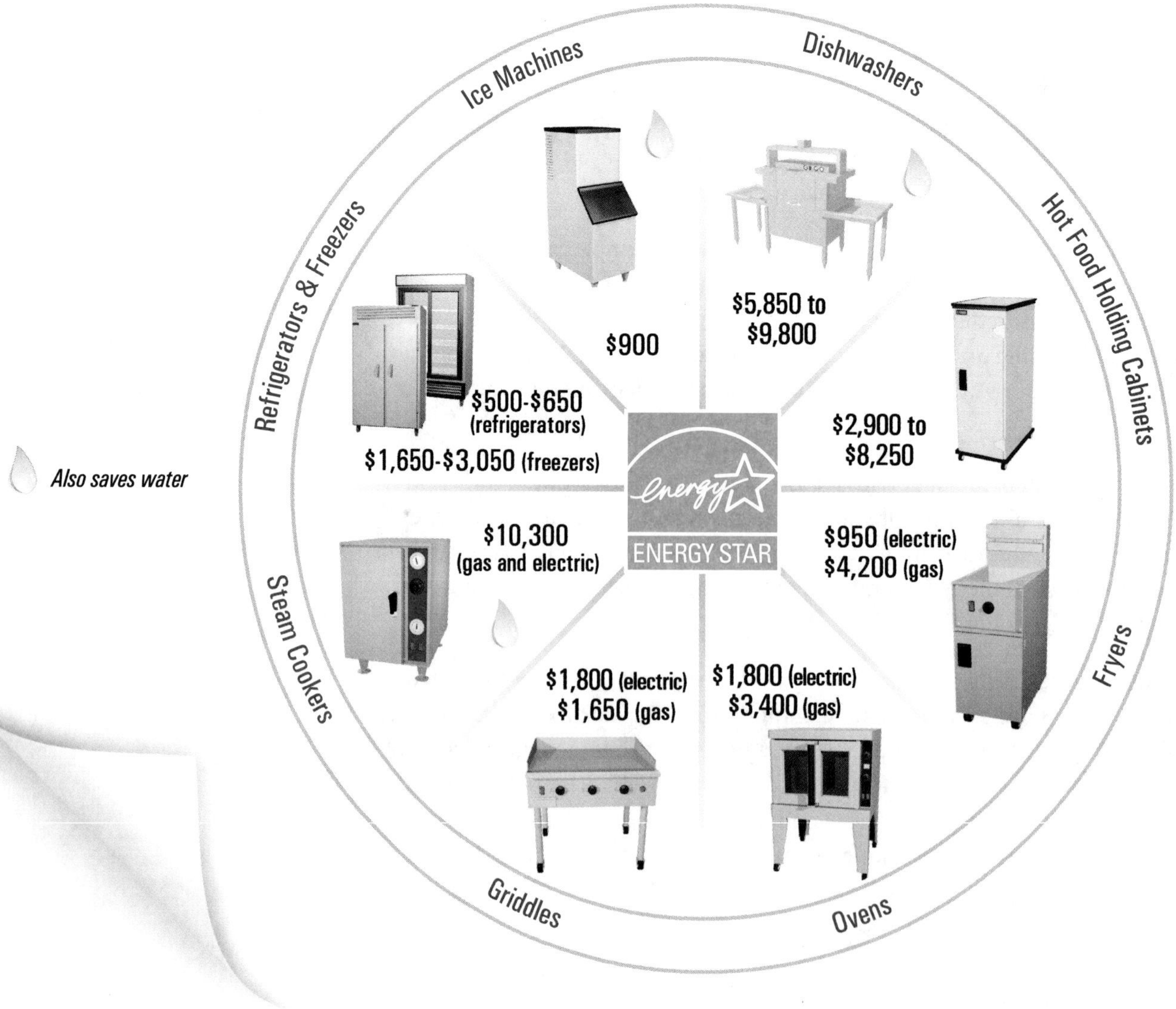

- Ice Machines: $900 (also saves water)
- Dishwashers: $5,850 to $9,800 (also saves water)
- Hot Food Holding Cabinets: $2,900 to $8,250
- Fryers: $950 (electric) $4,200 (gas)
- Ovens: $1,800 (electric) $3,400 (gas)
- Griddles: $1,800 (electric) $1,650 (gas)
- Steam Cookers: $10,300 (gas and electric) (also saves water)
- Refrigerators & Freezers: $500-$650 (refrigerators) $1,650-$3,050 (freezers)

Also saves water

Management in the News *(Continued)*

Where to Start Saving: Five Easy Steps!

1. **Install ENERGY STAR compact fluorescent lamps** (CFLs) in your walk-in refrigerators and kitchen ventilation hoods (and throughout your restaurant where appropriate).
2. **Install a high-efficiency pre-rinse spray valve** in your dishroom and save hundreds of dollars a year! For more information, visit: www.fishnick.com/equipment/sprayvalves.
3. **Fix water leaks immediately**—especially hot water leaks: wasted water, sewer, and water heating costs can add up to hundreds of dollars a year.
4. **Perform walk-in refrigerator maintenance:** check and replace door gaskets; clean evaporator and condenser coils; check refrigerant charge.
5. **Replace worn-out cooking and refrigeration equipment** with ENERGY STAR qualified models!

Other Energy Star Qualified Products

- **Lighting**—Install ENERGY STAR qualified fixtures and CFLs in your dining area and reduce energy consumption and heat output by 75% per bulb without sacrificing aesthetics.
- **Televisions**—Turn your TVs green, even the big screens, by selecting ENERGY STAR qualified televisions.
- **Audio/Video (A/V) Products**—Outfit the rest of your restaurant's entertainment system with ENERGY STAR qualified A/V products, which include DVD and Blu-Ray disc players, receivers, amplifiers, and speakers.
- **Office Equipment**—Purchase ENERGY STAR qualified computers and monitors, enable power management and expect to save $10–85 per year.
- **Heating and Cooling**—To save additional money in your restaurant, look for the ENERGY STAR for bathroom (ventilating) fans as well as heating, ventilation, and cooling (HVAC) units.
  - Ventilating fans: save $75 per year
  - HVAC: save $430 per year or $4,200 over the equipment's lifetime

For additional information, please visit the ENERGY STAR Web site at: www.energystar.gov/products

Did You Know?

The annual cost to operate a single gas (or electric) fryer is often more than the annual gas (or electric) bill of an average U.S. house!

Show Me the Money!

Many utilities offer monetary incentives to offset the added purchase cost of ENERGY STAR qualified CFS equipment. Find out if there are incentives in your area by visiting: www.energystar.gov/ CFSRebate_Locator.

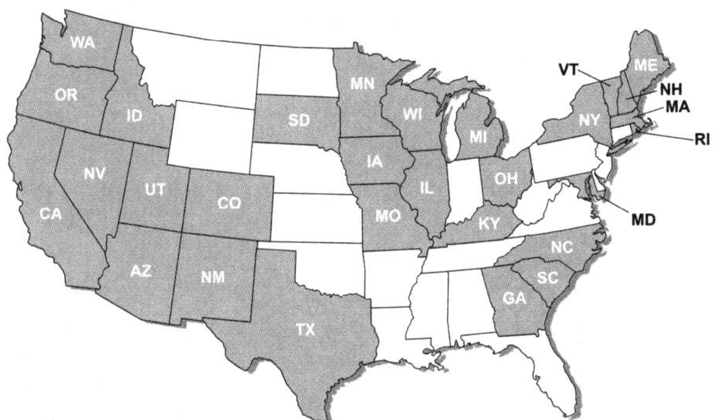

Blue states have utilities that offer incentives for energy-efficient CFS equipment

Join hundreds of other restaurants and work with ENERGY STAR to take part in the energy efficiency revolution: www.energystar.gov/restaurants.

430F09082

ENERGY STAR would like to thank the PG&E Food Service Technology Center (FSTC) for their assistance with this fact sheet and for the use of their equipment images. The PG&E FSTC program is funded by CA ratepayers under the auspices of the California Public Utilities Commission (CPUC) Energy Efficiency Program. Learn more at: www.fishnick.com.

END OF CHAPTER

Putting It Into Practice Questions & Answers

1. When considering design factors, how would your considerations for temperature and humidity be different for a kitchen versus a dining room?

   A. ***Kitchen:*** *Temperatures and humidity will vary greatly due to cooking and steaming equipment. Your menu will help you determine how much the cooking and steaming equipment will be used on the average. Then, you will need to select an appropriate hood ventilation system to handle the temperature and humidity needs. Another consideration is the noise level of the hoods. Will that interfere with conversation in the dining room...particularly with clients who might be hard of hearing? Suppliers can help you estimate your needs and determine if your hoods are compatible with the facility HVAC system.*

   Dining Room: *Temperatures, humidity, and noise levels will need to be maintained at a level comfortable with the clients.*

2. You are considering a culture change and plan to move away from a trayline and implement restaurant service in the dining room. What design considerations do you need to consider when planning for this change?

   A. *How will you serve in the dining room? Can the trayline steamtable be retrofitted to something that can be moved to the dining room during the service hours? Plates can be plated in the dining room based on client orders. Or, perhaps you will use the trayline steam table in the kitchen and use waitstaff in the dining room who will carry orders to the kitchen. Either way, the trayline assembly will need to be retrofitted or a new service system established.*

3. When developing a specification for a commercial food processor, what information would you need to consider?

   A. *The first question you need to answer is: how will this piece of equipment be used? Work with your cooks to determine how they see the equipment being used. For instance, if the cooks want equipment that can slice, dice, and shred, that will help you write the specification for the equipment. Secondly, how much and what products will be processed at one time will help you determine the size you need. Purchasing a small food processor when your cooks want to dice one hundred pounds of potatoes at a time may mean they won't be able to use it when it arrives.*

4. Over the past month a repair service has been called four times for your high-temp dishwasher that is 10 years old. What should you be documenting?

   A. *Document each time the service was called, the name of the technician, what was repaired and the cost of the service and repair. If the dishwasher was down over a meal and you had to use paper plates, be sure and add that cost to your documentation. Document any other costs associated with the repairs. For a dishwasher that is 10 years old, you will soon be able to provide justification for a new dishwasher, especially if the new dishwashers are more energy efficient.*

CHAPTER 15

Represent Department at External Meetings

Overview and Objectives

In any organization, you can expect to become involved in interdepartmental teams, committees, and task forces. Your obligation is to effectively represent your department by prepared, professional, and ensuring that department activities are coordinated with overall facility systems.

After completing this chapter, you should be able to:

- ✓ Communicate department goals and policies
- ✓ Describe interdisciplinary relationships
- ✓ Identify methods of communicating with other departments
- ✓ Suggest cooperative ways to solve problems
- ✓ Participate in state/national professional meetings
- ✓ Distribute client information assuring confidentiality
- ✓ Honor client (patient/resident) rights and confidentiality

In many respects, a Certified Dietary Manager functions as a communicator and facilitator. This role is especially true when representing your department at external meetings. You must understand both the facility needs and expectations and how your department team can carry them through. Ensuring that department activities are coordinated with overall systems requires cooperation and excellent ongoing communication at external meetings.

External Meetings

There are at least two categories of external meetings where you need to represent your department: Interdepartmental meetings and professional association meetings.

Interdepartmental Meetings

Care teams. In healthcare facilities, there is usually a team approach to the care of clients. The team may be composed of a Certified Dietary Manager, a Registered Dietitian, a diet technician, a nurse, a physical therapist, an occupational therapist, a speech therapist, a social worker, a clinical pharmacist, a physician, and/or many others. How a team is structured and the roles of each team member are governed by healthcare standards as well as the policies and practices of each facility.

Task Forces and Committees. As a Certified Dietary Manager, you may be asked to represent the foodservice department on a number of facility committees and task forces. Committees and task forces are formal units chaired by an appointed chairperson. Meetings are regularly scheduled. In meetings such as these, attendance and minutes typically are recorded and distributed to all members. Committees and task forces are established to:

- ✓ Coordinate activities within the organization
- ✓ Solve problems
- ✓ Evaluate or revise systems
- ✓ Devise plans for meeting objectives.

As a Certified Dietary Manager, you may be asked to serve on facility-wide committees such as:

- ✓ Infection Control. This committee's usual purpose is to develop policies and procedures for sanitation techniques, isolation procedures, reporting of infectious diseases, and educating and training all personnel.
- ✓ Safety Committee. A typical purpose of this committee is to review all unsafe acts within the facility, both for clients and others; to establish fire safety and disaster preparedness; to implement OSHA and other regulatory standards; and to provide education and training materials for all personnel.
- ✓ Cost Control. The purpose of this committee may be to provide, develop, and implement cost-effectiveness procedures and plans.
- ✓ Quality Assessment and Improvement. The purpose of this committee is to monitor, evaluate, and document actions for the provision of quality service and products for all clients.
- ✓ Customer/Client Service. A committee such as this may focus on ways to improve customer/client service and satisfaction in all areas.
- ✓ Marketing Committee. You will want to be involved if your facility is expanding services such as foodservice.

There may be other committees to which you belong. The number and types of committees vary from one facility to the next.

In a committee, a group of persons work together to solve problems and perform assigned administrative activities. This group is granted specific authority. Committees may be temporary or permanent. Committees are usually appointed for ongoing activities and may be mandated by regulatory agencies.

Task forces are usually appointed to deal with specific problems. Members of a task force analyze a problem, complete research, and make recommendations for action. Once the problem is solved, the task force is usually disbanded. For example, a healthcare facility may set up a task force to examine how well systems serve clients and to recommend revisions. Another facility may set up a task force to examine whether or how to use Web-based purchasing.

Professional Association Meetings

As you complete your training to become a Certified Dietary Manager, you may wonder what should happen next. Most likely, you will seek certification as proof of your newly developed competencies. You may also consider joining one or more professional associations. Joining an association of like professionals allows you to grow both professionally and personally. The following are some examples of the benefits of membership:

- ✓ Networking opportunities. Networking, or interacting with others in your profession, can be an excellent source of support, resources, ideas, and friendship. By networking with others, you usually discover that your management challenges are not unique, and that you and colleagues can help each other advance the practice of foodservice management. Some professional associations, such as Association of Nutrition & Foodservice Professionals, offer Web-based discussion areas or chat rooms, where members can meet with others from diverse locations to discuss professional issues. These associations may also offer local meetings where you can become involved in joint projects or joint problem solving.
- ✓ Educational opportunities. Professional associations are one of the best resources for educational sessions, meetings, and materials that help develop your own skills and continue professional growth.
- ✓ Research. A professional association typically conducts research on matters of interest to its members, such as salaries, professional practices, and other issues. This research is shared with members.
- ✓ Publications. A professional association issues publications that address the unique needs and interests of its members.
- ✓ Employment services. Many professional associations operate job boards on the Web. Here, you may find information about employment opportunities that relate to your own qualifications.
- ✓ Contact with suppliers. Through trade events and vendor relationships, professional associations become a conduit for information about suppliers and vendors who may specifically address the business needs of members.
- ✓ Legislative activity. A professional association may lobby for the interests of its members in state and regional governments, supporting legislation that supports the interests of the profession and the industry.

Joining a professional association presents many opportunities. Once you belong, you may take a passive or an active role. Most professionals agree that you gain a great deal by contributing time and energy to an association. Joining in activities, serving on committees, or becoming a leader all advance your professional development. Whatever your role, remember you are representing your facility and your department.

Certified Dietary Manager Role

To work well in a team, it is important to understand your role. Roles of the members of the foodservice team have been defined by the Academy of Nutrition and Dietetics (AND) [formerly known as the American Dietetic Association (ADA)] through its role delineation studies and the Association of

Foodservice & Nutrition Professionals (ANFP) in its role delineation studies. The AND and the ANFP are responsible for setting educational requirements, program approvals, and continuing education standards for their credentialed members.

In addition, each of these organizations provides standards of practice for professional members. Standards of practice serve as the basis for quality in professional activities. As a manager, you can use standards of practice to clarify and assess your own work, and the work of other professionals to whom the standards apply. Figure 15.1 provides an example of a ANFP standard of practice.

When you serve on interdepartmental teams or professional association task forces, you will be successful if you have commitment to: the meeting, the client and the team members, the mission, and resolving conflict.

The meeting. A commitment to the meeting means you attend scheduled meetings on time; you come prepared to work and meet deadlines; you participate as appropriate in the discussions.

The client and the team members. A commitment to the client and the team members means maintaining confidentiality as required. Use the opportunity to build relationships with others outside your department, be flexible and work as a team player; and always keep the focus on what is best for the client(s).

The mission. A commitment to the mission means knowing the scope, function, and authority of the group; knowing how your department goals and objectives fit with the overall mission of your facility; accepting responsibility for jobs that need to be done; and communicating your successes and failures back to your department.

Resolving conflict. A commitment to resolving conflict means if you make a mistake, own it, apologize for it, fix it, and learn from it; attack problems, not people; be willing to confront someone on the team if you have an issue and then listen attentively.

Additional Tips for Personal Professionalism

As a professional, by this point you are realizing that you have many responsibilities. You may quickly become an expert in many tasks, and a master of many skills. You may wonder what to do first, and how to assure that you are always up to the task at hand. There are four tips for personal professionalism that will help when you are representing your department at external meetings and with all other parts of your job: professional ethics, managing your time, managing your stress, and lifelong learning.

Professional Ethics

The concept of ethics refers to views, attitudes, and practices about what is right or wrong. It describes moral standards. This is subjective information. There are no absolute and uniform standards from which to devise a set of ethics. However, culturally, we tend to share many basic values. Among them are integrity, honesty, fairness, responsibility, and trust. Professional ethics take into account many of these basic values.

Figure 15.1 **ANFP Standard of Practice: Menu Planning, Calories, and Portion Sizes**

STANDARD 1

The Certified Dietary Manager (CDM) shall ensure that a menu planning process is in place in the facility. Menus shall meet the needs of the clientele as well as the facility.

Criteria

1.1 The menu will include a variety of foods from day to day.

1.2 The general menu will meet a government food guide such as Choose MyPlate or the Recommended Dietary Allowances. (e.g. Menu will include a food from Vitamin A group every other day and from Vitamin C group daily).

1.3 The menu will avoid repeating the same food on the same day of the week. Cycle menus should be set up so they are not divisible by seven to help avoid this (e.g. a cycle menu that is five days long).

1.4 New food will be introduced regularly; selective menus will include a familiar food with a new food.

1.5 The menu will include a variety of preparation methods and offer a contrast in texture and flavor.

1.6 The menu should be planned for eye appeal and include at least one or two colorful foods on each menu.

1.7 The menu includes foods that can be prepared with available personnel and equipment.

1.8 Menu planning guides such as those from vendors or books such as *Food for Fifty* or *Menu Solutions—Quantity Recipes for Regular and Special Diets* are available in the foodservice department.

1.9 Food preferences of clientele are periodically assessed or when complaints warrant (e.g. resident council meetings, quarterly assessments, individual complaints, or surveys).

1.10 Staff uses a checklist with criteria such as 1.3-1.5 above when serving meals.

1.11 Staff receives training on how to add eye appeal, prepare foods with a contrast in texture and flavor, and keep food costs within the budget allowance.

1.12 Staff receives training on the proper substitutions for food groups (e.g. What to serve to replace a Vitamin A group).

Assessment

1.1 Checklists used by staff are evaluated weekly and menus corrected as needed.

1.2 Training records are evaluated to make sure all cooking staff has received training in food preparation, sanitation, meal service, etc.; training records are maintained in the foodservice department.

1.3 Data from food preference surveys are used for menu planning purposes.

STANDARD 2

The Certified Dietary Manager (CDM) shall ensure that procedures for determining menu calorie count and portion sizes for small, regular, and large servings are established according to regulatory agency guidelines or facility policies.

Criteria

2.1 The Certified Dietary Manager works with the dietitian to establish a procedure or a standard for determining menu calorie count, including calorie levels for small, regular, and large servings, and modified diets.

2.2 The therapeutic menu is approved by the facility dietitian.

2.3 The CDM works with the cook staff to assure standard portion sizes for small, regular, and large servings.

2.4 The general/regular menu will provide approximately 1800-2200 calories each day, not including snacks.

In addition to your personal values, you may learn more about ethics by consulting with professional organizations, many of which have their own codes of professional ethics for members. For example, Association of Nutrition & Foodservice Professionals presents a code of ethics for its members, illustrated in Figure 15.2.

You can also learn from your own facility, which may define some basic ethical principles for employees. Some ethical codes stem, at least in part, from law as well. For example, avoidance of discrimination is not only a good idea from a moral perspective, it is also law.

Some ethical issues are fairly straightforward. For example, a policy about client confidentiality tells you that you should not disclose information about your clients to others who are not directly involved in their care.

From time to time, you have to make ethical choices as a professional that are less clear. For example, ethical practices in purchasing usually suggest that you avoid accepting gifts from a supplier or potential supplier.

Now, what happens when you attend a food show and are invited to register for a free drawing? Are you accepting a gift? Are you violating sound ethical practices? This question, recently discussed by Certified Dietary Managers in an online forum, can bring on a range of answers. One manager says that this is clearly unethical. Another says the intent of the no-gift practice is to avoid influencing purchasing decisions, and this drawing has no impact. Yet another manager says that her superior goes to the shows with her and they both register for the drawing.

Figure 15.2 ANFP Code of Ethics

The Code of Ethics for members of the Association of Nutrition & Foodservice Professionals (ANFP) has been adopted to promote and maintain the highest standards of foodservice and personal conduct among its members. Adherence to this code is required for membership and serves to assure public confidence in the integrity and service of ANFP.

As a member of ANFP, I pledge myself to:

- ✓ Reflect my pride in my competence as a dietary manager by wearing my pin and emblem and displaying my certificate.
- ✓ Use only legal and ethical means in the practice of my profession.
- ✓ Use every opportunity to improve public understanding of the role of the dietary manager.
- ✓ Promote and encourage the highest level of ethics within the industry.
- ✓ Refuse to engage in, or countenance, activities for personal gain at the expense of my employer, the industry, or the profession.
- ✓ Maintain the confidentiality of privileged information entrusted or known to me by virtue of my position.
- ✓ Maintain loyalty to my employer and pursue their objectives in ways that are consistent with the public interest.
- ✓ Always communicate administrative decisions of my employer in a truthful and accurate manner.
- ✓ Communicate to proper authorities, but disclose to no one else, any evidence of infraction of established rules and regulations.
- ✓ Strive for excellence in all aspects of management and nutritional practices with constant attention to self-improvement.
- ✓ Maintain the highest standard of personal conduct.

This is an example of an ethical decision that professionals must make. Another type of dilemma arises when two moral values come into conflict with each other. Many issues related to the care of terminally ill clients center on conflicting values.

When you are faced with an ethical dilemma, what should you do? A few steps can help you reach a resolution. First, check the codes of ethics for your professional association(s) and your facility. Sometimes, you can gain insight by checking the codes of ethics of other related associations.

Next, talk the situation over with peers and colleagues. Ask whether they have faced a similar dilemma. If so, ask how they considered the issue, and what resolution they reached. Of course, think about the situation from your own perspective. What feels right to you—and why?

Furthermore, you should always discuss a job-related ethical dilemma with your supervisor. If you are going to make a difficult choice: 1) your supervisor may be able to help, drawing from additional experiences, and 2) your supervisor should know what you are doing, so there will be no surprises or questions down the line. Enlisting approval and support ahead of time protects you, your supervisor, and the facility.

In most respects, ethical practices come naturally to individuals with well-developed personal value systems. Nevertheless, an occasional challenge does arise. Self-reflection and other people can be of great help in clarifying ethics.

Managing Your Time

Time is, like many resources you use at work, limited and precious. Just like supplies, time is a resource that you as a Certified Dietary Manager have to manage. What's the technique? An easy answer is just to work longer hours to get things done, and this does happen to managers in many facilities. Managers in foodservice are especially vulnerable to this problem, as foodservice facilities tend to operate for long hours each day.

The key to managing time is to plan and organize—two basic management skills. Often, you are so busy working that you may have difficulty even planning your time. A first step is to analyze your time. For a few days, keep a log of what you do from hour to hour. Note why you do it, where you do it, and whether you knew you would need to be doing it. Then, study the log and look for patterns. Group similar tasks and then ask:

Could I do more of these tasks together? This uses the principle of efficiency. It usually takes time to gather materials, orient yourself to the task, and even move yourself to the right location to perform a certain task. If you can group items, you may be able to reduce the total time involved.

Do I handle paper or stop and start the same small task more than once? This also uses the principle of efficiency. Reading the mail, putting it down, reading it again, and responding takes time. Only handle mail once. Most managers find that time is used most efficiently when they perform small tasks immediately and dismiss them from the to-do list.

Putting It Into Practice: 1

You are attending a state-wide meeting with your chef. The meetings last a day and a half and are in a nearby resort city. The meeting location is near a golf course that your chef says is a great place to play; you notice there is a lunch break on the first day. You are tempted to skip the early afternoon meetings to play a quick round of golf with your chef before you return to the meetings. The chef is new and it would be a good opportunity to get to know him better. Is this ethical?

(Check your answer at the end of this chapter)

Could someone else do some of these tasks? This uses the principle of delegation, or assigning tasks to others. Before you delegate, you need to assure that the task you intend to delegate is within another's realm of authority and responsibility. You need to assure that the person to whom you plan to delegate has the skills and training to assume the task. Of course, you also need to be sure the person has time to perform the work. Delegation can be a motivating and satisfying event. Employees given further responsibility may thrive on the challenge and rewards.

Are you spending time resolving crises that could be prevented? This uses the principle of proactive management. If you anticipate situations that may consume resources, such as time, you can prevent them through routine, sound management practices.

Are you accomplishing work at a solid rate? This uses the principle of productivity. Through careful analysis, you may realize that basic tools might whittle away time from certain tasks and improve your productivity. Computerized food purchasing is an excellent example of this.

Are you keeping tasks in sequence? This uses the principle of setting priorities. Sometimes, you have to acknowledge that you can't do everything—at least not all at once. You may need to set priorities and keep yourself on task.

Are you doing most things right the first time? This uses the principle of quality management. If you are performing poorly, you may be spending undue time correcting your own errors. A secret of quality management is that often the procedures that most support quality also support economy.

Are you taking breaks and having appropriate fun on the job? This uses the principle of stress management. If you are experiencing a great deal of stress, you may not be working as efficiently and effectively as you would like. Stress management is addressed below.

Certified Dietary Managers use various tools to assist with time management. A simple calendar posted on the wall or on a phone and carried in your pocket is a start. Personal calendar systems also help organize and track to-do items. As you make to-do lists, you can set priorities for each item to help stay focused as interruptions or surprises occur throughout the day. If you cannot accomplish everything on the list, at least you can accomplish the most important tasks in order. A sample to-do list appears in Figure 15.3.

To track commitments further in the future and follow up on action items, and/or the time-related responsibilities of others who report to you, you may also use a tickler list. A tickler list is designed to "tickle" your memory about selected items or tasks. Figure 15.4 illustrates a tickler list.

Today, you also have access to a wide variety of computer-based tools to help with time management. Some Certified Dietary Managers use e-mail to manage a calendar, track recurring events, and manage to-do and tickler lists. The calendar may also issue an audible alarm or reminder when you have an upcoming deadline or appointment.

Figure 15.3 To-Do List

To Do: Week 2/3-2/10	Priority
Attend safety meeting (2/6)	1
Rewrite job description (due 2/11)	1
Work on budget (due 3/10)	2
Go to Sally's luncheon	3
Review CQI (due 2/17)	2
Attend staff meeting	1
Call John in New Orleans	3
Answer mail	2
Meeting with the "Boss"	1

Figure 15.4 Tickler list

Tue., Feb 1	• Announce inservice on using personal protective equipment • Quality report due
Wed., Feb 2	• Print production sheets for new menu cycle • Check inventory—staples; place order • Ozzie's performance review due
Thur., Feb 3	• Supplies management committee meeting • Post employee schedule • Review temp. logs • Self-audit for production areas

Today's cell phones provide excellent tools with the additional advantage of portability. In some facilities, a project management software application is used throughout the facility to help track and coordinate work. Through e-mail and voice mail, you may also be able to pass messages and instructions on to others very expediently.

Managing Your Stress

Stress is a condition that arises from physical or mental strain, anxiety, and overwork. It is a familiar word not only to Certified Dietary Managers, but to most employees in a foodservice environment. The demands and schedules of the job can be strenuous. Client interactions can be satisfying, but draining. Along with work-related stress, you may experience stress from factors outside the workplace. This compounds your experience of stress.

Stress is a natural experience, and it is not unique to Certified Dietary Managers. A few ideas can help manage stress in your life:

✓ Take breaks. Physical breaks, emotional breaks, and mental breaks are all important. Examples include: talking a walk, stopping to enjoy a joke, or switching tasks for a while. Each of these helps to restore energy.

Putting It Into Practice: 2

You are always busy but your work this morning seems overwhelming. Here are the items on your to-do list at 7:30 am:

- Cooler temperature was too high this morning as reported by am cook
- Weekly production meeting at 8:30 am
- Care planning meeting at 10:00 am for a client who is losing weight
- New employee orientation, third session, meeting at 9:00 am to go over typical work day
- First draft of next year's budget is due to administrator by noon today

How would you prioritize these tasks to better manage your time?

(Check your answer at the end of this chapter)

✓ Accept what you cannot change. You can consume a lot of emotional energy worrying about things you cannot control, or feeling angry about something you cannot influence.

✓ Use relaxation exercises. Physical and mental relaxation exercises can help loosen tense muscles or release negative thoughts.

✓ Take things one at a time. When you work, focus on one task at a time so you can concentrate your energy. Thinking about other tasks at the same time only creates more stress.

✓ Focus on the positive results of your efforts. While you may work very hard and experience a great deal of pressure sometimes, you can usually see results and satisfaction in the outcomes. Many Certified Dietary Managers say the results of their work, such as superb food and satisfied clients, outweigh the stress of the work.

✓ Express your feelings. Safe and appropriate outlets for your emotions are healthy.

✓ Be realistic about yourself. Accept who you are and what you do. Accept your own mistakes as positive learning experiences.

✓ Keep a positive outlook. A healthy perspective is one in which you remember the big picture, and focus on the things you value that little problems cannot destroy; it is one in which you believe in yourself and others.

✓ Seek help if you need it. If stress is taking a toll, do not hesitate to seek professional help. The ability to ask for support and locate resources is a sign of managerial strength.

Lifelong Learning

As you continue on your career path, you may become interested in developing new skills. It is not uncommon for a Certified Dietary Manager to pursue additional training at some point during a career. One may choose to go to culinary school. Another may choose to obtain an associate or bachelor's degree. Another may pursue a degree in business management. Yet another may seek additional credentials.

When you are planning your own development, give some thought to both short-term and long-range goals. In the short term, you may need to learn more about standards, or labor unions, or another specific topic. As you do for other members of your staff, you can plan some of your own training and development based on desired outcomes. If this is something you need to do—or will need to do soon—you can list results-oriented objectives, and then work backward to identify resources for training or acquiring training.

Resources for your own development may come from a professional association, in-house training department, community resources, local schools, business seminars, the Internet, and self-study courses. Representing your department at external meetings will help you develop both personally and professionally. An online or advanced study course is one way a Certified Dietary Manager can pursue additional education while still holding down a full-time job with variable hours. Along with formal training, you can develop your knowledge through DVDs, videotapes, food books, trade magazines, and Websites.

You and your staff have had a very hectic week in the foodservice department. It was the first week of May and you had extra catering duties to celebrate National Older American's Month and then the week ended with an elaborate tea for Mother's Day. What might you do to reduce your own stress and your employee's at the same time?

(Check your answer at the end of this chapter)

END OF CHAPTER

Putting It Into Practice Questions & Answers

1. You are attending a state-wide meeting with your chef. The meetings last a day and a half and are in a nearby resort city. The meeting location is near a golf course that your chef says is a great place to play; you notice there is a lunch break on the first day. You are tempted to skip the early afternoon meetings to play a quick round of golf with your chef before you return to the meetings. The chef is new and it would be a good opportunity to get to know him better. Is this ethical?

   A. *Who is paying for the meeting and your time? If you are being paid by your facility to attend the meeting and receiving salary while you are attending, the answer is no, it is not ethical. If you want to get to know the chef better on the golf course, ask your administrator. If the administrator agrees you could miss the early afternoon meeting, then go play golf. Keep in mind that you are setting an example for the chef. If you choose to leave meetings early or skip out altogether, your chef may decide that behavior is acceptable at future meetings.*

2. You are always busy but your work this morning seems overwhelming. Here are the items on your to-do list at 7:30 am:
   - Cooler temperature was too high this morning as reported by am cook
   - Weekly production meeting at 8:30 am
   - Care planning meeting at 10:00 am for a client who is losing weight
   - New employee orientation, third session, meeting at 9:00 am to go over typical work day
   - First draft of next year's budget is due to administrator by noon today

   How would you prioritize these tasks to better manage your time?

   A. *Your first job is to prioritize these jobs in terms of importance:*

   #1 The cooler needs attention and that cannot be put off. (Ask one of your employees to take the temperature of foods in the cooler to determine their safety. If the food is above 41°, then you need to dispose of potentially hazardous foods since you don't know how long they have been in the danger zone. The cook should be able to make those decisions; you should call for repairs to the cooler.)

   #2 You need to be prepared for the care planning meeting about the client. You need at least 30 minutes to review the chart and department documentation on the client.

   #3 You have to have the first draft of the department budget to your administrator by noon and you need at least two hours to complete the draft.

   #4 You may be able to delegate the production meeting to one of the cooks; you may be able to delegate the orientation meeting to the employee who will be working with the new employee.

3. You and your staff have had a very hectic week in the foodservice department. It's the first week of May and you had extra catering duties to celebrate National Older American's Month and Mother's Day. What might you do to reduce your own stress and your employee's at the same time?

   A. *A number of companies are using 'monotony breakers' to help employees keep a positive outlook and focus on the results of their efforts. Some companies take their department employees off campus for an event to relax and mingle. This might be difficult in the foodservice department since the meals still have to be served; however, here are some activities you can do:*

   - *Offer everyone an ice cream break*
   - *Have a local caterer bring lunch and have a picnic outside*
   - *Order balloons, one for each employee and have them delivered*
   - *Hire a local massage therapist to give 5 minute massages to your staff*

   Whatever you do, make sure you focus on the positive result of your work.

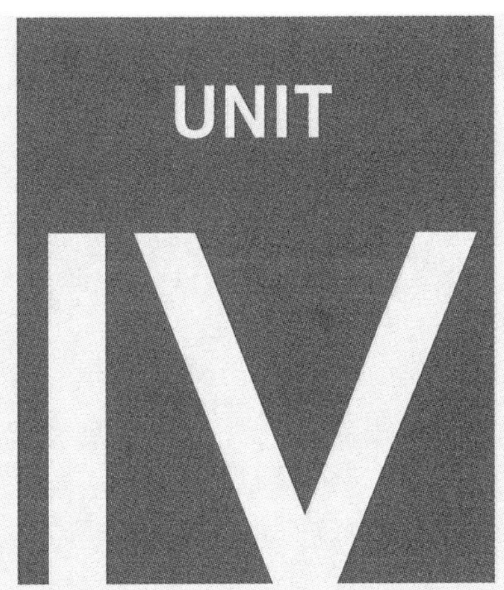

Manage Supplies, Equipment Use, Sanitation and Safety

An unknown author once said, "When safety is a factor, call in a contractor." The contractor for food safety is the Food and Drug Administration ***plus*** you! This unit is based strictly on the 2009 FDA Food Code. Each state has its own Sanitation Code adapted from the FDA Food Code; use your own state code in conjunction with this unit. While managing sanitation and safety is just one unit in this textbook, assuring the safety of your clientele and staff is a critical part of the job of any contractor and especially, the Certified Dietary Manager.

Purchase, Receive, Store, and Distribute Food Following Sanitation/ Quality Standards

Overview and Objectives

Ensuring food safety depends on selecting a safe food vendor, obtaining food from approved sources, and carefully controlling the receiving, storage, and distribution practices.

After completing this chapter, you should be able to:

✓ Identify appropriate grades and inspections for food
✓ Procure food and water from approved sources
✓ Verify the quality and quantity of food supplies and equipment received
✓ Check supplier invoices against facility purchasing order
✓ Recognize the hazards associated with types of food packaging
✓ Recognize the signs of contamination upon receipt and in storage
✓ Process rejections for unacceptable products
✓ Label, date and monitor food to ensure rotation
✓ Prevent environmental contamination of food
✓ Establish and maintain security procedures
✓ Ensure all product is received and stored at appropriate temperatures

Purchasing

For a foodservice operation, purchasing is the first step in the flow of food. Food and water must be purchased from approved sources. An approved source is one that is inspected based on federal, state, or local laws and has appropriate HACCP procedures in place. Purchasing specifications should include:

✓ Quality standards, such as grading and HACCP verification
✓ Wholesomeness indicators, such as inspection.

In addition, delivery times and intervals can also be included in specifications. The manager must exercise careful planning when purchasing food. Purchasing excessive quantities of food can result in spoilage, increased costs, and an increased likelihood of foodborne illness. Perishable products—such as fresh produce, fresh seafood, fresh meats, eggs, and dairy products—should be purchased in a quantity that can be used within a very short time period.

Non-perishable foods such as canned and frozen foods can be purchased in quantities that allow for longer storage times, if desirable.

Inspection

All food shipped in interstate commerce (from one state to another) must meet the requirements of one or more federal laws. The U.S. Department of Agriculture (USDA) has established uniform standards for state and federally inspected meats, poultry, and eggs. **Inspection** is a mandatory process that addresses wholesomeness and safety of fresh meats, dairy products, and produce. Some products that are not shipped across state lines may have to be inspected by state programs with their own standards—some higher than those of federal programs. Foodservice operations may only purchase meat, poultry and eggs that have been inspected by the USDA or by a state department of health or agriculture. Inspected food is considered to be safe for consumption, but inspection does not imply any quality standard.

Seafood and fish must be purchased from approved suppliers. This is especially important for molluscan shellfish such as oysters, scallops, mollusks, and clams, because they may be consumed raw or undercooked. To ensure safety when received, these foods must be accompanied by a certification that documents where and when they were harvested (**Shellfish Identification Tags**). This certification must be kept for 90 days to allow time for evidence of a Hepatitis A virus infection. Figure 16.1 provides the requirements for shellfish harvesters in the State of Oregon. Check your own state regulations for similar requirements.

The Public Health Service maintains lists of Certified Shellfish Shippers. Suppliers should be selected from this list or from state-approved lists.

Figure 16.1 Oregon State Requirements for Shellfish Harvesters

Shellfish Tagging—Harvesters and growers must attach to each container of shellfish a durable, waterproof tag sized: 2⅝" x 5¼" with information in the following order:

- Harvester's certificate number (i.e., OR 777 HV)
- Harvest date
- Harvest area (bay or beach)
- Type and quantity of shellfish
- This statement: "This tag shall be attached until container is empty or retagged and kept on file for 90 days."

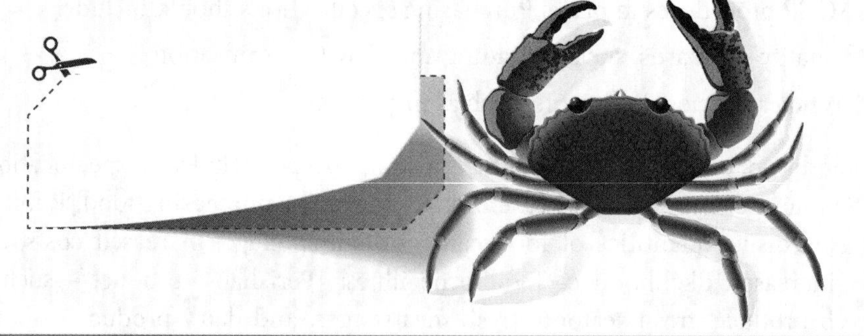

http://oregon.gov/ODA/FSD/program_shellfish.shtm, accessed January 5, 2011

Glossary

Inspection
A mandatory process that addresses wholesomeness and safety of fresh meats, dairy products, and produce

Grading
A voluntary process providing a descriptive term or number to designate quality

Shellfish Identification Tags
Special labels that can be used to trace a product such as oysters, mussels, clams, back to the source in the event that illness occurs

Figure 16.2 USDA Inspection Stamps and Grade Shields

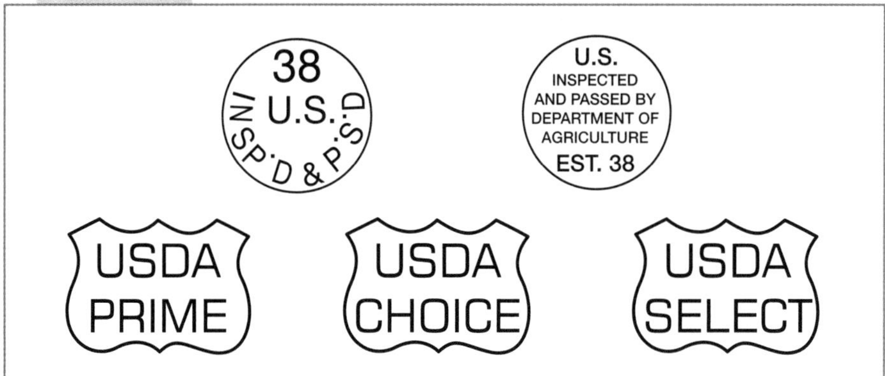

Grading

Grades are classifications of foods by a descriptive term or number to ensure the uniform quality and give an indication of the desirableness. **Grading** is a voluntary process. Most grades are assigned by government agencies and follow strict guidelines. Grades refer to attributes such as visual appearance, color, size, marbling, and uniformity.

Canned vegetables and fruits are usually graded and each vendor has its own terminology. Beef, veal, pork, and lamb are graded by the USDA. For beef, the USDA grades are: prime, choice, select, standard, commercial, utility, cutter, and canner. The last three grades are not used in foodservice operations. Examples of inspection stamps and grade shields appear in Figure 16.2.

Vendor Selection

Selecting a vendor is an important part of the purchasing process. Find out if you are required to purchase exclusively with a vendor. The Certified Dietary Manager must consider the extent to which the potential vendor will be able to meet the quality, service, and cost expectations of the foodservice operation. The relationship between the manager and the vendor must be one of mutual cooperation and trust. Past experience, good or bad, can serve as a basis for selection. Visits to the vendor's distribution center and inspections of delivery vehicles are advisable in the process of selecting a vendor. Once a reputable vendor is found, it is important to monitor quality continuously to ensure that the vendor has a long-term commitment to providing safe, quality food. Note that food prepared in the home cannot be served in quantity foodservice operations. Some of the considerations leading to selection of a safe food vendor include:

- ✓ Is the vendor inspected by an independent source to ensure food safety?
- ✓ Can the supplier provide you with written proof of government inspection for meats?
- ✓ Does the vendor have a Hazard Analysis Critical Control Point (HACCP) system in place?
- ✓ Will the vendor allow the manager to set delivery times?
- ✓ Are the vendor's delivery vehicles clean and well maintained?
- ✓ Are the delivery trucks for refrigerated foods adequately refrigerated?

Putting It Into Practice: 1

On which foods should you look for an inspection stamp when receiving food items?

(Check your answer at the end of this chapter)

✓ If purchasing frozen foods: do delivery trucks have freezer sections?

✓ Can the vendor provide business references?

✓ Can the vendor meet the delivery needs (daily, weekly, monthly) of the facility to ensure a safe flow of food?

✓ Does the vendor clarify their canned fruit and vegetable grading terminology?

✓ Does the vendor have a reputation for providing quality products?

✓ Will the vendor allow staff to inspect products upon receipt?

✓ Is the vendor cooperative if you refuse products because of food safety concerns?

✓ Where is the vendor located relative to the foodservice operation? A closer vendor would reduce delivery time and may reduce the possibility of contamination or time/temperature abuse of food.

Receiving

Receiving is an important phase in the flow of food through a foodservice operation. Food items must be carefully inspected before being placed into storage. The person receiving food must be knowledgeable of food safety, quality standards, and purchasing specifications. It is essential that food is inspected immediately upon delivery. Food not meeting the facility's quality and safety standards should be refused and returned to the vendor. Schedule deliveries at times convenient for the receiver to inspect food carefully. Even government inspected foods must be examined since federal inspection programs do not inspect food at every step in the flow of food from producer to vendor to foodservice operation. Storage areas should be prepared to accept new deliveries; and, staff must be available to compare the invoice to the order, and store the food immediately.

Of special concern today is fish such as large tuna or farm-raised (aquaculture) fish that might be consumed raw or undercooked such as in Sushi. If you purchase frozen fish for this purpose, it must contain a label indicating that is was frozen properly. These fish may contain a parasitic worm that can infect your clients. Thorough freezing at a low temperature for a long time can kill these parasites.

Purchased juice products, including pureed fruit and vegetables that are served to highly susceptible populations such as the sick and the elderly, must contain a label stating that the products have been pasteurized.

Potentially hazardous foods must be received at a temperature of 41°F or below.

A frozen food must be received in a frozen state and at 0°F or below in most cases. Carefully inspect refrigerated and frozen foods for any sign of temperature abuse during transportation and delivery. For instance, large ice crystals are evidence that frozen food was thawed and refrozen—and should be rejected at delivery. A receiving checklist (Figure 16.3) can help employees check and document condition of foods. Figure 16.4 shows how to check temperature of foods, and Figure 16.5 shows quality and safety indicators to check for many common foods.

Putting It Into Practice: 2

While checking in an order, you notice that one jar of mayonnaise in the case has a bulging lid. What should you do?

(Check your answer at the end of this chapter)

When receiving food:

✓ Reject food in damaged packaging.

✓ Check for inspection stamps, date codes, labels/tags for fish or juice.

✓ Check the temperature of frozen and refrigerated foods, including milk.

✓ Verify freshness by color, odor, touch, and package condition.

✓ Look for signs of pest infestation and/or spoilage.

Food Packaging

Technologies for packaging food to promote safety are constantly evolving. Some of the technologies used are discussed below.

Modified Atmosphere Packaged Foods (MAP). Most spoilage microorganisms are **aerobic** meaning they need oxygen to grow. In modified atmosphere packaging, oxygen is commonly replaced with a mixture of ozone, carbon dioxide or nitrogen. This type of packaging can extend freshness by maintaining a reduced-oxygen environment. Many food products are now packaged this way including vegetables, salad greens, fresh pasta, meat, fruit, cheese, seafood, and pre-prepared foods such as sandwiches and bakery products.

Although the packaging can extend shelf life, it will not always prevent microbial growth. For example, an anaerobic pathogen such as Clostridium botulinum may thrive in this low-oxygen environment. Another concern with MAP foods is that they may not "look" or "smell" spoiled when, in fact, they may have become unsafe for consumption. It is up to the manufacturer to protect the client from illness by providing storage instructions and date markings on how to store and handle the product safely. It is up to you to make sure that these products are received and stored properly. Thus when receiving and storing MAP foods, you should:

✓ Read the label. Note that recommended handling practices vary from product to product.

✓ Check for a **time/temperature indicator (TTI) strip**. This strip changes color if the product is outdated or has been temperature abused.

✓ Check for an expiration date or use-by date on the package. Do not use packages past recommended dates.

✓ Check for air bubbles; vacuum packaged foods should be free of air bubbles.

✓ Maintain MAP packages under refrigeration.

✓ Keep MAP packages sealed until you are ready to use them. Once a MAP package has been opened, the advantages of a low-oxygen environment disappear. Pathogens can now grow more rapidly.

Modified Atmosphere Packaging (MAP) techniques are very safe and provide advantages. However, a Certified Dietary Manager must nevertheless recognize and control hazards, as with any food product.

UHT or Ultra High Temperature Processing. UHT products are treated by flash sterilization and then packed into sterilized, airtight containers. Milk that is processed using the Ultra High Temperature method (shelf-stable milk) can

Glossary

Modified Atmosphere Packaging
A type of packaging that extends the life of the product by maintaining a reduced oxygen environment

Aerobic
Requires oxygen to survive. Many microorganisms are aerobic.

Time/Temperature (TTI) Strip
A smart label that shows the accumulated time and temperature history of a product

UHT
Ultra High Temperature Processing

Figure 16.3 Receiving Checklist

Received by: ______________________________ Date: ____________ Page #:________ of ______

Item	Item Matches PO	Actual Temp.[1]	Packaging Intact?		Use-By Date Valid?		Accepted	Rejected[2]	Stored[3]
			Y	N	Y	N			

1 Receive refrigerated food at 41°F or below. Receive frozen food at 0°F. Ice cream may be received at 6°F - 10°F.
2 If rejected, write comments on the back of this form.
3 Check to confirm that the item was stored.

Figure 16.4 Verifying Food Temperature During Receiving

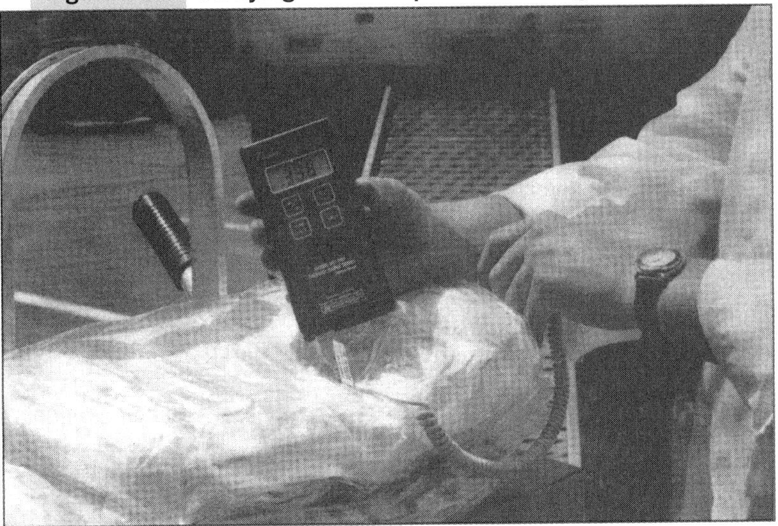

Courtesy: Cooper Instrument Corporation

Figure 16.5 Quality Indicators for Receiving Safe Food

Food Item	Accept...	Reject...
Fresh Beef	• Light pink to bright red color (aged beef may be darker) • Firm and elastic	• Dark brown or greenish color, sour or rancid smell
Fresh Poultry	• Slightly yellow appearance • Firm flesh • Not sticky to touch	• Dark appearance under wings • Sticky to touch
Marine Foods	• Gills of fresh fish are pink • No iridescence (shimmering) • Eyes clear, not sunken	• Excessive fish or ammonia color
Milk and Dairy Products	• Intact packaging • Clean containers • Butter with firm texture • Cheese free of mold	• Damaged or leaking containers • Expired dates
Egg and Egg Products	• Clean eggs, uncracked shells • Received at or below 45˚F	• Cracked or dirty eggs
Fresh Produce	• Bright color, no mold or wilt	• Signs of insect damage or plant disease • Bruises or soft produce
Canned Foods	• No dents • All foods labeled	• Dented or rusted cans
Dry Goods	• Intact packaging	• Ripped or torn packaging
Frozen Fish	• Labeled that it was frozen properly	• If label is missing
Molluscan Fish	• Contains a shellfish ID tag	• If tag is missing
Juice or Pureed Fruits/Vegetables	• Is labeled "pasteurized"	• If not pasteurized

be stored at room temperature for the time period indicated on the label. The most common UHT products are dairy products, but the use is expanding to fruit juices, wine, soups, and stews. After opening, the product must be refrigerated and used within the time listed on the product label. For instance, a milk-based soup that was processed with UHT has the following directions on the label: "After opening, keep refrigerated and use within 7-10 days."

Storage

Proper storage is an important aspect of food protection. Storage is more complex than simply having adequate space. Storage involves the variables of light, temperature (see Figure 16.6), ventilation, and air circulation. Food must be stored 6" above the floor, on clean, slatted racks or shelves, and in a manner that prevents environmental or cross-contamination. Food must also be stored away from walls and ceilings. Food not intended for further preparation before serving must be stored in a way that prevents contamination from food requiring preparation. For instance, raw foods—such as meat—should never be stored above ready-to-eat foods—such as fresh fruit, salads, or desserts. The raw food may splash or drip onto the ready-to-eat food and result in cross-contamination. Food may not be stored in locker rooms, toilet areas, dressing rooms, in garbage rooms, mechanical rooms, under sewer lines that are not adequately shielded, under open stairwells, under a water leak, or near any other potential source of contamination. Chemicals must never be stored near food.

Figure 16.6 Storage Temperatures

Dry storage	50°F - 70°F
Refrigerated storage	41°F or below
Deep chilling storage	26°F - 32°F
Freezer storage	0°F or below

Every food has a shelf life, which is the amount of time the product can be expected to remain reasonably safe if stored properly. Foodservice staff must monitor the dates on foods to ensure foods are used before expiration. New deliveries must be stored behind previous deliveries to ensure that the oldest product is used first. This method of stock rotation is called **First In, First Out (FIFO)**.

Certain foods may be difficult to identify after they are removed from their original packaging. Foods such as salt and sugar look the same, but if they are mixed up for clients on special diets, it could be disastrous. Some oils or granulated foods may look like cleaning compounds. Packaged food labels contain nutrition information as well as valuable ingredient information that you may need for consulting with clients with allergies. For that reason, containers holding food or food ingredients that are removed from original packaging for use in the foodservice operation should be labeled with the common name of the food and the date the package was opened. Slatted shelving allows for proper air circulation around food, and should not be covered with foil or other material.

Glossary

FIFO
First in, first out. A storage method to assure that older products are used first

Figure 16.7 Storage Temperature Log

Storage Area: ____ Page #: __________ of ________

Date	Storage Temperature		Comments/Corrective Actions
	A.M.	P.M.	

Dry storage: 50˚F-70˚F | Refrigerated Storage: 41˚F or below | Deep chilling storage: 26˚F-32˚F | Freezer Storage: 0˚F or below

Figure 16.8 Guidelines for Purchasing, Receiving, and Storing Food

Food Item	Purchase	Receive	Store	Shelf Life
Meat	• USDA or state inspected	• Receive frozen at 0°F • Receive refrigerated at 41°F or below	• Store frozen at 0°F or below • Store refrigerated at 41°F or below, separate from poultry	• Fresh beef: 6-12 mos. in freezer; 3-6 days in refrigerator • Ground beef: 3-4 months in freezer; 1-2 days in refrigerator
Poultry	• USDA or state inspected	• Receive frozen at 0°F • Receive refrigerated at 41°F or below	• Store frozen at 0°F or below • Store refrigerated at 41°F or below	• 6 months in freezer; 1-2 days in refrigerator
Fish and Shellfish	• From an approved supplier • Shellfish must have shellfish identification tag	• Receive frozen at 0°F • Receive refrigerated at 41°F or below	• Store frozen at 0°F or below • Store refrigerated at 41°F or below, separate from poultry	• All: 2-4 months in freezer • 1-2 days in refrigerator
Milk and Dairy Products	• Pasteurized milk and milk products	• Receive frozen (ice cream) at 6°F to 10°F • Receive refrigerated at 41°F	• Store frozen at 0°F or below • Store refrigerated at 41°F or below • Unopened UHT package may be stored at room temperature.	• Milk: Use by expiration date on carton • Ice cream: 6 months in freezer

When storing raw meats, fish and pork should be kept separate from poultry because of the possible higher bacterial count in the poultry. As mentioned, meats should be stored below ready-to-eat foods to avoid drippage during thawing.

Food storage areas must be equipped with thermometers accurate to ±3°F. The temperature of storage areas should be monitored not less than once a day and the actual temperatures documented on a temperature log (Figure 16.7).

Dry storage area temperatures should be maintained between 50°F-70°F. For short-term holding of perishable foods, maintain refrigerators between 34°F-41°F. Sometimes, a food is not quite as cold as the temperature around it. Maintaining refrigeration temperatures below 38°F will help ensure that actual food temperatures remain out of the hazard zone. The Food Code suggests placing a thermometer in the warmest part of the refrigerator. New technology allows employees to measure a simulated product temperature for better accuracy.

Figure 16.8 provides a summary of guidelines for purchasing, receving, and storing food.

Ideally, meats, poultry and fish should be stored in a deep chilling unit. Very low temperatures may damage food and affect quality for some items such as produce. A summary of suggested practices for storing food appears in the Appendix C.

Putting It Into Practice: 3

You are storing the following items in a cooler: a case of lettuce, a case of cottage cheese, a case of chicken breasts you want to thaw, and a bowl of tuna salad prepared for tomorrow's lunch. Where would you place these items in your cooler and why?

(Check your answer at the end of this chapter)

END OF CHAPTER

Putting It Into Practice Questions & Answers

1. On which foods should you look for an inspection stamp when receiving a food order?

   A. *Review what foods are required to be inspected. Meats, poultry, and eggs are required to be inspected.*

2. While checking in an order, you notice that one jar of mayonnaise in the case has a bulging lid. What should you do?

   A. *Since you don't know what caused the bulging lid, it could be the entire case was subjected to high temperatures. You should return the entire case of mayonnaise.*

3. You are storing the following items in a cooler: a case of lettuce, a case of cottage cheese, a case of chicken breasts you want to thaw, and a bowl of tuna salad prepared for tomorrow's lunch. Where would you place these items in your cooler and why?

   A. *Each of these foods is potentially hazardous so you want to place them in the coldest part of the cooler—near the back, away from the door, and on the lower shelves. The chicken breasts should be on the lowest shelf in case juices from thawing run out of the case box. The other items should be placed above the case of chicken breasts but still on lower shelves.*

Protect Food in All Phases of Preparation, Holding, Service, Cooking, and Transportation, Using HACCP Guidelines

Overview and Objectives

Did you ever consider how many processes food goes through before we actually consume it? Safe purchasing, receiving and storage procedures are just the beginning of processes needed to keep our food safe. You will evaluate foodborne diseases and their causes, explain all phases in the flow of food, and review HACCP guidelines in this chapter.

After completing this chapter, you should be able to:

- ✓ Identify potentially hazardous foods and foodborne pathogens and their control
- ✓ Recognize the causes, symptoms, and types of foodborne illnesses including biological, chemical and physical types
- ✓ Monitor time and temperature to limit growth of or destroy microorganisms
- ✓ Enforce employees' compliance with safe food preparation practices
- ✓ Prevent cross-contamination of food
- ✓ Identify appropriate techniques for temperature retention
- ✓ Ensure the safe cooling of food
- ✓ Establish critical limits
- ✓ Establish the corrective action to be taken when critical limits are exceeded
- ✓ Establish procedures to identify and monitor critical control points (CCP)
- ✓ Establish effective record-keeping systems that document HACCP
- ✓ Anticipate emergency preparedness procedures necessary to assure a safe food supply

SECTION A Foodborne Illness: Causes & Prevention

Foodborne illness is a major public issue. In 2011, the Food Safety Modernization Act was implemented to expand and improve the security and safety of our nation's food supply. This was historic legislation designed to build a new system of food safety oversight. Why do we need this important legislation? According to the Center for Disease Control (CDC), "each year, foodborne illness strikes 48 million Americans, hospitalizing a hundred thousand and killing over three thousand."

In addition, many people experience foodborne illness and do not report it, brushing off symptoms as "the flu." A **foodborne illness** is a disease that is transmitted by food. The most frequent cause is harmful microorganisms—or poisons produced by harmful microorganisms. Symptoms vary according to the cause of the illness and the person who is afflicted. However, common symptoms may include vomiting, diarrhea, fever, and headache. In some cases, death is a very real risk.

Some individuals are more susceptible to foodborne illness than others. Their symptoms may be more severe, and their risk of death may be higher. Preschool age children, the elderly, pregnant women, and persons with weakened immune systems are considered to be high-risk groups for foodborne illness, also called **highly susceptible populations**. Serving these groups requires special awareness of high vulnerability—and sometimes, special precautions in ingredient selection and food preparation.

Often, when there is one case of foodborne illness, there are more cases related to the same food item. A **foodborne illness outbreak** occurs when two or more persons become ill after ingesting the same food, and a laboratory analysis confirms that food was the source of the illness. If foodborne illness is caused by a chemical, this is also defined as an outbreak, even if there is only one case.

The annual cost of foodborne illness is estimated to be $152 billion. According to the CDC, more than 250 different types of diseases are caused by contaminated food or beverages. New strains of harmful foodborne microorganisms are constantly evolving.

Food Hazards

Food can become unsafe in a number of ways. There are many **hazards** in the environment that affect the safety and quality of food served. Hazards are present in the air, in water, in other foods, on work surfaces, and on the hands and bodies of foodservice employees. Food-related hazards fall into three major categories: biological, chemical, and physical, as shown in Figure 17.1. The presence of substances in food that could cause harm is called **contamination**.

Glossary

Foodborne Illness
A disease that is transmitted by food

Highly Susceptible Population
Persons who are more likely to experience foodborne disease because they are immunocompromised (already ill), preschool age children, or older adults

Foodborne Illness Outbreak
Occurs when two or more cases of a similar illness result from eating a common food

Contamination
The presence of biological, physical, or chemical substances in food that could cause harm

Hazards
Biological, chemical, or physical property that may cause an unacceptable consumer health risk. Hazards must be controlled.

Biological Hazards
A living organism such as bacteria, virus, parasite, fungi, that can cause harm to humans

Aerobic
Requires oxygen to survive; many microorganisms are aerobic

Anaerobic
Can grow without the presence of oxygen

Facultative
Can grow with OR without the presence of oxygen

Biological Hazards

Biological hazards include bacteria, viruses, parasites, and fungi. Viruses and bacteria are most commonly cited in foodborne illness outbreaks, but all present a threat to the safety of the food supply. Bacteria are plentiful in the environment and in our bodies. While some serve useful purposes, others cause serious foodborne illnesses. Microorganisms that cause foodborne illness are called pathogens. Pathogens may already be in the food supply or may be introduced at any time from the point of harvest to the food processor or manufacturer to the distributor to the foodservice operation. Improper operating procedures and food preparation practices allow pathogens to survive and grow. In turn, these events increase the risk of foodborne illness (see Figure 17.2).

Bacteria. There are many types of bacteria, with differences in their growth habits and requirements. **Anaerobic** bacteria grow in an environment with little or no oxygen. These bacteria might contaminate canned foods or modified atmosphere packaged products, or they may grow in the center of large quantities of food. **Aerobic** bacteria require air to grow. Many bacteria associated with foodborne illness can grow either with or without oxygen and are called **facultative**. When growth conditions are unfavorable, some bacteria form spores, exist in a dormant state, and then begin growing again when conditions are ripe. Spores are difficult to kill, and can function as a foodborne illness timebomb. Sound food protection practices, though, can keep them under control.

Types of Illness—Exactly how pathogens cause illnesses varies. Some microorganisms enter the body in an active state and continue to grow. The type of illness that results is called a **foodborne infection**, because the person who eats the food is literally infected with the pathogens. For example, Salmonella

Figure 17.1 Food Hazards

Biological Hazard Examples	Chemical Hazard Examples	Physical Hazard Examples
• Bacteria • Parasites • Viruses • Fungi • Natural Toxins • Prions	• Pesticides • Toxic Metals • Cleaning Chemicals	• Dirt • Hair • Broken Glass • Metal Shavings

Figure 17.2 Causes of Foodborne Illness

Pathogens are naturally present in the food supply.

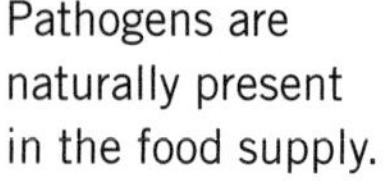

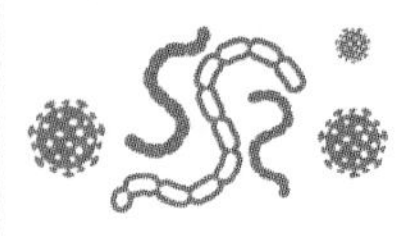

Contamination or mishandling occurs during processing, transport, storage, preparation, and/or service.

Pathogens may grow. New pathogens may be introduced. Other biological, chemical, and physical contaminants may also enter food.

Food is consumed and foodborne illness results.

bacteria enter the body in a live state and grow in the body, causing fever, nausea, diarrhea, and other symptoms. This illness is called Salmonellosis.

Other microorganisms produce a poison or toxin that may not be destroyed in cooking. The bacteria may not be alive anymore, but their toxins nevertheless cause illness. This type of illness is called a **foodborne intoxication**. For example, Clostridium Botulinum bacteria produce a toxin. The illness that results from eating an affected food is called botulism.

Finally, some microorganisms enter the body in a live and growing state—and produce toxins in the body. The resulting illness is a **toxin-mediated infection**. Shiga toxin-producing E. coli bacteria (STEC), for example, operate this way, producing an illness that involves severe diarrhea and vomiting.

Types of Pathogens—Details about common pathogens appear in Figure 17.3. Due to environmental and growth conditions, most pathogens favor certain foods. For example, Listeria bacteria are often associated with unpasteurized cheese and processed meats, Salmonella with eggs, Shiga toxin-producing E. coli with ground beef, and Norwalk virus with shellfish. You should be able to recognize symptoms that could signal foodborne illness and warrant medical evaluation. However, it is most important to note that control mechanisms for foodborne illness are fairly universal. A comprehensive set of food protection practices can prevent illness from a wide range of pathogens. The CDC lists the top five pathogens causing illness, hospitalization, and death: Norovirus (a virus, formerly called Norwalk virus), Salmonella (bacteria), Clostridium Perfringens (bacteria), Campylobacter (bacteria), and Staphylococcus aureus (bacteria). These top five pathogens are highlighted in Figure 17.3.

Conditions for Bacterial Growth and Toxin Formation—To protect clients from foodborne illness, first consider the conditions that allow bacteria to grow or toxins to develop. The conditions are similar to what humans need: air, food, moisture, and warmth. Bacteria require food for themselves. Often, they favor food high in protein, such as meat. But sometimes, they settle for vegetables, fruits, and other plant foods. In addition to food, bacteria need other factors to grow. They grow most rapidly in an environment that also provides them with moisture, warmth, neutral or slightly acid pH, oxygen at a level favored by the bacteria, and time. Moisture is measured as available water (a_w) in a food. Examples of food with a high a_w content include meat, cheese, and produce. Meats, fresh fruits, and fresh vegetables, for example, have an a_w of close to 1.0, while crackers have an a_w of 0.1.

The term pH describes level of acidity or alkalinity. Optimal conditions for microorganisms are typically neutral or slightly acid. Generally, as foods become more acid, they are less likely to support bacterial growth. Meats, fish, and vegetables tend to be slightly acidic and support bacterial growth. Foods that are very acid, with a pH below about 4.2, do not favor bacterial growth. Based on a_w and level of acidity, you can see why traditional methods of food preservation use techniques like dehydrating food products (to reduce a_w) and pickling or adding vinegar (to reduce pH to extremes where bacteria cannot thrive).

Glossary

Foodborne Infection
When pathogens enter the body in an active state and continue to grow (e.g. Salmonella)

Foodborne Intoxication
An illness that occurs from the toxin or poison left from bacteria that are no longer alive (e.g. Clostridium botulinum)

Toxin-Mediated Infection
When live bacteria enter the body and produce a dangerous toxin (e.g. E. coli bacteria)

Figure 17.3 Common Foodborne Pathogens

Type	Source	Symptoms and Complications	Prevention
Bacillus Cereus Bacteria	Milk, cereals, rice, and starchy foodstuffs	Nausea, diarrhea and vomiting are common symptoms. Onset is usually 6-15 hours.	Keep food out of the hazard zone. Keep dry products away from moisture.
Campylobacter Jejuni Bacteria	**Raw meat, poultry and shellfish; contaminated water and unpasteurized milk**	**Muscle pain, headache and fever followed by diarrhea, abdominal pain and nausea. Onset is usually 2-5 days.**	**Thoroughly cook meat and poultry. Use pasteurized milk and products. Control time/temperature. Use clean utensils. Use chlorinated drinking water.**
Clostridium Botulinum Bacteria	Grows in anaerobic environment—canned and reduced-oxygen packaged foods, or soups and sauces that have been improperly cooled. Also found in honey. Produces a toxin.	Double vision and difficulties in speaking, swallowing and breathing. May result in nerve damage and life-threatening illness. Illness is called botulism. Onset is usually 12-48 hours.	Dispose of canned foods that are leaking or bulging, or are dented or damaged. Inspect vacuum-packaged foods for tears and time/temperature abuse.
Clostridium Perfringens Bacteria	**Naturally present in the soil. Any raw food may contain the spore or bacteria. Called the "cafeteria germ" because many outbreaks result from large quantities of food being held at room temperature or cooled too slowly.**	**Abdominal pain and diarrhea. Onset is usually 8-22 hours.**	**Thoroughly cook foods containing meat or poultry. Maintain food at safe temperatures. Cool food quickly by dividing into small, shallow containers. Use ice as an ingredient, use an ice bath, or use a blast chiller. Reheat refrigerated foods adequately.**
Listeria Monocytogenes Bacteria	Commonly found in the intestines of animals and humans, in milk, soil, and leafy vegetables. Also found in unpasteurized dairy products and processed meats.	In adults: sudden onset of fever, chills, headache, backache, abdominal pain, and diarrhea. In newborns: may cause respiratory distress, refusal to drink, and vomiting. Can cause miscarriage or stillbirth in pregnant women. Onset 3-70 days.	Avoid unpasteurized milk and dairy products. Cook ground meats thoroughly. Maintain food temperature out of the hazard zone. Bacteria may grow at refrigerated temperatures, so follow use-by and sell-by dates on processed foods.
Salmonella Enteritidis Bacteria	**Often found in meat and poultry products. Can survive in frozen food and grow with or without oxygen. Common cause is poor personal hygiene or cross-contamination.**	**Nausea, vomiting, cramps and fever. Onset is within 12-36 hours. Can be fatal to high-risk groups, such as the elderly.**	**Avoid serving raw eggs or undercooked poultry. Never pool eggs. Use pasteurized egg products. Sanitize work surfaces and utensils. Cook food thoroughly.**
Shiga Toxin-Producing Escherichia coli (STEC) Bacteria	Ground beef has been implicated in several severe outbreaks. Beef was often contaminated during processing and then mishandled during preparation. Also found in raw seed sprouts, lettuce, unpasteurized milk.	Produces a toxin which causes hemorrhagic colitis. Symptoms include abdominal cramps, watery diarrhea, nausea, vomiting, and low-grade fever. Acute kidney failure is a possible complication. Onset is usually 3-8 days.	Cook ground beef to 155°F for 15 seconds or more. Reheat properly. Use good sanitation and hygiene practices. Store and hold foods properly.

(Continued)

Figure 17.3 Common Foodborne Pathogens *(Continued)*

Type	Source	Symptoms and Complications	Prevention
Shigella Bacteria	An infected foodservice employee (carrier) or contaminated water supply are frequently cited sources. Prepared salads, gravies, and milk have been implicated.	Symptoms include diarrhea, fever, chills, and dehydration. Onset is usually within 12-50 hours.	Ensure a safe source of water. Restrict foodservice employees with infectious disease from the foodservice operation. Ensure good personal hygiene.
Staphylococcus Aureus Bacteria	**Illness is caused by a toxin. Improperly sanitized equipment and poor handwashing practices are culprits. Ham, cold meats, custards, cream-filled desserts are implicated foods.**	**Nausea, vomiting, and abdominal cramps. Can be fatal to elderly, infants, and other high-risk populations. Onset 1-6 hours.**	**Keep food out of the hazard zone by storing and cooking properly. Ensure good personal hygiene. Do not allow employees with infected cuts to handle food.**
Yersinia Enterocolitica Bacteria	Found in meats, oysters, fish, and raw milk. Poor sanitation and food preparation practices contribute to outbreaks.	Fever, headache, nausea, abdominal pain, and diarrhea. Onset 24-48 hours.	Heat food thoroughly to destroy the bacteria. Practice effective handwashing.
Giardia Parasite	Found in contaminated water, infected food handlers, possibly fresh produce.	Diarrhea, abdominal cramps, bloating, weight loss, or malabsorption. Typical onset is 1-2 weeks after contact; may last 6 weeks or much longer. Person may have no symptoms.	Practice proper handwashing and good personal hygiene. Use approved water sources.
Anisakis Parasite	Roundworm found in fish, transmitted through ingestion of raw or partially cooked marine foods.	Can be painful and is often misdiagnosed as appendicitis, Crohn's disease or gastric ulcer. Can require surgery to remove the parasite.	Cook marine foods thoroughly to destroy the parasite.
Trichinella Spiralis Parasite	Roundworm found in pork and wild game. Illness caused by consuming pork that was not thoroughly cooked.	Muscle pain and fever.	Thoroughly cook pork to destroy parasites.
Hepatitis A Virus	Virus is transmitted from one person to another through food. Water, shellfish and salads are frequently implicated foods.	Fever, abdominal pain, loss of appetite and jaundice. Typical incubation time is 10-15 days, but could be up to 50 days.	Practice proper handwashing and good personal hygiene. Restrict infected persons from foodservice operation.
Norovirus Virus	**Contaminated shellfish or foods washed in contaminated water. Employees infected with the virus.**	**Nausea, vomiting, diarrhea and abdominal pain.**	**Avoid serving raw shellfish. Observe good personal hygiene and cooking practices.**
Vibrio Vulnificus	Contaminated shellfish especially from warm seawater	Fever, skin lesions, collapse, systic shock	Avoid serving raw shellfish.

Time and temperature are critically interrelated in controlling bacterial growth and formation of toxins. When all other conditions are suitable for microorganisms, a key question is: How much time does the microorganism have in which to flourish? Under one favorable temperature and time combination, you may see certain results. However, if you keep the temperature the same and then give bacteria twice as much time to grow, there may be a hundred times more bacteria present! The more time a microorganism has under favorable conditions, the more it will multiply or produce toxins. This is one reason that holding time, cooling (for hot foods), reheating time (for leftovers), storage time, and other time-related factors are important for ensuring safe food. Conditions that help bacteria grow can be summarized by the acronym, **FOTTWA**, shown in Figure 17.4.

Figure 17.4 Conditions for Bacterial Growth: "FOTTWA"

Food:	Food must contain appropriate nutrients for growth. Bacteria generally require protein and carbohydrates.
Oxygen:	Some bacteria require oxygen (aerobic). Some bacteria cannot tolerate oxygen (anaerobic). Others grow with or without oxygen (facultative).
Temperature:	Temperature is probably the most critical factor in the growth of bacteria. The hazard zone of 41°F-135°F is the range in which microorganisms grow and produce toxins most rapidly.
Time:	A single bacterial cell can multiply into 1 million cells in 5 hours under ideal conditions. A general rule is that food in the hazard zone for 4 or more hours may be unsafe.
Water:	Moisture is measured based on water activity (available water or a_w). Pathogens generally grow in foods with an a_w value greater than 0.85.
Acidity:	Many pathogens tend to prefer conditions that are near a pH of 4.3-7.5, which is neutral or slightly acid.

Foods that require control of time and temperature for safety in order to prevent growth of pathogens or formation of toxins are called potentially hazardous foods (time/temperature control for safety), or **PHF/TCS**. Examples include: meat, poultry, eggs, fish, seafood, cut melons, raw seed sprouts, garlic/oil mixtures, baked potatoes, cooked plant foods such as beans or rice, and some fresh vegetables (e.g. lettuce, tomatoes). These foods typically contain the nutrients, available water, and acidity levels that bacteria require for growth. Shell eggs that have been treated to destroy possible Salmonella bacteria are omitted from the list of PHF/TCS. These are often called "pasteurized in-shell" eggs. Many plant foods are PHF/TCS. In fact, foodborne illness outbreaks over recent years have been traced to plant foods such as chopped parsley, lettuce, spinach, fresh berries, green onions, tomatoes, fruit juices, and other products.

The 2009 FDA Food Code definition of PHF/TCS emphasizes the fact that PHF/TCS requires control of both time and temperature to control hazards. The old definition targeted foods that might support "rapid and progressive growth" of pathogens. Today, however, "rapid" is not as meaningful. Some foods may be stored for much longer times than they used to be. In these, pathogens do not need to grow rapidly to create illness. Progressive growth, such as that of Listeria bacteria in lunch meats or hot dogs held under refrigeration for very long periods of time, is enough to cause illness.

Putting It Into Practice: 1

From Figure 17.3, what are the common threads in prevention of foodborne illnesses and what type of contamination is most likely to occur from unwashed hands?

(Check your answer at the end of this chapter)

Hazard Zone—An awareness of FOTTWA is the first step towards understanding how to prevent growth of harmful bacteria in food. Many food protection practices involve controlling food temperatures. The temperature range in which most bacteria grow rapidly is called the **hazard zone**. The hazard zone is the range from 41°F -135°F, as shown in Figure 17.5. This temperature range is also commonly known as the danger zone. The terms hazard zone and danger zone can be used interchangeably. By controlling the time food spends in a temperature range favorable to bacterial growth, the Certified Dietary Manager can minimize growth during preparation and service. In general, temperature control means keeping cold food cold and hot food hot, while minimizing the time a food spends in the hazard zone. In fact, a potentially hazardous food that is allowed to remain in the hazard zone for a cumulative time of four hours or more during all phases of receiving, storage, preparation and service is considered unsafe to eat.

Figure 17.5 Hazard Zone

135˚ SAFE ZONE

40 60 80 100 120 140 160 180 °F

The safe temperature zone for hot foods is 135˚F or higher

41˚ DANGER ZONE! 135˚

40 60 80 100 120 140 160 180 °F

The hazard zone is the temperature range between 41˚F and 135˚F, where pathogens grow most rapidly.

SAFE ZONE 41˚

-40 -20 0 20 32 40 60 80 100 °F

The safe temperature zone for cold food is 41˚F or below.

Glossary

FOTTWA
Acronym for the conditions needed for bacterial growth: food, oxygen, temperature, time, water, acidity

PHF/TCS
Abbreviation for Potentially Hazardous Food (time/temperature control for safety); designation of foods that require control of time and temperature for safety

Hazard or Danger Zone
The temperature range in which most bacteria grow rapidly (41°F-135°F)

Putting It Into Practice: 2

In the following recipe, which foods would be considered potentially hazardous?

- 1 lb. boneless chicken breast, ½" pieces
- 2 cups diced potatoes with onion
- 3 Tbsp. flour
- 3 cups fat-free chicken broth
- 2/3 cups frozen mixed vegetables
- Salt, pepper, sage, thyme to taste

(Check your answer at the end of this chapter)

Virus. A **virus** is the smallest and simplest form of life known. Viruses can be transmitted from a foodservice employee to a client through food, but do not grow or multiply in food. Viruses need a living host such as humans, animals, or fish in which to grow. Marine foods (fish and shellfish), can also be sources of foodborne viruses. Preventing viral foodborne illness requires health screening of employees, exclusion of employees who may have viral illness, sound personal hygiene habits, and careful selection of marine foods.

Parasites. A **parasite** is a small or microscopic organism that lives within another organism, called a host. The parasite can be transmitted from animals to humans if food is not cooked thoroughly. For example, Trichinella is a parasite found in pork and wild game. It's actually a roundworm that causes an infection (Trichinosis) in the person who consumes it. Cooking pork to the proper temperature and holding that temperature for a recommended minimum time destroys the parasite.

Fungi. Molds and yeasts are types of **fungi**. Some play a role in food processing. For example, yeasts are used in the production of bread, and molds are used in the processing of cheese. However, molds and yeasts can also be a threat to food safety. Molds grow well on most types of food and appear as brightly colored, fuzzy growth. Certain molds produce a toxin, which can result in a foodborne illness. Toxins produced by fungi are called mycotoxins. Mycotoxins may be found in dry and/or acidic foods. Guidelines for handling food that has mold appear in Figure 17.6.

Figure 17.6 Guidelines for Handling Foods Containing Mold

Some foods that develop mold must be discarded. Other foods can be used, but first cut out the mold and at least an inch of food under and around it.

Discard	Cut and Use
• Cucumbers	• Bell Peppers
• Tomatoes	• Broccoli, Cauliflower
• Spinach, Lettuce, Leafy Greens	• Cabbage
• Bananas, Peaches, Melons	• Garlic, Onions
• Berries	• Potatoes
• Breads, Cakes, Rolls, Flour	• Turnips
• Soft Cheeses like Brie or Mozzarella	• Zucchini, Winter Squash
• Lunch Meat and Cheese (slices)	• Apples, Pears
• Yogurt, Tub Spreads, Cream Cheese	• Hard Cheeses like Cheddar or Swiss
• Canned Foods	
• Peanut Butter	
• Juices	
• Cooked Leftovers	

Glossary

Virus
Source of foodborne illness that does not grow in food but is transmitted from people, animals, or fish/shellfish

Parasite
A small organism that lives within another living organism such as Trichinella that lives in pork or wild game

Fungi
Molds or yeast that can cause an illness or produce a toxin that causes the illness

Prions. Prions are biological agents in a very unique category. They are small, protein-like particles responsible for illnesses such as bovine spongiform encephalopathy (BSE), commonly know as mad cow disease. Unlike other pathogens, they are not affected by conditions for pathogen growth (FOTTWA). They are *not* destroyed by heat, as many pathogens are. They cause infection only when one animal (or person) consumes food made from an animal infected with the prion. For example, the mad cow outbreak in Great Britain in the 1980s was traced to feeding cows with meat and bone products that came from infected sheep. Human infection is extremely rare, but government officials are taking many precautions to protect the U.S. food supply from potentially infected meat. Chronic Wasting Disease (CWD) in deer and elk is also caused by a prion. CWD is in 12 states and deer and elk meat from these locations should not be consumed.

Yeasts. Yeasts are not a significant cause of foodborne illness, but can contaminate food and cause it to spoil. Yeasts prefer sweet, liquid foods and are well known for fermenting cider and fruit juices. An indication of yeast spoilage is a fermenting, alcoholic smell, and discoloration.

Natural Toxins. Toxins can occur naturally in foods such as fish, shellfish, mushrooms, and certain plants. A foodborne illness called ciguatera (pronounced "sig-wah-terrra") is caused by consuming fish that has, in turn, ingested toxins present in algae. Shellfish can also be toxic due to algae they consume. An example of shellfish-related illness is paralytic shellfish poisoning. Scombroid poisoning is the result of eating certain varieties of fish that release a toxin called histamine when they begin to spoil. Mushroom poisoning can result from eating certain varieties of mushrooms. Generally, these toxins are not destroyed by cooking. So the best protection is prevention: purchase seafood and mushrooms only from approved sources. See *Management in the News* at the end of this chapter.

Chemical Hazards

Chemical hazards include pesticides that are sprayed on food, preservatives used to maintain food, toxic metals in cooking equipment and utensils, and chemical cleaning materials used in the foodservice operation.

Preservatives and Food Additives. Some chemicals are added to food to help preserve the quality. Sulfites are one example that are used for fresh fruits and vegetables, shrimp, lobster, and wine. Sulfites may cause an allergic reaction in some people so sulfiting agents added to a product in processing plant must be declared on labeling. Do not use a sulfiting agent on raw produce.

Other chemicals added to enhance food quality that may cause allergic reactions are nitrites/nitrates in meats and MSG (monosodium glutamate) used in Asian or Latin American foods.

Putting It Into Practice: 3

A Certified Dietary Manager notices a client wheezing after eating a stir-fry dish that was fried with peanut oil. What should the manager do first? Why might this have happened?

(Check your answer at the end of this chapter)

Allergens. Food allergies are a separate, but classified as chemical, type of food-related illness warranting the attention of Certified Dietary Managers. The FDA Food Code has added an emphasis on food allergies: "Food allergy is an increasing food safety and public health issue affecting approximately 4 percent of the U.S. population or twelve million Americans." The 2009 FDA Food Code lists the following topics that managers need to know regarding food allergies:

✓ The eight major food allergens

✓ Food allergen ingredient identities and labeling

✓ How to avoid cross-contamination during food preparation and service.

A food allergy is an adverse reaction to food that involves the immune system. An allergic reaction depends upon an allergen, a specific protein in the food that triggers an immune system response. For example, the protein in peanuts or eggs may function as an allergen for sensitive individuals. Figure 17.7 shows the foods associated with the most common food allergies. The best control measure to use in the foodservice department is to prevent cross-contamination between allergenic and non-allergenic ingredients. For a full discussion on food allergies, see Chapter 5 in the *Nutrition Concepts and Medical Nutrition Therapy* textbook.

Pesticides. Chemicals used to keep produce grown in the United States free from plant diseases and insect infestations are regulated by the government and should not cause foodborne illness when applied at recommended levels. But some foods originate from international sources, with less government regulation and monitoring. Wash all fresh fruits and vegetables to remove chemical residues before serving.

Figure 17.7 The Most Common Food Allergens

- Milk
- Eggs
- Fish
- Shellfish (e.g. crab, lobster, shrimp)
- Tree Nuts (e.g. almonds, pecans, walnuts)
- Wheat
- Peanuts
- Soybeans
- A food ingredient derived from one of these, e.g. peanut oil, baked goods containing eggs, sauces containing wheat flours, etc.

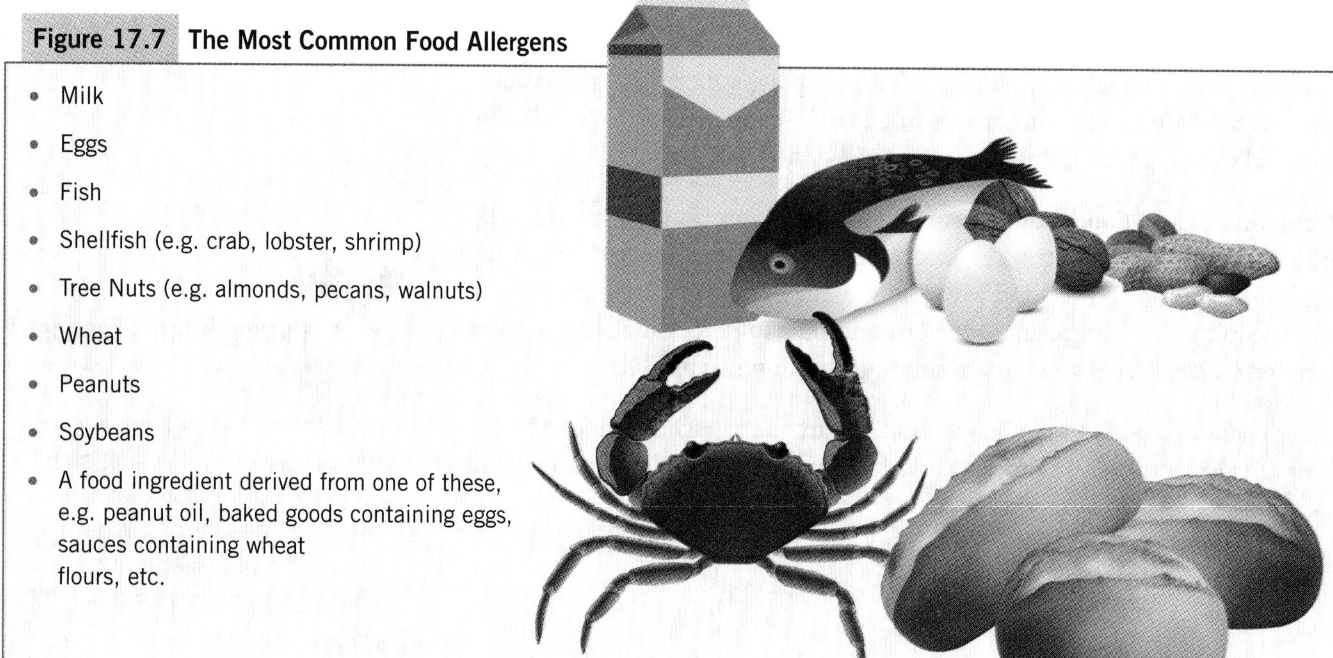

Toxic Metals. Metals that can cause foodborne illness include cadmium, antimony, lead, zinc, and copper. Antimony, zinc, and copper may cause contamination after prolonged contact with acid foods. Carefully select foodservice equipment to control this hazard.

Cleaning Supplies. Cleaning products may also cause contamination when improperly used or stored. Cleaning supplies and other toxic materials must be stored separately from the food preparation area. Never use a food container to store chemicals, and never use chemical containers to store food. Containers used for cleaning—such as buckets and pails—should be clearly marked and dedicated for use in cleaning only.

Physical Hazards

Physical hazards are foreign materials that enter food accidentally. Examples are glass fragments, pieces of bone, metal shavings, staples from produce crates, and other objects that fall into food and cause serious physical harm or injury.

Examples of techniques to prevent contamination of food from physical hazards include: visually inspecting food during preparation, maintaining equipment in good repair, keeping food covered to prevent fragments from falling into it, and discarding food that has been exposed to broken dishware.

Foodborne Illness Prevention

Foodborne illness is a real and present danger. This places a great responsibility on every Certified Dietary Manager and foodservice staff member to protect clients. It is essential to take steps to protect food and control hazards. The steps follow the flow of food throughout your operation—from purchasing ingredients to receiving and storing, to preparing and serving food, to managing leftovers.

United States government research indicates that the five top causes of foodborne illness outbreak are:

- ✓ Improper holding temperatures
- ✓ Contaminated equipment
- ✓ Poor personal hygiene
- ✓ Inadequate cooking
- ✓ Food from unsafe sources.

This textbook addresses essential food protection practices that relate to these concerns, as well as other causes of foodborne illness. A Certified Dietary Manager must ensure safe practices in all phases of foodservice management. How do we know what is a safe practice? The Food and Drug Administration (FDA) has developed one set of food protection standards, the FDA Food Code. The standards recommended in the Food Code provide the basis for this unit.

Glossary

Physical Hazards
Foreign materials that enter food accidentally

Summary

Anyone managing a foodservice operation must be aware of the constant hazards that can result in foodborne illness. In the U.S. today, foodborne illness is a serious public health concern. In some cases, failure to observe food-safe practices can result in illness, hospitalization, or even the death of a client. While the responsibility is grave, we fortunately have a wealth of knowledge about the factors that can cause foodborne illness and the means to control them. This is the charge of every Certified Dietary Manager.

SECTION B Protect Food in the Preparation and Service of Safe Food

The movement of food through the various stages of purchasing, receiving, storage, preparation, transport, holding, service, cooling, and reheating is called the **flow of food**. Each step in this flow presents hazards and challenges for food protection. In this section, we will focus on the latter segment of this flow, beginning with food preparation.

Preparing Safe Food

Temperature is a critical variable in protecting food. Food temperature must be monitored at each step in the flow of food. It is important to keep food out of the hazard zone for food temperatures. To ensure that food is being safely maintained, keep temperature logs in all storage, preparation, and service areas. Involve all staff members in monitoring food temperatures, and be sure all staff are trained in proper procedures for recording food temperatures.

Time is also an important control technique for food protection. When moving food from storage to preparation areas, label it to indicate the latest time for use. Once food has been removed from a monitored, temperature-controlled environment, serve or dispose of it within four hours. For instance, if you have room service and you prepared the lunch entree at 10:00 am for a room service request, it must be served or refrigerated properly before 2:00 pm. Dispose of food if it is in unmarked containers, or if the expiration date has passed. Communicate food labeling and monitoring practices to all members of the foodservice team.

Cross-Contamination

During all phases of food preparation and service, foodservice professionals must take steps to prevent cross-contamination. **Cross-contamination** is the transfer of pathogens from any item to food. The source of contamination may be a non-food item, such as a work surface, another food item, or the hands of a foodservice employee. Figure 17.8 identifies examples of how cross-contamination can occur. To prevent cross-contamination:

- ✓ Follow proper procedures for cleaning and sanitizing equipment and utensils.
- ✓ Observe handwashing practices and standards for glove use.
- ✓ As much as possible, isolate raw foods from ready-to-eat or prepared foods in all phases of the flow of food.

Glossary

Flow of Food
Movement of food through a foodservice facility including purchasing, receiving, storage, preparation, transport, holding, service, cooling, and reheating

Cross-Contamination
The transfer of pathogens from any item or human to food

Figure 17.8 Examples: How Cross-Contamination May Occur

- A foodservice staff member prepares tuna salad while wearing gloves and then puts a pan of macaroni and cheese into the warmer without changing gloves and washing hands.
- A cook dices beef for stew on a cutting board, and then chops onions on the same board without cleaning and sanitizing the surface between jobs.
- A cook uses the same spatula to put raw burgers on the grill and to remove cooked burgers from the grill.
- A foodservice staff member allows raw egg mixture to splash over prepared foods near the steam table.
- An employee picks up trash from the floor, and then enters the walk-in refrigerator without first washing hands.

Raw fruits and vegetables must be thoroughly washed in water to remove soil and other contaminants. They should be washed before being cut, combined with other ingredients, cooked, served, or offered for service in a ready-to-eat form.

Pathogens such as salmonella or chemicals such as pesticides may be present on the outside surface of fruits and vegetables. The 2009 FDA Food Code says, "All fresh produce, except commercially washed, pre-cut, or bagged produce, must be thoroughly washed under running, potable water before eating, cutting, or cooking." This is required even if you plan to peel the produce prior to eating. If you are using pre-washed, bagged produce in an opened bag, it must be considered a potentially hazardous food at that point.

Ice that is used for displaying fresh produce or cooked shellfish cannot be used further for cooking or service.

Thawing

Foods must be thawed in a manner that avoids placing the food in the hazard zone for an excessive amount of time. Frozen food should never be thawed at room temperature. Following are four options for thawing food safely:

- ✓ Thaw gradually under refrigeration that maintains the food temperature at 41°F or less.
- ✓ Thaw completely submerged under cold, potable, running water (70°F or less), with water pressure sufficient to continuously agitate any food particles off the surface. With this method, thawing time should be less than two hours, or until food reaches 41°F. This method may not be effective for thawing large pieces of meat.
- ✓ Thaw during the cooking process by cooking frozen food in the oven in a continuous process.
- ✓ Thaw and cook single-service items completely in the microwave from a frozen state and then cook immediately.

Food that is removed from the freezer to thaw gradually under refrigeration should be date-marked to indicate the date by which the food should be consumed. The food should be consumed seven days or less after the food was removed from the freezer and should be held at 41°F or below.

Slacking

Slacking is the process of moderating temperature of frozen foods before preparation (such as deep-fat frying). For example, if you are deep-fat frying chicken nuggets that are at -10°F, maybe you wish to bring them up to 32°F first. Regulations about slacking PHF/TCS foods vary from one jurisdiction to another.

The FDA Food Code says that if you practice slacking, you should:

✓ Maintain the temperature of the food you are slacking at or below 41°F, under refrigeration, or

✓ Maintain the product at any temperature, as long as the product remains frozen.

Cooking

Cooking is a very important step in the flow of food. Failure to cook PHF/TCS food thoroughly can cause foodborne illness. Cooking food thoroughly destroys most (but not all) biological hazards.

For PHF/TCS foods, the FDA Food Code suggests cooking standards that combine time and temperature. An **endpoint temperature** is the temperature a food reaches at the end of cooking.

Endpoint temperature should be measured with a calibrated measuring device, such as a thermometer or thermocouple. Measure in the part of the food that is heated last—usually the center or thickest part of the food. See Figure 17.9 for more tips on measuring temperatures.

Endpoint Temperature
The temperature a food reaches at the end of cooking

A foodservice employee is preparing French toast for a special brunch. He uses a spatula to transfer the egg-wash covered French toast to the griddle. He flips the French toast on the griddle and uses the same spatula to transfer the cooked French toast to the steam table pan for service. Is this a concern and why or why not?

(Check your answer at the end of this chapter)

Figure 17.9 Measuring a Food Temperature

Food Item
- Insert thermometer into geometric center or into thickest portion.
- Insert away from the bone, fat or gristle on a food product.
- Insert sideways into small items.

Food Packaging
- By folding the bag over the thermometer or probe for bulk milk or liquids
- Place between frozen packages of food.

General Guidelines
- Wait 5-10 seconds for an accurate reading.
- Sanitize thermometer after each use.
- Until at least 2 inches are submerged in milk and other liquids

In addition, the Food Code specifies that when measuring the temperature of thin foods, use a temperature measuring device (thermometer) with a suitable, small-diameter probe. Typically, this is a thermistor or thermocouple thermometer, rather than a bi-metallic stem thermometer. A bi-metallic stem thermometer needs to contact food all along its sensitive stem, often about 3 inches, in order to obtain a valid reading. In contrast, small, thin probes available with thermocouple or thermistor thermometers may capture an accurate reading with less contact surface.

After using a thermometer probe, always clean and sanitize it, such as with an isopropyl alcohol wipe. The Food Code stipulates that a thermometer is like a utensil because it contacts food, and therefore requires sanitization.

For any thermometer, calibration is also essential (see Figure 17.10). A thermometer used for measuring food temperatures should be accurate to ±2°F. Note that this is more rigorous than the calibration requirement for a thermometer used to measure ambient temperatures in storage areas.

Figure 17.10 Calibrating a Bi-Metallic Thermometer—Slush Method

Step 1: Fill an insulated container (like a foam cup) full of potable, crushed ice.

Step 2: Add cold water and stir.

Step 3: Allow time for the mixture to come to a 32˚F temperature (about 4-5 minutes).

Step 4: Insert a bi-metallic stemmed thermometer into the geothermal center of the cup (away from the bottom and sides).

Step 5: Hold thermometer until the temperature stabilizes, and record the temperature.

Step 6: Repeat two times to verify the temperature reading.

Step 7: If the temperature is not 32˚F, use pliers on the calibration nut under the top of the thermometer to adjust the temperature to 32˚F.

Reaching a specified temperature alone is not adequate for ensuring destruction of pathogens. Cooks should be instructed to hold the endpoint temperature for a specified length of time, as shown in Figure 17.11. For mixed foods, such as casseroles and soups, find the ingredient with the most stringent time and temperature standard—and apply that standard. Cooks should monitor and record cooking times and temperatures in a log, as shown in Figure 17.12.

Some PHF/TCS foods pose special concerns. Cooking pork and game animals is imperative to destroy possible parasites. Ground meats and seafood have an increased surface area resulting from grinding. This creates more opportunity for pathogens to flourish. Stuffed foods, such as ravioli or stuffed turkey, also provide favorable breeding ground for foodborne pathogens. The FDA time and temperature standards reflect these concerns.

Figure 17.11 Cooking Time and Temperature Guide (Suggested Minimums)

Food Item	Temperature	Time	Comments
All whole cuts of meat such as pork, steaks, roasts and chops	145°F	for 15 seconds	Allow the meat to rest for 3 seconds before consuming.
Poultry, game, stuffed fish, stuffed meat, stuffed pasta	165°F	for 15 seconds	
Chopped or ground seafood or meat (includes ground beef, ground pork, veal, lamb and mechanically tenderized meat)	155°F	for 15 seconds	
Fish, seafood, meats not listed above	145°F	for 15 seconds	
Eggs on steam table	155°F	for 15 seconds	Cooked to hold
Egg, single-serving	145°F	for 15 seconds	Cooked to order
Fruits and vegetables	135°F	No time standard	
Food cooked in microwave	165°F	hold 2 minutes after cooking	

Note: These are standards recommended in the 2009 FDA Food Code and the 2011 Update Bulletin. Please consult your local standards, which may be different. Also review manufacturers' instructions for processed foods.

New to the 2009 Food Code are greater controls if you are partially cooking a product with the expectation of fully cooking it at a later date or time. If your facility follows this practice for foods such as large roasts, you must now establish and follow a written HACCP plan. The plan has to ensure that the stages of cooling, storage, reheating, cooling, and storage are completed within time and temperature parameters that adequately prevent pathogen survival and growth. They must also be clearly labeled so they are not accidently served to the client in a partially cooked state.

Highly Susceptible Populations

If you are serving a highly susceptible population, be aware that both eggs and juice receive special attention in the Food Code. You should generally avoid using fresh, shell eggs for food preparation. Instead, use pasteurized egg products for quantity cooking and for recipes in which eggs will not be thoroughly cooked (such as eggnog). A whole, fresh egg may be used only for a single-service item prepared for immediate service. Today, fresh eggs are also available pasteurized in-shell. This means the whole, fresh egg has been pasteurized, typically at low temperatures. Pasteurized in-shell eggs are fine for both single-service and quantity production.

With the implementation of juice HACCP regulations in 2002, juices you serve must be treated by the processor to control foodborne illness risks through a HACCP process (e.g. pasteurized). Be aware that if you prepare your own juices on-site to serve any population, you must use a HACCP plan for

Figure 17.12 **Endpoint Temperature Log**

Date: ________________ Page #:_____________ of ____________

Item	Time	Temperature	Cook's Initials	Endpoint ✓*

** Check to indicate that this was the endpoint of cooking.*

managing juice-related hazards. Note that juice, as defined in the Food Code, includes liquids, purees, or concentrates.

For highly susceptible populations, the Food Code also prohibits the use of fresh seed sprouts, such as mung bean or alfalfa sprouts. It also stipulates that raw or undercooked meats, such as raw, marinated fish; soft-cooked eggs; or rare meat may not be served. (In foodservice operations serving a general population, this may be permitted as long as the operation provides a consumer advisory about the associated risks.)

New to the 2009 Food Code: A children's menu may not list undercooked hamburger or other groundmeat.

Microwave Cooking

When preparing food in a microwave:

- ✓ Rotate or stir the food item throughout or at the midpoint of cooking to distribute heat evenly.
- ✓ Cover to retain surface moisture.
- ✓ Cook to a temperature of at least 165°F in all parts of the food item.
- ✓ Allow to stand covered for two minutes before serving to obtain temperature equilibrium.

Serving Safe Food

During service, a combination of time and temperature is used to prevent or slow microbial growth. PHF/TCS foods must be held out of the hazard zone as much as possible, as shown in Figure 17.13. Figure 17.14 illustrates examples of monitoring temperature during preparation and service. A log (Figure 17.15) can help employees monitor and document holding temperatures, which should be measured at least every two hours.

Putting It Into Practice: 5

You observe a foodservice staff member replenishing chili on the steam table. She carefully stirs the chili on the steam table, takes and records the temperature. Then she adds fresh chili to the batch in the steam table, being careful to thoroughly stir the two batches together. Is this a concern? Why or why not?

(Check your answer at the end of this chapter)

Figure 17.13 Hazard Zone with Cooking and Holding Temperatures

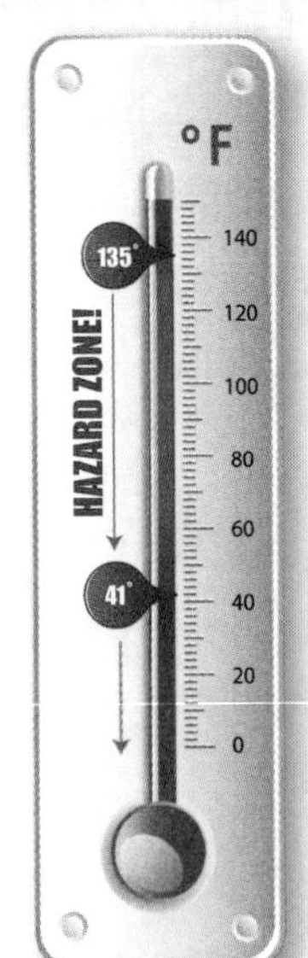

Above 135°F
Hold hot foods above 135°F to prevent growth of microorganisms. Cook food to recommended time/temperature standards to destroy microorganisms.

41°F -135°F
Hazard Zone

Below 41°F
Hold cold food below 41°F to slow bacterial growth and extend shelf life.

Figure 17.14 Monitoring Temperatures During Preparation and Service

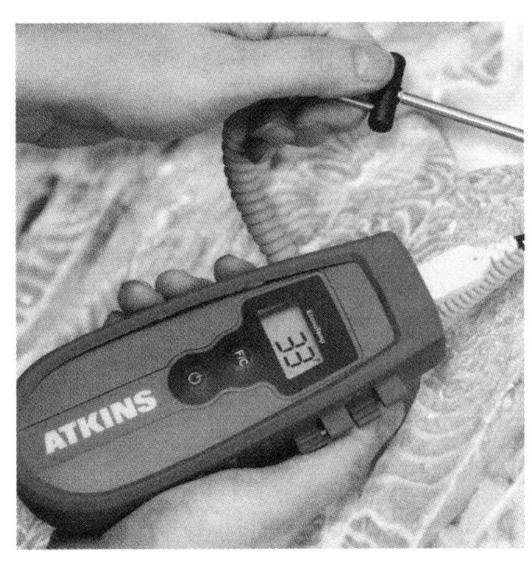

Images courtesy of Cooper Instrument Corporation

Hot Holding

Hot foods must be held at 135°F or above, with the exception of roasts cooked to a time and temperature shown in Figure 17.11. Stir foods during holding to redistribute heat throughout the food product. Keep food containers covered to retain heat and to prevent environmental contaminants from entering the food.

Steam tables and food warmers are examples of equipment that may be used to retain heat and control food temperatures. Steam tables are not meant to cook foods—only to hold them after cooking. Food warmers are usually equipped with an ambient thermometer. Steam tables usually have a temperature control knob but may not measure the actual food temperature. When holding hot foods for service, measure the food temperature at least every two hours. If the food temperature falls into an unsafe range, immediately follow procedures for reheating previously cooked food. When re-stocking hot food products, finish one pan before bringing in a refill; do not pour new product on top of older product.

Cold Holding

Cold food must be held below 41°F. Holding food below this temperature slows the growth of bacteria. Special considerations are required for using ice as a coolant. Packaged food may not be stored in direct contact with ice or water if the entry of water is possible due to the nature of the packaging or its positioning in the ice or water. Ice that has been used as a coolant may not be used as a food or food ingredient. Unpackaged food may not be stored in direct contact with undrained ice, with these exceptions:

- ✓ Whole, raw fruits or vegetables—such as celery or carrot sticks or whole potatoes—may be immersed in ice or water.
- ✓ Raw chicken and raw fish that are received immersed in ice in shipping containers may remain in that condition while in storage awaiting preparation or service.

Putting It Into Practice: 6

How would you cool the following?

- Chicken salad make from canned chicken
- Beef stew

(Check your answer at the end of this chapter)

Figure 17.15 **Holding Temperature Log**

Date: ________________ Page #:____________ of ____________

Item	Time	Temperature	Cook's Initials	Corrective Action

Keep food out of the Hazard Zone: Hold cold foods below 41°F. Hold hot foods above 135°F

During holding and service, utensils should be kept in the food. Utensil handles should be kept above the top of the food and the container. Between uses, a utensil can be stored in water that is at least 135°F. During service, food on display must be protected from contamination. During transport, food items must be maintained out of the hazard zone, and food must be covered to prevent contamination.

Self-Service Food Bars

Self-service food bars, such as buffets and salad bars, present special food protection risks. Client actions and habits create the potential for food contamination. Label all food items in self-service areas to discourage clients from sampling food items. Sneeze guards must be used on service lines, salad bars, and display cases. Self-service food bars should be monitored by foodservice employees trained in food protection practices. Clients are required to use a clean plate for each service from a food bar to prevent contamination from soiled dishes and utensils.

Cooling

Large food masses, such as roasts, turkeys, and large containers of rice, refried beans, or soup/stews take longer to cool because of the mass of food. According to the FDA Food Code, PHF/TCS food should be cooled from 135°F to 41°F within a total maximum time of six hours. The first step of this process must get food down to 70°F within the first two hours.

If you begin with food at room temperature, such as canned tuna, cool it down to 41°F within a maximum total time of four hours. Figure 17.16 identifies methods for speeding the cooling process. Once cooled, food should be covered, dated, and labeled according to date marking standards.

Figure 17.16 Proper Cooling Methods

- Place food in a shallow container (2" deep) to increase surface area and reduce cooling time
- Divide a large food mass into several smaller masses (e.g. a 20-lb roast into five 4-lb pieces)
- Stir the food in a container placed in an ice water bath
- Use rapid cooling equipment, such as a blast chiller
- Add ice as an ingredient

Date Marking

PHF/TCS food prepared in the foodservice operation and held at or below 41°F should be labeled at the time of preparation with the date by which the food should be consumed. Prepared foods should be used within seven days or less of preparation if held at 41°F or below.

The practice of date marking is detailed in the FDA Food Code. When you mark a date on a food product, you are indicating the date by which the product must be used or discarded. A key objective of this practice is to address the time element of bacterial growth. The longer a PHF/TCS food remains in storage, the more opportunity Listeria bacteria have to grow—and they can do so even at or below 41°F.

Date marking applies not only to leftovers. Generally, after opening a package of PHF/TCS food, you must date mark it as well. You should use or discard it within seven days, counting the day you open the package as Day 1.

Certain products, such as hard cheeses or cheeses that contain up to 50 percent moisture (e.g. cheddar, Parmesan, gorgonzola, jack), yogurt, sour cream, buttermilk, and certain shelf-stable processed meat products are exempt from date-marking procedures. Date-marking guidelines also do not apply to deli salads you obtain from a food processing plant, because they apply processes to prevent bacterial growth. Instead, refer to the manufacturer's use-by date. Remember that if PHF/TCS food in storage is not maintained at or below 41°F, you should still discard it.

Reheating

Frozen, ready-to-eat food taken from a commercially prepared, intact package must be heated to at least 135°F for hot holding. Reheating for hot holding should be done as rapidly as possible.

A previously cooked food (a food that was prepared, cooked, and cooled in the foodservice operation) must be reheated to an internal temperature of 165°F for a minimum of 15 seconds. This process must be completed within two hours.

Reservice of food is also governed by the FDA Food Code. Food that is unused or returned by the client may not be offered to others. If the food is individually packaged such as crackers, salt, pepper, or sugar packets, it may be reserved if the packaging is in sound condition. No food, including secure packets may be reserved if it is returned from clients in medical isolation or quarantine.

Putting It Into Practice: 7

You are preparing leftover rice for storage. If the rice was prepared on January 9, what would you put on the label?

(Check your answer at the end of this chapter)

Summary

Referring to the conditions for growth of pathogens, FOTTWA, it is clear that a Certified Dietary Manager has many opportunities to ensure food safety in the process of food production, continuing through service and management of leftovers. In all, time and temperature are critical factors for making food safe.

SECTION C Protect Food Using HACCP Guidelines

HACCP Basics

Hazard Analysis Critical Control Point (HACCP) is an important development in food protection. The **HACCP** system is a preventative food safety program that greatly reduces the likelihood of foodborne illness. HACCP (pronounced has-sip) was developed years ago to ensure a safe food supply for astronauts. It is now being implemented throughout the food processing and service industries. In this section, you will learn the principles of HACCP and discover how to apply them to a foodservice operation.

HACCP uses a systematic approach to identify, evaluate, and control food safety hazards. It focuses on the flow of food rather than on individual procedures. A Certified Dietary Manager who uses HACCP principles in combination with basic sanitation and a solid employee training program, can prevent, eliminate or reduce the occurrence of foodborne illness in his/her facility.

HACCP builds on essential food safety practices that should already be in place. These are called standard operating procedures (SOPs). SOPs include the sanitation guidelines outlined in the FDA Food Code and discussed in other chapters of this book—such as your practices for purchasing, receiving, and storing food; your personal hygiene policies; your procedures for thawing, cooking, holding, and cooling food; and your procedures for cleaning and sanitizing. They are prerequisites for implementing an effective HACCP plan. Without them, any HACCP plan may fail.

Although using HACCP is not directly part of the Food Code, the FDA recommends implementing HACCP throughout the food industry. HACCP plans may be required in foodservice operations processing juice in-house, preparing pureed food, or operating a cook-chill system. Furthermore, school foodservice operations participating in the National School Lunch program are required to have HACCP plans. In addition, your local health department may require you to implement a HACCP system.

The success of HACCP is dependent on a number of variables. Certified Dietary Managers learn HACCP principles and concepts and demonstrate their ability to effectively organize a HACCP system by applying their knowledge. Managers must educate all members of their foodservice team on the principles of HACCP and on the team's role in its implementation. Staff training is essential to the successful implementation of HACCP.

Implementing a HACCP System

A HACCP system revolves around seven principles, summarized in Figure 17.17.

1—Analyze Hazards

Identify hazards associated with foods in your recipes and on your menus. These items could be hazardous due to ingredients, the processes involved in preparation, how the product is held or handled during service, or its

Glossary

HACCP
Hazard Analysis Critical Control Point

Figure 17.17 Seven Principles of HACCP

Principle #1: Analyze hazards.

Principle #2: Identify critical control points (CCPs).

Principle #3: Establish critical limits for critical control points (CCPs).

Principle #4: Establish procedures for monitoring critical control points.

Principle #5: Establish corrective actions.

Principle #6: Establish a record-keeping system.

Principle #7: Establish procedures to verify that the system is working.

ultimate use. Hazards may vary from one foodservice operation to another—even with the production of the same menu item—because of differences in ingredient sources, formulations, processing or packaging techniques, preparation methods and equipment, storage and service plans, who will be consuming the food, or employees' understanding of safe food practices. Figure 17.18 lists some questions you can ask to decide what hazards are present.

While HACCP is concerned with the safety of all food, particular attention should be given to PHF/TCS foods. These foods can support progressive bacterial growth or development of toxins. It's also important to examine the flow of food through your own foodservice system. As you track each PHF/TCS food, where are the hazards? Where could dangerous microorganisms have an opportunity to grow? Developing a flow chart or diagram of the flow of a food can help you identify hazards and control points.

2—Identify Critical Control Points

Points in the flow of food at which a potential hazard can be controlled or eliminated are called **control points.** Control points occur throughout the flow of food, such as during receiving, storage, thawing, cooking, holding, and chilling, and are generally addressed through standard operating procedures. For each control point, ask this question: Could loss of control here lead to an unacceptable health risk? If so, it's called a **critical control point (CCP)**. To determine whether a step is a CCP, refer to the CCP Decision Tree (Figure 17.19). Critical control points vary depending on the food item being prepared and the preparation techniques being used. Often, cooking to recommended time and temperature standard becomes a CCP. However, in a cook-chill operation, blast chilling food to a recommended temperature within a specified time may also be a CCP.

Following the CCP Decision Tree, you can see that there is generally only one CCP for any food or menu item. However, advice varies on this. You may see HACCP examples where only one step in the flow of food is designated as a CCP, and other models where several are. Whether you designate one or several CCPs for any given recipe is not an issue, because either way, you are implementing critical control. However, beware of designating too many steps as CCPs. This can make the system too complex for employees to carry out. Instead, review your standard operating procedures and use them as control points (not CCPs with documentation requirements) as appropriate.

Glossary

Control Point
Point in the flow of food where a hazard can be controlled, a step can be taken to minimize the risk of foodborne illness

Critical Control Point (CCP)
Step in the flow of food which, if not controlled, could lead to an unacceptable health risk for consumers of the food

Figure 17.18 Analyzing Hazards: Questions to Ask

Q: Does the food contain any sensitive ingredients that may present known hazards (e.g., Salmonella, Staphylococcus, aflatoxin)?

Q: What are the sources (e.g., geographical region, specific supplier)?

Q: Does the process include a controllable processing step that destroys pathogens? If so, which pathogens?

Q: Does the microbial population change during the normal time the food is stored prior to consumption?

Q: Does the layout of the facility provide an adequate separation of raw materials from ready-to-eat (RTE) foods if this is important to food safety? If not, what hazards should be considered as possible contaminants of the RTE products?

Q: Will the equipment provide the time-temperature control that is necessary for safe food?

Q: Is the equipment properly sized for the volume of food that will be processed?

Q: Can the equipment be sufficiently controlled so that the variation in performance will be within the tolerances required to produce a safe food?

Q: Is the equipment reliable or is it prone to frequent breakdowns?

Q: Is the equipment designed so that it can be easily cleaned and sanitized?

Q: To what degree will normal equipment wear affect the likely occurrence of a physical hazard (e.g., metal) in the product?

Q: Is the package clearly labeled "Keep Refrigerated" if this is required for safety? Does the package include instructions for the safe handling and preparation of the food by the end user?

Q: Is each package and case legibly and accurately coded? Does each package contain the proper label?

Q: Can employee health or personal hygiene practices impact upon the safety of the food being processed?

Q: Do the employees understand the process and the factors they must control to assure the preparation of safe foods?

Q: Will the employees inform management of a problem which could impact upon safety of food?

Q: What is the likelihood that the food will be improperly stored at the wrong temperature?

Q: Would an error in improper storage lead to a microbiologically unsafe food?

Q: Will the food be heated by the consumer?

Q: Will there likely be leftovers?

Q: Is the food intended for the general public?

Q: Is the food intended for consumption by a population with increased susceptibility to illness (e.g., infants, the aged, or immunocompromised individuals)?

Source: FDA

3—Establish Critical Limits for Critical Control Points

There must be a critical limit for each CCP identified. A **critical limit** identifies the limits of certain properties that you will accept for a given product at a given stage in the flow of food. It is observable and measurable. For a cooked food, a critical limit might specify minimum internal temperature for the endpoint of cooking, along with the minimum time that temperature must be held. The standards you use for critical limits should come from your local food code, the FDA Food Code, or a similar guideline.

4—Establish Procedures for Monitoring CCPs

Determine how and by whom CCPs will be monitored. **Monitoring** procedures may be included in standardized recipes. Observe and measure to determine whether critical limits are met. Critical limits may also be included in recipes, and foodservice personnel should be required to measure all CCPs and document them in HACCP logs (such as the Cooking Temperature Log in Chapter 16).

5—Establish Corrective Actions

When monitoring shows that a critical limit has not been met, there must be an established procedure to follow. These procedures, called **corrective actions**,

Putting It Into Practice: 8

In a traditional baked chicken breast recipe, what would the critical control point(s) be?

(Check your answer at the end of this chapter)

Glossary

Critical Limits
Specified limits or characteristics of a physical, chemical, or biological nature that help you measure whether you have adequately controlled a hazard at a CCP

Monitoring
Checking that a processing or handling procedure does not exceed the established critical limit at each critical control point. It involves systematic observation, measurement, and/or recording. More than one observation may be necessary at a particular critical control point. The monitoring procedures chosen must enable action to be taken to correct an out-of-control situation or to bring the product back into acceptable limits.

Corrective Action (HACCP)
The procedure to follow when monitoring shows that a critical limit has not been met

Dry Lab
Recording temperatures without actually taking them

Verification
The use of equipment to determine that the HACCP system is in place and achieving the desired objectives

are specific to each foodservice operation. Corrective actions should be clearly written and understood by foodservice personnel. For example, let's say you are baking meatloaf (a CCP), and the critical limit is to reach 155°F for a minimum of 15 seconds. You check the temperature in the deepest part of the meatloaf at the end of cooking, and it's only 140°F. Your corrective action might be to return the meatloaf to the oven immediately and continue cooking to reach 155°F. Other examples of corrective actions might be: contacting the Certified Dietary Manager for direction, reheating immediately to a specific temperature, or disposing of food that was improperly cooled.

6—Establish a Record-Keeping System

A record-keeping system documents HACCP activities and includes time and temperature monitoring records. Use forms to document the flow of food products, time and temperature, and corrective actions. Maintain daily HACCP logs in a notebook accessible to all members of your foodservice team. Your HACCP log may identify critical limits to check, and include a place for employees to document corrective actions taken. Be alert to **dry lab**, the practice of entering time and temperature measurements without actually taking them. Dry lab can undermine the success of any HACCP program.

7—Verify that the System is Working

Calibration of temperature monitoring devices and review of HACCP logs for accuracy and completeness will help to verify the system is fulfilling its mission to improve food safety. Review HACCP logs, records of monitoring CCPs, and corrective actions taken by staff members. Conduct random checks to ensure that CCPs are being monitored appropriately by staff and that temperature monitoring equipment is working properly. Figure 17.20 lists some activities a manager may use in the **verification** process.

HACCP and Planning

As you analyze HACCP records, look for patterns that indicate a need for employee training, equipment repair or replacement. Sometimes HACCP information will indicate a need to change kitchen layout, menus, ingredient selection, preparation methods, processes, or procedures. HACCP records can provide a valuable tool for planning and refining a safe foodservice system. Consider the flow of food as you make decisions that will affect your foodservice systems, and update your HACCP plan as you make changes. For example, as you review HACCP logs, you may find that it is difficult to meet cooling recommendations for tuna salad. As you review the flow of food for tuna and mayonnaise, you realize that food preparation is starting with ingredients at room temperature. As a result, you decide to change the procedure and pre-chill potentially hazardous ingredients. In another example, you are evaluating plans to re-design the kitchen. As you map out the flow of food for some of your key menu items, you notice that your current layout presents opportunities for contamination that could be avoided: The trash room occasionally overflows into an area where fresh meats are received, and food waste from dining service is being processed very close to the cold food preparation area. As you work with an architect, you specify that food

receiving and preparation areas must be isolated from sources of contamination. In yet another example, you review the hazard associated with cross-contamination. You decide to use color-coded cutting boards to reinforce safe practices among employees.

Figure 17.19 CCP Decision Tree

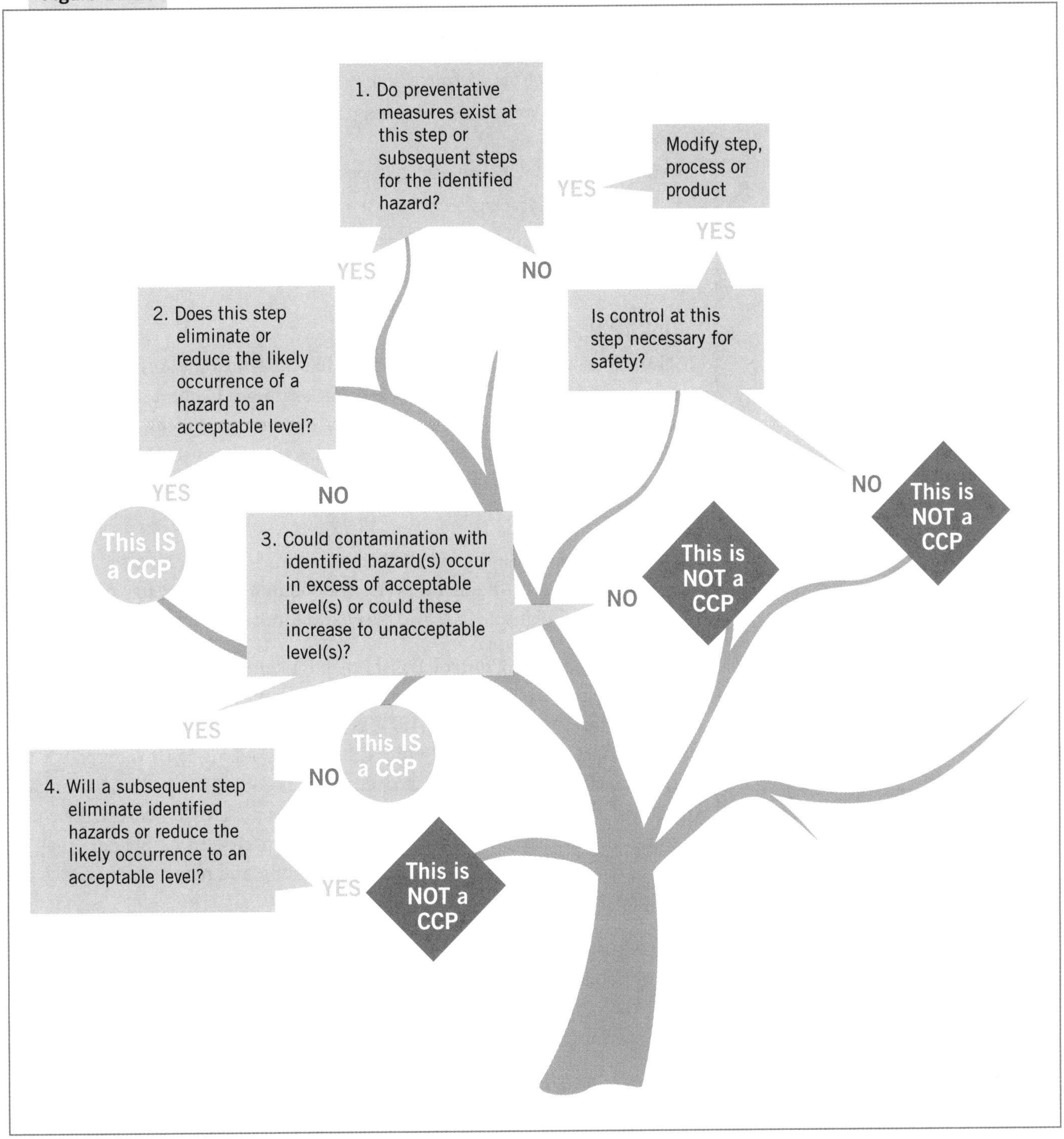

Source: FDA Food Code

Figure 17.20 HACCP Verification Activities

- Establishment of appropriate verification schedules
- Review of the HACCP plan for completeness
- Confirmation of the accuracy of the flow diagram
- Review of the HACCP system to determine if the facility is operating according to the HACCP plan
- Review of CCP monitoring records
- Review of records for deviations and corrective actions
- Validation of critical limits to confirm that they are adequate to control significant hazards
- Validation of HACCP plan, including on-site review
- Review of modifications of the HACCP plan
- Sampling and testing to verify CCPs

Source: FDA

A HACCP Plan Case Example

A HACCP plan is a written document that describes the formal procedures for following HACCP principles. In this example, Community Hospital is implementing a HACCP plan. To begin the process, Community Hospital has assembled a HACCP team that includes the: Certified Dietary Manager, receiving clerk, cook, and trayline supervisor. See Figure 17.21 for a sample HACCP plan.

1—Analyze Hazards. The HACCP team begins by identifying the PHF/TCS foods on each day of the menu cycle. The menu for the first day of the menu cycle appears in Figure 17.22. The PHF/TCS foods are circled.

2—Identify Critical Control Points. After identifying the PHF/TCS foods, the team begins to develop a flow chart to identify the critical control points in the flow of food for each PHF/TCS food. Flow charting requires taking a closer look at the recipe for PHF/TCS foods. Cooking is considered a CCP here, because failure to impose proper controls could lead to an unacceptable health risk for clients. In this example, holding is not a CCP because the entire holding process is completed in less than two hours. Some peppers may be saved as leftovers, stored under proper conditions, and reheated for service the following day. Therefore, reheating is also a CCP.

3—Establish Critical Limits for Control Points. After identifying the critical control points, the team determines the critical limit for each critical control point. The critical limits are listed along with the CCP in the HACCP recipe in Figure 17.23.

4—Establish Procedures for Monitoring Control Points. The team next determines who will be responsible for monitoring the critical limits. The team must decide what forms will be necessary to document monitoring activities, and how staff will be informed of their responsibilities for monitoring. Monitoring information is included in the HACCP plan and in the recipe.

Figure 17.21 **HACCP Plan for Stuffed Peppers**

Steps 1-2: Analyze hazards, identify critical control points

		CCP?
Purchase	USDA inspected beef	No
Receive	Frozen beef at 0°F or below	No
Store	0°F or below	No
Prepare	Thaw at 41°F or below	No
Cook	Cook to 165°F	Yes
Hold	Hold at 135°F	No
Cool	Cool from 135°F to 70°F within 2 hrs, and from 70°F to 41°F within 4 hrs	No
Reheat	Reheat to 165°F within 2 hrs	Yes

Steps 3-6: Establish critical limits, procedures for monitoring, corrective action, record-keeping

CCP	Critical Limit	Standard	Corrective Action
Cooking beef/rice mixture	Cook to 165°F for at least 15 seconds	**Monitor:** observation **Stuffed food:** Cook thoroughly to destroy pathogens (high risk for STEC). **Monitor:** record temperature	Continue cooking until critical limit is reached
Reheating	Reheat to 165°F within 2 hrs	**Monitor:** Check time/temperature during reheating	Dispose of food that is not properly reheated

5—Establish Corrective Actions. When monitoring shows that a critical limit has not been met, there must be an established procedure to follow. Corrective actions are included in the HACCP plan.

6—Establish a Record-Keeping System. The team will develop log sheets and records to be used by staff to verify that the HACCP system is being used. The log sheets should be simple to use and understand. All staff must be trained in the proper techniques for monitoring CCPs and recording data on the log sheets.

7—Establish Procedures to Verify that the System is Working. The team agrees to meet on a regular basis to review HACCP logs, to ensure that records are being completed and to identify any necessary changes.

Figure 17.22 Identifying PHF/TCS Foods on a Menu

Breakfast

- Orange juice
- Scrambled eggs
- Canadian bacon
- Toast with jelly

Lunch

- Tossed salad
- Beef barley soup
- Turkey club sandwich
- Cherry cake

Dinner

- Peach salad
- Stuffed pepper
- Whipped potatoes
- Baby carrots
- New York style cheesecake

The Process Approach to HACCP

In a foodservice operation, HACCP may take a different form than in a food processing or packaging environment, notes the FDA, explaining, "The resources available to help you identify and control risk factors common to your operation may be limited." The report advises that a "complete HACCP system" is ideal, but variations are acceptable, as long as the plan is designed to control risks and incorporate "some, if not all" of the HACCP principles. Because each set of procedures for production and service is different, "HACCP has no single correct application," according to the FDA.

While a food manufacturer generally focuses on one food product at a time in its HACCP plan, says the FDA, a foodservice operation weaves together the flow charts of many distinct foods to produce a meal, which calls for a different approach. The recommended approach targets processes rather than individual foods.

In a process approach, you assign sets of food flow charts to process-related categories and manage them as groups. See Figure 17.24 for examples. The FDA suggests three types of processes:

✓ Process 1: Food preparation with no cook step, where the flow of food is: receive > store > prepare > hold > serve. Examples: salads, cold sandwiches.

Putting It Into Practice: 9

What is the best way to train staff on HACCP plans?

(Check your answer at the end of this chapter)

- ✓ Process 2: Preparation for same-day service, where the flow of food is: receive > store > prepare > cook > hold > serve. Examples: baked chicken, meatloaf.
- ✓ Process 3: Complex food preparation, where the flow of food is: receive > store > prepare > cook > cool > reheat > hot hold > serve. Examples: casseroles in which meats or other ingredients are cooked and cooled the day before assembly, or leftovers that are reheated and served at another meal.

Figure 17.23 **HACCP Recipe for Stuffed Peppers**

Yield: 24 portions

Ingredients	Amount	PHF/TCS Food
Green peppers, large	12	
Rice	10 oz.	
Ground beef	2½ lb.	✓
Onion, fine dice	10 oz.	✓
Chopped garlic	1 tsp.	
Tomato sauce	3 pt.	
Oil	3 oz.	
Water		

Directions *(CCP = Critical Control Point)*

1. Wash hands before beginning food preparation. Use clean and sanitized utensils and equipment.
2. Thaw ground beef under refrigeration (41˚F or below), 2 days.
3. Wash the peppers before cutting. Cut the peppers in half lengthwise. Remove seeds and core.
4. Blanch the peppers in boiling salted water or in a steamer for 4-5 minutes. (Peppers should be partially cooked but still crisp and firm.) Cool quickly in cold water.
5. Cook the rice by steaming. Cook to internal temperature of 165˚F at endpoint of cooking.
6. Cool to 41˚F within 4 hours. Use a cold water rinse to expedite cooling.
7. Sauté the onions and garlic in oil until lightly browned. Cool.
8. Combine rice, onions, meat and tomato sauce.
9. Fill each pepper half with 4 oz. meat mixture.
10. Arrange peppers in baking pans and add about ¼" water to the bottom of the pan (do not pour it on the peppers).
11. (CCP) Bake at 350˚F for 30-35 minutes until internal temperature is 165˚F for 15 seconds and the tops are browned.
12. Hold for service at 135˚F or above.

Figure 17.24 Process Examples

PROCESS 1: No Cook • Example: Fruit Salad
Receive—Control measures: known source, receiving temperatures
Store—Control measures: proper storage temperatures, prevent cross-contamination, store away from chemicals
Prepare—Control measures: personal hygiene, restrict ill employees, prevent cross-contamination
CCP: Cold Holding—Critical limit: hold at 41° or below.* Check and record temperatures
Serve—Control measures: no bare hand contact with ready-to-eat food, personal hygiene, restrict ill employees
PROCESS 2: Same Day Service • Example: Baked Chicken
Receive—Control measures: known source, receiving temperatures
Store—Control measures: proper storage temperatures, prevent cross-contamination, store away from chemicals
Prepare—Control measures: personal hygiene, restrict ill employees, prevent cross-contamination
CCP: Cook—Critical limit: internal temperature of 165°F for 15 seconds.* Check and record temperatures
CCP: Hot Hold—Critical limit: hold at no less than 135°F.* Check and record temperatures
Serve—Control measures: no bare hand contact with ready-to-eat food, personal hygiene, restrict ill employees
PROCESS 3: Complex Food Preparation • Example: Beef and Bean Tamale Pie
Receive—Control measures: known source, receiving temperatures
Store—Control measures: proper storage temperatures, prevent cross-contamination, store away from chemicals
Prepare—Control measures: personal hygiene, restrict ill employees, prevent cross-contamination
CCP: Cook—Critical limit: Cook to 165°F for at least 15 seconds.* Check and record temperatures
CCP: Cool—Critical limit: Cool to 70°F within 2 hours and from 70°F to 41°F or lower within an additional 4 hours.* Check and record temperatures
CCP: Reheat—Critical limit: heat to 165°F for at least 15 seconds.* Check and record temperatures
CCP: Hot Hold—Critical limit: Hold for hot service at 135°F or higher.* Check and record temperatures
Serve—Control measures: no bare hand contact with ready-to-eat food, personal hygiene, restrict ill employees

Thermometer icon means that taking a temperature is necessary; Clipboard icon means recording data is necessary.

**From the 2005 FDA Food Code*

Source: USDA. Guidance for School Food Authorities: Developing a School Food Safety Program Based on the Process Approach to HACCP Principles, 2005. www.fns.usda.gov/cnd/Lunch/Downloadable/HACCPGuidance.pdf

Figure 17.25 **Examples of Hazards and Control**

Measures for Same Day Service Items		
Process 2: Preparation for Same Day Service		
Example Products	**Baked Meatloaf**	**Baked Chicken**
Example Biological Hazards	*Salmonella* spp.	*Salmonella* spp
	E. coli O157:H7	*Campylobacter*
	Clostridium perfringens	*Clostridium perfringens*
	Bacillus cereus	*Bacillus cereus*
	Various fecal-oral route pathogens	Various fecal-oral route pathogens
Example Control Measures	Refrigeration at 41°F or below	Refrigeration at 41°F or below
	Cooking at 155°F for 15 seconds	Cooking at 165°F for 15 seconds
	Hot Holding at 135°F or above OR Time Control	Hot Holding at 135°F or above OR Time Control
	Good personal hygiene (No bare hand contact with RTE food, proper hand-washing, exclusion/restriction of ill employees)	Good personal hygiene (No bare hand contact with RTE food, proper hand-washing, exclusion/restriction of ill employees)
RTE = Ready-to-Eat Food		

Source: 2009 Food Code Annex, pg. 525

There can be variations in these processes, but they characterize the foodborne illness risks fairly well, and examples of the risks are outlined in the FDA Annex. Process 3 includes at least two trips through the hazard zone, so it carries the greatest risks. It clearly requires carefully managed temperature control, especially in cooling and reheating steps. Date marking and storage are also important.

You can target food-flow steps involving the hazard zone and apply controls to manage the hazards in all processes. For Process 1, where there is no cooking to destroy potential pathogens, controls focus more on purchasing specifications, receiving check-in, date marking, and storage time and temperature. For Process 2, cooking (endpoint temperatures) and holding will require your most active managerial control.

Processes may also merge for menu items. A chicken salad sandwich, for example, may include elements of Process 3 (receive, store, prepare, cook, cool) and Process 1 (store, prepare, hold, serve). Figure 17.25 illustrates examples of hazards and controls for foods prepared for same-day service.

If you group foods according to their flow in your operation, you do not need to map out a flow of food for each individual food item on your menu, says the FDA, adding that "a hazard analysis on individual food items is time and labor intensive and generally unnecessary." Managing the steps in a process "achieves the same control of risk factors as preparing a HACCP plan for each individual product," suggests the report.

Summary

HACCP is a proactive method for managing food safety. It allows a Certified Dietary Manager to focus resources where they are needed most, at critical control points (CCPs) in the flow of food. Although not required for most foodservice operations today, HACCP is a great idea because it is an effective management tool for control. HACCP builds upon standard operating procedures. It requires documentation and monitoring. In foodservice, it is not always necessary to create a flow chart for every food in order to implement HACCP. Instead, a manager can group foods according to the types of preparation processes used.

Management in the News

Fish Should Not Smell Fishy

by Melissa Vaccaro, MS, CHO

Melissa Vaccaro, MS, CHO is a Food Program Specialist for the PA Department of Agriculture and an Executive Board Member for the Central Atlantic States Association of Food and Drug Officials (CASA). Contact her at mvaccaro@state.pa.us

Has sushi made an appearance in your town? How about the raw oyster bar? Sushi (raw fish with rice) and sashimi (raw fish) are a popular and growing trend in the food industry. Where once you would only have found sushi in fine dining restaurants (or in Japan), now most large supermarket chains carry sushi or have a sushi chef on staff.

You can now find raw oyster bars in your local high-end grocery stores. Nutritional diets include lots of fish as a good alternative to higher calorie, higher fat meats. With all this promotion of fish and shellfish consumption, do you know how to choose fish or shellfish when you are standing at the market? Fish come with a variety of concerns for harvesters, producers, distributors and customers alike, that every consumer of fish and should know about. Fish is a great source of nutrition, so don't stop eating it, just be educated about how to choose, handle, and consume fish wisely.

According to the National Oceanic and Atmospheric Administration's National Marine Fisheries Service, Americans consume 15.8 lbs of fish per person/year (2009). In 2009, US consumers spent $75.5 billion on fish. Fish is a huge part of the US diet. Imported fish made up 84 percent of the seafood eaten in the US in 2009. As such, the Hazards Guide now includes information on species of fish harvested and processed in non-US waters and facilities.

The Food and Drug Administration (FDA) publishes the "Fish and Fishery Products Hazards Guide," aka, "Hazards Guide." This resource is intended for harvesters (fishermen) and processors of fish and shellfish. This guide helps the industry (including the regulator) ensure that consumers don't become sick from the consumption of fish parasites, pathogens (including bacteria, virus, and fungi) and toxins (chemicals produced by the fish themselves). A processor will find information in this guide on what contaminants might be present and what controls should be used to eliminate them. Providing the latest scientific research to harvesters and producers of fish, the Hazards Guide helps assure that our fish supply is safe. But once the fish has moved from the processors to the retailers, does it remain safe? The FDA Model Food Code sets the standard for retail storage, processing, and sale of fish. If a retailer follows the requirements within the Code, they will be providing safe fish to their consumers.

The last link in the food chain is the consumer. What can a consumer do to protect themselves from illness caused by fish or fishery products? First, you must understand some basics about fish and associated illness.

Parasites in Fish

Fish are animals that live in water. Some fish are bottom feeders. Big fish eat small fish. Parasites also live in water. Parasites, mostly worm-like, are commonly found in fish flesh. Some you cannot even see with the naked eye. If you eat fish with live parasites, you too will have the parasite grow in your body. One of the biggest concerns with eating raw or undercooked fish is parasite infections. Freezing kills parasites; therefore, it is required that all fish intended to be consumed raw or undercooked, with the exception of some tuna

(Continued...)

Fish Should Not Smell Fishy *(Continued)*

species, be frozen prior to consumption. This is true for sushi, sashimi, and other raw or undercooked fish preparations. The FDA requires that fish be frozen at -20°F or below for a minimum of 7 days or at -35°F or below for a minimum of 15 hours.

Freezing will not kill other pathogens; therefore, good sanitation is very important to control contamination or growth of other pathogens. Unless served within 4 hours, sushi or other similar fish preparations should be refrigerated to control the growth of microorganisms.

Toxins and Other Bacteria in Fish

There's another important food safety concern with fish...scombrotoxism. Scombroid poisoning is a food-related illness associated with fish. It resembles an allergic reaction. A histamine (scombrotoxin) is produced which poisons the food and leads to the reaction. If exposed to elevated temperatures at any point from harvest to consumption, fish can produce this very dangerous toxin which will cause human illness. This bacteria, which naturally exists on the gills and inside live saltwater fish, can continue to grow even on dead fish, especially if the fish are not kept chilled properly. Scombroid is caused by bacterial spoilage of certain finfish such as tuna, mackerel, bonito, and, rarely, other fish, therefore temperature control of fish is very important. The Hazards Guide addresses Scombroid from harvest (control measures at sea) through distribution.

Other marine toxins such as *Ciguatera poisoning, Paralytic shellfish poisoning*, and *Neurotoxic shellfish poisoning*, all caused by marine dinoflagellates, are of concern in marine fish. Dinoflagellates are the creatures that cause 'red tides.' Harvesting waters are monitored very closely by regulatory agencies. Buying fish from reputable suppliers is very important.

Vibrio is a naturally-occurring organism commonly found in waters where oysters are cultivated. When the appropriate conditions occur with regard to salt content and temperature, Vibrio thrives. Vibrio is a bacterium. Harvesting areas are monitored for conditions that may increase the chance of Vibrio growth and could be closed until such time as conditions return to normal; as such, purchasing shellstock from reputable dealers who harvest only from approved waters is most important. Of course, if you choose to eat shellstock raw, you are still eating a raw, unprocessed animal and are still taking a chance with your health. Pasteurized shellstock are a great alternative!

Mercury in Fish

Some fish are known to be high in mercury. Pregnant women, women trying to get pregnant, and young children are at highest risk for mercury poisoning due to elevated mercury levels in certain species of fish. Fish is a good healthy food, so don't stop eating fish. Simply be aware of the amount of fish you consume.

To reduce exposure to mercury, FDA recommends the following:

- If you are a susceptible population, do not eat shark, swordfish, king mackerel, or tilefish. They are very high in mercury.
- Continue to eat up to 12 oz. a week of a variety of fish and shellfish with low mercury levels, such as shrimp, canned light tuna, salmon, pollock, and catfish.
- Albacore has high levels of mercury compared to canned light tuna. Eat only 6 oz. of albacore per week.
- If you are fishing in local waters, be aware of any elevated mercury information from those waters. If no information is available, eat up to 6 oz. of local water fish and don't consume other fish that week.

(Continued...)

Fish Should Not Smell Fishy *(Continued)*

Consumers of Fish

Fish and shellfish are an important part of a healthy diet. They are low calorie, rich in high quality protein and other essential nutrients, low in saturated fat, and contain omega-3 fatty acids. So keep them in your diet, but be cautious and understand what you are buying.

Hopefully with a better understanding of fish and shellfish safety, your next trip to the grocery store or market will end in a great piece of SAFE fish in your cart for your evening meal.

Safety Tips for Purchasing and Consuming Fish and Other Fishery Products

- When buying fish or shellstock, always buy from a reputable dealer.
- If fishing, make sure you are fishing in waters that have not been designated as waters of concern for algal blooms, dinoflagellate growth or "red tide" conditions.
- Watch your seafood counter personnel. Are they practicing good personal hygiene and proper food handling practices? Does the area look and smell clean? Is it free of flies? If not, walk away.
- When selecting fish at your local store, choose fish that do not smell fishy. The only fish that smell fishy are those that are beginning to decompose. The flesh should be springy, eyes clear but bulging just a small bit (if buying whole, except Walleye pike which have naturally cloudy eyes), firm flesh with a nice shine. The skin and flesh of the fish should not look dry or show darkening at the edges. Note: fish that have been previously frozen may have lost some of their shine but are still fine to eat.
- Do not buy or consume shellstock that are cracked, broken, or dead.
- Buy only fish or shellstock that is refrigerated or packed in ice to 38°F or below. When at home, keep fresh fish refrigerated at 38°F or below to control histamine production or those fish listed above that are natural histamine producers. Toxins are not destroyed with cooking. Once they are formed, they are there for good.
- Once at home, consume fish within two days. If not used, wrap tightly and freeze.
- Thaw frozen fish/shellfish in the refrigerator, never out at room temperature. You can also immerse packaged fish in cool running water for a short time to thaw your product faster just prior to preparation or cooking.
- Wash your hands thoroughly before and after handling raw or partially cooked fish/shellfish.
- Be careful not to cross-contaminate your kitchen. Wash all surfaces thoroughly before and after fish preparation. Be aware of items that may have come in contact with the raw product and clean those areas thoroughly. You can even sanitize the area with bleach water (1 tablespoon of bleach to 1 gallon of water but DON'T mix with soap, unless you desire a trip to the hospital).
- Highly susceptible populations (those who may be immune compromised) should not consume raw fish or shellstock.
- Consume only pasteurized raw shellstock if at all possible. Raw oysters are still raw and can still have pathogens. Hot sauce and alcohol will not kill the pathogen.
- When eating sushi or sashimi, be sure that the fish, except tuna, has been frozen as required to eliminate parasites. Note: freezing does not kill other harmful pathogens.
- Have a working and accurate food thermometer and cook all seafood to 145°F.
- Relax and enjoy your fish and shellfish dinner!

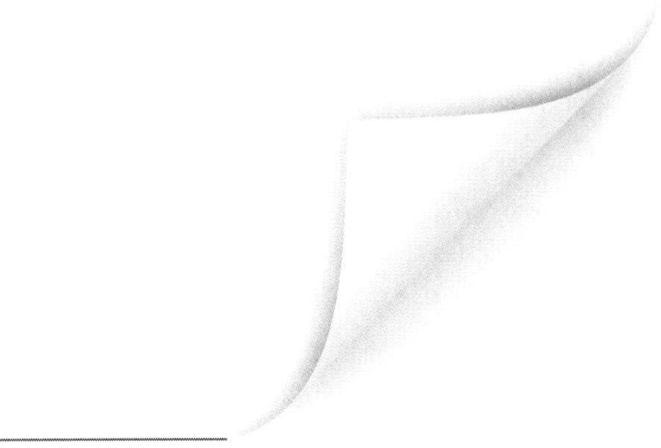

END OF CHAPTER

Putting It Into Practice Questions & Answers

1. What type of contamination is most likely to occur from unwashed hands?

   A. *You need to know what type of contamination is spread through human contact. In most cases that would be viruses. A virus is a biological contamination. Viruses most likely spread from unwashed hands are Hepatitis A, Norovirus, and Vibrio. Common symptoms include nausea, diarrhea and vomiting. Common sources of the virus include contaminated meat and poor sanitation habits (such as improper handwashing). Common ways to prevent the virus are temperature control and proper handwashing.*

2. In the following recipe, which foods would be considered potentially hazardous?
   - 1 lb. boneless chicken breast ½" pieces
   - 2 cups diced potatoes with onion
   - 3 Tbsp. flour
   - 3 cups fat-free chicken broth
   - ⅔ cups frozen mixed vegetables
   - Salt, pepper, sage, thyme to taste

   A. *Foods that are potentially hazardous are high in protein, have a higher pH, and a higher moisture content. In this recipe the two items that best fit that criteria are the chicken breast and the chicken broth. Potatoes that are left at room temperature could also be a concern.*

3. A Certified Dietary Manager notices a client wheezing after eating a stir-fry dish that was fried with peanut oil. What should the manager do first? Why might this have happened?

   A. *The client could be having an allergic reaction and you should first call for a nurse. Perhaps the client was allergic to peanuts and even if the stir fry didn't contain peanuts, if it was fried in peanut oil that could be the cause.*

4. A foodservice employee is preparing French toast for a special brunch. He uses a spatula to transfer the egg-wash covered French toast to the griddle. He flips the French toast on the griddle and uses the same spatula to transfer the cooked French toast to the steam table pan for service. Is this a concern and why or why not?

   A. *Transferring cooked French toast with the same spatula used to transfer raw French toast is a concern due to cross-contamination. The cooked French toast could be contaminated with salmonella from the egg wash and then transferred to other pieces of cooked French toast. Even if the steam table was hot, it is not meant to continue the cooking process. Either use tongs to transfer the cooked French toast to the steam table or use pasteurized eggs in the egg wash for the French toast.*

5. You observe a foodservice staff member replenishing chili on the steam table. She carefully stirs the chili on the steam table, takes and records the temperature. Then she adds fresh chili to the batch in the steam table, being careful to thoroughly stir the two batches together. Is this a concern? Why or why not?

   A. *Yes, this is a concern. She was correct in stirring the chili on the steam table and taking and recording the temperature. However, you should NOT mix a fresh batch of chili with one on the steam table because of the potential for contamination from the chili on the steam table. If the chili needs to be replenished, initially use smaller amounts on the steam table and replace the entire pan with a fresh batch.*

(Continued)

Putting It Into Practice Questions & Answers *(Continued)*

6. How would you cool the following products:
    1. Chicken salad made from canned chicken
        A. *Canned chicken taken from the storeroom is at room temperature. Therefore, the chicken salad must be cooled to 41°F within 4 hours of preparation.*
    2. Beef stew
        A. *Beef stew should be cooled in a 2 step process: rapid cooling from 135° to 70°F within 2 hours then from 70°F to 41°F within 4 hours.*
7. You are preparing leftover rice for storage. If the rice was prepared on January 9, what would you put on the label?
    A. *The label would show the name of the item, date of preparation, the last date to be used (seven days out counting the day it was prepared), and the initials of the person putting it into storage. So it would read: white rice,1/9/12, 1/15/12, sda*
8. In a traditional baked chicken breast recipe, what would the critical control point(s) be?
    A. *Remember the critical control point is the point where if you don't intervene, a foodborne illness could occur. For a baked chicken breast, if it isn't cooked properly and is served undercooked, it could cause a foodborne illness. The CCP would be COOK TO 165° FOR 15 SECONDS. If the leftover chicken breasts are to be used for another recipe, such as chicken stir-fry, the reheat step would also be a CCP. It would read: REHEAT TO 165° WITHIN TWO HOURS.*
9. What is the best way to train staff on HACCP plans?
    A. *The best way to train staff in HACCP is to involve them in developing the HACCP plans and recipes for your facility. They are the people who actively follow the flow of food and can make developing a HACCP plan more efficient and accurate.*

Manage Physical Facilities to Ensure Compliance with Safety and Sanitation Regulations

Overview and Objectives

The 2009 FDA Food Code uses the term "active managerial control" to describe a foodservice facility's responsibility for developing and implementing controls to "prevent, eliminate, or reduce the occurrence of foodborne illness risk factors." This chapter outlines your active managerial control for regulations, employees, and physical facilities.

After completing this chapter, you should be able to:

✓ Identify federal safety laws/regulations for a facility

✓ Identify appropriate environmental controls for water supply, waste disposal and ventilation

✓ Prepare a safety inspection checklist

✓ Write an inspection report on hazards control

✓ Assure cleaning and sanitation of equipment and utensils

✓ Anticipate emergency preparedness procedures necessary to ensure a safe food supply

✓ Develop a crisis management plan to address an outbreak of foodborne illness

SECTION A Manage Regulations and Crises

Federal Safety Laws and Regulations

Regulatory inspections are part of everyday life in foodservice facilities. Regarding sanitation, regulatory inspections will be assessing the control you have over the foodborne illness risk factors. The FDA lists the elements of an effective food safety management system in the 2009 Annex. They include principles for protecting food through the flow of food in a foodservice facility. The elements also include the following:

1. Certified food protection managers who have shown a proficiency in required information by passing a test that is part of an accredited program
2. Standard operating procedures (SOPs) for performing critical operational steps in a food preparation process
3. Equipment and facility design and maintenance

4. Record keeping
5. Manager and employee training
6. On-going quality control and assurance

Foodservice operations must comply with many local, state, and federal regulations. Each of the elements above are required for some state and federal regulations. You may wonder why they all aren't required. The answer is because it depends upon the state and how they interpret federal laws.

Regulations

Each of the three branches of the government is involved in protecting the safety of the food supply and public health. See Figure 18.1 for an explanation of each. Congress and the Senate comprise the legislative branch and they pass laws regarding food handling and protection. Agencies like the FDA, within the executive branch of the government, develop regulations to implement the laws; and the judicial branch reviews the policies and procedures of regulatory agencies to protect the rights of both private businesses and the public. Laws usually state broad objectives and need to be interpreted. Regulations are more specific and give guidance in how to comply with the law. Several regulations may be necessary to implement one law.

A foodservice operation may be required to comply with a number of different laws and regulations regarding safety and sanitation. Laws and regulations addressing food protection are present at the federal, state and local level. It is important for the Certified Dietary Manager to learn about standards and expectations of different regulatory agencies and to develop policies and procedures to achieve compliance. Different agencies may have different expectations. For instance, local laws may be stricter than state laws. In this case the foodservice operator must comply with the most stringent standard. When in doubt, the Certified Dietary Manager should consult a representative of the regulatory agency or their administrator to review the regulations.

Local or Municipal Laws and Regulations. Depending on the size of the community and the number of foodservice operations it has, the county or municipal government may have a department of health or food protection that enforces local laws.

State Laws and Regulations. All states have a department charged with protecting the safety of food produced, served, and transported in the state. The office may be within the department of public health or the department of agriculture.

Federal Laws and Regulations. Federal laws and regulations exist to protect food safety by requiring inspection, controlling food additives, and regulating the transport of food across state borders.

Figure 18.1 Regulatory Agencies and Resources

Food and Drug Administration (FDA)

The FDA, an agency of the Department of Health and Human Services Public Health Service, is responsible for ensuring the safety and wholesomeness of all foods sold in interstate commerce except for meat, poultry and eggs, all of which are under USDA jurisdiction. FDA develops standards for the composition, quality, nutrition, and safety of foods. It collects and interprets data on nutrition, food additives, and environmental factors, such as pesticides, that affect foods. FDA also sets standards for certain foods and enforces federal regulations for labeling, food and color additives, food sanitation, and safety of foods. FDA monitors recalls of unsafe or contaminated foods and can seize illegally marketed foods.

Department of Agriculture (USDA)

Through inspection and grading, the USDA enforces standards for wholesomeness and quality of meat, poultry, and eggs produced in the United States. USDA food safety activities include inspecting poultry, eggs, and domestic and imported meat; inspecting livestock and production plants; and making quality (grading) inspections for grain, fruits, vegetables, meat, poultry, and dairy products (including cheeses). The USDA's education programs target family nutritional needs, food safety, and expanding scientific knowledge.

Centers for Disease Control and Prevention (CDC)

An agency of the Department of Health and Human Services, CDC becomes involved as a protector of food safety—including responding to emergencies when foodborne illnesses arise. It directs and enforces quarantines, and it administers national programs for prevention and control of vector-borne diseases (diseases transmitted by a host organism) and other preventable conditions. It maintains statistics on foodborne illnesses.

National Marine Fisheries Service (NMFS)

A part of the Department of Commerce, NMFS is responsible for seafood quality and identification, fisheries management, habitat conservation, and aquaculture production. NMFS has a voluntary inspection program for fish products. Its guidelines closely match regulations for which FDA has enforcement authority.

Department of Health & Human Services, Centers for Medicare and Medicaid (CMS)

Provides guidance to surveyors for regulatory tags that include F tag 371 §483.35(i)—Sanitary Conditions, and the requirement at 42 CFR 483.65(b) (2) regarding preventing the spread of infection. Even if you are surveyed by CMS, you will also have to follow your local and state sanitation regulations.

State and Local Governments

State and local government agencies cooperate with the federal government to ensure the quality and safety of food produced within their jurisdictions. FDA and other federal agencies help state and local governments develop uniform food safety standards and regulations, and assist them with research and information. States inspect restaurants, retail food establishments, dairies, grain mills, and other food establishments within their borders. In many instances, they can embargo illegal food products, which gives them authority over fish, including shellfish, taken from their waters. FDA provides guidelines to the states for this regulation. Many states have their own fish inspection programs. The FDA also provides guidelines for state and local governments for regulation of dairy products and restaurant foods.

FDA Food Code

The FDA Food Code is a framework upon which an effective retail food safety program can be built. Today, the FDA's purpose in maintaining an updated model food code is to assist food control jurisdictions at all levels of government by providing them with a scientifically sound technical and legal basis for regulating the retail segment of the food industry. The retail segment includes those establishments or locations in the food distribution chain where the consumer takes possession of the food.

The Food Code is neither federal law nor federal regulation, and it does not replace local regulations. Rather, it represents FDA's best advice for a uniform system of regulation to ensure that retail food is safe and properly protected and presented. Although not federal requirements (until adopted by federal bodies for use within federal jurisdictions), Food Code provisions are designed to be consistent with federal food laws and regulations, and are written for ease of legal adoption at all levels of government.

The most current FDA Food Code recommendations may or may not apply in the particular jurisdiction where you work, so it is important to become familiar with all sanitation regulations that apply to your facility.

Inspections

One way agencies and governments assess compliance with regulations is through the inspection process. The FDA recommends that foodservice operations be inspected once every six months. An inspection often begins with an inspector or sanitarian identifying him or herself and presenting the appropriate identification. If an inspector does not present identification, be sure to ask for it. In most cases inspections are unannounced. In some areas of the country, inspections only occur in response to complaints. In other areas, routine inspections can be expected by every foodservice operation. Some foodservice operations may be inspected by several different agencies.

Inspection Process. When interacting with inspectors or surveyors, remember to show professional courtesy. If possible, accompany the inspector during the visit. This way you will be available for questions that the inspector may have, and you can ask the inspector questions if you do not understand a regulation or violation. The key to success with inspections is to view them as a source of help and not a hindrance. Inspectors are well trained in the area of food protection and are a source of valuable information.

Areas that an inspector will probably address include such areas as:

- ✓ Food purchasing practices, including use of approved sources and potable water.
- ✓ Food storage practices, including the cleanliness and temperature of food storage areas; indication that proper stock rotation methods (FIFO) are being used; labeling and dating practices for food products; protection of food in storage from cross-contamination; and proper storage of chemicals away from food preparation areas, in clearly marked containers.

Putting It Into Practice: 1

List some steps to prepare your staff for a sanitation inspection.

(Check your answer at the end of this chapter)

- ✓ Food preparation and service practices, including the thawing, cooking, holding, transporting, serving, cooling, and reheating of food. The inspector may want to review temperature logs, measure temperatures, review date-marking procedures, and observe staff work habits.
- ✓ Personal hygiene of employees, including the cleanliness of staff, use of disposable gloves and utensils to avoid hand contact with food, presence of any staff with reportable symptoms or illnesses, and accessibility and use of handwashing sinks and supplies. The inspector may interview staff about work habits and practices. See *Management in the News* at the end of this chapter.
- ✓ Cleaning and sanitization practices, including manual and mechanical warewashing practices, proper dilution of chemical sanitizers, and proper water temperature. The inspector will tour the premises and inspect equipment to determine overall cleanliness. The inspector may request a copy of cleaning schedules.
- ✓ Facilities, including safe water supply, proper sewage disposal and backflow prevention with air gap or approved device, absence of pest infestation, and pest control methods and techniques employed.

While the FDA Food Code provides a sample inspection form and guidelines, the form and criteria used for your locale may vary. You should have food temperature logs and staff training records available for the inspector. Some facilities are required to have a manager certified in foodservice sanitation on the premises at all times. Be sure that the proper records and evidence of certification are available and current.

An inspector who discovers minor infractions will establish a deadline for correction. Correct violations immediately—even before the inspector leaves the premises if possible. Take notes during inspection. The notes will help you to make any necessary improvements and are a resource to prepare for future inspections. A health inspector can serve as a resource, too. If there is anything you don't understand—ask. If a serious problem or imminent health hazard is noticed, the inspector may order the facility to close immediately. A foodservice operation that fails to correct problems by established deadlines risks fines and loss of the permit to operate.

HACCP-Based Inspections. Some local health departments have changed their inspection process to one based on HACCP principles. Instead of traditional inspections that focus on the foodservice operation, a HACCP-based inspection focuses on the flow of food. A HACCP-based inspection might take several days as inspectors follow food through the operation. Inspectors measure and observe controls at each step in the flow of food. In a traditional inspection, you might be penalized once for a refrigerator that was not in the proper temperature range. In a HACCP-based inspection, you may be penalized for each food in the refrigerator found at an unsafe temperature.

The inspector will also review HACCP logs during the visit. Reviewing the logs allows the inspector to inspect food safety practices over a long period of time rather than just on the day of the inspection.

Inspection Preparation. An inspector will usually leave a written report that notes areas for improvement and any violations. Study the written report to identify why violations occurred and to develop an action plan to avoid having the same violation occur a second time. To improve compliance during inspections, follow these guidelines:

- ✓ Plan and Prepare: Obtain a copy of applicable regulations and review them in advance. If you have questions about the regulations, contact the regulatory agency that enforces them. Develop policies and work practices that comply with the regulations.
- ✓ Use Self-Inspection: Conduct routine self-inspections to determine strengths and weaknesses of the facility. Ask an inspector for blank inspection reports, or create self-inspection forms specifically for your foodservice operation. Several examples of self-inspection forms are included in this textbook. Correct problems that you discover during self-inspections.
- ✓ Network: Through professional organizations, discuss regulations and compliance issues with peers. Identify common strategies and resources.
- ✓ Train and Educate Staff: Train all staff members in safe food preparation practices and regulations applicable to their own jobs.

Crisis Management

A crisis is a sudden change, often an unstable condition, that requires decisive action to be taken. Often a crisis endangers the health of a client or employee, or it threatens the safety and security of the foodservice operation. A crisis can occur in any type of foodservice operation. Some examples of crisis situations are:

- ✓ Fire
- ✓ Flood
- ✓ Tornado or hurricane
- ✓ Utility (water or gas) loss
- ✓ Delivery driver strike
- ✓ Food tampering by client or employee
- ✓ Sudden illness of an employee or client
- ✓ Workplace violence
- ✓ Bomb threat
- ✓ Robbery or theft
- ✓ Vandalism
- ✓ Act of terrorism
- ✓ Foodborne illness outbreak

Crisis Management Plan. Imagine being the Certified Dietary Manager of a foodservice operation that has been flooded and is without utilities. What if the foodservice operation were at a hospital, nursing home or other facility where you were expected to continue providing meals. How would you do it? How could you be sure that the food being served is safe? To handle such a situation properly, it is necessary to plan in advance. Anticipate the type of crisis situations that your operation might face and develop a plan of action. Examples of advance planning and preparation for crisis situations are:

- ✓ A nursing home maintains a supply of bottled water and a one-week supply of disposable dishes for use in the event the water supply becomes contaminated or water service is lost.

What principles of purchasing must you keep in mind even if you are in a crisis?

(Check your answer at the end of this chapter)

✓ A correctional facility maintains an emergency menu and food supply for use in case power is lost or weather prohibits delivery of food.

✓ A fire evacuation plan is established for a fine dining restaurant and employees are trained in the use of fire extinguishers.

✓ Employees at a hotel are trained in procedures to follow if they receive a bomb threat, such as what to listen for and what to ask the caller.

✓ A hospital has an agreement with a regional food supplier to provide a refrigerated truck.

✓ A fast food restaurant has an established procedure to follow if they receive a complaint about foodborne illness.

✓ Emergency phone numbers for police, fire, and medical personnel are posted by each telephone in a college dining hall.

✓ Employees of a correctional facility are trained in non-violent intervention techniques.

✓ A resort maintains a crisis management manual with procedures to follow in the event of most emergency situations.

A Certified Dietary Manager should always have a written plan about how to feed clients in an emergency. Food preparation in situations where power is lost or food deliveries are impossible may require a pre-planned menu that includes foods that do not require cooking, such as peanut butter sandwiches, fresh or canned fruit, and similar items. In creating a plan, consider what supplies are likely to be on hand, how to handle a severe staffing shortage if employees cannot get to work, and whether the operation will feed extra people. In some healthcare facilities, an emergency staffing plan may include drawing on employees from other non-client care departments. Staff need to be aware of the emergency plan so they will be ready to activate it at any time.

Foodborne Illness Outbreak. A foodservice operation may at some time receive a complaint about foodborne illness. Every foodservice operation should have a plan in place to deal with such complaints. Questions that should be asked of the complainant include:

✓ What is your name, address and phone number?

✓ When did you eat at the foodservice operation (day and time)?

✓ What were you served?

✓ When did you become ill?

✓ Have you sought treatment? Where?

✓ Was anyone else with you when you ate at the foodservice operation?

✓ If yes, are they ill and what did they have to eat?

Do not accept responsibility for the illness or agree to pay for medical care, but do encourage the complainant to seek medical care. After receiving the complaint, contact the local department of health. Reporting the complaint to local public health officials should be done quickly to prevent possible illness from spreading further. If the suspect food is still in service, immediately take it out of service and save it. A laboratory analysis can help to confirm the presence of foodborne pathogens—or establish the safety of the food item. Some facilities even have a procedure to save a plate of food from each meal served. After securing the food sample and reporting the complaint to the health department, you may wish to contact your liability insurance carrier and to interview staff involved in the preparation of the suspect food.

The local health department will investigate the complaint of foodborne illness. A team of investigators will interview the victim, visit the foodservice operation to interview management and personnel, take samples of suspected food items, and evaluate the food protection practices of the foodservice operation. HACCP logs can provide a record of food handling practices in the facility.

Since foodservice staff may be carriers of an illness, the team may request that cultures be taken from all staff to detect the presence of a communicable disease. Bacterial sampling of work surfaces and equipment may also be done to determine if they are contaminated. During an investigation, it is very important for management and personnel to cooperate fully.

Crisis Communications. In the event of a crisis situation, there should be one designated person responsible for contact with members of the media. All other staff should decline answering questions and refer members of the press to the designated spokesperson. Before answering any questions, the spokesperson should determine the facts surrounding the emergency or crisis situation. In many cases, the spokesperson should consult with legal counsel before answering questions if possible. During an emergency, spokespersons are also encouraged to follow these do's and don'ts:

- ✓ Do provide factual information.
- ✓ Don't speculate or guess or provide false information.
- ✓ Do develop a prepared statement of exactly what information you want to release and then follow your statement.
- ✓ Don't feel obligated to answer all of the questions you are asked.
- ✓ Do communicate in a clear and concise manner.
- ✓ Don't use jargon or lurid descriptions.
- ✓ Do ask technical experts to provide explanations of complex situations if necessary.
- ✓ Don't allow pointed questions to alarm you.
- ✓ Do inform the media that public health and safety is your priority and that you are cooperating with regulatory agencies.
- ✓ Don't appear uncooperative or intimidated.

Food Security

In today's world, food security is a growing concern. The FDA recommends that Certified Dietary Managers consider the possibility of food tampering, or other criminal or terrorist actions that may result in unsafe food. Terrorist activity could occur at any point in the flow of food—on the farm, in a food processing facility, in a warehouse, or in a foodservice operation. A manager needs to be alert to this possibility, and can definitely take proactive steps to help prevent or limit this kind of crisis in a foodservice department. FDA advice for foodservice operations includes the following:

- ✓ Train staff to report any unusual or suspicious behavior.
- ✓ Promote security awareness among employees. Ask them to notice and report signs of tampering.
- ✓ Supervise and observe foodservice activities.
- ✓ Screen employees before hiring.
- ✓ Provide work assignments and schedules, and insist that each employee wear an ID badge.
- ✓ Restrict access. Do not allow employees in work areas when they are off-duty, and do not allow others into food storage and food production areas.
- ✓ Prevent staff from bringing personal items into non-public food preparation or storage areas.
- ✓ Monitor activity in self-service areas, such as salad bars.
- ✓ Limit access to and secure storage areas for chemicals used in your operation (e.g. no public access; secure with lock and key).
- ✓ Monitor inventory, and report unusual changes: disappearance of products, or unauthorized appearance of products.
- ✓ Establish a chain of communications. Train staff to inform a designated manager of any concerns.
- ✓ Have a crisis response plan, and keep all emergency contact numbers for your community readily accessible. Include the FDA emergency number on your contact list: 301-443-1240. Also include the phone number for your state complaint coordinator.

Summary

A number of government agencies at all levels, from federal through local, participate in ensuring food safety. A Certified Dietary Manager should be familiar with regulations that apply to the foodservice department, and work diligently to comply with them on a routine basis. While the FDA Food Code provides a model for sanitation regulations, each health jurisdiction sets its own standards. Routine inspections are a means through which government agencies help to ensure the safety of foodservice clients. A crisis can occur in any type of foodservice operation. Thus, a manager must be prepared with a plan.

Personal hygiene, practices of cleanliness or personal care habits—especially handwashing—are among the most critical employee practices a Certified Dietary Manager can cultivate. Never to be underestimated, employee effectiveness in protecting food depends on training.

SECTION B Manage Employees

Foodservice Managers

The Food Code provides special definitions for Certified Dietary Managers. The **permit holder** is the entity that is legally responsible for the operation of the food facility and possesses the valid permit to operate the facility. For example, a permit holder might be a school system or a nursing facility. A manager who oversees the foodservice operation is defined as the person in charge. More specifically, according to the 2009 FDA Food Code, "the person in charge is accountable for developing, carrying out, and enforcing procedures aimed at preventing food-borne illness." The Certified Dietary Manager may be the **person in charge** or may report to a foodservice director who qualifies as the person in charge. The person in charge may vary from one day to another, depending on staffing. A person in charge should be on the premises at all times during operations. A person in charge should be a certified food protection manager who has passed a recognized exam. Key changes to the 2009 Food Code include requiring that foodservice operations have a certified food protection manager on staff.

The responsibilities of the person in charge are many and equally important. They must demonstrate knowledge in:

- ✓ Preventing foodborne illness
- ✓ HACCP and critical control points
- ✓ The impact of personal hygiene on food safety
- ✓ Symptoms of foodborne illness
- ✓ Time and temperature control standards for cooking PHF/TCS foods
- ✓ The hazards of consuming undercooked meat, poultry, eggs, and fish
- ✓ Temperatures for hot holding, storing, cooling, and reheating PHF/TCS food
- ✓ Prevention of cross-contamination
- ✓ Standards for avoiding bare hand contact with food
- ✓ Adequate and effective handwashing
- ✓ Cleaning and sanitation
- ✓ Food-safe equipment
- ✓ Safe water
- ✓ Safe use of chemicals
- ✓ Employee health restrictions/exclusions
- ✓ Food allergy awareness
- ✓ Properly training employees in food safety, including food allergy awareness.

In addition to demonstrating this knowledge, they have additional duties to ensure food safety. Those duties are listed in Figure 18.2. If you are the designated person in charge, you should work with your staff and administration to develop policies and procedures for carrying out these duties.

Glossary

Permit Holder
The entity that is legally responsible for the operation of the food facility such as the hospital, nursing facility, or school district

Person in Charge
The manager of the foodservice operation who is accountable for developing, carrying out, and enforcing procedures aimed at preventing foodborne illness

Figure 18.2 The Person in Charge Must Ensure That:

A. Food establishment operations are not conducted in a private home or in a room used as living or sleeping quarters;

B. Persons unnecessary to the food establishment operation are not allowed in the food preparation, food storage, or warewashing areas, except that brief visits and tours may be authorized by the person in charge if steps are taken to ensure that exposed food; clean equipment, utensils, and linens; and unwrapped single-service and single-use articles are protected from contamination;

C. Employees and other persons such as delivery and maintenance persons and pesticide applicators entering the food preparation, food storage, and warewashing areas comply with this Code;

D. Employees are effectively cleaning their hands, by routinely monitoring the employees' handwashing;

E. Employees are visibly observing foods as they are received to determine that they are from approved sources, delivered at the required temperatures, protected from contamination, unadulterated, and accurately presented, by routinely monitoring the employees' observations and periodically evaluating foods upon their receipt;

F. Employees are properly cooking potentially hazardous food (time/temperature control for safety food), being particularly careful in cooking those foods known to cause severe foodborne illness and death, such as eggs and comminuted meats, through daily oversight of the employees' routine monitoring of the cooking temperatures using appropriate temperature measuring devices properly scaled and calibrated;

G. Employees are using proper methods to rapidly cool potentially hazardous foods (time/temperature control for safety foods) that are not held hot or are not for consumption within 4 hours, through daily oversight of the employees' routine monitoring of food temperatures during cooling;

H. Consumers who order raw or partially cooked ready-to-eat foods of animal origin are informed that the food is not cooked sufficiently to ensure its safety;

I. Employees are properly sanitizing cleaned multiuse equipment and utensils before they are reused, through routine monitoring of solution temperature and exposure time for hot water sanitizing, and chemical concentration, pH, temperature, and exposure time for chemical sanitizing;

J. Consumers are notified that clean tableware is to be used when they return to self-service areas such as salad bars and buffets;

K. Except when approval is obtained from the regulatory authority, employees are preventing cross-contamination of ready-to-eat food with bare hands by properly using suitable utensils such as deli tissue, spatulas, tongs, single-use gloves, or dispensing equipment;

L. Employees are properly trained in food safety as it relates to their assigned duties; and

M. Food employees and conditional employees are informed of their responsibility to report in accordance with law, to the person in charge, information about their health and activities as they relate to diseases that are transmissible through food. *It can be verified that all employees are informed.

N. *All operating procedures required by the Food Code are developed and implemented.

** Supplement to the 2009 FDA Food Code*
Source: 2009 FDA Food Code

Foodservice Staff

Foodservice staff must observe personal hygiene practices to reduce the likelihood of contaminating food and must also observe safe work practices. It is the responsibility of the Certified Dietary Manager to develop and implement policies for foodservice employee hygiene. It is the obligation of every foodservice employee to observe standards of personal hygiene in order to ensure food safety. Personal hygiene and handwashing are critical controls for food safety, because many foodborne illnesses travel from people to food, and then back to other people, who become ill. Foodservice employees should observe the following standards for personal hygiene:

✓ Bathe daily.

✓ Cover mouth when coughing or sneezing and then wash hands.

✓ Do not eat, drink, or use tobacco or gum while preparing food. Wash hands after doing these activities on break.

✓ Restrain and cover hair.

✓ Frequently wash hands following established procedures.

Lavatory Facilities and Supplies

Foodservice personnel must be provided with a sink specifically intended for washing hands. It is not acceptable to wash hands in sinks intended for food preparation or to perform food preparation activities in hand sinks. At least one sink must be provided, and more may be required to ensure convenient use by employees. The sinks should be easily accessible by employees. Handwashing sinks should be available in food preparation, foodservice, and warewashing areas, as well as in restrooms. A handwashing lavatory must provide water at a temperature of at least 100°F through a mixing valve or faucet. Some models of hand sinks are equipped with infrared sensors or flow control devices, which eliminate the need for staff to touch sink faucets (see Figure 18.3). The lavatory must be supplied with a hand cleanser and materials for hand drying such as individual, disposable towels, a heated-air drying device, or a non-heated pressurized air device. When food exposure is limited and handwashing lavatories are not conveniently available—such as in some mobile or

Figure 18.3 **Hand Sink with Infrared Sensor**

Courtesy: Fisher Manufacturing Co.

Putting It Into Practice: 3

Your cook is breading chicken for the evening meal when a foodservice staff member requests more rolls for the lunch meal. The cook picks up a basket of rolls and takes it to the staff member. Then she returns to breading the chicken. Is this a concern? Why or why not?

(Check your answer at the end of this chapter)

temporary food operations or at some vending machine locations—employees may use chemically treated towelettes for handwashing. Towelettes are not as effective as handwashing, and are not accepted by all local food codes.

Handwashing and Hand Care

Preparing and serving foods with hands is a common way to transfer pathogens and other food hazards from people to food. Handwashing is the most important step that all foodservice employees can take to protect food. All employees should be trained in proper handwashing procedures. To reinforce this important practice, you can post reminder signs at every handwashing sink employees might use. The most effective way to determine employee compliance with handwashing standards is to observe on-the-job practices. Hands must be kept clean before, during, and after preparing foods.

According to the FDA Food Code, hands should be washed:

- ✓ After touching bare human body parts
- ✓ After using the restroom
- ✓ After coughing, sneezing, using a tissue, using tobacco, eating, or drinking
- ✓ After handling soiled equipment or utensils
- ✓ Before food preparation
- ✓ During food preparation, as often as necessary to remove soil and avoid cross-contamination
- ✓ When switching between raw foods and ready-to-eat foods
- ✓ After engaging in any activity that might contaminate hands.

Foodservice personnel must clean their hands, wrists, forearms, and other exposed parts of their body with a cleaning compound (antibacterial soap

Figure 18.4 Handwashing Procedure

1. Rinse under clean, running warm water.
2. Apply an amount of cleaning compound recommended by the cleaning compound manufacturer.
3. Rub together vigorously for at least 10-15 seconds while:
   a. Paying particular attention to removing soil from underneath the fingernails during the cleaning procedure, and
   b. Creating friction on the surfaces of the hands and arms or surrogate prosthetic devices for hands and arms, fingertips, and areas between the fingers.
4. If using antimicrobial soap, 15 seconds of vigorous washing is required.
5. Thoroughly rinse under clean, running warm water.
6. Immediately follow the cleaning procedure with a thorough drying method, such as individual, disposable towels; or a continuous towel system that supplies the user with a clean towel; or a heated-air device.

NOTE: To avoid re-contaminating hands, food employees may use disposable clean towels or similar clean barriers when touching surfaces such as manually operated faucet handles or the handle of a restroom door.

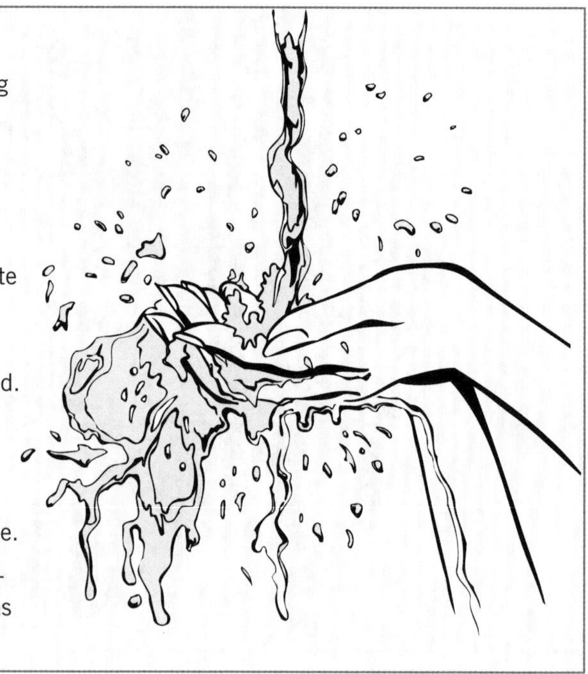

Adapted from 2009 FDA Food Code, sections 2-301.12 to 2-301.16

recommended). As shown in Figure 18.4, proper handwashing requires application of the cleaning compound and vigorously rubbing the hands for at least 10-15 seconds, followed by a rinse with potable water.

Ensuring the cleanliness of areas underneath fingernails and in between fingers is particularly important. A nail brush may be used to clean under fingernails, particularly after handling raw food which may be trapped under the fingernails, or after using the restroom. Recommendations about whether to use nail brushes vary. If you use one, sanitize it on a regular basis.

Foodservice staff must keep their fingernails trimmed, filed, and maintained so the edges and surfaces are cleanable and not rough. Fingernail polish or artificial nails are not allowed for employees working with food, unless covered by a sanitary, disposable glove in good condition.

Hand Antiseptics

Hand antiseptics (previously called hand sanitizers) are permitted, according to the FDA Food Code. A hand antiseptic solution should be an approved drug (per the FDA), or use antimicrobial ingredients listed by the FDA. A hand antiseptic may be used only after an employee has washed hands, following established procedure. In other words, using a hand antiseptic is not a substitute for washing hands. It is only a supplementary option.

Jewelry

Foodservice staff should limit jewelry to one single band ring. Jewelry can trap microorganisms and is difficult to keep clean.

The Food Code clarifies use of medical alert jewelry, such as a band indicating a drug allergy or medical condition. Medical information jewelry is not an exception to the "no-jewelry" guideline. It is not permitted on hands or arms. The Food Code guidance explains that an employee could wear an alert bracelet as a necklace or on the ankle.

Disposable Glove Usage

The use of disposable gloves in foodservice operations is increasingly common. It is important to note that wearing gloves is not a substitute for appropriate, effective, thorough, and frequent handwashing. Use single-use gloves that are stored and dispensed in a manner that prevents contamination. Gloves should be intact and free of tears or other imperfections. Before putting on a glove, wash hands, following the established procedure. Replace gloves at least hourly; when changing food preparation tasks; or after sneezing, coughing, touching hair, face, or non-disinfected surfaces. Skin lesions, cuts on the hands, wrists, or exposed portions of the arm must be covered with an impermeable cover such as a finger cot or stall. If on the hands or wrists, a disposable glove should be worn over the impermeable cover.

Clothing

Foodservice employees should always wear clean clothing to prevent contamination of food, equipment, utensils, and linens. If employees are expected to change into a uniform after reporting to work, provide a suitable changing area

You observe a foodservice staff member replacing ready-to-eat items in the cafeteria. She is wearing disposable gloves. At that moment, a client is waiting at the cash register. Your cook quickly removes her gloves, wipes her hands and helps the client at the cash register. She then returns to replacing the ready-to-eat items after putting on new gloves. Is this a concern? Why or why not?

(Check your answer at the end of this chapter)

separate from food preparation and storage areas. Employees should not bring personal items such as coats, hats, and purses into food preparation areas.

To further minimize the risk of foodborne illness transmission from employees or employee work habits, protective clothing should be worn to keep body parts from coming in contact with exposed foods. Hair restraints and beard restraints should be worn to reduce contact with human hair. Aprons and disposable gloves may also be used to reduce the transfer of microorganisms to an exposed food. Aprons and disposable gloves should be changed frequently.

Foodservice Practices

Avoid Hand Contact with Food. In addition to handwashing, the risk of foodborne illness can be reduced by eliminating direct contact of hands with ready-to-eat food. Except when washing fruits and vegetables, foodservice employees may not contact exposed, ready-to-eat food with their bare hands. Instead, they should use suitable utensils such as deli tissue, spatulas, tongs, single-use gloves, or dispensing equipment. Foodservice personnel should also minimize bare hand and arm contact with exposed food that is not in a ready-to-eat form.

Tasting Food. Foodservice personnel should be trained in proper tasting techniques. To prevent contamination, employees should not taste food while standing over it. A foodservice employee may not use a utensil more than once to taste food that is to be sold or served. A utensil used to taste food cannot be returned to the pot.

Handling Sanitary Surfaces. Employees should avoid touching the eating ends of the utensils, the tops or insides of drinking glasses, the surfaces of plates, or any other utensil or serviceware in a manner that might allow hands to contaminate the item.

Employee Health

Foodservice personnel who are suffering from illnesses that can be transmitted through food can present a major risk for any foodservice operation. For example, many pathogens travel through what is called a fecal-oral route. This means an employee who does not wash hands after using the restroom may have pathogens on the hands, and later contaminate food with these pathogens. Clients who consume the food may become ill. In addition, some employees may themselves be ill with a pathogen that can be foodborne, such as Norovirus or Hepatitis A. Those employees carry the pathogens on their hands and can contaminate food. Key changes to the 2009 Food Code require that "food establishments have a plan for responding to and properly cleaning up after an employee or client becomes physically ill in areas where food is prepared, stored, or served."

Furthermore, some people can carry pathogens without actually having symptoms. Certain foodborne illnesses are primarily the result of carriers contaminating food. A **carrier** may "carry" and transmit pathogens without having any symptoms of illness. For example, a person with Hepatitis A may pass along

Glossary

Carrier
An individual who may 'carry' or transmit pathogens without having any symptoms of illness

the virus for weeks before actually becoming ill. Some people carry Salmonella bacteria, and foodborne illness outbreaks have been traced to this problem.

Staphylococcus aureus and other bacteria may thrive on skin and in infected wounds. These bacteria can cause foodborne illness. By scratching an infected cut or pimple and then touching food, employees can pass the bacteria to food, where it can multiply to numbers sufficient to produce illness in a person consuming the food. Also, pus in an infected wound could ooze into food or onto food contact surfaces and thus contaminate food.

With these risks in mind, a Certified Dietary Manager must take special precautions to identify any employee who may be capable of transmitting foodborne pathogens at any point in time, and to limit the possibility of transmitting illness. The 2009 Food Code describes two categories of employees for whom the manager must enforce special policies to prevent transmission of illness: foodservice employees and conditional employees.

A **foodservice employee** is just what it sounds like—a person working with food, food equipment or utensils, or food-contact surfaces.

A **conditional employee** is one who has been offered a job in foodservice. The offer is considered conditional on responses to medical questions or examination, or health screening. The objective of health screening is to identify anyone who may have an illness that can be transmitted through food. According to the 2009 FDA Food Code, a conditional employee who reports specific symptoms that could indicate foodborne illness, a current diagnosis of a foodborne illness, past foodborne illness, or a history of exposure to foodborne pathogens must meet certain criteria before becoming employed. Generally, they must be cleared by a qualified medical practitioner, in writing. A conditional employee who cannot meet the criteria should not be hired. Figure 18.5 is a sample interview form that can be used for screening a conditional employee.

During health screening, a Certified Dietary Manager needs to be aware of conditional employees' rights. The Equal Employment Opportunity Commission (EEOC) offers advice about how to conduct screening and manage other health-related personnel activities without violating rights specified under Title I of the Americans with Disabilities Act (ADA). See Figure 18.6.

Reportable Health Information

The 2009 Food Code lists a number of health conditions that food employees must report to the person in charge. Each employee bears responsibility for reporting information that may have an impact on food safety. The FDA Food Code draws special attention to five pathogens that may be transmitted by foodservice employees: Norovirus, Shigella, Hepatitis A, Salmonella typhi, and Shiga toxin-producing E. coli (STEC). An employee diagnosed with one of these illnesses should report this to the person in charge. The person in charge is responsible for taking action to prevent disease transmission.

In addition, the Code says that even if employees have only symptoms—such as diarrhea, fever, vomiting, jaundice (yellowing of the skin, which can be a

Glossary

Foodservice Employee
An individual working with unpackaged food, food equipment or utensils, or food contact surfaces

Conditional Employee
A potential foodservice employee to whom a job offer is made conditional on responses to subsequent medical questions or examinations

Figure 18.5 Health Screening Sample Questionnaire

FORM 1-A: Conditional Employee and Food Employee Interview

Preventing Transmission of Diseases through Food by infected Food Employees or Conditional Employees with Emphasis on illness due to Norovirus, Salmonella Typhi, Shigella spp., Enterohemorrhagic (EHEC) or Shiga toxin-producing Escherichia coli (STEC), or Hepatitis A Virus

The purpose of this interview is to inform conditional employees and food employees to advise the person in charge of past and current conditions described so that the person in charge can take appropriate steps to preclude the transmission of foodborne illness.

Conditional employee name *(print)* ______________________________

Food employee name *(print)* ______________________________

Address ______________________________

Telephone *(Daytime)* ______________________ *(Evening)* ______________________

Are you suffering from any of the following symptoms? *(Check one)*	YES	NO	If YES, Date of Onset
Diarrhea			
Vomiting			
Jaundice			
Sore Throat with Fever			
OR			
Infected cut or wound that is open and draining, or lesions containing pus on the hand, wrist, an exposed body part, or other body part and the cut, wound, or lesion not properly covered *(Examples: boils and infected wounds, however small)*			

In the Past:	YES	NO	
1. Have you ever been diagnosed as being ill with typhoid fever *(Salmonella Typhi)* If YES, what was the date of the diagnosis?:			
2. If within the past 3 months, did you take antibiotics for S. Typhi? If YES, how many days did you take antibiotics?:			
3. If you took antibiotics, did you finish the prescription?			

History of Exposure:	YES	NO	
1. Have you been suspected of causing or have you been exposed to a confirmed foodborne disease outbreak recently? If YES, date of outbreak:			
a. If YES, what was the cause of the illness and did it meet the following criteria:			

Cause:	Date of Illness Outbreak
i. Norovirus *(last exposure within the past 48 hours)*	
ii. E. coli O157:H7 infection *(last exposure within the past 3 days)*	
iii. Hepatitis A virus *(last exposure within the past 30 days)*	
iv. Typhoid fever *(last exposure within the past 14 days)*	
v. Shigellosis *(last exposure within the past 3 days)*	

(Continued...)

Figure 18.5 Health Screening Sample Questionnaire *(Continued)*

	YES	NO
b. If YES, did you:		
i. Consume food implicated in the outbreak:		
ii. Work in a food establishment that was the source of the outbreak:		
iii. Consume food at an event that was prepared by person who is ill?		
	YES	NO
2. Did you attend an event or work in a setting, recently where there was a confirmed disease outbreak?		
If YES, what was the cause of the confirmed disease outbreak:		
a. Norovirus *(last exposure within the past 48 hours)*		
b. E. coli O157:H7 or other EHEC/STEC *(last exposure within the past 3 days)*		
c. Shigella spp. *(last exposure within the past 3 days)*		
d. S. Typhi *(last exposure within the past 14 days)*		
e. Hepatitis A virus *(last exposure within the past 30 days)*		
Do you live in the same household as a person diagnosed with Norovirus, Shigellosis, typhoid fever, Hepatitis A, or illness due to E. coli O157:H7 or other EHEC/STEC? If YES, Date of onset of illness:		
3. Do you have a household member attending or working in a setting where there is a confirmed disease outbreak of Norovirus, typhoid fever, Shigellosis, EHEC/STEC infection, or Hepatitis A? If YES, Date of onset of illness:		

Health Practitioner Information

Name ______________________________

Address ______________________________

Telephone *(Daytime)* ______________________ *(Evening)* ______________________

Signature of Conditional Employee ______________________ Date __________

Signature of Food Employee ______________________ Date __________

Signature of Permit Holder or Representative ______________________ Date __________

Source: 2005 FDA Food Code

symptom of Hepatitis), sore throat with fever, or an infected wound that is open, draining, and/or contains pus—this is cause for action. Each of these may potentially indicate that a foodborne pathogen is at play. Thus, each of these must be reported to the person in charge.

As a Certified Dietary Manager, what should you do when an employee reports a diagnosis or symptom? For some symptoms or diagnoses, the answer depends upon what type of client group you serve. If you serve a highly susceptible population, such as nursing home clients, young children, or hospitalized patients with compromised immune systems, you must take conservative action to protect clients. This is to exclude the employee (e.g., except for an infected wound). See Figure 18.7 for a summary of requirements for symptomatic employees.

Exclude simply means to prohibit employees from coming to work. A medical clearance is required for the employee to return to work. Also note that if an employee is actually diagnosed with a foodborne illness, you should exclude the employee and notify your health department. Guidelines offered by the Food Code may be considered minimum standards based on commonly cited culprits in actual foodborne illness outbreaks. Local authorities and/or your facility's health policy may dictate further restrictions.

If the employee has an infected wound, the employee can come to work but must cover the wound with an impermeable cover.

Guidelines for responding to symptoms or illness are more liberal if you serve a general, healthy population. Rather than exclude employees, you may restrict employees who have Norovirus with no symptoms, STEC with no symptoms, or sore throat with fever, for example. **Restrict** means to limit an employee's activities, so that there is no risk of transmitting foodborne illness. For example, a restricted employee should not work with food, clean equipment, clean dishes or utensils, or clean linens. An infected cut or wound must be bandaged and covered with an impereable cover. If the wound is on the hand or wrist, this must also be covered with a clean, disposable glove.

If you have questions regarding who to restrict or not, review the current Food Code or contact your regulatory authority.

The Food Code also addresses the concern of an employee who suffers sneezing, coughing, or a runny nose. Any employee who has a discharge from eyes, nose, or mouth should not work with exposed food; clean equipment, utensils, or linens; or unwrap single-service items. This means that if you notice an employee has a common cold, you may need to restrict the employee.

Viruses cannot multiply in food but can be transmitted through food. Examples of such viruses include Hepatitis A and Norovirus. Other viruses, such as the HIV virus, are very fragile outside of the human body and cannot be transmitted through food. Foodservice employees with HIV or AIDS should not be excluded unless they are suffering from another illness or infectious disease.

Glossary

Exclude
Prohibit employees from coming to work

Restrict
To limit an employee's activities so there is no risk of transmitting foodborne illness (such as to reassign the employee to a non-food related position)

Putting It Into Practice: 5

It is a hectic day in the foodservice department because two employees are off sick. Your cook explains that he isn't feeling well and has visited the bathroom several times in the past two hours. What should you do?

(Check your answer at the end of this chapter)

Figure 18.6 ADA and Employee Health

ADA regulations protect persons with disabilities. They prohibit discrimination in employment decisions. They also stipulate that an employer must make reasonable accommodations for an employee who has a disability. As defined by the law, a disability is a medical condition or disorder that substantially limits a person in doing basic life activities. According to EEOC guidance, an employee who suffers key symptoms that could indicate foodborne illness is NOT disabled. Because a foodborne illness is generally a short-term condition, the ADA regulations do not apply. In other words, a manager can restrict or exclude an employee, following Food Code guidance.

However, a foodborne illness occasionally leads to long-term disability, such as chronic liver failure following Hepatitis A. If this occurs, ADA regulations do apply. In this case, you must follow the steps outlined by the ADA. First, determine whether there is a reasonable accommodation that would eliminate the risk of the employee transmitting illness. If not, or if accommodations would create undue hardship on your business, you should next investigate reassignment to a non food-handling position. According to the EEOC guidance, even when the Food Code says to exclude the employee, you still have an obligation to follow a thinking process and plan of action outlined by the ADA. Furthermore, you must handle health issues carefully when making hiring decisions. Here are some do's and don'ts as spelled out by the EEOC:

DON'T ask a job candidate about health status (including foodborne illness) before making a conditional job offer.

DO ask about health status (including foodborne illness) after offering a job, as part of a procedure that you apply uniformly to everyone.

DON'T hire an employee whose pre-employment medical review indicates the applicant is diagnosed with one of the five illnesses listed in the Food Code (Norovirus, Hepatitis A, Shigella, STEC, or Salmonella typhi). If the applicant has a disability because of this illness, the position is a food handling job, and there is no reasonable accommodation that prevents the risk, you have a right to cancel the job offer.

DO require current employees to report symptoms, diagnosis, or a past history of illness with the five illnesses described above.

DON'T dismiss an employee who has a foodborne illness without following all the steps outlined by the ADA.

DO hold a job open for an excluded employee with a foodborne illness AND a disability, unless this causes undue hardship for your organization.

DON'T allow an employee who does NOT qualify as having a disability to work in a foodservice establishment serving high-risk clients (e.g. a nursing home) if the employee has symptoms or diagnosis of foodborne illness.

DO require an employee who has qualifying symptoms or diagnosis to obtain a medical clearance to return to work before you lift a restriction or exclusion.

DON'T mention the name of an employee who has a symptom or diagnosis of foodborne illness to other employees or allow access to this information on your computer.

DO keep employee medical information confidential as part of your HIPAA compliance.

DON'T discriminate against an employee who has AIDS or an HIV positive diagnosis.

DO allow an employee who is HIV positive to work in a foodservice department, because HIV is not transmitted through food.

DON'T allow a service animal in food preparation areas.

DO allow an employee to use a service animal at work if this does not create significant risk or harm. (This is a reasonable accommodation.) Do require the employee to wash hands after touching the animal.

DON'T allow co-workers to harass an employee who has a disability.

Reprinted from Food Protection Connection, Dietary Manager Magazine, May 2005; updated to reflect 2005 Food Code standards.
Reference: EEOC. How to Comply with the ADA: A Guide for Restaurants and Other Food Service Employers, 2005.

Figure 18.7 Summary of Requirements for Symptomatic Food Employees

Symptom	EXCLUSION OR RESTRICTION		Removing Symptomatic Food Employees from Exclusion or Restriciton	RA Approval Needed to Return to Work?
	Facilities Serving an HSP	Facilities Not Serving an HSP		
Vomiting	EXCLUDE 2-201.12(A)(1)	EXCLUDE 2-201.12(A)(1)	When the excluded food employee has been asymptomatic for at least 24 hours or provides medical documentation 2-201.13(A)(1). *Exceptions:* If diagnosed with Norovirus, Shigella spp., E. coli 0157:H7 or other EHEC/STEC, HAV, or typhoid fever (S. Typhi) (see Tables 1b & 2).	No if not diagnosed
Diarrhea	EXCLUDE 2- 2-201.12(A)(1)	EXCLUDE 2-201.12(A)(1)	When the excluded food employee has been asymptomatic for at least 24 hours or provides medical documentation 2-201.13(A). *Exceptions:* If Diagnosed with Norovirus, E. coli 0157:H7 or other EHEC/STEC, HAV, or S. Typhi (see Tables 1b & 2).	No if not diagnosed
Jaundice	EXCLUDE 2-201.12(B)(1) if the onset occurred within the last 7 days	EXCLUDE 2-201.12(B)(1) if the onset occurred within the last 7 days	When approval is obtained from the RA 2-201.13 (B), and: • Food employee has been jaundiced for more than 7 calendar days 2-201.13(B)(1), or • Food employee provides medical documentation 2-201.13(B)(3).	Yes
Sore Throat with Fever	EXCLUDE 2-201.12(G)(1)	RESTRICT 2-201.12(G)(2)	When food employee provides written medical documentation 201.13(G) (1)-(3).	No
Infected Wound or Pustular Boil	RESTRICT 2-201.12(H)	RESTRICT 2-201.12(H)	When the infected wound or boil is properly covered 2-201.13(H)(1)-(3).	No

Notes:

- Food employees and condition employees shall report symptoms immediately to the person in charge.
- The person in charge shall prohibit a conditional employee who reports a listed symptom from becoming a food employee until meeting the criteria listed in section 2-201.13 of the Food Code, for reinstatement of a symptomatic food employee.

Key for Tables 1, 2, 3, and 4:

RA = Regulatory Authority

EHEC/STEC = Enterohemorrhagic, or Shiga toxin-producing Escherichia coli

HAV = Hepatitis A virus

HSP = Highly Susceptible Population

Source: FDA 2009 Food Code Annex 3 – Public Health Reasons/Administrative Guidance, pg. 347
Additional Exclusions and Restrictions can be located on pages 348-355

Health Policies and Documentation

One of the stipulations introduced in the 2005 Food Code is the concept of an employee health reporting agreement. The Food Code requires that both conditional and regular food employees acknowledge, in writing, their responsibility for reporting certain symptoms, diagnoses, and health conditions to the Certified Dietary Manager. Employees must also acknowledge their responsibility to comply with restriction or exclusion, when applicable. At the same time, the person in charge must acknowledge, in writing, the responsibilities outlined in the Food Code for managing employee health. This means, for example, that when your facility offers a foodservice job to someone, you should ask that person to sign a reporting agreement. The FDA provides a sample form for this, shown previously in Figure 18.5.

In addition, the Food Code stipulates that a foodservice operation must have a written employee health policy. The policy must address, at a minimum, how the operation complies with the rules for reporting illness/symptoms and managing restrictions or exclusion.

SECTION C Manage Physical Facilities

A foodservice operation must provide documentation that employees' hands are washed before food preparation and as necessary throughout the work day. Some Certified Dietary Managers may choose to fulfill this requirement by using checklists that employees sign throughout the day. Others may choose to implement some of the handwashing technologies on the market today. Some handwashing systems, for example, can control and track the length of time a faucet runs while an employee is washing hands.

The equipment used to prepare food and the physical facilities of the foodservice operation have a tremendous impact on the safety of food served. In this section, we will consider what characteristics enable foodservice equipment and facilities to support safe food.

Cleanability

Cleaning and maintenance are important considerations when designing a foodservice facility and when purchasing equipment. A well-designed foodservice operation utilizes materials that are durable, non-porous and easy to clean. Regulations for foodservice operations have changed considerably over the last several years, so it is important to consult new standards before making any construction, remodeling, or major purchasing decision. The sanitary design of a foodservice facility is often governed by a variety of laws, including public health, building, and zoning. The primary consideration for the sanitary design of foodservice facilities is cleanability. **Cleanability** is the extent to which an item is accessible for cleaning and inspection, and ease with which soil can be removed by normal cleaning methods.

Cleanability
The ability of a piece of equipment to be easily accessible for cleaning, soil removal, sanitizing, and inspection

Some examples of how food safety can be part of a facility design are:

- ✓ Equipment is easily dissembled
- ✓ Finishes are durable and easy to clean
- ✓ Equipment is attached to the wall, eliminating legs, which makes it easier to clean under the equipment
- ✓ Equipment racks have a minimum number of legs
- ✓ Garbage disposals are placed in work areas to facilitate waste disposal
- ✓ Shelves under tables are designed to be portable, so they can be cleaned easily.

Construction Materials and Considerations

Floors, Walls, and Ceilings. The materials for floors, walls, and ceilings are selected on the basis of ease in cleaning, resistance, and durability. Utility service lines should not be unnecessarily exposed and should not obstruct or prevent cleaning. Walls and ceilings should be light in color to distribute light and to make any soil more noticeable.

Floors. The floor in food preparation and utility areas should be easy to maintain, wear resistant, slip resistant, and non-porous. Common materials for floors are quarry tile, terrazzo, and sealed concrete. Other materials may be used in dining rooms. For instance, tightly woven carpeting would be acceptable in a dining room but not in a food preparation or storage area.

Vinyl tile is not recommended, even for dining rooms, because it is difficult to maintain and wears out quickly. Ceramic tile is a common floor finish for public restrooms and other high traffic areas. Floor mats, if used, should be easy to remove and to clean.

Floor Drains. Floors that are flushed with water for cleaning or are subject to frequent liquid spills should have adequate drains to allow the liquids to drain off by themselves.

Walls. The best wall finish in food preparation areas is structural glazed tile or ceramic tile. Both withstand heat, grease, and frequent cleaning. Structural glazed tile is also resistant to impact from movable carts and equipment, which is important to prevent chips. Surfaces that are chipped or cracked allow microorganisms to attach themselves.

Floor and Wall Junctures. Coving is required at the juncture of floors and walls. Coving at a floor-wall joint facilitates cleaning by preventing accumulation of bits of food that attract insects and rodents.

Ceilings. A wide variety of construction materials is available for ceilings, including: acoustical tile, painted drywall, painted plaster, and exposed concrete. Acoustical tile is a common choice because it is economical and has sound-absorbing qualities. Special non-absorbent acoustical tiles have been developed. Tiles are easier to replace when needed.

The cook was slicing ham for the noon meal when he noticed that the blade had a chip in it. The chip was not there prior to slicing the ham. What should you do?

(Check your answer at the end of this chapter)

Heating, Ventilation, Air Conditioning Systems. Heating, Ventilation, and Air Conditioning (HVAC) systems should help maintain appropriate temperatures and air flow. The elements of an HVAC system—including hoods, vents and filters—should be inspected and cleaned on a regular basis to ensure efficient operation and to prevent the risk of a fire from grease build-up. Hoods can be commercially cleaned to eliminate grease build-up, which is a fire hazard. All preparation and work areas where odors, fumes, or vapors accumulate should be vented to the outside. Heating, ventilating, and air conditioning systems should be designed and installed so that make-up air intake and exhaust vents do not cause contamination of food, food contact surfaces, equipment or utensils. Vents and hoods should be maintained in a clean condition and air filters, if used, should be changed regularly.

Lighting. Lighting should be: adequate so that dirt and soil are visible; easy to clean; and bright enough to prevent accidents from poor lighting. Lighting is measured in foot-candles. Work areas require 50 foot-candles of light. Storage areas and walk-in coolers require at least 10 foot-candles. In food preparation and warewashing areas, lighting must be shielded and shatter-resistant.

Special Area Considerations

Dry Storage Areas. Storage areas should be well ventilated, dry, and constructed of easy-to-clean surfaces. Concrete or tile floors, cement block walls with epoxy paint, and acoustic ceilings are common for all storage areas except those that are refrigerated. Three- or four-level metal shelving is commonly used in storage areas. Slatted or louvered shelves are recommended for storage areas because they permit proper air flow. Storage areas should be maintained at 50˚F - 70˚F.

Warewashing Areas. Warewashing areas must be designed so that they are easy to sanitize and can withstand wet conditions. Common construction materials include slip-resistant quarry tile floors, ceramic or structural glazed tile walls, and moisture-resistant acoustic ceilings.

Preparation Areas. A major consideration in preparation areas is work surfaces. A common material used in the construction of work surfaces is stainless steel. Stainless steel is non-corrosive, non-absorbent, and non-toxic—making it a very suitable material for use in foodservice operations. All food contact surfaces must be accessible for cleaning and sanitizing.

Toilet and Handwashing Facilities. Toilets should be conveniently located but separate from food preparation areas. The number of toilets and sinks required will vary by the size of the foodservice operation and is usually determined by state and local regulations. Separate restrooms for employees and clients are recommended. The doors to toilet areas must be tight-fitting and self-closing.

Foodservice Equipment

Equipment Standards. Many utensils and products intended for household use are not appropriate for use in foodservice operations. A Certified Dietary Manager should purchase only equipment that is intended for use in the foodservice industry. In general, foodservice equipment should be designed to be easily cleaned, maintained, and serviced—either in the assembled or disassembled state.

Metal pieces such as slicer blades and mixer pieces should be made of heavy gauge metal and checked frequently for nicks or broken areas.

One way to identify properly designed and constructed equipment is to look for the NSF International mark. (See Figure 18.8) The NSF International mark of approval is a recognized standard of acceptance for many pieces of equipment. This seal assures the manager that the equipment meets certain construction standards for sanitation and safety.

Another important standard is the Underwriter's Laboratories (UL) mark, which indicates compliance of the equipment with electrical safety standards. (See Figure 18.8) UL has developed nearly 20 safety standards for the commercial foodservice industry. Only equipment meeting these standards can display the blue UL sanitation certification mark. The following are examples of characteristics to look for when purchasing foodservice equipment:

- ✓ Easy disassembly for cleaning
- ✓ Durable, corrosion resistant and non-absorbent
- ✓ Materials that do not impart any significant color, odor, or taste to food
- ✓ Smooth surfaces free of pits, crevices, ledges, bolts and rivet heads
- ✓ Coating materials that are resistant to cracking and chipping
- ✓ Rounded edges and internal corners with finished smooth surfaces.

Figure 18.8 Equipment Standards Marks

Putting It Into Practice: 7

Your foodservice assistant comments that the cooler temperature seems warm but the cooler temperature log indicates that the cooler hasn't varied more than three degrees throughout the day. What is the first action you should take?

(Check your answer at the end of this chapter)

Refrigeration Equipment. Refrigeration equipment is important to food protection. To ensure maximum performance of refrigeration units, follow these steps:

✓ Check to see that gaskets and hinges fit tightly and that there is no air leaking.

✓ Clean or replace the air filter.

✓ Clean the condenser.

Some foodservice operations connect thermostats on refrigerators to security or other monitoring equipment. Maintenance or management personnel can be notified immediately if the equipment fails—rather than discovering food spoilage several hours after the fact. Thermal barriers made of flexible, overlapping, PVC strips can be mounted on the doors of walk-in refrigerators and freezers to help maintain temperatures even when the door is opened. There should be room inside or on the door for a temperature log that is filled out three times a day. Take the actual food temperature if there has been a disruption in service, or if you believe the thermometer is off.

Equipment Installation. Equipment that is fixed because it is not easily mobile should be installed so that it is spaced to allow access for cleaning along the sides, behind and above the equipment. Equipment that is not easily movable should be sealed to the floor or elevated on legs that provide at least 6" (15 cm) clearance between the floor and the equipment. Equipment mounted on concrete bases or on small steel legs can interfere with proper cleaning. Easier access for cleaning can also be provided by mounting equipment on wheels so it can be moved, or by using wall-mounted equipment.

Cutting Boards. Surfaces such as cutting blocks that are subject to scratching and scoring should be resurfaced if they can no longer be cleaned and sanitized effectively; or, they should be discarded if they cannot be resurfaced. Wooden cutting boards may be prohibited in some areas; if used they must be made of hard maple. Cutting boards made of food-grade seamless hard rubber or acrylic are recommended.

Color-coded cutting boards are available: red for meat, yellow for poultry, white for dairy, green for fruits and vegetables, beige for cooked poultry, and blue for seafood. Even a two-board combination (such as red for raw foods and beige for cooked foods) will reduce the risk of cross-contamination.

Thermometers: Monitoring proper storage, cooking, holding, cooling and reheating temperatures is vital to food protection. The most common thermometer used in foodservice is the bi-metallic stem type. Bi-metallic stem thermometers are made of two metal strips which are joined together. The expansion and contraction of these strips move a pointer on a dial face. Bi-metallic thermometers need to be calibrated on a regular basis to ensure accuracy. Technology offers some alternatives to bi-metallic thermometers. As more foodservice operations implement HACCP food safety programs, other types of foodservice thermometers are becoming more common.

Thermocouple and Thermistor. The probes of these electronic thermometers can measure the temperature of food and provide a digital display. Some have

Figure 18.9 Monitoring Temperature of a Thin Food like Salmon Steak

Image courtesy of Cooper Instrument Corporation

additional electronic features, such as the ability to store temperature readings. Most have interchangeable probes, which allow you to match the probe to the food or equipment. A thermometer with a small, thin probe allows for greater accuracy in checking temperatures of thin foods, such as ground beef patties, fish filets, or strips of meat for stir-fry. In fact, the Food Code stipulates using one of these for thin foods. See Figures 18.9 and 18.10.

An important consideration with any type of temperature-measuring device is cross-contamination. A thermometer used to measure the temperature of a raw food and then used to monitor a prepared food can contaminate the prepared food with bacteria. Probes should be sanitized with an approved sanitizer after each use. Foodservice storage areas should be equipped with thermometers to measure the ambient temperature. Grill and oven thermometers may be used to verify the calibration of cooking equipment.

Clean-in-Place Equipment (CIP). Clean-in-place equipment must be self-draining and designed so that cleaning and sanitizing solutions circulate throughout a fixed system and contact all food-contact surfaces. Clean-in-place equipment that cannot be disassembled for cleaning should have access points to allow inspection of interior food contact surfaces. CIP equipment and pieces that can be disassembled need the same steps for cleaning and sanitizing: wash, rinse, sanitize, air dry.

Equipment Calibration. Storage equipment is essential for maintaining proper food temperatures. Cooking and holding equipment—such as ovens, grills, steam tables and food warmers—should be calibrated on a regular basis. Equipment that is not calibrated may not cook food thoroughly or hold food at a safe temperature.

Mechanical Warewashing Equipment. Dishmachines must be equipped with a temperature measuring device that indicates the temperature of water in each tank and the temperature of water during the sanitizing final rinse. Warewashing machines should be equipped with internal baffles, curtains, or other

Putting It Into Practice: 8

You are observing a new employee as she disassembles and cleans the slicer. She puts on safety gloves, disassembles the slicer, takes the portable pieces to the dishwasher and runs them through. She carefully washes the blade of the slicer and then reassembles the slicer. What step(s) has she overlooked?

(Check your answer at the end of this chapter)

Figure 18.10 Verifying Temp. of Salad with Bi-Metallic Stem Thermometer

Image courtesy of Cooper Instrument Corporation

means to minimize internal cross-contamination between the solution in the wash and rinse tanks. In mechanical dishwashing, adequate dwell time is also a consideration. Dwell time is the time that dishes spend in contact with heat during sanitization.

Manual Warewashing Equipment: A sink with at least three compartments must be provided for manually washing, rinsing, and sanitizing equipment and utensils. A temperature-measuring device must be provided for frequently measuring the washing and sanitizing temperature of the water. Dishwasher temperatures should be monitored and recorded. Test strips may be used to monitor concentration of chemical sanitizing agents. A warewashing machine installed after 2001 should meet additional requirements: It should be equipped to dispense detergents and sanitizers automatically. It should also have a visual signal or audible alarm to indicate a failure to dispense these chemicals.

Developing a Cleaning Program

Maintaining a clean environment for food preparation is an important part of food safety. The presence of bacteria and the likelihood of foodborne illness increase if a foodservice operation fails to use appropriate cleaning and sanitizing techniques. Equipment, food contact surfaces, and utensils must be clean to sight and touch. The food contact surfaces of equipment should be free of any encrusted grease deposits and other soil accumulations. The plumbing under the dishmachine should be clear of rust and lime build-up. Non-food contact surfaces should be kept free of dust, dirt, food residue and debris. A philosophy of clean-as-you-go should be instilled in all foodservice staff. A cleaning program will most likely be effective if the Certified Dietary Manager incorporates a system of self-inspection and training.

Maintaining a clean foodservice operation requires that Certified Dietary Managers use their skills in planning, organizing, staffing, training, and directing. The manager must first determine what the cleaning needs of the operation are, and when these functions need to be carried out. The manager must then determine who will be responsible for carrying out the cleaning. Some cleaning may be done by contract personnel, but most will be completed by foodservice employees. The manager must provide adequate staffing so that employees will be able to carry out the planned cleaning activities. The manager must train employees in proper cleaning techniques and safe use of chemicals. Finally, the manager must evaluate the cleaning program on an ongoing basis to ensure its effectiveness and to correct any identified problems.

A written schedule, such as that in Figure 18.11, can be developed to outline the cleaning program and employee responsibilities. A self-inspection checklist (Figure 18.12) can be used to evaluate the effectiveness of the cleaning program. Detailed instructions on proper cleaning techniques should be incorporated into employee training programs. An example of this appears in Figure 18.13.

Cleaning Products. Detergents are powerful dirt-removing cleaning agents. Types of cleaning products are described in Figure 18.14. A cleaning supply vendor can assist you in selecting the right chemical for the right job. Or, your local or state regulatory agency may be able to provide a list of approved chemical products. Factors in selecting a detergent include:

✓ Dissolvability: how well the detergent disperses with water

✓ Wetting ability: how well it saturates the surface of the object to be cleaned

✓ Emulsification ability: how well the detergent suspends the fats in water and keeps them suspended

✓ Free rinsing ability: how well the detergent keeps soil from returning to the cleaned object

✓ Deflocculation ability: how well the detergent puts lumps of food-soil in suspension in water

✓ Non-toxicity: the extent to which the detergent is free of toxins and other elements harmful to humans

✓ Corrosiveness: how great a corroding effect the detergent has on the surface of the item to be cleaned.

Wiping Cloths. Cloths that are used for wiping food spills should be used for no other purpose. Wet cloths used for wiping food spills should be stored in a sanitizing solution. Dry or moist cloths that are used with raw animal foods must be kept separate from cloths used for other purposes, and moist cloths used with raw animal foods must be kept in a separate sanitizing solution. Wiping cloths that you use just to wipe spills from tables and carry-out containers can be stored and used dry. Sponges should not be used on any food-contact surface.

Clean vs. Sanitary. Clean does not mean sanitary. **Clean** means free of visible dirt or debris. Cleaning is accomplished by physical and/or chemical means and is a two-step process:

1. Wash with an approved detergent
2. Rinse with clear water

Glossary

Clean
Free of visible soil

Sanitary
Free of harmful levels of microorganisms

Figure 18.11 **Sample Daily Cleaning Schedule**

Area: ______________________ Week of: ______________

Item	Person Responsible	Initial When Completed						
		Sun	Mon	Tue	Wed	Thur	Fri	Sat
Grill	Cafe Employee 1							
Fryer	Cafe Employee 1							
Reach-in Refrigerator	Cafe Employee 1							
Food Warmer	Cafe Employee 2							
Steam Table	Cafe Employee 2							
Salad Bar	Cafe Employee 3							
Serving Line	Cafe Employee 3							
Soda Dispenser	Cashier							
Dining Room Table	Cashier							
Floor	Utility Aide							
Garbage Cans	Utility Aide							

Sanitary means free of harmful levels of microorganisms. It is almost impossible to sanitize equipment and facilities unless they are first clean. Clean foodservice equipment may appear safe to use, but if it is not sanitized, then a hidden threat to food safety exists. Equipment and utensils must be sanitized after cleaning. The FDA Food Code defines a thermometer probe as a utensil, too, so it must also be sanitized.

Sanitizing. Sanitizing is the process of making equipment and work surfaces sanitary. There are two major methods of sanitizing: heat sanitization and chemical sanitization.

✓ Heat sanitization: The procedure is to expose an object to sufficiently high heat for a sufficient period of time to sanitize it. According to the FDA Food Code, cleaned food contact surfaces can be sanitized by immersion in water that is 171°F or above for at least 30 seconds.

Figure 18.12 **Sample Cleaning Self-Inspection Checklist**

Area	Clean		Action Taken
	Yes	No	
KITCHEN			
Floors			
Walls			
Ceilings			
Baseboards			
Hoods and Vents			
Light Fixtures			
Counters			
Filters			
Fans			
Garbage Cans			
DINING ROOM			
Floors			
Walls			
Ceilings			
Baseboards			
Light Fixtures			
DRY STORAGE AREA			
Floors			
Walls			
Ceilings			
Baseboards			
Light Fixtures			

Figure 18.13 Sample Cleaning Procedure for Floors

How to Clean Floors	
Equipment Needed: • Broom • Dust Pan • 2 Mops • 2 Mop Buckets	**Supplies Needed:** • Heavy-Duty Detergent
What to Do	**How to Do It**
1. Sweep	• Sweep the floor with a broom, making sure to get under equipment. • Minimize dust by using short, controlled strokes. • Use dust pan to pick up debris.
2. Set up mop buckets	• Fill each bucket 3/4 full with hot tap water. • Put the appropriate amount of cleanser in one of the buckets.
3. Apply cleanser to floor	• Dip first mop into cleanser solution and wring out. • Mop small section of floor using a figure-eight motion. • Allow detergent to loosen soil for a few minutes.
4. Rinse floor	• Dip the second mop into the rinse water, wring out, and use the mop to pick up the dirt and cleaning solution. • Change detergent solutions and rinse water often.
Safety Considerations	
• Check product label and refer to MSDS for precautions and emergency procedures in the event of an accident • Follow manufacturer's directions on detergent label to ensure the proper dilution. • Use "wet floor" signs to prevent accidental slips and falls.	

Figure 18.14 Types of Cleaning Products

Alkaline Detergents	The most commonly used detergents. General-purpose alkalines are only mildly alkaline and are usually applied to walls, ceilings, and floors. Heavy-duty types are highly alkaline for use in dishwashing machines.
Abrasive Cleaners	Effective in scouring off rust, grease, and heavy soil but can scratch certain surfaces such as stainless steel. Use caution with abrasive cleaners, as scratches in food contact surfaces can harbor bacterial growth.
Acid Cleaners	Acid cleaners have more specialized uses, such as deliming dishmachines and removing water spots. Use acid cleaners with caution to avoid skin irritation.
Degreasers	Degreasers are highly alkaline and can remove grease build-up from floors, ovens, and vents. Degreasers are also known as solvent cleaners.

Note: To avoid producing a poisonous gas, never mix chemicals together.

✓ Chemical sanitization: **Sanitizers** are chemicals that destroy harmful pathogens. The dilution or strength of a sanitizing solution is measured in parts per million (ppm). Dispensing equipment for sanitizers should be calibrated on a regular basis and the strength of a sanitizing solution should be checked with a chemical test strip on a daily basis. Chemical test strips are often available from the chemical supply vendor. Keep in mind that the effectiveness of a sanitizer may be affected by the temperature, hardness, and/or pH of the water in which it is mixed. Also, some chemical solutions lose their strength over time. Chemical sanitizers are summarized in Figure 18.15.

Figure 18.15 Chemical Sanitizers

Product	Dilution in Parts Per Million (ppm)	Water Temperature	Immersion Time
Iodine	12.5-25	75°F-120°F	30 seconds
Chlorine	50-100	75°F-115°F	30 seconds
Quaternary Ammonium Compounds	180-200	75° (minimum)	30 seconds

General guidelines only; follow manufacturer's directions or local regulations.

Dishwashing

Manual Cleaning and Sanitizing. Manual cleaning and sanitizing is generally done with a three-compartment sink. Some municipalities are now requiring a four-compartment sink. The additional compartment is designated for prescraping. If you are using a three-compartment sink, remember to pre-scrape utensils and cooking equipment before placing them in the first sink compartment. The steps in manual cleaning and sanitizing using a three-compartment sink are:

1. Pre-clean to remove loose food soil.
2. Wash in the first sink using an approved detergent with a water temperature of 110°F-120°F.
3. Rinse in the second sink, using clear water.
4. Sanitize in the third sink using an approved sanitizer at the appropriate concentration and temperature. See Appendix E.
5. Allow dishes to air dry and store in a clean, dry, protected area.

Remember to change the water as necessary to maintain the temperatures and to clean the sink after each use. Use cleaned and sanitized drain boards to stack the equipment and utensils during air drying.

Mechanical Cleaning and Sanitizing. While there are various sizes and types of dishmachines (see Figure 18.16), the following steps will apply to most operations. These six steps are necessary in any mechanical warewashing operation. Each step is equally important in obtaining clean and sanitary dishware.

Sanitizers
Chemicals that destroy microorganisms

What cleaner would you recommend to your staff to remove the grease buildup from the back of the range?

(Check your answer at the end of this chapter)

Figure 18.16 Mechanical Dishmachine Temperatures

Type of Machine	Temperature of Wash Solution	Temperature of Sanitizing Rinse
Stationary rack, single temperature machine	165°F	165°F
Stationary rack, dual temperature machine	150°F	180°F
Single tank, conveyor, dual temperature machine	160°F	180°F
Multi-tank, conveyor, multi-temperature machine	150°F	180°F

Notes:

- The temperature of sanitizing rinse should not exceed 194°F.
- The actual temperature attained within a hot water sa.itizing machine (at utensil surface) should be at least 160°F when measured by a thermometer or temperature test strip.

The steps are:

1. Separate: Separate any items that will require special attention, such as items that are heavily soiled or have burned-on residue.
2. Pre-scrape or pre-flush: Excess food soil and pieces of paper straws or napkins will clog the dishmachine, scrap trays, pump and wash arms—and reduce their effectiveness. Excess food soil in the wash tank also uses up more detergent and requires more frequent changes of water in the wash tank.
3. Rack dishes: Proper racking of dishes is essential for getting good results. All of the racks should be filled with similar items. A rack should contain cups only, or plates only, or bowls only, etc. Avoid mixing loads. The dishmachine works by spraying water at the dishes, and if the water cannot reach all of the dish surfaces, the dishes can't get clean.
4. Wash: Washing dishes requires a properly operating dishmachine and the proper detergent usage. You must be sure to use the right detergent, make sure that the machine is set up properly, and see that it is free of paper, straws, and excess food.
5. Perform sanitizing rinse: Rinsing is done automatically and requires only the proper water flow, proper water temperature, and the proper rinse aid. Visually inspect the machine to ensure that the rinse jets are not clogged. Verify that rinse temperature is reaching the appropriate point and that the rinse injector is supplied with the proper rinse aid, and that dwell time is adequate.
6. Air Drying: Air drying the dishes requires nothing but time. Wait until the dishes are completely dry before putting them in a clean, dry storage area. Avoid stacking utensils within one another until they are completely dry.

Dish and Utensil Storage. After cleaning and sanitizing, all dishes and utensils must be stored dry and in clean, dust-free areas above the floor and protected from dust, splashes, spills and other forms of contamination.

The dishwasher just informed you that sometime while running the evening dishes, the soap dispenser quit working. What would you recommend?

(Check your answer at the end of this chapter)

Management in the News

Importance of Employee Health and Hygiene

Poor Personal Hygiene

Employee health and hygiene are significant factors in preventing foodborne illness. This has been demonstrated in the population at large, commercial food service establishments, and in nursing facilities. Foodborne illness in nursing homes has been associated with Norovirus. Because "infectious" individuals (persons capable of transmitting an infection or communicable disease whether they be colonized or infected) are a source of Norovirus, proper hand washing techniques and exclusion of infectious workers from handling food are critical for prevention of foodborne illness.

Source of Contamination	Primary Agents of Concern	Primary Control Strategies
Hazards that are likely to occur—strategies that must be in place to prevent foodborne illness.		
Eggs, raw or unpasteurized	• Salmonella	• PHF/TCS • Cook to proper temperature • Prevention of cross-contamination to ready-to-eat foods
Poultry, raw	• Campylobacter • Salmonella	• PHF/TCS • Cook to proper temperature • Prevention of cross-contamination to ready-to-eat foods
	• Clostridium perfringens	• PHF/TCS • Cook to proper temperature
Meat, raw	• E. coli O157:H7 • Salmonella • Campylobacter	• PHF/TCS • Cook to proper temperature • Prevention of cross-contamination to ready-to-eat foods
	• Clostridium perfringens	• PHF/TCS • Cook to proper temperature

(Continued...)

Importance of Employee Health and Hygiene *(Continued)*

Source of Contamination	Primary Agents of Concern	Primary Control Strategies
Infectious food workers	• Norovirus • Hepatitus A virus • Shigella • Salmonella	• Exclusion of infectious workers • Proper hand-washing procedures • Avoid bare-hand contact with ready-to-eat-foods
	• Staphylococcus aureus	• PHF/TCS • Proper hand-washing procedures • Prevention of cross-contamination to ready-to-eat foods
Hazards that may occur as a result of adulteration of food products, and for which good food handling practices are needed to minimize the potential for foodborne illness transmission.		
Fruits and vegetables, fresh	• E.coli 0157:H7 • Salmonella • Norovirus • Hepatitus A virus • Shigella	• Wash prior to use (unless pre-washed) • Keep cut and raw fruits and vegetables refrigerated
Ready-to-eat meat and poultry products	• Listeria monocytogenes	• Proper refrigeration during storage
Pasteurized dairy products	• Listeria monocytogenes	• Proper refrigeration during storage
Ice	• Norovirus	• Cleaning and sanitizing the internal components of the ice machine per manufacturer's guidelines

Source: CMS Manual System Revisions to Appendix PP, "Guidance to Surveyors of Long Term Care Facilities" Effective June 12, 2009.

END OF CHAPTER

Putting It Into Practice Questions & Answers

1. List some steps to prepare your staff for a sanitation inspection.

   A. *1. Provide continuous training for your staff that includes someone acting as the sanitation inspector each week.*

   2. Involve your staff in developing cleaning and documentation procedures.

   3. Encourage staff to cooperate with any inspectors.

   4. Make sure staff knows what documentation might be required: purchasing specs, time and temperature logs, HACCP documentation, assurance of appropriate handwashing practices.

2. What principles of purchasing must you keep in mind even if you are in a crisis?

   A. *Food must be procured from an approved source, including water. Refrigerated/Frozen foods must be delivered in refrigerated/frozen trucks. Setting up provisions for emergency delivery from your current food vendor is an item that could be in your crisis plan.*

3. Your cook is breading chicken for the evening meal when the foodservice staff member requests more rolls for the lunch meal. The cook picks up a basket of rolls and takes it to the staff member. Then she returns to breading the chicken. Is this a concern? Why or why not?

   A. *Yes, this is a cross-contamination concern, even if she didn't touch the rolls. She still touched the basket and the basket could be the transfer of Salmonella to the rolls. She should have washed her hands, taken the basket, rewashed her hands, and continued with the breading.*

4. You observe a foodservice staff member replacing ready-to-eat items in the cafeteria. She is wearing disposable gloves. At that moment, a client is waiting at the cash register. Your cook quickly removes her gloves, wipes her hands and helps the client at the cash register. She then returns to replacing the ready-to-eat items after putting on new gloves. Is this a concern? Why or why not?

   A. *Your staff cannot move from the cash register to food prep without washing their hands, even if they put on gloves to continue the food prep. Money contains many microorganisms. Hands should be clean prior to putting on gloves.*

5. It is a hectic day in the foodservice department because two employees are off sick. Your cook explains that he isn't feeling well and has visited the bathroom several times in the past two hours. What should you do?

   A. *Ask your cook what his symptoms are. If they are vomiting, diarrhea, sore throat, or fever, he should be sent home until he is cleared by a physician.*

(Continued)

Putting It Into Practice Questions & Answers *(Continued)*

6. The cook was slicing ham for the noon meal when he noticed that the blade had a chip in it. The chip was not there prior to slicing the ham. What should you do?

   A. *1. Remove the ham that was being sliced from service and destroy it. Metal chips are a physical contamination and even if you found the chip, there might be minute pieces remaining in the ham.*

   2. Remove the slicer from service until a new blade can be replaced.

7. The foodservice assistant comments that the cooler temperature seems warm but the cooler temperature log indicates that the cooler hasn't varied more than three degrees throughout the day. What is the first action you should take?

   A. *Take the temperature of food in the cooler. If food is in the danger zone, remove any potentially hazardous food from future service because you don't know how long it has been at that temperature. Then, contact your repair person. If food is still within safe temperatures, contact your repair person and monitor the temperature of the potentially hazardous foods until the repairs are completed. If possible, move the food to another cooler or freezer until the repairs are made.*

8. You are observing a new employee as she disassembles and cleans the slicer. She puts on safety gloves, disassembles the slicer, takes the portable pieces to the dishwasher and runs them through. She carefully washes the blade of the slicer and then reassembles the slicer. What step(s) has she overlooked?

   A. *All parts of the slicer that are not movable, including underneath the slicer, need to be washed, rinsed, and sanitized. The blade also needs to be sanitized after washing and rinsing.*

9. What cleaner would you recommend to your staff to remove the grease buildup from the back of the range?

   A. *The best cleaner for removing grease build up is a degreaser or solvent cleaner.*

10. The dishwasher just informed you that sometime during the running of the evening dishes, the soap dispenser quit working. What would you recommend?

    A. *Replace the soap in the dispenser and run the dishwasher to make sure the soap dispenser is working. If it is, rerun the evening dishes. If it is not, rewash the evening dishes and all subsequent dishes with a five-step manual process (pre-wash, wash, rinse, sanitize, air-dry) until repairs are made.*

CHAPTER 19

Conduct Routine Maintenance Inspection of Equipment

Overview and Objectives

Keeping equipment and facilities in good repair is both a cost saving and a time saving practice. This chapter reviews preventative maintenance, environmental controls, and pest management that will benefit sanitation management.

After completing this chapter, you should be able to:

- ✓ Follow an integrated pest management (IPM) system
- ✓ Identify appropriate environmental controls for water supply, waste disposal, and ventilation
- ✓ Identify equipment maintenance requirements from manufacturer's manuals
- ✓ Correct equipment malfunctions and potential problems
- ✓ Monitor preventative maintenance schedule and contracts

Preventative Maintenance

Preventative maintenance of equipment and facilities is required as an on-going process in order to keep foodservice facilities in good repair and condition. Preventative maintenance goes beyond the daily cleaning tasks. Some preventative maintenance responsibilities will undoubtedly be carried out by foodservice staff, while others may be performed by the facility maintenance staff, or through a contract with a commercial equipment maintenance company. It is important to determine what duties foodservice and maintenance will perform.

Preventative maintenance includes weekly, bi-monthly, monthly, quarterly, and semi-annual cleaning responsibilities. Figure 19.1 shows a partial preventative maintenance cleaning schedule. When assigning these cleaning duties, it is important to include the who, what, when, and how that are part of any cleaning schedule. How do you decide who should do which cleaning duties? Obviously, no one wants to be assigned to clean the grease traps each time. Determining who does what cleaning would be a great topic for a department meeting. Get input from your staff as to how cleaning duties should be divided up. One facility uses a job jar and each week, employees pull a job from the jar.

It is the Certified Dietary Manager's responsibility is to make sure that cleaning is done properly and according to schedule.

Figure 19.1 Preventative Maintenance Cleaning Schedule for Facilities and Equipment

What to Clean	When to Clean	How to Clean	Person Responsible	Initial When Complete
Drain Covers	Monthly	Remove and wash thoroughly with detergent or degreaser if necessary		
Walls	Monthly	Wash with detergent or degreaser if necessary		
Ceiling Vents	Monthly	Wash with detergent or degreaser if necessary		
Hood Filters	Monthly	Wash filters, replace if necessary		
Grease Traps	Every 2 months	Clean with degreaser		
Fans	Monthly	Wipe down blades and fan cover		
Ice Machine	Quarterly	Remove ice, clean interior surfaces with detergent, flush ice-making unit		
Cooler/Refrigerator	Bi-monthly or more often as needed	Wipe down racks, clean floors, and fan with detergent		
Freezer	Bi annually	Empty, defrost, wash racks, floors, fans with detergent		
Steamer	Weekly	Use approved de-liming agent		
Dishwashing Machine	Weekly	Use approved de-liming agent		
Dish Racks	Weekly	Scrub with detergent		
Food Carts	Weekly	Scrub with detergent or use steam cleaner		
Garbage Cans	Weekly	Scrub with detergent or use steam cleaner		
HVAC	Every 6 months	Steam clean		

A checklist should be used to ensure that equipment and facilities are properly maintained, as shown in Figure 19.2. Whatever the schedule, make sure that proper tools, equipment, and cleaning materials are available when needed. The manager is also responsible for making sure that employees are thoroughly trained in the procedure and cleaning materials for each task. For example, one facility noticed a significant increase in the cost of sanitizers. Upon investigation, one of the staff believed that if some sanitizer was good, double the amount would be better. Training needs to include why the concentration of sanitizer is important.

Preventative Maintenance Records

There are different types of preventative maintenance records. Two are temperature logs and equipment repair records.

Temperature logs. Temperature logs should be established for equipment where maintaining temperature is critical. These logs can be set up on a monthly

Figure 19.2 Equipment Cleaning Checklist

Equipment	Clean?		Operational?		Action Taken
	Yes	No	Yes	No	
Oven					
Range Top					
Broiler					
Tilting Skillet					
Fans					
Hood Filters					
Food Carts					
Steamer					
Trunnion Kettles					
Steam Jacketed Kettle					
Dish Racks					
Cooler/Freezer					
HVAC					
Fryer					
Steam Table					
Food Warmer					
Walls					
Ceiling					
Grease Trap					

Figure 19.3 Dishwasher Temperature Log

Month: ____________________ Year: ____________________

Instructions: Record temperatures for dishwasher at each meal. Keep this form on the clipboard throughout the month. Report any problems to your supervisor.

Date	Breakfast			Lunch			Dinner		
	Wash	Rinse	Hold	Wash	Rinse	Hold	Wash	Rinse	Hold
1									
2									
3									
4									
5									
6									
7									
8									
9									
10									
11									
12									
13									
14									
15									
16									
17									
18									
19									
20									
21									
22									
23									
24									
25									
26									
27									
28									
29									
30									
31									

basis and maintained by an assigned staff person. Temperature logs are essential to help you determine the time when the equipment stopped working. Since time AND temperature are important in maintaining food safety, temperature logs are part of preventative maintenance. Temperature logs can be useful during inspections if they are maintained and completed appropriately. Figure 19.3 shows a sample of a dishwasher temperature log. Similar logs could be set up for coolers and freezers.

Equipment Repair Records. Certified Dietary Managers should maintain a record of repairs for each piece of major equipment. An equipment repair record that contains the number of repairs and the cost of each is essential when

Figure 19.4 Equipment Repair Record

<table>
<tr><td>Name of Equipment:</td><td>Brand:</td><td>Purchase Date:</td><td colspan="2">Purchase Price:</td></tr>
<tr><td>Model #:</td><td>Serial #:</td><td></td><td colspan="2"></td></tr>
<tr><td colspan="2">Name of Manufacturer or Vendor:</td><td colspan="3">Representative's Phone #:</td></tr>
<tr><td colspan="2" rowspan="5">Warranty Information (includes recommended preventative maintenance):</td><td colspan="3">Representative's Email:</td></tr>
<tr><td rowspan="2">Date of Repair</td><td colspan="2">Cost of Repair</td></tr>
<tr><td>Material</td><td>Labor</td></tr>
<tr><td></td><td></td><td></td></tr>
<tr><td></td><td></td><td></td></tr>
<tr><td colspan="2" rowspan="6">Repair Log (attach copy of repair bill and name of person doing repair):</td><td></td><td></td><td></td></tr>
<tr><td></td><td></td><td></td></tr>
<tr><td></td><td></td><td></td></tr>
<tr><td></td><td></td><td></td></tr>
<tr><td></td><td></td><td></td></tr>
<tr><td></td><td></td><td></td></tr>
</table>

writing a justification for new equipment. The equipment repair record should be established as soon as a new piece of equipment is received. In today's electronic age, there is unlimited room for computerized equipment repair records ,including setting up reminders for periodic maintenance. See Figure 19.4 for a sample equipment repair record form.

Equipment Replacement Decisions. Sometime during your experience as a Certified Dietary Manager, you will be expected to recommend for purchase or purchase new equipment. Your equipment maintenance record will assist you in deciding when to purchase, what to purchase, and why. The steps in replacing or purchasing new equipment include:

1. Conducting Cost Analysis: A cost analysis compares the cost of upgrading a piece of equipment with the cost of repairs. A repair log can provide you with the cost of repairs information. When the cost of materials and labor to repair equipment is near to or greater than the cost of replacement, the equipment should be replaced.

   When writing a cost analysis/justification for replacement, you can estimate repair costs by comparing the warranty information for the life of equipment or talking with others who have had experience with that brand of equipment. You may get up to three bids and compare that to what it cost to repair the equipment, including labor.

2. Developing Equipment Specifications: When the decision has been made to replace equipment, the Certified Dietary Manager should develop a specification for the new equipment. Considerations for developing purchase specifications include:
   - ✓ Will the equipment provide the time and temperature control that is necessary for safe food?
   - ✓ Is the equipment properly sized for the volume of food that is prepared?
   - ✓ Is the equipment reliable or is it prone to frequent breakdowns?
   - ✓ Is the equipment designed so that it can be easily cleaned and sanitized?
   - ✓ Is the equipment easy to use?
   - ✓ Will the equipment fit into the assigned space?

3. Installation and Staff Training: The manufacturer or supplier should assist in ensuring that the new equipment is properly installed and in providing training to staff. Often, vendors will charge an additional fee for equipment manuals. Certified Dietary Managers and other purchasers should attempt to negotiate the price of equipment operation manuals, staff training, and other support into the purchase price of the equipment.

Water, Plumbing, & Waste Management

Working with maintenance or a local plumbing firm during construction times or after emergency situations such as a flood or tornado is extremely important. It is your responsibility to make sure that maintenance staff know the local, state, and federal sanitation regulations. One example is the FDA Food Code requirement that a drinking water system be flushed and disinfected before being placed in service after construction or an emergency situation.

You are having multiple maintenance calls for a mixer. What is the first step in justifying a new mixer?

(Check your answer at the end of this chapter)

Figure 19.5 Ice Management Practices

- Close or cover the ice bin when not in use.
- Wash hands following established procedures before scooping or dispensing ice. Realize that hands can transfer microorganisms directly to ice, and freezing temperatures do not destroy all pathogens.
- Use a scoop or designated utensil to transfer ice. (Do not use a glass.) Touch only the handle of the scoop.
- Store the scoop in or near the ice bin in a protected manner, or in a sanitizing solution (per your local health regulations), with handle up.
- Clean and sanitize ice scoops regularly.
- Do not store any food products or beverages in or directly above the ice bin.
- Report any concerns about equipment malfunction to a designated supervisor.
- Assure that cleaning compounds are stored and used in such a way that they cannot spill or spray into ice.
- Protect ice supplies from broken china or glasses. If glass breaks or a chemical spills in the vicinity of an ice bin, empty, clean, and sanitize the bin.
- Clean and sanitize the ice collection bin routinely.
- Follow the manufacturer's instructions for maintenance, which may include de-liming machines and replacing filters.

Source: Food Protection Connection, Dietary Manager Magazine, October 2005.

Water can be a vehicle for transmitting harmful microorganisms. Part of the food protection process involves selecting appropriate sources of water, and managing how clean and waste water are handled in the operation through the plumbing system. In addition, food safety requires proper management of refuse.

Sources of Water

Water served in a foodservice operation—as well as water used in food preparation, warewashing, and even handwashing—must be **potable**, or safe to drink. An approved source may be the local public water system. Alternately, it may be a non-public water system that meets National Primary Drinking Water Regulations, as well as state or local regulations. Water from a non-public source must be sampled and tested at least annually, and the report must be kept on file in the foodservice operation. Water must be received through an approved water main, or water transport vehicle. Bottled drinking water that meets appropriate standards is also permissible.

Ice is also a form of water and should be made from potable water. It is important to maintain ice machines in good repair and follow basic sanitation practices in serving ice to clients. Figure 19.5 summarizes some key practices to help ensure safe ice.

Plumbing

Plumbing systems also cover handwashing sinks. The FDA Food Code requires that handwashing sinks provide water at a temperature of at least 100°F. Handwashing sinks must be maintained so that they are accessible at all times to employees. Employees may ONLY use chemical hand sanitizers as a substitute for handwashing when food exposure is limited and handwashing sinks are not convenient, such as in an approved temporary food

Potable Water
Water that is safe to drink

operation like a mobile unit. An amendment to the 2009 FDA Food Code requires that toilets and urinals NOT be used for the disposal of mop water.

The plumbing system performs two very important functions. It brings potable water to the operation and it removes waste materials to a sewer or disposal plant. A major consideration for food protection is to avoid any connection between the two functions.

Fixtures and equipment that are used for food preparation, cleaning, or sanitizing may not allow a cross-connection—a dangerous link between an outlet of a drinkable water system and unsafe water. The link may allow contaminants to flow into potable water, making it unsafe. A **cross-connection** is a structural design issue.

If contaminated water does flow into potable water, this process is called **backflow**. For example, if a faucet is located below the flood rim of a sink, when the sink gets too full, dirty water may flow back into the faucet. Sometimes, rather than just flowing back into potable water, contaminated water is actually sucked into the clean water supply. This type of backflow is called **back-siphonage**. Back-siphonage occurs after a loss in pressure in the water supply; water is siphoned back into the drinkable water supply.

To prevent backflow, provide for an air gap. An **air gap** is an unobstructed air space between an outlet of drinkable water and the flood rim of a fixture or equipment. For example, space between the flood rim in a sink and the outlet of a faucet is an air gap. If an air gap is not present, then the equipment should be equipped with an approved mechanical device to prevent backflow.

Plumbing should be kept in good repair. Be alert to leaks or drainage issues that might contaminate food or food preparation areas. Get to know your local code, as plumbing regulations vary. Always use the services of a licensed, qualified plumber for installing or repairing plumbing systems.

Waste Management

Proper management of waste and garbage will help to maintain a clean, sanitary foodservice operation and to prevent pest infestations. As quickly as possible, garbage should be removed from food preparation and serving areas. Trash holding areas should be located as far as possible from food.

Garbage cans should be sturdy and easy to clean. They should be equipped with tight-fitting lids and covered when not in use. Garbage cans should be cleaned on a routine basis, and garbage cans with cracks or leaks should be replaced immediately. Indoor trash areas should be cleaned on a regular basis, and garbage should be picked up at regular intervals to prevent excess odors and reduce food sources for pests.

If your facility has a recycling program, make sure you are aware of the local, state, and federal sanitation requirements. For instance, the FDA Food Code requires that recyclables be kept covered if the containers contain food residue, or after a recycling container is filled.

Cross-Connection
A dangerous link between an outlet of drinkable water system and unsafe water

Backflow
When contaminated water flows back into potable water

Back-Siphonage
When water is siphoned back into potable water supply after a loss in water pressure

Air Gap
An unobstructed air space between an outlet of drinkable water and the flood rim of a fixture or equipment

Where would you expect to find an air gap in your kitchen?

(Check your answer at the end of this chapter)

Chemical Safety

The use of chemicals is an essential component of a foodservice operation. Chemicals are used in cleaning and sanitizing, and sometimes in office operations. Chemicals that are stored or used incorrectly pose hazards to food, because they can contaminate food and make it unsafe. Chemical safety is an important part of a comprehensive food protection program. In addition, the federal government imposes regulations on chemical use for foodservice operations. A related issue is the safe practice for preventing and eradicating pests.

Chemical safety is addressed by **OSHA**, a government agency responsible for protecting the safety of employees, including those in foodservice operations. OSHA has issued a regulation requiring employers to inform employees about the possible dangers of chemicals they use to do their jobs, and to train them to use chemicals in a safe manner.

The regulation is called the **Hazard Communication Standard**, or "Right to Know" Law. The purpose of the Hazard Communication Standard is: to ensure that all employers receive the information they need to inform employees about chemicals they work with; to train their employees properly on the hazardous substances they work with; and to help design and institute employee protection programs. It also provides necessary hazard information to employees, so they can participate in and support protective measures.

Material Safety Data Sheet. By law, a document called a **Material Safety Data Sheet (MSDS)** must be made available by every chemical manufacturer (see Figure 19.6). You should have an MSDS for every chemical used in your operation, and place sheets in a location that is readily accessible to all employees. The MSDS addresses safe use of a chemical, as well as hazards, safety precautions, proper disposal practices, and how to deal with accidents. In some cases, the MSDS may suggest the use of personal protective equipment, such as rubber gloves or goggles. Material safety data sheets are not easy to read, so employees will require orientation in how to use them. Be sure that employees understand 1) what to use each chemical for, 2) how to mix each chemical, 3) what protective equipment is required, 4) where to find the MSDS for a chemical and 5) how to read it, and 6) what to do in case of an accident or spill. Suggested training content is summarized in Figure 19.7.

To comply with the Hazard Communication Standard:

✓ Review the Hazard Communication Standard.

✓ Develop an inventory of chemicals used in the foodservice operation.

✓ Request a Material Safety Data Sheet (MSDS) for each chemical used in your operation, and make it available to all employees.

✓ Make sure that all chemicals are in labeled containers.

✓ Include safe chemical use in the new employee orientation and as part of annual training for all employees.

Glossary

OSHA
Occupational Safety and Hazard Administration responsible for enforcing chemical safety standards

Hazard Communication Standard ("Right to Know" Law)
Law that requires informing employees about chemicals they work with and to design and institute employee protection program

MSDS
Material Safety Data Sheet required for every chemical that addresses the safe use of the chemical

Putting It Into Practice: 3

One of your staff accidently spilled delimer on her arm. What is the first action you should take?

(Check your answer at the end of this chapter)

Figure 19.6 Sample Material Safety Data Sheet

Material Safety Data Sheet May be used to comply with OSHA's Hazard Communication Standard, 29 CFR 1910 1200. Standard must be consulted for specific requirements.	**U.S. Department of Labor** Occupational Safety and Health Administration (Non-Mandatory Form) Form Approved OMB No. 1218-0072
IDENTITY *(as Used on Label and List)*	**Note:** Blank spaces are not permitted. If any item is not applicable or no information is available, the space must be marked to indicate that.

SECTION I

Manufacturer's Name:	Emergency Telephone Number:
Address *(Number, Street, City, State, and Zip Code)*:	Telephone Number for Information:
	Date Prepared:
	Signature of Preparer *(optional)*:

SECTION II—Hazardous Ingredients/Identity Information

Hazardous Components *[Specific Chemical Identity, Common Name(s)]*	**OSHA PEL**	**ACGIH TLV**	**Other Limits Recommended**	**% (Optional)**

Figure 19.7 Hazard Communication Training Program Content

- Location of Material Safety Data Sheets (MSDS) in the operation
- Inventory list of hazardous chemicals used in the operation
- How to read product labels to learn potential hazards and directions for safe use
- Proper handling, application, storage, and disposal of chemicals
- Use and location of personal protective equipment
- Emergency procedures in the event of a spill or exposure

Chemical Storage. For food safety, it's also important to store chemicals away from food. Chemicals should be stored in their original containers and be clearly labeled. If transferring is necessary, transfer them only to durable, clearly labeled containers. Containers used to hold and dispense chemicals should be clearly marked, and should never be re-used for food storage. Likewise, discarded food containers should never be used for chemical storage, because someone may mistake the contents for food.

Medicines. Storage of medicines are also regulated by the FDA Food Code. The Food Code requires that "only those medicines that are necessary for the health of employees" are allowed in the foodservice department. They must be labeled with a manufacture's label and located to prevent contamination of food, equipment, utensils, linens, and single-service articles. Refrigerated medicines must be stored in a covered, leakproof container that is identified as a container for the storage of medicines. They must also be located so they are inaccessible to children.

Common Pests

A safe food operation is free of insects, birds, and other sources of contamination. Measures must be taken to prevent contamination of food, utensils, equipment and linens by pests. Many pests carry pathogens that can render food unsafe for consumption.

Putting It Into Practice: 4

In a day care facility, how would you handle refrigerated medicine brought in by parents for their children?

(Check your answer at the end of this chapter)

Cockroaches. Cockroaches are common pests in foodservice operations and they represent a significant threat. Cockroaches are carriers of disease and can multiply rapidly. Cockroaches are most active at night and in dark areas where there is less disturbance from people. While there are many different species of cockroaches, three types are frequently found in foodservice operations. German cockroaches, the most abundant species in the U.S., are pale brown with two dark-brown stripes behind the head. They seem to prefer warm places in the foodservice operation. American cockroaches are the largest in size and are reddish brown. They prefer open, wet areas and spaces that are slightly cooler than the favorite spots of German cockroaches. Oriental cockroaches are shiny and dark brown to black. They prefer conditions similar to those of the American cockroach.

Housefly. The common housefly is a great threat to food safety. Flies feed on animal and human waste and then transmit pathogenic organisms as they travel from item to item. Houseflies are numerous during late summer and early fall, since the population has been growing during the warmer weather.

Rats and Mice. Rats and mice can force their entry into a building through small openings. Both rats and mice are skilled swimmers and can enter a building through floor drains and toilet bowl traps. Rats and mice are both nocturnal creatures, being most active at night. One indication of an infestation is the presence of fecal droppings in foodservice areas. Another sign is the presence of gnaw marks on food and food containers in storage.

Birds. Birds, such as pigeons, sparrows, and starlings, are another pest of concern. Birds can enter a building through doors and windows that do not have screens and through ventilation openings. Birds can be carriers of mites and harmful microorganisms such as Salmonella.

Pest Control

Pest control is the reduction or eradication of pests. One of the safest and most effective methods of fly control is the use of insect light traps. Light traps must be enclosed so that pests entering the trap are contained within and cannot fall out into the foodservice operation. Mechanical traps can be used with birds and rodents. Glue traps are also effective in capturing mice. Pesticides, insecticides and repellents are other control techniques. Extreme caution should be exercised when using chemical control methods to prevent contamination of food. Only chemicals approved for application in foodservice operations may be used. Further, only individuals with the proper training and knowledge should apply pesticides. In addition, pesticide application must not occur during food preparation or service. Check local regulations for further restrictions on the use of pest control devices.

Pest control cannot be accomplished effectively unless proper cleaning has occurred. One method of pest control alone is not often effective. For this reason, many foodservice operations use an approach called **integrated pest management (IPM)**. IPM uses a variety of techniques and focuses on prevention. Certified Dietary Managers should implement an IPM including these elements:

- ✓ Routine inspection of incoming supplies and inspection of the premises for evidence of pests.
- ✓ Restrict access into the facility with screens and building maintenance.
- ✓ Reduce food sources for pests through good cleaning and sanitization practices.
- ✓ Control pests by working with a licensed pest control operator (PCO), someone who is trained and licensed in pest management and use of pest-control chemicals and devices.

All openings to the outside of the building must be closed to restrict access to the rodents. Screens in doors and windows can help to restrict the access of insects. Self-closing doors and proper seals around doors also reduce the accessibility of the foodservice operation to pests. Some facilities are required to use Fly Fans or air curtains. Check all deliveries for signs of pest infestation. All

Integrated Pest Management (IPM)
A coordinated approach with pest control and foodservice to manage pests

food storage and preparation areas must be kept in a clean and sanitary condition. Food spills are a source of food for pests. Food stored against the wall creates places for pests to hide, nest and multiply. Proper garbage management can reduce the risk of pest infestation.

Live Animals. Generally, live animals are prohibited from foodservice establishments. The FDA Food Code makes an exception for the following, if food, equipment, utensils, linens, and unwrapped single-service articles are kept sanitary:

✓ Decorative fish in an aquarium

✓ Patrol dogs accompanying police or security officers

✓ In areas that are not used for food preparation

✓ Pets in the common dining areas of facilities such as nursing homes, assisted living group homes, or residential care facilities at times other than during meals if the following conditions are met:

- Doors separate the common dining areas from food storage or food preparation areas
- Condiments, equipment, and utensils are stored in enclosed cabinets or removed from the dining areas when pets are present
- Dining areas, including tables and countertops are cleaned and sanitized before the next meal service.

END OF CHAPTER

Putting It Into Practice Questions & Answers

1. You are having multiple maintenance calls for a mixer. What is the first step in justifying a new mixer?

   A. *Review the equipment maintenance record to determine the cost of repairs over the past year. Use that information to conduct a cost analysis to compare the cost of replacement with the cost of repairs.*

2. Where would you expect to find an air gap in your kitchen?

   A. *Between the sprayer of the manual dishwashing sink and the edge of the sink (sprayers are often on a spring and when stretched from use, may hang below the edge of the sink causing a concern for back siphonage).*

3. One of your staff accidently spilled delimer on her arm. What is the first action you should take?

   A. *Locate the MSDS sheet for delimer. Read what the emergency procedures are in case of contact with skin. Follow the directions.*

4. In a day care facility, how would you handle refrigerated medicine brought in by parents for their children?

   A. *You should have a special container that is labeled and can be securely closed to store children's medicine. The medicine should be in a cooler on a shelf that is not within reach of the children.*

CHAPTER 20

Organize Work Flow and Use of Equipment

Overview and Objectives

Every employer has a responsibility to protect the safety and well-being of employees. Safety considerations when organizing work flow and the use of equipment is essential in the risk management of employees, and it has financial and regulatory ramifications. In this chapter, we examine the role of the Certified Dietary Manager in risk management in ensuring safety in the use of equipment and productivity through organized work flow.

After completing this chapter, you should be able to:

- ✓ Analyze tasks to determine overlapping effort or equipment use
- ✓ Plan proper placement and safety in use of equipment
- ✓ Simplify work procedures and steps
- ✓ Monitor work flow, identify and correct problems
- ✓ Assure adequate hand-washing sinks, lavatory facilities, and supplies

SECTION A Employee Safety

Risk Management

In a foodservice environment, risks confront both management and employees. Managing these risks can lead to lower employee injury rates and higher productivity. **Risks** are the possibility of injury. **Risk management** is the practice of managing the possibility of injury to employees or harm to the organization.

A foodservice department presents many risks. There are open flames, steam-releasing machines, sharp knives, hot liquids, wet or slippery floors, and heavy objects to move. Employees often move fairly quickly in efforts to meet deadlines. An accident can result in harm to an employee or client. It can damage morale and image. It can also generate lost work days, and other costs to a facility. The U.S. Bureau of Labor Statistics reports that industries with high rates of employee injuries are foodservice, hospitals, and nursing homes.

What causes accidents? Initially, there is the presence of a risk, or situation that is potentially dangerous. Examples of safety risks appear in Figure 20.1. As you

Glossary

Risks
The likelihood of a potentially dangerous situation

Risk Management
Managing the possibility of dangerous situations to employees or to the organization

Figure 20.1 Safety Risk Examples

- A pile of boxes obstructs a hallway where many employees need to walk or in aisle of store room or freezer.
- A ladder has a broken rung.
- A slicer has a frayed power cord.
- A puddle of water is accumulating on the floor.
- A pot has a loose handle.
- The hot water temperature is set too high.
- A loose tile sits awkwardly on the floor.
- A sharp knife is sitting in a sink full of soapy water.
- Knives in the kitchen have become dull, requiring an employee to use more pressure when using them.
- A cart used for transporting coffee has a loose wheel.
- The safety guard for a slicer or mixer is missing.
- An urn of hot coffee is balanced precariously on top of several trays on the counter.
- The safety valve on a steam-jacketed kettle is clogged.
- Broken mugs appear on the floor in the dishroom.
- Hallways or stairways are poorly lit.
- Heavy boxes are placed on higher shelving.

can see from these examples, a risk sets the stage for an accident to occur. For example, a sharp knife sitting in a sink full of soapy water is an invitation for an employee to reach his hand in and get cut. Water accumulating on the floor raises the likelihood that someone walking there will slip.

Risks are situations a Certified Dietary Manager can pinpoint and correct through routine inspection. The most important thing to do to manage risk is simply to notice them, so you can take action. A tool for accomplishing this is a safety inspection checklist. Figure 20.2 shows an example of a safety inspection checklist. Others are available in other foodservice management textbooks, food safety textbooks, and even from insurance companies and fire departments.

A self-audit such as this one helps you remember everything you need to keep in mind when you are examining your operation for risk. A structured inspection process is essential to help you monitor safety needs on a routine basis. A structured inspection process is one that has an established plan, time, forms and evaluation.

Who should perform a safety inspection? Ideally, a Certified Dietary Manager delegates responsibility to groups of employees, maintaining final responsibility and accountability. The task of conducting a safety audit may be rotated among small teams or work groups, for example. Involving all employees in safety audits builds awareness and commitment.

Frequency of a safety inspection may vary from one facility to the next, but should follow an established schedule. Some perform weekly inspections, and others do it bi-weekly. Regardless of the frequency, you need to build a state of daily watchfulness for risk among all employees. There may be an facility-wide safety team that visits each area of the workplace. This is valuable, as a new set of eyes studies the environment. If your facility is being inspected by a team, welcome the opportunity and learn all you can. Likewise, if you or someone in your department is invited to join a safety team, realize that this can be an excellent learning experience.

(Continued on page 387)

Figure 20.2 **Safety Inspection Self-Audit**

The following checklist covers both physical factors in the property and work practices of personnel. During your inspection, be as aware of unsafe acts as you are of unsafe conditions.

Area	Yes	No	Comments
Receiving Area:			
Are floors in safe condition? (Are they free from broken and defective floor tiles/boards? Are they covered with nonskid material?)			
Are employees instructed in correct handling methods for various containers that are received?			
Are garbage cans washed daily in hot water?			
Are garbage cans always covered?			
Are trash cans leak-proof and adequate in number and size?			
If garbage disposal area is adjacent to a part of the general receiving area, is there a program that keeps floors and/or dock areas clear of refuse?			
Is there a proper rack for holding garbage containers? Are garbage containers on dollies or other wheel units to eliminate lifting by employees?			
Are adequate tools available for opening crates, barrels, cartons, etc. (hammer, cutter, cardboard carton opener, and pliers)?			
Storage Area:			
Are shelves adequate to bear weight of items stored? Are employees instructed to store heavy items on lower shelves and lighter materials above?			
Is a safe ladder provided for reaching high storage?			
Are cartons or other flammable materials stored at least two feet from light bulbs?			
Are light bulbs provided with a screen guard?			
Is a fire extinguisher located at the door?			
Are employees carefully instructed in the use of detergents to prevent irritation or dermatitis, etc.?			
Do you have a program for disposition of broken glass or china?			
Where controls are in a passageway, are they recessed or guarded to prevent breakage or accidental starting?			
Are dish racks in safe condition (if wooden, free from broken slats and smoothly finished to eliminate splintering; if metal, free of sharp corners that could cause cuts)? Are these racks kept off the floor to prevent tripping?			
Serving Area:			
Are steam tables cleaned daily and maintained regularly? (Are gas or electric units checked regularly by a competent serviceperson?)			
Are safety valves on equipment operative?			
Are serving counters and tables free of broken parts and wooden or metal slivers and burrs?			

(Continued)

Figure 20.2 Safety Inspection Self-Audit *(Continued)*

Area	Yes	No	Comments
Serving Area: *(Continued)*			
Do you have regular inspections of:			
• Glassware?			
• China?			
• Silverware?			
• Plastic equipment?			
If anything breaks near the foodservice area, do you remove all food from service adjacent to breakage?			
Are tray rails adequate to prevent trays from slipping or falling off at the end or corners?			
Are floors and/or ramps in good condition (covered with nonskid material, free from broken tile and defective floor tiles/boards)?			
Are these areas mopped at least daily and waxed with nonskid wax when necessary?			
Is there effective traffic flow so that clients do not collide while carrying trays or obtaining foods?			
Dining Areas:			
Are floors free from broken tile and defective floor boards?			
Are they covered with nonskid wax?			
Are pictures securely fastened to walls?			
Are drapes, blinds, or curtains securely fastened?			
Are chairs free from splinters, metal burrs, broken or loose parts?			
Are floors "policed" for cleaning up spillage and other materials?			
Is special attention given to the floor adjacent to water, ice cream, or milk stations?			
Are vending machines properly grounded?			
If clients clear their own trays prior to returning to dishwashing area, are the floors kept clean of garbage, dropped silver, and/or broken glass and china?			
If trays with soiled dishes are placed on conveyor units, are the edges guarded to keep clients from catching fingers or clothing?			
If dishes are removed from dining areas on portable racks or bus trucks, are these units in safe operating condition (for example, are all castors working, all shelves firm)?			
Soiled Dish Processing Area:			
Are floors reasonably free of excessive water and spillage?			
Are floor tiles/boards properly maintained and in safe condition (free from broken slats and worn areas that cause tripping)?			
Are all electrical units properly grounded?			
Are switches located to permit rapid shutdown in the event of emergency?			
Can employees easily reach switches?			

(Continued)

Figure 20.2 Safety Inspection Self-Audit *(Continued)*

Area	Yes	No	Comments
Pots and Pans Area:			
Are duckboards or floor tiles/boards in safe condition (free from broken slats and worn areas which could cause tripping)?			
Are employees properly instructed in use of correct amounts of detergent and/or other cleaning agents?			
Are adequate rubber gloves provided?			
Is there an adequate drainboard or other drying area so that employees do not have to pile pots and pans on the floor before and after washing them?			
Do drain plugs permit draining without employee placing hands in hot water?			
Walk-in Refrigerators and Freezers:			
Are floors in the units in good condition and covered with slip-proof material? Are they mopped at least once a week (and whenever spills occur)?			
If floor tiles/boards are used, are they in safe condition (free of broken slats and worn boards which could cause tripping?)			
Are portable and stationary storage racks in safe condition (free from broken or bent shelves and set on solid legs)?			
Are blower fans properly guarded?			
Is there a by-pass device on the door to permit exit if an employee is locked in (or, is there an alarm bell)?			
Is adequate aisle space provided?			
Are employees properly instructed in placement of hands for movement of portable items to avoid hand injuries?			
Are heavy items stored on lower shelves and lighter items on higher shelves?			
Are shelves adequately spaced to prevent pinched hands?			
Is the refrigerant in the refrigerator nontoxic? (Check your refrigerator service manual.)			
Food Preparation Area:			
Is electrical equipment properly grounded?			
Is electrical equipment inspected regularly by an electrician?			
Are electrical switches located so that they can be reached easily in the event of an emergency?			
Are the switches located so that employees do not have to lean on or against metal equipment when reaching for them?			
Are the floors regularly and adequately maintained (mopped at least daily and waxed with nonskid wax when necessary; are defective floor tiles/boards replaced when necessary)?			
Are employees instructed to immediately pick up or clean up all dropped items?			
Are employees properly instructed in the operation of all machines?			
Are employees forbidden to use equipment unless specifically trained in its use?			
Are machines properly grounded?			

(Continued)

Figure 20.2 Safety Inspection Self-Audit *(Continued)*

Area	Yes	No	Comments
Lighting and Exits:			
Is lighting adequate in the:			
• Receiving area?			
• Storage area?			
• Pots and pans area?			
• Walk-in refrigerators and freezers?			
• Food preparation area?			
• Cooking area?			
• Serving area?			
• Dining areas			
• Soiled dish processing area?			
Do doors open into passageways where they could cause an accident? (List any such locations.)			
Are fire exits clearly marked and passages kept clear of equipment and materials? (List any violations.)			
Stairways and Ramps:			
Are they adequately lighted?			
Are the angles of ramps set to provide maximum safety?			
If stairs are metal, wood composition, or marble, have abrasive materials been used to provide protection against slips and falls?			
Are pieces broken out of the casing or front edge of the steps?			
Are clean and securely fastened handrails available?			
If stairs are wide, has a center rail been provided?			
Is Ventilation Adequate in the:			
• Receiving area?			
• Storage area?			
• Pots and pans area?			
• Walk-in refrigerators and freezers?			
• Food preparation area?			
• Cooking area?			
• Serving area?			
• Dining areas?			
• Soiled dish processing area?			
Other Safety Concerns:			
Do employees wear good shoes to protect their feet against injury from articles that are dropped or pushed against their feet?			
Is employee clothing free of parts that could get caught in mixers, cutters, grinders, or other equipment? Jewelry should be restricted to a single band.			
Are fire extinguishers guarded so they will not be knocked from the wall?			

(Continued)

Figure 20.2 **Safety Inspection Self-Audit** *(Continued)*

Area	Yes	No	Comments
Other Safety Concerns: *(Continued)*			
If doors are provided with a lock, is there an emergency bell or a by-pass device that will permit exit from the room should the door be accidentally locked while an employee is in the room?			
Is there a pusher or tamper provided for use with the grinders?			
Are mixers in safe operating condition?			
Do mixers and other dangerous pieces of equipment have protective guards (e.g. blade guard and are they used)?			
Are the mixer beaters properly maintained to avoid injury from broken metal parts and foreign particles in food?			

When a safety inspection has been completed, carefully review the results. Any risk identified should be corrected immediately. Some Certified Dietary Managers use a column on the inspection form itself to note corrections made, with a date and time.

Some of the ongoing risk prevention activities in a foodservice department involve equipment maintenance. When a steam release valve is clogged, for instance, or an electrical cord is frayed, the Certified Dietary Manager needs to identify this and take quick action to place any dangerous equipment or location "off limits" and arrange repairs. For detailed ideas about risks common in a foodservice operation and possible interventions, refer to Figure 20.3. Note that this is a great list of rules for any type of facility.

Employee Practices

Beyond risks, employee practices have a great influence on safety. Even in a safe environment, an employee can make an error that results in injury. In fact, a majority of foodservice accidents occur when an employee simply isn't paying attention or thinking about his or her action.

Here are some examples:

- ✓ A cook is feeling rushed to get the hot entree out to the dining room. She grabs a pan without using a pot holder.
- ✓ A cafeteria server uses a wet rag to wipe the counter, and then to handle a pan for the steam table.
- ✓ A stock employee opens a case of applesauce with a can opener.
- ✓ A pantry employee microwaves a covered tray of food, and then carelessly removes the cover with steam venting towards his hand.
- ✓ A cook decides to grab another box of cake mix from the top shelf of the storeroom. He stacks a couple of boxes and climbs up.
- ✓ A trayline employee had punched in late and begins running to the trayline.
- ✓ A supervisor rushes through the door to the cafeteria without checking to see if the doorway is clear.
- ✓ An employee in the dishroom tries to carry too many soiled dishes at a time.

Each of these—and many more—constitutes a situation in which human action is likely to cause an accident. An accident can affect the careless employee, co-workers, or clients, so each employee has a responsibility to everyone in the vicinity to work safely. Common accidents in foodservice operations include slips and falls, cuts, burns, and muscle strains. To manage the human factor, a Certified Dietary Manager can take the following actions:

Build awareness. While you as a Certified Dietary Manager are aware of the risk of accidents in your operation, not everyone walking through your doors will automatically have the same awareness. In orientation for new employees and in ongoing training sessions, explain to employees that the foodservice operation does indeed have hazards, and that each person plays a role in ensuring safety. Make sure that part-time employees also receive this training.

Define your expectations. Let every employee know that safety is your priority, and ask employees to make safety their priority, too. As possible, share your facility's safety statistics with your work team on an ongoing basis. If they are not optimal, ask the team for a commitment to improve them.

Build safety into procedures. As you train an employee to accomplish certain tasks and as you write procedures for aspects of the job, incorporate specific safety requirements. Explain what tools are required for safe work performance, such as a ladder for reaching high places, a dry pot holder for handling hot pots and pans, a blade guard for the slicer, and so forth. Then, include actions the employee must take during this procedure to provide protection. For example, a procedure for cleaning electrical equipment includes the basic step of unplugging the equipment first.

Make inspection everyone's job. Whether or not each employee is involved in formal safety inspections, tell employees what hazards to watch for. Ask them to identify and help correct (or report) safety risks.

Ask for caution. Remind employees to be alert, to focus on what they are doing, and to exercise care. Do not allow horseplay or other situations that could result in a loss of attention to safety. Ask employees not to distract each other when they are involved in dangerous tasks. You can also ask them to watch each other, and tell each other when they see a dangerous or careless action in progress.

Provide specific safety training. At least one inservice session per year should focus on employee safety. Even tenured employees should undergo periodic review sessions to keep safe practices paramount in their minds. The more specific you are in training, the more effective training will be. In other words, name situations that employees need to notice. Name practices in each work area that need to be avoided. Name actions an employee can take to ensure safety.

A foodservice employee notices that every time he comes near the food mixer, he gets an electrical shock. What is the first step you should take for his safety?

(Check your answer at the end of this chapter)

Figure 20.3 **Foodservice Employee Safety Rules—School Foodservice Department**

To Prevent Falls:

- Use a step ladder of safe construction.
- Keep floors dry and free from litter.
- Clean up spilled food, water or grease at once.
- Request for immediate repair any hazard such as a broken floor, fallen wires, etc.
- Keep traffic aisles and passages clear, including electrical cords.

To Prevent Burns:

- Turn handles of pans on range so that pans cannot be knocked off or caught in clothing and pulled off. Always use dry flame-proof pot holders to remove.
- To avoid scalds, tilt lids away and get help to remove.
- Prepare a place to put hot pots and pans before removing them from range or oven. Move hot food on a cart. Do not have pots and pans too full. (See "Safe Lifting Rules")
- Keep papers, plastic aprons and other flammable materials away from hot areas.
- Pull rack out part way or use puller to remove items from oven.
- Use pots and pans with sturdy handles.
- Pour hot fat into a metal container and allow it to cool before moving to store.
- Keep moisture at a minimum when putting food in fryer.
- Operate steam equipment according to instructions. Use caution in handling valves and pipes leading to equipment.

To Protect Against Cuts:

- Keep knives sharp and stored separately in a drawer.
- Use tools for purposes for which they were made. For example, do not use cleavers or knives to open cans or knife blades as a screw driver.
- Cut away from, never towards body.
- Be sure the can opener leaves no jagged edges on cans. Sweep up broken glass. To pick up very small pieces use wet toweling, then wrap all broken glass in paper. Dispose promptly.
- Use a NSF approved cutting board for cutting or chopping food. Keep tips of fingers back to prevent injury.
- Collect all sharp tools on a tray and wash each item separately from other utensils.
- Use plastic or paper for drinking glasses in the kitchen, never glass.

In Using Equipment:

- Always have hands dry, and stand on dry floor, when turning electrical equipment on or off.
- Have electrical cords or plugs in good working order.
- Follow manufacturer's instructions for safe operation of all equipment. Be sure that employees are trained in the use of each piece of equipment. Conduct demonstration on use of new equipment.
- Be careful in handling slicing, chopping, grinding and mixing equipment.
- Have all equipment that mixes, slices, chops or grinds equipped with safety guards.
- Keep hands and spoons away from moving parts, as in using mixer, grinder attachments and slicers.
- Turn off mixer and wait until all moving parts have stopped before adding ingredients, scraping down sides of bowls or removing foods.
- Turn off electrical switches and gas controls when equipment is not in use.
- Make sure that the pressure gauge is at zero before opening steamer.
- Prevent any water or steam from coming in contact with any electrical motor.
- Always unplug electrical equipment by grasping plug, not cord.
- Keep hands and arms away from ram shaft or garbage compactor (while in operation).
- Be sure that location of master cut off switch for kitchen equipment is known to employees.

(Continued)

Figure 20.3 Foodservice Employee Safety Rules—School Foodservice Department *(Continued)*

Vertical Cutter Mixers:

- Read operating instructions carefully and follow them "to the letter."
- Make sure bowl cover is closed and latched before turning on cutter motor.
- Allow knives to stop before opening bowl cover.
- Remove knives before emptying bowl.
- Turn off cutter and baffle motors before cleaning machine.

Clothing:

- Have dress pockets flat and high enough to avoid catching on door knobs or equipment.
- Avoid large, loose sleeves, neckties and strings or decorative clothing that may get caught in equipment.
- Wear protective, comfortable, low heel shoes, properly cleaned and in good repair.

Gas Leakage:

- Check pilot lights before turning on gas.
- Check for gas odor before lighting any range or oven.
- Be sure all needed burners are lit when lighting surface units or oven.

Lighting:

- Have all work areas, hallways, and stairwells well lighted. Request replacement of burned out bulbs.
- Have all light bulbs in the kitchen covered.

Fire Hazards:

- Keep fire extinguishers in convenient and visible locations.
- In case of fire, turn off ventilating system and close doors and windows to prevent drafts.
- Keep exhaust fans and hoods clean.
- Use proper cooking temperatures to avoid excessive heat.
- If grease should catch fire, cover immediately to smother.
- Pull the main switch if there is an electrical fire. Do not use water.
- Do not use excessive water around electrical outlets or equipment. Even damp cloths can be a hazard.
- Always use pilot lights for lighting burners.
- Never use ovens or food warmers as a way to dry dish towels.

Safe Lifting Rules:

- Size up the load; do not attempt to lift a load alone if you have any doubt of your ability to lift it.
- Always make sure your footing is secure.
- Place feet close to the base of the object to be lifted.
- Get a good grip on the load.
- Bend your knees; keep your back straight.
- Keep the load close to the body.
- Be sure you can see past the load.
- In team lifting, cooperate with your partner if carrying a long object; with a two-person carry, both should carry from the same side, be it left or right.
- When putting down a load, take care and reverse the lifting procedures.

(Continued)

Figure 20.3 **Foodservice Employee Safety Rules—School Foodservice Department** *(Continued)*

Other Accidents or Hazards:
• Keep all toxic or poisonous substances clearly marked. Never store toxins with food supplies, dishes or utensils.
• Keep drawers and doors closed.
• Do not carry heavy cans, boxes or other objects, but place on carts to transport.
• Place dishes, cans and containers firmly on shelves to prevent falling. Do not overcrowd or overload shelves.
• Discard broken or defective utensils.
• All unauthorized personnel should be excluded from the kitchen.
• Move cautiously rather than too hastily.
• Open crates, boxes and cases with caution.

Source: Pam Murphy, District Services Specialist, Leon County School Board, used with permission.

Involve Worker's Comp Insurance. They may offer to do an audit of your kitchen. Recommendations might include:

✓ Wear non-skid shoes, hand mitts

✓ Use fire resistant aprons when using the deep fryer

✓ Provide gloves and goggles in the chemical room

✓ Use an approved step ladder.

Offer ongoing reinforcement. As you walk through foodservice areas from day to day, observe what employees are doing. If you see an unsafe practice, tell the employee on the spot. If you see a safe practice, praise the employee. Safety, like sanitation, is a way of life. If the Certified Dietary Manager makes that an expectation, the employee will remember the importance of it.

Fire Safety

The potential for fire exists in all foodservice operations. Possible causes of fire include: unemptied grease traps, grease build-up on exhaust vents, equipment malfunction, faulty or frayed electrical cords, improper storage of flammable items, ignition of trash because of cigarettes being improperly discarded, or food left unattended during preparation. Employees must be familiar with possible sources and kinds of fire, the locations of fire suppression equipment, and the actions to take in the event of a fire. As with all safety issues, a self-audit is a strong preventative tool. A sample fire safety audit appears in Figure 20.4.

For responding to a fire, the first few minutes are the most important. A fire requires three conditions: fuel, oxygen, and a heat source. The goal in extinguishing a fire is to remove one or more of the required elements. Fires are classified according to the material combusting, as shown in Figure 20.5. Extinguishing Class B and Class C fires generally requires the removal of oxygen, while a Class A fire may require removing the heat or the fuel. Fire extinguishers have an identification system that indicates which type of fire they will extinguish.

The best all-purpose fire extinguisher for a foodservice operation is the multipurpose dry chemical type. Extinguishers should be inspected periodically to ensure that they are still properly charged.

You are observing a new employee as she disassembles and cleans the slicer. She puts on safety gloves, disassembles the slicer, takes the portable pieces to the dishwasher and runs them through. What safety step has she overlooked?

(Check your answer at the end of this chapter)

Figure 20.4 **Fire Safety Audit**

Description	Yes	No	Corrective Actions
Hoods and vents are clean and free of grease.			
Power cords are not frayed or damaged.			
Broiler, salamander, grill, fryer, and range top are clean and free of grease build-up.			
Smoking is limited to designated areas.			
Cigarette butts are being properly disposed of.			
Combustible materials, such as paper supplies, are properly stored—away from heat source.			
Staff are following safe work practices, e.g. hot pads are kept away from heat source.			
Preventative maintenance on electrical equipment is up-to-date.			
Fire extinguishers are charged and operable.			
Smoke detectors are functioning properly.			
Supplies are stored in a manner that will not interfere with the sprinkler system.			
Annual training is conducted and documented.			

Employees should receive regular training about fire safety. Training should include emergency response procedures. Topics to address include:

- ✓ Fire prevention plan and responsibilities
- ✓ Location, purpose, and use of devices in the department, such as heat detectors, smoke detectors, fire alarm box, fire extinguishers
- ✓ How to respond to a fire
- ✓ Sounding the alarm
- ✓ How to use a fire extinguisher
- ✓ How to protect yourself if your clothing catches fire
- ✓ Evacuation plan and exit routes
- ✓ Procedures for protecting/evacuating clients in case of an emergency

During training, employees should walk through the facility and locate signaling devices, and they should also walk the evacuation routes (not just view them on a map). In a controlled environment, it is also a good idea for employees to practice using a fire extinguisher. In some facilities, a fire safety officer or team will conduct fire safety training.

A common failing in fire response is waiting to see whether the fire will become "serious" before calling for help. In fact, some employees may hesitate, trying to extinguish a fire on their own first. It is always safer to call for help, even if it may not be needed. A Certified Dietary Manager should specifically direct employees to sound the alarm even if the fire seems small. There are several training aids that can help employees remember some basic response techniques, described in Figure 20.6.

Figure 20.5 **Fire Extinguishers**

Class	Type of Fire	Recommended Extinguisher	Comments
Class A	Normal combustible materials	Foam, soda acid, pump tank (plain water), gas cartridge, multipurpose dry chemical	
Class B	Grease and oil	Foam, carbon dioxide, multipurpose dry chemical, ordinary dry chemical	Never use plain water or a water extinguisher. This spreads the fire.
Class C	Electrical	Carbon dioxide, multipurpose dry chemical, ordinary dry chemical	Never use plain water or a water extinguisher. This can cause electrical shock.

Figure 20.6 **Training Aids for Fire Response**

RACE	PASS	STOP, DROP AND ROLL
RACE—Steps for responding to a fire: 1. **Remove** everyone from danger 2. Turn on the **Alarm** 3. **Confine** the fire 4. **Extinguish** the fire if you can do so safely	**PASS**—Steps for using a fire extinguisher: 1. **Pull** the pin 2. **Aim** at the base of the fire 3. **Squeeze** the trigger and keep the extinguisher in an upright position 4. **Sweep** from side to side	**Stop, Drop, and Roll** if your clothing catches on fire.

Heat Exhaustion

Another safety concern in a foodservice environment is heat stress. Any time employees find themselves in a hot, humid environment, everyone should be alert to symptoms of heat stress. Timely intervention can prevent serious problems. When a person becomes overheated, symptoms such as profuse sweating, muscle cramps, and skin rash may occur. These are early signs of heat exhaustion, a medical condition in which the body cannot cool itself quickly enough.

Left untreated, the condition progresses to symptoms of pale, clammy skin; weak, rapid pulse; low blood pressure; headache; intense thirst; weakness; dizziness; and nausea and vomiting. Intervention is important to prevent heat exhaustion from leading to heat stroke. In heat stroke, a person may develop a high fever (>102°F), experience seizures, or become unconscious. This is a medical emergency. Interventions are described in Figure 20.7. A Certified Dietary Manager needs to be aware of heat-related risks and prevent problems by using air conditioning and fans, encouraging employees to wear lightweight, loose-fitting clothing that conforms with the dress code, encouraging employees to take breaks if they are working in heat, and most importantly—encouraging employees to drink plenty of fluids when working in heat, even if they don't feel particularly thirsty. The FDA Food Code requires that employee beverages must be in a closed container.

Figure 20.7 Interventions for Heat Exhaustion

First Aid:	Do Not:	Call immediately for emergency medical assistance (911) if:
• Have the person lie down in a cool place. Elevate the person's feet about 12 inches. • Apply cool, wet cloths (or cool water directly) to the person's skin and use a fan to lower body temperature. Place cold compresses on the person's neck, groin, and armpits. • If alert, give the person beverages to sip (such as Gatorade), or make a salted drink by adding a teaspoon of salt per quart of water. Give a half cup every 15 minutes. Cool water will do if salt beverages are not available. • For muscle cramps, give beverages as above and massage affected muscles gently, but firmly, until they relax.	• **Do not** underestimate the seriousness of heat illness. • **Do not** give the person medications that are used to treat fever (such as aspirin or acetaminophen). They will not help, and they may be harmful. • **Do not** give the person salt tablets. • **Do not** give the person liquids that contain caffeine. • **Do not** use alcohol rubs on the person's skin. • **Do not** give the person anything by mouth (not even salted drinks) if the person is vomiting or unconscious	• The person loses consciousness or experiences a change in alertness (e.g., confusion or seizures). • The person has a fever over 102°F. • Other symptoms of heat stroke are present (like rapid pulse or rapid breathing). • The person's condition does not improve, or worsens despite treatment.

Source: US National Library of Medicine

Government Regulations—OSHA

The Occupational Safety and Health Act of 1970 was passed to "assure safe and healthful working conditions" for today's employees. It mandates that employers provide a safe work environment for employees. In 1971, the Occupational Safety & Health Administration (OSHA) was established to enforce this regulation. In some cases, OSHA enforcement is handled by state OSHA agencies.

OSHA is involved in all aspects of employee safety on the job. It provides standards to ensure a safe work environment. OSHA requires the maintenance of safety records, the filing of safety reports, and strict adherence to good safety practices. Employers are required to maintain records of employee accidents and to report serious accidents and fatalities to OSHA.

To monitor compliance, OSHA periodically inspects businesses to determine the level of compliance. If a business is found to be in violation of a health and safety regulation, OSHA may issue a citation, fine the employer, or in some cases, order the employer to close the business until compliance is attained.

OSHA also provides training information for employers and employees, compliance tools, and reference on its Web site at www.osha.gov. Specific OSHA standards relate to safe equipment, electrical safety, machine usage, fire safety, accident prevention, and sound ergonomic practices. Guidelines provided in this chapter reflect many of the OSHA standards.

To comply with OSHA standards, a Certified Dietary Manager needs to review standards, monitor and correct hazards, report and document injuries, and provide ongoing training for employees. Employers are required to display a poster prepared by the Department of Labor summarizing the major provisions of the Occupational Safety and Health Act and telling employees how to file a complaint. The poster must be posted in a conspicuous place where employees and applicants for employment can see it.

Accident Investigation and Reporting

If an accident or injury occurs in your operation, it is your responsibility to report the situation—and it is the law. Your own facility most likely has an accident or incident reporting form that you must complete. See Figure 20.8 for a sample reporting form provided by OSHA. OSHA advises completing a reporting form within seven days of an incident, and keeping it on file for five years after the incident. The form is a tool to help you gather all relevant information to support systematic information review. You and other reviewers need to look for causes and identify ways to prevent this type of accident from recurring. In addition, the employer (your facility) must maintain recordkeeping for OSHA. It is important to realize that the form contains confidential employee information, so you must handle the form in a confidential manner, sharing it only with those in your facility who need to review it in order to help manage safety concerns.

OSHA defines a **work-related injury** or illness as one that results in days away from work, restricted work activity or job transfer, medical treatment (beyond first aid)—or in the most extreme case—loss of consciousness or death. In addition, a needlestick, hearing loss, or tuberculosis infection may require reporting under certain circumstances.

As a critical personnel policy, you need to ask employees to report any accident or injury to a supervisor. If an accident occurs, your steps are to first take care of the employee, obtaining first aid or medical help as needed. Second, complete the accident reporting form. During this process, you will be asking questions about how the accident occurred. Then, consider how the accident could have been prevented. If the employee is in condition to discuss this, ask the employee to make suggestions. Finally, follow your internal procedures for handling the emergency and completing the form.

As accidents are tabulated and analyzed in your facility (such as by a safety committee or safety officer), you will want to review accident statistics and trends. You can target areas that need improvement, and use the steps outlined above to improve your safety record. Accident review should become an integral part of quality assurance activities.

Ergonomics in Foodservice

Another area of increasing concern today is the ergonomics of foodservice work. **Ergonomics** is the science of fitting the work environment to the employee. A key objective of ergonomic analysis and intervention is to prevent injury related to repetitive motions and related work factors.

Repetitive motion injuries are common in many industries, including foodservice. Unlike an accident or sudden event, a repetitive motion injury occurs gradually, over time. It comes from the motions an employee makes over and over.

Work-Related Injury
Injury that occurs at work that results in: days away from work, restricted work activity, medical treatment, loss of consciousness, or death

Ergonomics
The science of fitting the work environment to the employee

Your new employee just smashed her finger, resulting in a critical injury. What is the first action you should take?

(Check your answer at the end of this chapter)

Figure 20.8 Sample Employee Injury and Illness Reporting Form—OSHA

OSHA's Form 301

Injury and Illness Incident Report

Attention: This form contains information relating to employee health and must be used in a manner that protects the confidentiality of employees to the extent possible while the information is being used for occupational safety and health purposes.

U.S. Department of Labor
Occupational Safety and Health Administration

Form approved OMB no. 1218-0176

This *Injury and Illness Incident Report* is one of the first forms you must fill out when a recordable work-related injury or illness has occurred. Together with the *Log of Work-Related Injuries and Illnesses* and the accompanying *Summary*, these forms help the employer and OSHA develop a picture of the extent and severity of work-related incidents.

Within 7 calendar days after you receive information that a recordable work-related injury or illness has occurred, you must fill out this form or an equivalent. Some state workers' compensation, insurance, or other reports may be acceptable substitutes. To be considered an equivalent form, any substitute must contain all the information asked for on this form.

According to Public Law 91-596 and 29 CFR 1904, OSHA's recordkeeping rule, you must keep this form on file for 5 years following the year to which it pertains.

If you need additional copies of this form, you may photocopy and use as many as you need.

Completed by ______________________

Title ______________________

Phone (_____)______-________ Date ____/____/____

Information about the employee

1) Full name ______________________

2) Street ______________________

City ______________ State ______ ZIP ______

3) Date of birth ____/____/____

4) Date hired ____/____/____

5) ☐ Male
☐ Female

Information about the physician or other health care professional

6) Name of physician or other health care professional ______________________

7) If treatment was given away from the worksite, where was it given?

Facility ______________________

Street ______________________

City ______________ State ______ ZIP ______

8) Was employee treated in an emergency room?
☐ Yes
☐ No

9) Was employee hospitalized overnight as an in-patient?
☐ Yes
☐ No

Information about the case

10) Case number from the *Log* ____________ *(Transfer the case number from the Log after you record the case.)*

11) Date of injury or illness ____/____/____

12) Time employee began work ____________ AM / PM

13) Time of event ____________ AM / PM ☐ Check if time cannot be determined

14) ***What was the employee doing just before the incident occurred?*** Describe the activity, as well as the tools, equipment, or material the employee was using. Be specific. *Examples:* "climbing a ladder while carrying roofing materials"; "spraying chlorine from hand sprayer"; "daily computer key-entry."

15) ***What happened?*** Tell us how the injury occurred. *Examples:* "When ladder slipped on wet floor, worker fell 20 feet"; "Worker was sprayed with chlorine when gasket broke during replacement"; "Worker developed soreness in wrist over time."

16) ***What was the injury or illness?*** Tell us the part of the body that was affected and how it was affected; be more specific than "hurt," "pain," or sore." *Examples:* "strained back"; "chemical burn, hand"; "carpal tunnel syndrome."

17) ***What object or substance directly harmed the employee?*** *Examples:* "concrete floor"; "chlorine"; "radial arm saw." *If this question does not apply to the incident, leave it blank.*

18) ***If the employee died, when did death occur?*** Date of death ____/____/____

Public reporting burden for this collection of information is estimated to average 22 minutes per response, including time for reviewing instructions, searching existing data sources, gathering and maintaining the data needed, and completing and reviewing the collection of information. Persons are not required to respond to the collection of information unless it displays a current valid OMB control number. If you have any comments about this estimate or any other aspects of this data collection, including suggestions for reducing this burden, contact: US Department of Labor, OSHA Office of Statistical Analysis, Room N-3644, 200 Constitution Avenue, NW, Washington, DC 20210. Do not send the completed forms to this office.

Examples of repetitive motion include:

✓ Using a scoop over and over to portion applesauce into bowls

✓ Bending down to lift boxes and placing them on a shelf, over and over again

✓ Reaching for a plate cover and turning to place it on a tray moving along the trayline, over and over

✓ Racking plates for the dishmachine again and again.

Examples of injuries that can result from repetitive motions include:

✓ Carpal tunnel syndrome. This is an inflammation of tendons in the wrist, causing numbness or tingling.

✓ Tendonitis. This is inflammation of a tendon anywhere in the body. A tendon is connective tissue that attaches muscles to bones.

More broadly, experts are also looking at other factors that cause injury to muscles, nerves, tendons, ligaments, and joints. In addition to repetitive motion, factors such as awkward posture, force, and vibration can bring on injury. A broader term for injury related to work environment and tasks is musculoskeletal disorders (MSDs). These are disorders affecting any part of the systems of skeleton, muscles, and tendons.

Today, safety experts in all industries are focusing a great deal on how the work environment can be designed to help prevent these injuries. To help prevent MSDs, you can take several steps. First, ask employees to report and investigate symptoms that may indicate development of an MSD. These include:

✓ Painful joints

✓ Pain in wrists, shoulders, forearms, knees

✓ Pain, tingling or numbness in hands or feet

✓ Fingers or toes turning white

✓ Shooting or stabbing pains in arms or legs

✓ Back or neck pain

✓ Swelling or inflammation

✓ Stiffness

✓ Burning sensation.

In addition, review any information that becomes available in your workplace that can help you pinpoint MSDs that are occurring. Look carefully at the workplace, at posture of employees, and at movements. As you see opportunities, improve the work environment to minimize injury. Train employees how to use good body mechanics. Figure 20.9 lists ergonomic hazards in foodservice, along with solutions. Figure 20.10 lists examples of training points for preventing MSDs, and Figure 20.11 illustrates several ergonomically sound techniques for foodservice employees.

As many facilities face budget constraints, Certified Dietary Managers increasingly face the requirement to accomplish more, using fewer resources. One of the greatest resources to a foodservice operation is people—the employees. It is common for a foodservice operation to experience budget cuts and reductions in staffing. For this reason, managing productivity is of utmost importance.

Figure 20.9 Ergonomic Hazards and Solutions

Dietary employees must perform many lifting, reaching, and repetitive tasks as part of their job duties. Employee activities in this area, if occurring with sufficient duration, magnitude, and/or frequency, may create a musculoskeletal disorder (MSD).
For example:

Potential Hazard: Reaching/Lifting

Frequent elevated extended reaches for supplies or heavy containers can cause back and shoulder injury resulting in muscle strain, bursitis, tendonitis, and rotator cuff injuries. Example: A kitchen worker uses an extended high reach to get her hand into a box.

Possible Solutions

Assess worksites for ergonomic stressors and identify and address ways to decrease them such as:

- Provide height adjustable workspaces appropriate for the task being performed, so that workers can keep elbows close to the body. For example, lower countertops, or use height adjustable countertops or stands, or provide work stands for employees.
- Redesign or reposition tasks to allow elbows to remain close to the body, (e.g., turn boxes over on side to allow for easier access).
- Avoid awkward postures (e.g., reposition work in front of worker so that he does not have to reach above or behind to get supplies).
- Use mechanical aids to reduce the need to lift. Use a spring device to automatically lift a load (e.g., use automatic plate and cup riser dispensers).
- Lighten a load that needs to be lifted or get help when lifting.
- Train workers to use proper lifting techniques.

Potential Hazard: Repetitive Motions

Rapid hand and wrist movements from frequent cutting, chopping, or scooping may lead to hand disorders such as tendonitis or carpal tunnel syndrome. Example: A kitchen worker scoops ingredients with a flexed wrist.

Possible Solutions

Assess worksites for ergonomic stressors and identify and address ways to decrease them such as:

- Rotate workers through repetitive tasks.
- Use mechanical aids for chopping, dicing or mixing foods (e.g., food processors, mixers).
- Select and use properly designed tools. For example, kitchen scoops or kitchen knives that allow the wrist to remain straight.
- Maintain a neutral (handshake) wrist position.
- Restructure jobs to reduce repeated motions, forceful hand exertions, and prolonged bending.

Source: http://www.osha.gov/SLTC/etools/hospital/dietary/dietary.html

Figure 20.10 **Musculoskeletal Disorders (MSDs): Training Points**

- Use safe lifting techniques.
- Lighten the load; do not try to lift too much at once.
- Provide mechanical aids for lifting as warranted.
- Avoid reaching or working above shoulder height.
- Seek to avoid motions that require bending the wrists. Instead, try to keep wrists comfortably straight as much as possible.
- Teach safe postures: As often as possible, elbows should be at 90° angles; shoulders should be relaxed and low; and arms should be close to the body.
- Be sure standing workers are working at comfortable counter heights that do not require them to bend excessively.
- Avoid repeated twisting, and arrange the work area to support this.
- For workers involved in prolonged repetitive movements, provide frequent breaks from the task.
- Rotate workers through jobs, so that any one worker does not have as much repetition of movements.
- As possible, minimize the amount of force or pressure a worker has to use to accomplish a task.
- For repeated utensil use, look for utensils with ergonomically designed grips. These are thicker than ordinary handles, and may minimize strain.
- Ask a qualified expert, such as an occupational health nurse, to train employees to stretch safely to avoid injury.
- Talk with workers and ask them what steps they believe could make their jobs more comfortable.

Figure 20.11 **Ergonomically Sound Techniques**

Lifting

1. Get close to the load. Bend at the hips and knees. Firmly grasp the load.
2. Keep head and shoulders erect. Lift, using legs for power.
3. Maintain a wide base.
4. To transfer the load, turn with your feet. Do not twist at the waist.
5. Lower the load by bending at the hips and knees.

Straight Wrists

Avoid the situations illustrated below.
Instead, keep wrists as straight as possible.

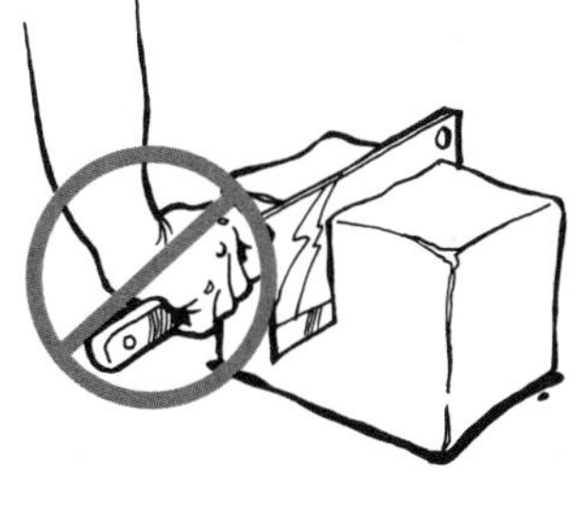

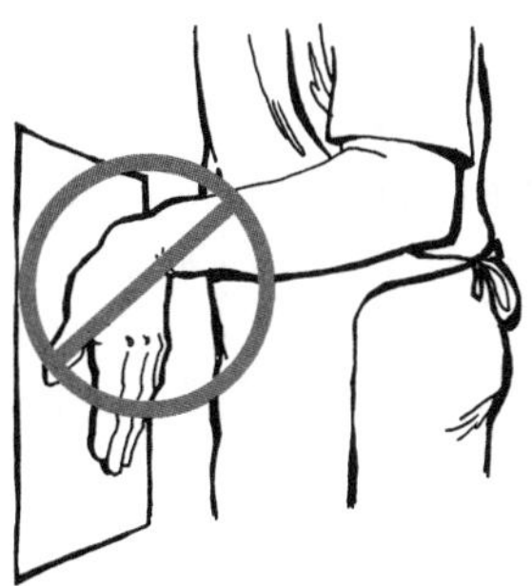

Holding a Can

Avoid picking up a large can with one hand.

Instead, pick up a large can with two hands on the sides.

Source: The Grossbauer Group. Used with permission.

SECTION B Employee Productivity

Employee productivity is the rate at which employees accomplish their work. Productivity can usually be calculated by some measure of the work performed. There are several formulas used to measure productivity. Here are the most common:

A. Meals per labor hour = $\frac{\text{total meals served per day}}{\text{total labor hours per day}}$

Example: Your staff prepared 300 meals yesterday. The total labor hours, including the Certified Dietary Manager hours was 40 hours. That would make the meals per labor hour 7.5.

B. Minutes per meal = $\frac{\text{total minutes per day}}{\text{total meals served per day}}$

Example: Using the example above, 40 hours is equivalent to 2400 minutes. Those minutes divided by total meals (300) is 8 minutes per meal.

C. Labor hours per meal = $\frac{\text{total labor hours}}{\text{total meals served}}$

Example: Using the example above, the total hours (40) divided by the total meals (300) is .1333 labor hours per meal.

Productivity in the form of meals or minutes per labor hour is considered a quantitative measure. **Quantitative** means the measure focuses on the quantity produced and is usually something that can be counted. The measures mentioned above apply more to long-term care where nonpatient meals are less common. In a hospital you may have a cafeteria and want to measure nonpatient meals. Those quantitative measures might be total nonpatient meals per labor hours, number of nonpatient transactions per cashier, or number of transactions per FTE.

Benchmarking. It is important to adopt a standard measure of productivity and record it over time to see trends. One way to do that is by benchmarking or comparing, on some standard scale, the operation of key departments. Having a record of productivity also helps you to benchmark with other like facilities. Your facility may already have productivity standards such as patient days, nonpatient meals, what staff hours go into labor hours, etc. What is most important is that you determine what factors go into measuring your department's productivity and then you measure it properly. The *Management in the News* at the end of this chapter provides the Association of Nutrition & Foodservice Professionals/Dietary Managers Professional Practice Standards for Measuring Meal Production. This Practice Standard shows some sample benchmark numbers.

Productivity is affected by the structure of the job, the process or procedure defined, and the tools provided. To meet operating requirements, a Certified

What are your meals per labor hour if you have the following numbers?

Census for this past week was 86 (assume you are serving three meals each day)

You have three full-time staff and two part-time staff (20 hrs/ week), including yourself.

(Check your answer at the end of this chapter)

Dietary Manager may continually examine ways to improve productivity.

Methods to help pinpoint opportunities for increasing productivity include the following:

- ✓ Increasing the number of meals served without greatly increasing labor hours, such as offering meal service to community senior meal sites.
- ✓ Increasing the number of liberalized diets, therefore reducing the number/kind of modified diets
- ✓ Using information technology (computerized client records) to reduce the number of late trays, meal scheduling issues
- ✓ Using more self-service or vending
- ✓ Sharing services with other departments such as clerical, cross-training for staff, purchasing

For example, with the task of performing nutritional assessments, a Certified Dietary Manager may determine that nutritional assessments are frequently delayed because medical records are not available at the time the technician tries to review them for pertinent data. One way of solving this might include computerized medical records. Another way of solving it might be to obtain more information through a computerized system that automatically deposits information, so that the diet technician does not have to go to medical records to retrieve the information. Once your facility has agreed upon productivity standards and are measuring them regularly, you will discover through analysis of the data that you may need to increase productivity. One way to do that is through work simplification techniques.

Work Simplification

An examination of productivity leads to a closely related idea—that of **work simplification**. Work simplification means simplifying a task so that it is performed as efficiently as possible. A Certified Dietary Manager who achieves work simplification may enjoy:

- ✓ A higher rate of productivity
- ✓ Shortened time for completing the job
- ✓ Better use of labor resources
- ✓ A reduction in operating costs.

In some situations, work simplification ties in with ergonomic principles, too. It is not uncommon for an ergonomically sound practice and a work simplification technique to be identical. Each has a different purpose, but in reality, they may overlap. Sometimes, work simplification enhances employee satisfaction as well. An employee may feel more comfortable completing a job in an efficient manner, and may enjoy the satisfaction of heightened accomplishment.

Part of work simplification means assuring that there are adequate hand-washing sinks. If your staff have to walk across a kitchen each time to wash their hands, it will raise one of two issues: they won't wash their hands as often, putting your client's safety at risk; or they won't be as productive and may be more

Glossary

Quantitative
A measure of productivity that measures quantity such as labor hours, time, number of transactions, staff turnover, and overtime usage

Benchmarking
Comparing, on some standard scale, the operation of key departments

Work Simplification
Simplifying a task so that it is performed as efficiently as possible

tired due to the excess walking. Your responsibility for work simplification also extends to having a nearby lavatory facility and adequate supplies close to each work area. To further emphasize the importance of conveniently located facilities, the FDA Food Code requires conveniently located handwashing sinks and toilet rooms.

Work simplification does not mean pressuring employees to just work faster. Instead, it means structuring the job so that it is as simple as possible. The following techniques are helpful in simplifying work.

- ✓ Break work into segments. Make a simple chart of the flow of movements and actions. Examine each piece of the job by itself.
- ✓ Perform a time and motion study. Using this flow chart, time each component of the task, and note what motions are required.
- ✓ Strive for economy of motion. Studying time and motion information, look at each movement an employee makes in performing a task, and consider whether there is a way to do it that requires less time and less motion.
- ✓ Examine the work station. Assure that all needed items in the work area are arranged in such a way that minimal movement is required.
- ✓ Streamline. Determine whether any tasks are repetitive or unnecessary. If possible, eliminate them.
- ✓ Check the sequence of tasks. Ask whether the tasks are happening in the right order. If necessary, rearrange the sequence to simplify the job.
- ✓ Group like tasks. If similar tasks repeat throughout the work flow, consider whether they can be grouped.
- ✓ Check for idle time. Some processes require idle time, or waiting. As you notice this, ask whether the idle time can be reduced, or whether the idle time can be used to accomplish something else.

Figure 20.12 lists examples of ideas that can simplify common foodservice jobs.

Putting It Into Practice: 5

In this scenario, what would you suggest to simplify the work of your employee?

You are working with a staff member to perform a time and motion study in the food prep area. You observe the staff member is very efficient at chopping raw vegetables for salads but has to leave her station once to locate a knife and a second time for a bowl for the vegetables.

(Check your answer at the end of this chapter)

Figure 20.12 Work Simplification Examples

Recipe Preparation
Group similar tasks so that the cook retrieves all needed items from storage in a single trip.

Breading Foods
Arrange containers in the order in which they are used to eliminate unnecessary back-and-forth movements. The first item in the line is a package of chicken to be breaded. The second container holds flour for dipping. The third container holds an egg wash. The fourth container holds crumbs for breading. The final item is a baking pan on which the chicken is placed.

Clean Dish Handling
Remove clean, dry flatware from the dishmachine and place it directly into the containers needed for cafeteria service setup.

Bringing Tray Tickets to Trayline
Ask staff who are preparing tickets to place them in a single stack. Designate one employee responsible to walk the entire stack to the trayline just before service.

These are just examples to illustrate the basic ideas of work simplification. As you examine specific jobs in your own facility, you will identify many more ideas.

Management in the News

Measuring Meal Production & Calculating Meal Equivalents

by Susan Davis Allen, MS, RD, CHE

Professional Standards of Practice serve as the basis for quality dietetic practice for dietary managers. The Standards published here provide guidelines for certified dietary managers to use when measuring meal production and calculating meal equivalents.

During these economic times, are you being challenged to reduce your staff to combat increasing healthcare costs? Are you prepared to provide staff level information to your supervisor to justify your employee's efficiency? This information should be at your fingertips at all times to demonstrate your lean focus. As you assess the efficiency of your department, ask and answer these questions: 1) What food cost data will be used to determine actual patient/client meals served: patient/client trays, Meals on Wheels, etc. 2) What food cost data will be used to determine a meal equivalent for non-patient/client meals: cafeteria, floor stock, catering from outside groups, staff, supplements? 3) Which labor hours will be used in the calculation of meal productivity: all staff involved in producing meals, management staff, clinical dietetics staff, support staff?

Background Information

Several calculations are used in the industry to measure meal productivity:

1. **Meals per labor hour**—This is calculated by dividing the total meals served by the total number of labor hours:

$$\frac{\text{Total meals served}}{\text{Total number of labor hours}}$$

2. **Minutes per meal**—This is calculated by dividing the total labor hours X 60 minutes by the total number of meals:

$$\frac{\text{Total labor hours X 60 minutes}}{\text{Total meals served}}$$

3. **Labor hours per meal**—This is calculated by dividing the total labor hours per meal by the total meals served:

$$\frac{\text{Total labor hours}}{\text{Total meals served}}$$

Once you have determined your method of measuring productivity,you'll want to compare it to an industry standard. Dietary Managers Association surveyed its membership in late 2009 to determine which of the above calculations were used in their facilities and what standard they used. The results are in the chart below.

Example for XYZ Long-Term Care Facility

First, answer the questions asked in the beginning paragraph above:

A. What food cost data will be used to determine actual patient/client meals served: patient/client trays, Meals on Wheels, etc.? *Patient/client trays, Meals on Wheels; document an actual count of these meals monthly.*

- *Actual meals for XYZ facility for October: 9,300 meals*

(Continued...)

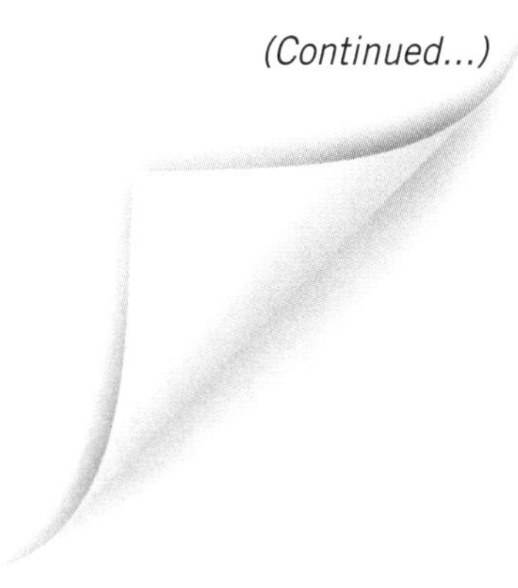

Measuring Meal Production & Calculating Meal Equivalents *(Continued)*

B. What food cost data will be used to determine a meal equivalent for non-patient/client meals: cafeteria, floor stock, catering from outside groups, staff, supplements? *Cafeteria, floor stock, catering from outside groups, staff meals, tube feedings; use a market basket price cost for a typical cafeteria meal. Cost out floor stock, tube feedings, catering, and cafeteria costs and divide by the market basket price to determine meal equivalents. Add this to the count of actual meals served from A above.*

- *Meal equivalents for XYZ facility for October: 4,500 meals*
- *9,300 meals + 4,500 meals = 13,800 total meals/meal equivalents served in October*

C. Which labor hours will be used in the calculation of meal productivity: all staff involved in producing meals, management staff, clinical dietetics staff, and support staff? *All staff involved in producing meals, certified dietary manager, consulting dietitian; total all of the hours for the production staff, CDM, and consulting dietitian.*

- *Total hours = 1,975*

Insert these numbers into the formulas (1-3 above) to determine:

1. Meals per labor hour: $\frac{13,800}{1,975}$ = 7 meals per labor hour
2. Minutes per meal: $\frac{1,975 \times 60 \text{ minutes}}{13,800}$ = 7 meals per meal
3. Labor hours per meal: $\frac{1,975}{13,800}$ = .14 labor hours per meal

Work with your facility to apply the Professional Practice Standard that follows.

Standard

The certified dietary manager (CDM) assures that productivity for patient/client services is measured and compared to a standard productivity equivalent.

1.1 CDM will work with management staff and fiscal staff to select a method for measuring meal production (see examples within this article).

1.2 CDM will work with management staff and fiscal staff to determine which staff will be included in total hours for selected productivity standard. (Examples: all food production staff, support staff, food management staff, clinical management staff)

1.3 CDM will work with management staff and fiscal staff to determine what will be used to calculate meal equivalents. (Examples: using a market basket* for café/catering/guest meals, staff meals; using a standard for nourishments and/or tube feedings, such as three nourishments are equivalent to one meal.)

1.4 Actual meals are counted using a standardized method (see sample form provided).

- Count every tray delivered for patients/clients.
- Count every meal delivered for Meals on Wheels.
- Count every meal delivered for medical doctors.

1.5 Total actual meals/trays served are recorded on a weekly productivity form by category (see sample form provided).

1.6 Meal equivalents (as determined in 1.4 above) are counted.

1.7 Total meal equivalents are recorded on a weekly productivity form (see sample form provided).

1.8 Labor hours are tracked for foodservice personnel (as determined in 1.2 above) and recorded on the productivity form.

1.9 Meals per labor hour, minutes per meal, or labor hours per meal are determined for patient/client and non-patient/client services.

(Continued...)

* *Market basket (in 1.3 above) is the term for a typical meal cost, such as 4 oz. chicken breast, starch, vegetable, fruit, beverage, dessert*

Measuring Meal Production & Calculating Meal Equivalents *(Continued)*

Assessment

1.1 CDM prepares a written summary of meal production and meal equivalents and compares them to facility standard (see worksheet provided).

1.2 CDM follows up on decreases in productivity by checking variances in the patient/client meals, non-patient/client meals, meal equivalents.

1.3 CDM designates an employee trained in these procedures to act in their absence.

1.4 CDM measures meal production to assist in calculating FTE (full-time equivalent) needs.

Summing it Up

These guidelines offer help for CDM, CFPPs responsible for measuring meal production and calculating meal equivalents. Refer to them as needed.

DMA survey results as compared to industry averages (from Sneed and Dresse, 1989)

Low	LTC/CCRC*	Hospital	School Foodservice	Corrections	Sneed and Dresse, 1989
Meals Per Labor Hour	6-12	6-12	12-18	6	3.5-5.5
Minutes Per Meal	18	18	22	22	NA
Labor Hours Per Meal	0.3	0.19-0.3			0.19-0.29

[1]Results form those facilities that used a standard; the majority of the LTC/CCRC respondents did not use any standard.

Measuring Meal Productivity Sample Form

	January				February				March			
Variables	**Wk 1**	**Wk 2**	**Wk 3**	**Wk 4**	**Wk 1**	**Wk 2**	**Wk 3**	**Wk 4**	**Wk 1**	**Wk 2**	**Wk 3**	**Wk 4**
Total Actual Trays/Patient/ Client Meals												
Total Non-Patient/Client Meal Equivalents **TOTAL MEALS** Total Hours Worked for Selected Staff												
Meals Per Labor Hour **OR**												
Labor Hours Per Meal												
Facility Standard												

REFERENCES

1. R. Puckett, Food Service Manual for Health Care Institutions, Josey-Bass, 2004, pg. 160.
2. Dietary Managers Association Education Survey Results, 2009.

Susan Davis Allen, MS, RD, CHE is Director of Institutional Advancement at Southwest Wisconsin Technical College in Fennimore, WI. She serves as an advisor to the Certifying Board for Dietary Managers and has authored many publications for ANFP and other professional groups.

END OF CHAPTER

Putting It Into Practice Questions & Answers

1. A foodservice employee notices that every time he comes near the food mixer, he gets an electrical shock. What is the first step you should take for his safety?

   A. *Immediately unplug the mixer and remove it from service until your maintenance staff or contract company can repair or replace it.*

2. You are observing a new employee as she disassembles and cleans the slicer. She puts on safety gloves, disassembles the slicer, takes the portable pieces to the dishwasher and runs them through. What safety step has she overlooked?

   A. *She should unplug the slicer before she disassembles it.*

3. Your new employee just smashed her finger, resulting in a critical injury. What is the first action you should take?

   A. *The first step is to address the need of your staff member by helping her get medical aid. The second step would be to investigate the cause of the accident.*

4. What are your meals per labor hour if you have the following numbers?
   - Census for this past week was 86 (assume you are serving three meals each day)
   - You have three full-time staff and two part-time staff (20 hrs/week), including yourself.

   A. 1. *Determine the meals served for the week: 86 x 3 x 7 = 1806 meals served*
   2. *Determine the number of labor hours for the week: (3 x 40) + (2 x 20) = 160*
   3. *Meals per labor hour means dividing the number of meals served by the labor hours worked: 1806 ÷ 160 = 11.285 meals per labor hour.*

5. In this scenario, what would you suggest to simplify the work of your employee?

   You are working with a staff member to perform a time and motion study in the food prep area. You observe the staff member is very efficient at chopping raw vegetables for salads but has to leave her station once to locate a knife and a second time for a bowl for the vegetables.

   A. *There are several answers to making this task more efficient. It is most important to discuss the scenario with the staff member to see if she has a suggestion, first. Two possible solutions are: 1) to work with your staff to make sure that they have all of the equipment needed for the job before they begin the task; 2) place the knives and bowls needed for chopping vegetables close to the prep table.*

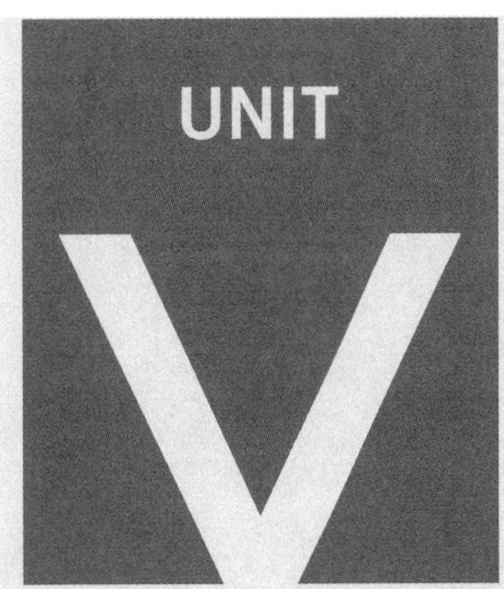

Manage Production

Confucius once said: "Success depends upon previous **preparation**, and without such **preparation** there is sure to be failure." Nothing could be more true when it comes to managing food production. Managers are expected to be decision makers. Production (**preparation**) decisions include deciding how much food to **prepare**, the quality of the food to **prepare**, and taking corrective action if necessary. This chapter provides an overview of production controls that are needed to manage production. You may prefer to use additional resources to this unit in the form of a production textbook such as *Food for Fifty* by Mary Molt.

Prepare Standardized Recipes for Food Production

Overview and Objectives

Even if you work in a corporate-owned facility where menus and recipes are pre-determined, it's important to be able to create and use standardized recipes. A standardized recipe is an essential tool in controlling costs in foodservice. It is a recipe for managing and controlling many aspects of the foodservice operation.

After completing this chapter, you should be able to:

- ✓ Identify food elements of a standardized recipe
- ✓ Calculate menus, recipes, diet census, tally sheets, and cafeteria needs to develop requisitions
- ✓ Compute proper portions using appropriate food charts/references
- ✓ Identify ways of calculating cost and nutrition content of a standard recipe
- ✓ Standardize recipes
- ✓ Evaluate client acceptance of new recipes

A menu serves as a master plan for the food you serve. From the menu, a Certified Dietary Manager uses/develops recipes. A recipe is the ultimate formula for the control of food. Each recipe has an effect on quality, cost control, and client satisfaction. A standardized recipe assures consistency in quality, yield, nutritional value, the time required to prepare it, and staffing requirements. It is a fundamental and essential tool in the foodservice department.

A Recipe: The Ultimate Formula

A recipe is a formula for preparing a menu item. As such, it plays a strong role in control of your operation. It tells what ingredients to include and in what amounts. It tells how to prepare, portion, and present the food. It specifies what equipment and techniques to use. It controls what nutrients you will be serving clients.

Consider this scenario: You have just calculated the cost for a turkey casserole served every other week at lunch. It is coming out too high. To change this cost, one of your options is to go back to the recipe and adjust it. You can look at the cost and quantity of each ingredient. You may choose a different, less expensive form of turkey. Or, you may change the quantities you use for turkey, the most expensive ingredient. If your nutritional analysis tells you that scaling back the turkey will still allow the menu to meet nutritional standards, you may do just this. Alternately, you may see that you are using a cream soup base in the casserole. You may determine that you can accomplish a similar result with a small amount of milk, at a lower cost. This is just an example to demonstrate that a recipe indeed has clout, with financial impact.

Now, consider actual production procedures. One way to prepare a turkey casserole is to buy a frozen convenience food. In this case, the cook's task is to re-heat it according to directions. Another way to prepare it might involve using pre-cooked turkey cubes and a cream soup base as ingredients. Yet another might involve cooking raw turkey, chilling it, and cubing it. Again, it is evident that the recipe exerts control. The production methods specified in recipes control:

- ✓ How much time it will take to prepare an item (and how much lead time will be needed)
- ✓ What the labor cost of the recipe will be
- ✓ What level of skill will be needed among preparation staff
- ✓ What requirements for equipment the recipe will impose.

What about final quality? A recipe capable of producing good results will contain the proper balance of ingredients. If you are making something as simple as gelatin, the amount of water added to the flavored powder makes all the difference in final quality. For a homemade minestrone soup, think about the seasonings included. Too much or too little can make the product unacceptable. Preparation procedures affect quality, too. For example, a prime filet of fish will not turn out well if your procedure calls for baking it too long. Or, a stir-fry recipe will not turn out well if your procedure has you simmer the crisp vegetables in sauce for an extended period. In fact, the accuracy of a recipe, the procedures it defines, and even the ingredients it requires all affect final food quality. If you make changes to the recipe, you have to evaluate the quality of the final product, and exercise good judgment.

Standardized Recipes

Once you have selected or developed a recipe for a menu item, it's important to plan how you will make products turn out consistently every time you produce them. This is where standardization comes into play. A **standardized recipe** is a recipe that contains detailed specifications, and has been adapted and tested in your own operation. A standardized recipe tells exactly how much of each ingredient to use. It tells how to add ingredients and in what sequence. It tells what procedures to use in producing the item.

By becoming very specific in a recipe, you can give instructions that can be repeated again and again, even by different staff members. This can be a great advantage, particularly in situations where a minimally trained employee may need to produce food, or numerous employees may rotate through an assignment.

Quality. The result of using a standardized recipe is that you can produce a consistent product. The product is consistent in quality; it always looks and tastes the same. Clients notice this consistency; particularly if you have long-term clients, you can count on certain expectations. A client who enjoyed the banana bread last week expects to enjoy the same product again this week, and may be disappointed if it turns out differently.

Yield. A standardized recipe is consistent in **yield** and number of servings at a given portion size. A recipe for 100 servings always yields 100 servings. This is critical in assuring you have enough food ready for service at any given time. You need to be able to tell a cook how much food to make—and then tell how much of each ingredient to include to assure this happens.

Nutritional Value. A standardized recipe is also consistent in nutritional value. A serving that contains 8 grams of protein this week will contain 8 grams of protein again next week. In most non-commercial foodservice situations, you are responsible for assuring nutritional consistency. If you are complying with specific nutritional guidelines, standardized recipes become the formula for reliable nutrition. If you are not, you may still be marketing nutritional aspects of your products to clients. For example, the low-fat fare in a business dining setting needs to be reliably low in fat.

Time. In addition, a standardized recipe is consistent in time required for preparation. If it takes 75 minutes to prepare, you can generally count on that time and schedule the product to be ready for service. It is consistent in its labor requirements as well. This time-and-labor aspect of standardization is critical for devising effective employee schedules, and for assuring timeliness of service.

Cost. A standardized recipe is developed with specific amounts of ingredients and a given yield of servings. Because of this factor, you can use a standardized recipe to cost out your menus. What if employees choose not to follow a standardized recipe by increasing ingredient amounts or serving larger portion sizes and the cost has been figured into your department budget? You will be over budget, so making a standardized recipe work requires attention to the human factor as well.

It is important to note that a recipe out of a cookbook does not qualify as a standardized recipe. Why? Because the equipment may vary, cook's interpretation of "cook until done" or "add seasonings to taste" may vary, and the portion utensils and ingredients availability may vary. Each recipe needs to be standardized to your kitchen and staff.

The bottom line is that standardization allows you to manage the operation effectively. You want to be able to predict the inventory needed for food preparation, quantify purchasing needs, and have ingredients on hand in time for production. You can predict and control expenses in your operation. You can also predict staffing needs, and prepare an employee schedule far in advance. You need to plan exactly how much food to produce for each meal in order to feed all clients. For each of these tasks, standardization provides a useful

Glossary

Standardized Recipe
A recipe that contains detailed specifications, and has been tried, adapted and retried in your facility

Yield
The number of servings a recipe will produce at a given portion size

Figure 21.1 **Example of a Standardized Recipe**

1284: Alaska Cod Chowder with Black Beans and Corn

Category: Soups | **Yield:** 50 Servings | **Portion:** 1½ cups | **Batch Qty:** 4.5 gal.

Ingredients

8 cups	onions, halved and sliced
1 (#10) can	diced tomatoes in juice
1 (#10) can	black beans, drained and rinsed
1 (#10) can	corn, drained
5 cups	chopped green chilies, canned or fresh/seeded
3 gal + 2 cups	chicken or fish broth
½ cup	fresh lime juice
¼ cup	chili powder
1 Tbsp	garlic powder
2 Tbsp	toasted cumin seeds, crushed
8 lbs, 4 oz	Alaska Cod, thawed if necessary, cut in 1" pieces
½ cup	vegetable oil

Directions

1. In a large stockpot or steam-jacketed kettle, combine onions, tomatoes in juice, black beans, corn, and chilies.
2. Add broth, lime juice, chili powder, garlic powder, and cumin seeds. Bring to boil; reduce to simmer and cook 10 minutes.
3. Pan-sear cod in lightly oiled non-stick skillet about 3 minutes; add cod to chowder.
4. Simmer chowder an additional 20 minutes over medium-low heat. Verify that serving temperature is 155°F or higher.
5. For each serving, **portion** 1½ cups soup into shallow bowl.

CCP Verify that serving temperature is 155°F or higher, held for a minimum of 15 seconds.

Source: Adapted from Alaska Seafood Marketing Institute

planning tool. From the recipes, you know what you will need and can exercise strong management of the entire process.

Components of a Standardized Recipe

Now that you understand the concept of a standardized recipe, let's examine the details that define its consistency. An example of a standardized recipe appears in Figure 21.1. As you can see, the standardized recipe contains some key elements. These are described below.

Title. Each recipe must have its own unique title or name. The title in Figure 21.1 is *Alaska Cod Chowder with Black Beans and Corn.* While the need for recipe names may seem obvious, in operational practice, confusion actually can occur without attention to this detail. Let's say that you have two types of beef stew. One uses traditional carrots and potatoes, while another uses leeks and peas. You will need to distinguish these clearly from each other to avoid production errors. For clients, too, unique names make it easier to distinguish one menu item from another.

Category. Most facilities use a category designation to help keep recipes organized. Figure 21.2 provides some examples of category designations for recipes. Using categories helps you assign recipe production to the intended staff members. It also helps you group recipes for production on any given day. It helps you locate recipes for special menus as needed. If you use a computerized recipe system, categories help you use search features to find recipes. There is no right or wrong way to develop categories for your own operation. Categorization is simply a logical grouping that is useful to you.

Figure 21.2 Sample Categories for Recipes

Starters	Sides
• Soups • Appetizers 	• Side Salads • Salad Dressings • Rice and Pasta Sides 
Entrees	**Hot Vegetables**
• Beef • Pork • Poultry • Seafood • Vegetarian • Salads • Pureed 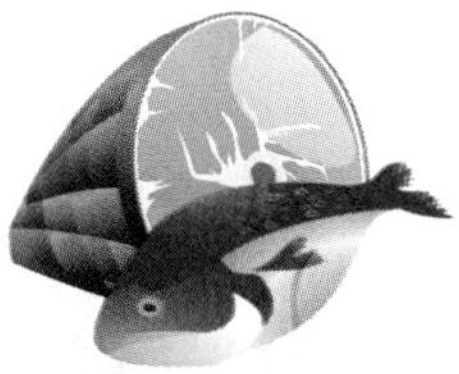	• Potatoes • Other 
Breads	**Desserts**
• Quick Breads and Muffins • Yeast Breads and Rolls 	• Cakes • Cookies • Pies • Fruit • Other 

Recipe number. As you adopt recipes into your own facility, you will probably assign a recipe number to each as an additional way of identifying and controlling your bank of recipes. A computerized system typically requires a recipe number as a way of ensuring a unique identity for each recipe in the database. Some operations use numbering systems that relate to the categories. For example, a series of recipes beginning with 5000 may represent quick breads and muffins. So, a cinnamon muffin recipe may be number 5001. An apple walnut quick bread may be number 5026, and so forth.

Yield. A yield is the number of servings a recipe will produce. Yield is closely related to portion size.

Batch quantity. Sometimes yield is shown as a total volume of the batch, such as 4 gallons or 7.5 pounds.

Portion size. This tells what size each portion will be. It is expressed as a measurement. In the example shown in Figure 21.1, the recipe yields 50 servings of 1½ cups each. Note that the same recipe would alternately yield 100 servings of ¾ cups each. Thus, it's important to specify portion size in every recipe. Otherwise, the yield becomes meaningless.

Portion sizes occasionally vary for use in different menus. This soup, for example, may be used as a ¾ cup portion when the soup is an appetizer on a dinner menu. However, when it is featured as a main lunch entree, the larger portion may be more appropriate. Traditionally, a "cup" of soup is ¾ cup and "bowl" of soup is 1 cup.

Sometimes, even at a single meal, portion sizes may vary for special diets. On a renal menu used for clients with limited kidney function, there is typically a restriction on meat, which contains protein. A standard portion of roast beef for a dinner meal may be 4 ounces. On a renal diet, though, it may be 2 ounces. In this case, each portion size must be specified on the recipe.

Ingredients. A standardized recipe specifies each ingredient. As with recipe naming, ingredient naming is a task that must always be tackled with precision. For instance, if you use flour in your operation, you need to be sure the names of various types are clearly distinguished. You may have all-purpose flour, self-rising flour, pre-sifted flour, whole wheat flour, cake flour, bread flour, and/or others. The success of a recipe for baked goods will depend on your cook selecting the proper ingredient. Very simply, a clear and precise name for the ingredient, used consistently, helps to make this happen. Computerized systems use ingredient numbers along with names to track, distinguish, and describe ingredients.

Typically, a recipe for quantity food production shows all ingredients in the order in which they are added. It is essential that every ingredient used in a recipe appear on the ingredient list. The list itself may serve as a tool for cooks in organizing their work. A common procedure is to measure each ingredient and have it ready before beginning production. The ingredient list in each recipe forms a basis for evaluating purchasing needs. An item that misses the list may not be purchased, and may not be available when needed. So, oversights in the ingredient list can lead to unnecessary work and error, and thoroughness is worth the effort.

Weights or measures. An essential control in food production is measurement of ingredients. For most operations, three basic options present themselves. One is to measure ingredients by volume. Another is to measure by weight. Another, only feasible with certain ingredients, is to measure by count, or by the "each." Figure 21.3 gives examples of measurements. It is more accurate to weigh large amounts of dry ingredients and more cost effective.

Figure 21.3 Examples of Weights and Measures for Ingredients

Measurement by Weights	Measurement by Volume	Measurement by Count
• 3.5 lbs. all purpose flour • 2 oz. iodized salt • 2.5 lbs. sugar • 12 lbs. turkey roast • 6.5 lbs. crushed pineapple • 1 oz. cinnamon • 12 lbs. raw apples • 5.5 lbs. chopped fresh white onions • 8 lbs. margarine	• 9 qts. all purpose flour* • ¾ cup baking powder • 2 Tbsp. ground sage • 1¾ cups skim milk • 3 cups margarine *Note: If accurate scales are available, dry ingredients should be weighed rather than measured.*	• 11 fresh white onions • 3 lemons • 45 bananas • 7 cloves of garlic • 3, #10 cans of tomato sauce

Food safety information. To support a food safety system, many Certified Dietary Managers also provide sanitation-related information on recipes. In a proactive system for managing food safety called HACCP, a particular step of the recipe may be identified as being critical for ensuring food safety. This step is called a critical control point (CCP). The CCP may be noted on the recipe for reference and use by food preparation employees.

Some foodservice operations control ingredients by using an ingredient room. An ingredient room is a unique location where an assigned employee measures ingredients for all recipes, packages them, and labels them. Pre-measured ingredients are then distributed to assigned preparation staff. The ingredient room concept imposes several forms of control in the kitchen. First of all, it ensures that ingredients are carefully measured by someone with specialized focus on measurement. This can support consistent yields and adherence to the measurements required for standardized recipes. Secondly, an ingredient room allows managers to limit access to food storage areas, which may be kept locked. This prevents pilferage or theft in a foodservice operation. Beyond these benefits, an ingredient room allows cooks to work very efficiently during the production process. In an ingredient room model, it is very common for all ingredients to be weighed.

Directions or procedure. Detail and clarity in the directions for preparing a recipe help make it reproducible from one employee to the next. Steps for preparation must be presented in a logical sequence.

Pan size. Many types of recipes include specifications for a pan size. A cake, for example, may use a 12" x 20" x 2" pan. Instructions for employees should indicate how to portion a pan (e.g., cut 8 x 10), or cut a pie (e.g., 6 slices). The pan specification may also relate to a layout for a steam table. Then, it is especially important that the cook use the right pan, so it will fit the layout. See Figure 21.4 for pan and portion sizes.

Batch unit. Sometimes called unit of production, this figure tells in what batches you must make a recipe. This figure may not appear on all recipes, but is sometimes critical. Often, the quantity you choose to produce for any given recipe does not match the yield you have it in at the moment. So, the

Your new chef is anxious to introduce his new recipes to your clients. What would you suggest he do first?

(Check your answer at the end of this chapter)

Figure 21.4 Pan and Portion Chart

Pan Size	Pan Depth	Pan Capacity		Size of Portion		# of Portions Yielded*
		Quarts	Cups	Cup	Scoop #	
Full Size 12" x 20"	2¼"	7½	30	¼	18	120
				⅓	12	90
				⅜	10	80
				½	8	60
	4"	13	52	¼	16	206
				⅓	12	156
				⅜	10	138
				½	8	104
	6"	19½	78	¼	16	312
				⅓	12	234
				⅜	10	208
				½	8	156
				1	6 oz. ladle	78
Half Size 12" x 10"	2½"	3¾	15	¼	16	60
				⅓	12	45
				⅜	10	40
				½	8	30
	4"	6½	26	¼	16	104
				⅓	12	78
				⅜	10	69
				½	8	52
	6"	9¾	39	¼	16	156
				⅓	12	117
				⅜	10	104
				½	8	78
				1	8 oz. ladle	39
Third Size 12" x 6⅞"	2½"	2⅖	9⅗	⅛	2 Tbsp.	76
				¼	16	38
				⅓	12	28
				⅜	10	25
	4"	3⅞	15½	⅛	2 Tbsp.	124
				¼	16	62
				⅓	12	46
				⅜	10	41

Adapted from The Foodservice Tune Up *by Wayne Toczek, Innovations Services, and Tim Bauman.*

** Rounded down to lower portion*

recipe has to be scaled. **Scaling** a recipe means adjusting ingredients upward or downward to generate specific yields. Other terms for this are extending or factoring the recipe. When you scale recipes, you have to recognize batch units, if applicable. Consider this example:

> You are making apple pies. Each pie yields 6 servings, with a portion of 1⁄6 of a pie. You need to serve pie to 211 people. To determine how many pies, divide 221 by 6.
>
> 211 ÷ 6 = 35.17
>
> Since you cannot make a fraction of a pie, you have to round this up and make 36 pies. In portions, this is a yield of 216, or 5 more servings than you estimated you would need.

If your facility maintains vending machines, consider putting the five extra pieces in the vending machine.

A batch unit may be important for a meatloaf, a cake, a quick bread, a roast, and other products that will only be successful when prepared in groups of servings. When and how you will round yields upward depends on the batch unit. If you are preparing products such as chili, stew, or soups, and you need 6.1 batches, consider rounding down. You would over-produce too much to round up. For some products, the batch unit is irrelevant, because you can scale the recipe into batches of single servings. Examples include cookies, soups, sandwiches, and individual chicken pieces.

Recipe sources. Generally, Certified Dietary Managers strive to find recipes that have been developed specifically for quantity production. This is primarily a time-saver. Adapting a home recipe to large-scale production has some pitfalls and requires a fair amount of effort. So, a practical question to ask as you evaluate new recipes is: Has this been refined for quantity production? Even if you have a corporate office providing your recipes, you will want to address the following questions:

- ✓ What does this recipe cost per serving?
- ✓ What is the labor cost in producing this recipe?
- ✓ Do we have the proper equipment to produce it well?
- ✓ Do we have the match of skills required to produce a high-quality product?
- ✓ How does this recipe meet the nutritional requirements of our menus and recipes?
- ✓ How does this recipe fit the tastes and needs of our clients?

Steps in Adapting and Testing a Recipe

As you find recipes you wish to use in your operation, you are ready to begin adapting and standardizing them. When you obtain a recipe for foodservice that has already been standardized, you still need to test it in your own facility. Why? The standardization may change a little bit with the specific ingredients and equipment you use. Furthermore, variations occur with altitude. If a recipe for baked goods was tested at sea level, and you are at an altitude of 4,000 feet,

Glossary

Scaling
Adjusting standardized recipes upward or downward to provide a specific yield

Putting It Into Practice: 2

Complete this question using Figure 21.4. Your lasagna recipe yields about 24 lbs. What would be the best size pan to cook and serve it in? (Note: Assume that 1 lb=1 pint)

(Check your answer at the end of this chapter)

you will need to make adjustments to create a similar product. In addition, a standardized recipe that meets one facility's standards may not meet another's. Thus, a safe practice is: *Don't believe it until you prove it in your own facility.* This assures you know you have standards upon which you can depend.

The steps in adapting and standardizing a recipe are as follows.

Step 1: Assure that directions, techniques, ingredients and equipment specified all apply to your own facility. Edit them if necessary.

Step 2: Produce the original recipe in your own facility, using the equipment you expect to use for routine production. Portion out servings according to your portion and yield figures, and verify the numbers and acceptability.

Step 3: Name and categorize the recipes in a way that makes sense for your own facility.

Step 4: Specify the portion size you wish to use to comply with your own menu needs.

Step 5: Set the yield for which you wish to standardize the recipe. This should be the yield in which you expect to produce it most often.

Step 6: Scale and cost out the recipe accordingly (described under *Recipe Math* below).

Step 7: Assure that measurements are expressed in terms you always use for each ingredient and are easy to understand.

Step 8: Prepare the new recipe. Taste and evaluate the final product for quality. This is often done through a taste panel, a group of individuals who all taste and evaluate the food. A sample evaluation for members of a taste panel appears in Figure 21.5.

Step 9: Document any adjustments needed, and re-test if warranted. Some experts advise adjusting only one ingredient at at time, so that you may fully evaluate the impact of each change.

Step 10: Prepare a finalized, clearly documented version of the recipe for reference. At this point, you may be entering it into a computer-based management system, or, you may be filing an original copy in a secure location.

In large facilities, recipe testing occurs in a test kitchen. A test kitchen is simply a designated location with proper equipment and staffing for trying out, verifying, adjusting, and standardizing recipes. Whether or not you have a test kitchen, the steps are similar.

The most important consideration in this process is precision and accuracy. The more careful you are in adapting and testing the recipe, the more certain you can be that you have developed a meaningful, standardized recipe.

Realize, too, that as you adapt recipes, you may make adjustments that affect both cost and nutrients. Many managers run both cost and nutrient analyses when the standardization is complete, and again verify that all figures are acceptable.

Glossary

Conversion Factor
The number by which you adjust each recipe ingredient to arrive at a new yield

Figure 21.5 **Recipe Evaluation for Taste Panel**

Date: ________________ Menu Item: Blueberry Muffins

Evaluator: ________________ Recipe Number: ________________

Instructions: Check (✓) your reaction to each of the following factors used to describe the menu item.

Evaluation Factor	Exceptional	Like Very Much	Acceptable	Like Slightly	Unacceptable
Evenly browned.					
Rounded, not peaked top.					
No tunnels.					
Blueberries evenly distributed.					
Cake-like texture.					

Comments:

Recipe Math

Scaling a recipe to produce different yields calls for some recipe math. First, you convert the yield from old to new. Then, you need to adjust measurements of all ingredients accordingly. Let's take a closer look at the calculations.

The most common method is to come up with a **conversion factor**. A conversion factor is the number by which you will (initially) adjust everything to arrive at a new yield. The steps for scaling a recipe are as follows.

Step 1: Divide the new yield by the original yield. This gives you a conversion factor. Note that when you are reducing a yield, the conversion factor will be less than 1.0. When you are increasing a yield, the conversion factor will be more than 1.0.

Example: Your original recipe yields 100 portions. You want a yield of 225 portions.

New yield ÷ original yield = 225 ÷ 100 = 2.25

2.25 is your conversion factor.

(Tip: Remember that *n* comes before *o* in the alphabet. To obtain a conversion factor, use *new* yield divided by *old* yield.)

Your chef wants to standardize a new recipe. The old recipe yield is 20 servings and she wants the new yield to be 75 servings. What is the conversion factor? Use that conversion factor to determine how much chicken is needed in the recipe if the old amount was 4 lbs.

(Check your answer at the end of this chapter)

Figure 21.6 Example of Weight and Volume Conversions for Flour

Background

- You are scaling a recipe that contains all-purpose flour.
- Your original recipe calls for 5 cups of flour.
- You wish to scale this recipe to a higher yield, using a conversion factor of 3.3.

Convert to Weight

- First, you need to convert cups to a weight.
- You look up the volume-to-weight equivalent in a cookbook and find that 4 cups all-purpose flour = 1 lb.
- You create an equation to show the relationship:

  4 cups/1 lb. = 5 cups/? lb.

  Tip: When you are setting up an equation like this one, always put the volume measurement on the top of each side, and the weight measurement on the bottom of each side (or vice versa). This assures that you have set up the equation correctly.

To solve this, you cross multiply the top (numerator) of one side by the bottom (denominator) of the other to create a new equation:

$$\frac{4}{16} \times \frac{5}{x} = 5 = 4x$$

The next step is to divide each side by 4.

5 ÷ 4 = x

So, x = 1.25 lbs.

Scale the Measurement

Now, you need to scale the measurement for the new yield. Multiply the original measurement in weight by the conversion factor:

1.25 lbs. x 3.3 = 4.125 lbs.

Convert to Volume

This is an optional step. If you measure flour by volume, it is important. If you measure flour by weight, you can stop here. You create an equation to show the relationship:

$$\frac{x}{4.125} \times \frac{4}{1}$$

To solve this, you cross multiply the top (numerator) of one side by the bottom (denominator) of the other to create a new equation:

4 x 4.125 = 1 x (x) or

4 x 4.125 = 16.5 cups

Make it Easier

To make this measurement easier, convert this final volume measurement to a manageable unit. From a cookbook, you can also learn that 4 cups = 1 quart. So, you may change this figure to: 4 pt. ÷ ½ cup.

Food Production references such as *Food for Fifty* by Mary Molt provide direct reading tables so you don't have to calculate.

Step 2: Multiply the measurement for each ingredient by the conversion factor.

Example: The original recipe calls for 3 oz of sugar. The new measurement is:

3 oz x conversion factor = 3 oz x 2.25 = 6.75 oz

Step 3: Consider additional adjustments that may be necessary. Some ingredients do not need to follow the conversion factor precisely. Spices and seasonings, for example, can appear in smaller quantities than you might calculate. Oil used for sautéing vegetables may not need to increase in proportion.

Step 4: Specify and verify the batch unit if applicable. So, if you are adjusting a recipe for whole pies, be sure the final quantities you have determined will make some number of whole pies. Likewise, if you are working on a recipe that must be prepared in steam table pans, baking pans, or something similar, examine the batch unit.

In Step 2 of this process, most experts suggest you use only weight measurements. In other words, if you have flour in cups, first change it to pounds and ounces. This is generally the most precise, and it is also easiest to convert. To do this, you may need a reference table of conversions from weights to measures. This table is available in many quantity cookbooks, such as *Food for Fifty,* and is also built into many computer-based recipe management systems. When you are finished, you can use the same table to convert back to volume measurements if desired. Figure 21.6 shows an example of a set of weight and volume conversions for flour.

As you can see, converting a recipe to new yields requires careful attention to proper calculations. In addition, your final answer may come out as a unit of measure that is not usable in daily operation. Or, it may come out as a decimal, such as 2.79 teaspoons. In this case, you need to round the decimal to a usable fraction, such as 2¾ teaspoons. Keep in mind how the recipe will be used, and strive to make it clear and simple for kitchen employees. Finally, after scaling a recipe and converting measurements, it is wise to re-test the recipe.

Using Standardized Recipes to Determine Standard Portion Costs

Additional math that can be performed with a standardized recipe is costing. A standardized recipe helps you with cost control because the amount the recipe produces and the number of portions are predetermined and standardized. Costing out a recipe without a computer program can be time consuming. As the Certified Dietary Manager, you should decide whether to include ingredient costs on the standardized recipe. Perhaps you could begin with the recipes that are most expensive, such as your meat items and your supplements. Regardless of whether you use ingredient costs on your standardized recipes, you need to know how to calculate the cost of a recipe.

Step 1: Create a standard recipe costing form such as the one in Figure 21.7 and fill in the ingredient and amount columns.

Step 2: Locate the ingredient unit cost from your invoices or calculate the unit cost and then calculate the total cost of the ingredient item.

Total cost of the ingredient item = unit cost x the quantity/amount of the ingredient.

Unit Cost = Total cost ÷ by number of servings per package

Example of calculating unit cost: Bacon comes in 2 lb. packages for $7.78 per package. The salad recipe calls for 12 pieces of bacon. You know that bacon is usually 1 oz per piece. Two lbs is equivalent to 24 pieces. Determine the unit price by dividing the total cost of the package by 24: $7.78 ÷ 24 = $.32 per piece/unit. This becomes the unit price on the recipe. The total cost of that ingredient is then $.32 x 12 pieces called for on the recipe or $3.84.

Step 3: Determine if any of your recipe ingredients have a different yield from the amount purchased. (See the section on Understanding Product Yields.) Calculate the edible portion cost.

Step 4: Total all of the ingredient costs.

Step 5: Divide by the total number of portions for the recipe to determine the cost per portion.

Figure 21.7 Standardized Recipe Cost Sheet Sample

Menu Item: French Dip Sandwich						
Total Yield: 50 Sandwiches	Portion Sizes: 3 oz. meat, 1/4 cup au jus					
Ingredients			Ingredient Cost			
Item	Amount	Unit Cost	AP $	Yield %	EP $	Total Cost
Roast Beef*	15 lb. AP	$2.39/lb	$2.39	66% or .66	$3.621	$36.21
Au Jus, canned product	3 qts, 1c (2-51 oz cns)	$5.38/cn				$10.76
Kaiser Roll	50 each	$.17 ea				$8.50
					Total Recipe Cost:	$55.47
* Roast Beef purchased raw and then cooked.					# of Portions:	50
					Cost per Portion:	$1.11

Understanding Product Yields

When you purchase fresh produce, you will clean it, peel it, core it, etc. before you use it. This preprocessing reduces the final amount available for a recipe. You might also remove skin from chicken pieces, trim fat from pork chops or remove bone from a ham steak. You are changing the amount purchased (aka **As Purchased** [**AP**]) to an **Edible Portion** (**EP**) amount. For costing purposes, you must calculate the cost of the edible portion of a food. Thus, the ingredient information in recipes must be adjusted or converted to reflect the cost of what is actually consumed.

Cooking may also change the amount purchased to an edible portion amount. You know when cooking a roast, turkey, or ground beef that the amount you end up with is less than the amount you started with.

How do you know what the edible portion (EP) is for any produce you use? You can weigh the product in its as purchased (AP) form, and then weigh it again after you have completed the preparation or cooking. There are many reliable resources available that provide you with tables showing the **yield percentage** of an as purchased amount to an edible portion. One such reference is *Food For Fifty* by Mary Molt. This book includes many food production tables and quantity recipes and would be a valuable resource for any foodservice department.

Calculating Edible Portions from As Purchased Amounts. Most facilities use a yield percentage to determine the ingredient amount from the raw purchased or AP amount. The yield percentage is the percentage available after preproduction, portioning, or cooking has been completed.

Edible portion (EP) cost = AP cost ÷ yield percentage

Example of determining the edible portion cost of a recipe ingredient: The yield percentage table (from a reference book) indicates that each pound of 85% lean ground beef yields 0.80 pounds of cooked, drained ground beef. 10 pounds x 0.80 = 8 pounds of cooked ground beef. The AP price of 85% lean ground beef is $13.90 for 10 lbs. The EP cost = $13.90 ÷ .80 or $17.38 for 10 lbs. To determine the price per pound, divide the total EP cost of $17.38 by 10 =$1.74 (round up) per EP pound.

Example of determining ingredient cost using yield percentage: Recipe calls for 15 lbs of fresh green beans. The unit cost of the green beans is $.69 per pound. The yield percentage on fresh green beans is 88% or .88. The EP cost of one pound of green beans then is $.69 ÷ .88 = $.78/pound.

Figure 21.7 shows ingredient costing where the AP and the EP are the same and an example of calculating an ingredient cost where the AP and EP are different. Figure 21.8 shows an example of calculating a yield percentage.

Note: This process is also very important when determining the nutrient value of a recipe ingredient. The nutrient content should be determined based on the edible portion, not on the amount purchased.

Computerized Recipe System

Now that the effort involved in scaling and costing recipes is apparent, you probably also realize that scaling and costing recipes on a daily basis would require a great deal of time. Many Certified Dietary Managers scale a single recipe to several common quantities, and simply use these. With chicken soup, one manager may maintain a reference recipe scaled to 200, 250, and 300 servings. When a recipe calls for 215 servings one day and 235 for another day, the facility may produce 250 servings.

This is practical and expedient, but also results in over-production of food. When amplified by dozens of food items in a single day, this over-production

Glossary

AP
As purchased or raw weight, without any preproduction

EP
Edible portion; the final quantity of a product after all preparation is done

Yield Percentage
Edible portion weight divided by the as purchased weight

Putting It Into Practice: 4

Calculate the yield percentage of ground beef if the AP weight is 10 lbs. and the EP weight is 7.5 lbs. Using the yield percentage, calculate the ingredient cost of two pounds of ground beef if the AP price is $1.69 per lb.

(Check your answer at the end of this chapter)

Figure 21.8 Sample EYF Calculation

This example uses fresh strawberries:

A kitchen employee removes 10 pounds of strawberries from the case.

AP: 10 lbs. This is the net weight of the strawberries as purchased.

A kitchen employee washes the strawberries, cuts off the leaf-ends, and slices the strawberries for shortcake. To determine EP, he weighs the strawberries again.

EP: 7.6 lbs. This is the weight after pre-preparation processing.

A Certified Dietary Manager wants to know the EYF for use in purchasing. He calculates it as follows:

EYF = EP ÷ AP

EYF = 7.6 ÷ 10 = 0.76 or 76%

incurs significant unnecessary expense. Depending on how a manager uses the extra food, there may be food waste. In dollars, some managers have described this over-production as representing 5-10 percent of the food budget.

This is one reason that many managers choose to use a computer-based system for recipe management. Software can scale and re-scale recipes at any time. So, if a core recipe is in the computer, the system may produce scaled recipes for each day of production, based on projected usage figures the manager specifies (or the system calculates). In the above example, this would mean the system produces a recipe for chicken soup scaled to 215 servings on one day, and 235 on another. Thus, it reduces food waste.

Calculating recipe costs using computer software expedites the process of calculating food costs. If the software is linked to your electronic inventory program, your recipes costs can be updated as prices change, thereby providing more current information. The more current your recipe costs are, the more accurately you can stay within budget.

Encouraging the Use of Standardized Recipes

Making standardized recipes work requires communication. Remind your staff of the importance of standardized recipes by holding short inservices annually to review how and why to use them. Make sure that your department standards (such as standardized recipes) are part of your new employee orientation. If you notice over or under production problems, follow up on them immediately with the cooking staff. In addition, there are several ways to make a standardized recipe user-friendly and improve compliance:

Sequence of ingredients. As you list ingredients on a recipe, assure that the sequence of ingredients matches the sequence in which they are used. This helps to prevent oversights and errors.

Consistent units of measure. Recognize that there are many ways to measure any given ingredient, and standardize your units of measure for each one you use in your operation. For example, if you decide that flour will be measured by volume, then be sure it is always done this way on every recipe. There can be a few exceptions to this practice, where ingredients are used quite differently in

Putting It Into Practice: 5

Your facility is researching the need to expand their computer system and have asked for your input. Currently all you have is a computerized inventory system. How would you justify expanding the computerized inventory system by adding a computerized recipe system?

(Check your answer at the end of this chapter)

one recipe or another. In a computer-based system, a user may actually specify two different ingredients that can appear on recipes, such as: margarine, measured in 1-lb blocks; and margarine, measured by volume. Also assure that for whatever measurements you specify, measuring utensils are available. For example, if you use quart measurements, have a quart measure on hand.

Consistent abbreviations. There are variations in abbreviations used to describe common measurements. For example, teaspoons may be: tsp or t. Tablespoons may be: Tbsp or TB or T. Pounds may be: lb or #. There is no right or wrong to any of these designations. However, the use of abbreviations must be standardized and consistent on all recipes to minimize confusion.

Consolidated measures. In scaling a recipe, you may arrive at measurements such as: 18 cups or 24 teaspoons. If you ask an employee to make these kinds of measurements, you lengthen the time required for production. Think how long it would take to portion 18 cups of peanut butter one cup at a time. In addition, you increase the opportunity for error. Thus, it is helpful to consolidate these to larger units, using a chart of equivalents available in *Food for Fifty*. For example, 18 cups becomes 4.5 quarts, and 24 teaspoons becomes ¼ cup. See Figure 21.9 for common equivalents.

Figure 21.9 **Common Equivalents**

Volume Measurements	Fluid Measurements	Weight Measurement
1 bushel = 4 pecks	1 gallon = 4 quarts	1 pound = 16 ounces
1 peck = 8 quarts	1 quart = 4 cups = 2 pints	1 ounce = 30 grams
1 gallon = 4 quarts	1 cup = 8 fluid ounces	
1 quart = 2 pints	1 fluid ounce = 2 tablespoons	
1 pint = 2 cups		
1 cup = 16 tablespoons		
½ cup = 8 tablespoons		
⅓ cup = 5 ⅓ tablespoons		
¼ cup = 4 tablespoons		
1 tablespoon = 3 teaspoons		

Consistent temperature standards. It is also helpful to standardize all temperature measurements to one system, such as degrees F or degrees C. Generally, this has to match available readings on actual equipment, and many operations use Fahrenheit.

Proofread recipes. As you finalize tested recipes, take the time to proofread them carefully. Small errors can magnify in the kitchen. Imagine the results that could occur if you omitted baking powder from the cornbread recipe, or accidentally noted teaspoons instead of tablespoons, or specified a baking temperature as 425° instead of 325°F. Check final amounts carefully. In addition, assure that every ingredient in the ingredient list is used in the text of the procedure—and that every ingredient called for in the procedure appears on the ingredient list. Finally, make sure the procedure is clear and cannot be misunderstood. Attention to detail helps assure the recipe will be carried out as it is intended it to be.

To ensure the ongoing success of standardized recipes, it's also important to encourage feedback from production employees. Tell employees that if they encounter suspected errors in recipes, or believe that a standardized recipe is producing unacceptable results, you would like to hear about it. Encouraging communication allows you to pinpoint areas for correction and involve production staff in tweaking recipes.

Employees who feel they cannot talk to the Certified Dietary Manager about recipe problems are much more likely to make their own adjustments to "fix" a recipe. In this way, a flawed recipe can slip through the system for a long time. When a new employee comes in and prepares the same recipe, it can flop. So, it's always better to edit the recipe and create a document that can generate reproducible results.

Using Standardized Recipes

Standardized recipes are useful for more than just production needs. Use them to determine your requisition needs and to improve portion control.

Requisitions

In large facilities, there may be one staff member whose job is to retrieve items from the storeroom for production needs. That person will work from a requisition that lists all of the items needed for the day's production. If your standardized recipes are computerized, your computer software can generate the requisition from those recipes. If your recipes are not computerized, you can still generate a requisition from the standardized recipes. This will improve the storeroom process and the requisitions can also be used for establishing a purchase order.

Portion Control
Control of serving sizes so they are standardized

Disher/Portion Scoop
A portion control utensil used for dishing vegetables, fruits, desserts, or starchy products such as rice and potatoes. It is also commonly known as a portion scoop.

What portion control utensil would be best to list on a standardized recipe for rice pilaf?

(Check your answer at the end of this chapter)

Portion Control

Ensuring that food served matches portions specified in standardized recipes and on menus is critical because portion control is intertwined with recipe yields. **Portion control** is essential for all the controls you wish to implement with a standardized recipe, such as predictable costs, predictable nutrient content of menu items, and predictable number of servings for each product. Portion control also builds client satisfaction, as the portion sizes of foods are predictable and consistent.

Responsibility for portion control may be shared among various employees, from production staff to trayline employees to servers. For example, portion control for applesauce pre-portioned into dishes in the cold food production area becomes the responsibility of a cold food production employee. Meanwhile, portion control for hot mashed potatoes served on a buffet becomes the responsibility of the server. As the Certified Dietary Manager, you need to explain and reinforce the importance of portion control to all involved employees, provide training, and allow employees to practice the techniques. For example, have them practice using a common big spoon, a spoodle and a disher to portion a set number of portions of mashed potatoes. Usually, these portion sizes will vary and will demonstrate the need for a standard portion utensil.

Carrying through portion control often requires some tools for measurement. For example, when you specify ½ cup as a portion size, how do you know it will be served that way? Common measurement tools used in foodservice facilities include portion/dishers, scoops, and ladles. Portion scoops/dishers, and ladles designed for non-commercial foodservice have standardized sizes and are an aid in portion control. Portion scoops/dishers have designated numbers. For example, a #8 disher equals ½ cup, and a #16 equals ¼ cup. This number is equivalent to the number of servings in a quart or 32 oz. So a #8 **disher** means 8 servings in a quart. (Note: a disher is frequently called a scoop or an ice cream scoop. The proper term is disher or portion scoop so it is not confused with another utensil called a scoop and used for dry ingredients such as flour.)

For some foods, portioning is achieved by weighing on a scale. For example, the 2-ounce serving of beef for a renal diet may be weighed to assure compliance with the diet order. However, it is not always practical or cost-effective to weigh every portion of a food. In portioning the roast beef for a trayline service, a cook may weigh several portions in order to establish the thickness and dimensions of a 4-ounce serving, and use this as a visual guide for the remaining portions. Finally, managers have many pre-portioned foods available to them today. These eliminate many of the challenges related to portion control. For example, you may purchase pre-portioned chicken breasts or fish filets for service. Figure 21.10 provides examples of how portions may be measured.

As you have seen, one advantage of standardized recipes is that you can specify standard portion sizes. But how do you know what the portion size should be? There are many references that describe standard portion sizes such as the Academy of Nutrition and Dietetics (AND) [formerly known as The American Dietetic Association (ADA)] Exchange Lists. The *Management in the News* section at the end of this chapter puts portion sizes into perspective from the Dietary Guidelines. Check out what the USDA considers to be standard portion sizes for various calorie levels.

Standardized recipes are more than recipes for simple food products. They are also a recipe for managing and controlling many aspects of food production.

Figure 21.10 How Portions Are Measured

Product	Portion	Method
Diced peaches	½ cup	Cook uses a #8 disher/portion scoop to portion individual servings into bowls.
Individual chicken filets	5 oz. cooked weight	Server portions each as one serving.
Vanilla cake	1/24 of pan	Cook slices cake as 6 x 4 servings, taking care to ensure the cuts are even. Each piece becomes a portion.
Apple pie	1/8 pie	Cook slices pie into eight equal pieces. Each piece becomes a portion.
Hearty chicken stew	1 cup	Server uses 8 oz. ladle to portion into bowls at the point of service.
Mashed potatoes	½ cup	Server uses #8 disher/portion scoop to portion individual servings onto plates.
Whole banana	1 each	Server offers one banana.

Management in the News

Putting the Guidelines Into Practice. March 2002. Center for Nutrition Policy and Promotion. United States Department of Agriculture. Home and Garden Bulletin, No .267-1.

How Much are You Eating? Dietary Guidelines for Americans

Many people feel that the bigger the portion, the better. But is that so? Not if you're trying to manage your weight. One key to getting or keeping your weight in a healthy range is to eat sensible portions. That's easy to say—but not always so easy to do! This brochure gives tips to help you decide what sensible portions are for you, and to help you stick to those reasonable portion sizes.

How Much Do You Eat?

Suppose you had dinner at an Italian restaurant last night. You ordered spaghetti with meatballs. While you were waiting for your order, you ate 2 slices of garlic bread. How can you tell if this dinner is too much food for you? You need to estimate how much you ate, and then compare that to Food Guide Pyramid recommendations.

Think about your plateful of spaghetti and meatballs. Estimate the amounts of spaghetti, sauce, and meat. You may decide for example, that the spaghetti portion was about 2 cups, the tomato sauce looked like about 1 cup, and the meatballs were about 5 ounces. With the 2 slices of garlic bread, you now have an idea about how much you ate for dinner. But how do your portions translate into standard servings? Chart 1 lists the serving sizes for each Food Guide Pyramid food group. According to the Pyramid, your portions equal the following number of servings:

Spaghetti Dinner

Food	Your Portion	Choose MyPlate	Choose MyPlate Group	Number of Choose MyPlate Servings You Ate
Spaghetti	2 cups	6-8 oz	Whole Grains	2
Garlic Bread	2 slices	1 slice	Grams	2
Tomato Sauce	1 cup	1/2 cup	Vegetables	2
Meatballs	6 oz.	5-6 oz.	Meat and Beans	1-2

Pyramid/Choose MyPlate Recommendations

To figure out if your spaghetti dinner was the right amount of food for you, use the Pyramid. Chart 1 also lists the number of servings recommended for each Pyramid food group, based on your calorie needs. Over a day, you should plan on eating the number of servings recommended from each group.

The number of servings from each food group recommended by the Choose MyPlate depends on your calorie needs.

- Children ages 2 to 6 years, many inactive women, and some older adults may need about 1,600 calories per day.
- Most children over 6, teen girls, active women, and many inactive men may need about 2,200 calories per day.
- Teen boys and active men may need about 2,800 calories per day.

(Continued...)

How Much Are You Eating *(Continued)*

For example, if you need about 1,600 calories a day, the Choose MyPlate recommends 4-6 daily servings from the Grains (Bread, Cereal, Rice and Pasta) group. How does this compare to your spaghetti dinner? Your dinner had 6 servings—the total daily recommendation for someone with your calorie needs. If you had counted your portions of spaghetti and bread as only 1 serving each, you might think you had only eaten 2 servings from the Grains group. But, you actually ate 6! By comparing the portion you ate with a standard serving, you can judge whether your daily intake is right for you.

Serving sizes and the recommended number of servings from each group are *guides* to help determine your daily intake. Your portions do not have to match the standard serving size—they can be larger or smaller. But the amount you eat over the day should match the total amount of a food that is recommended. *Often, the food portions of grains and meats that people choose are larger than the Choose MyPlate serving size. Be especially careful when counting servings from these groups to figure out how many servings are in your portions.*

How Can You Follow Pyramid Recommendations?

Let's go back to the spaghetti dinner. In this example, you know that you should have 6 daily servings from the Grains group. Before dinner, you estimate that you have already had 3 Grains group servings. So, only 3 more servings would meet your recommended intake. To keep to 3 servings, you eat only one slice of garlic bread. When you see the large plate of spaghetti, you set aside half on your plate and ask for a "doggie bag" to take it home. Then, the following would have been your choices from the Grains group over the day:

Meal	Grains Group Portions		Pyramid Grains Group Servings
Breakfast	1/2 cup of oatmeal	=	1 serving
Lunch	1 hamburger bun	=	2 servings
Dinner	1 slice of garlic bread	=	1 serving
Dinner	1 cup of spaghetti	=	2 servings
TOTALS	**4 portions**	=	**6 servings**

In 4 sensible portions, you have consumed your recommended 6 servings of grains. Note that an active man may need about 2,800 calories each day. Checking Chart 1, this man's Grains group recommendation would

(Continued...)

Portions and Servings—What's the Difference?

A **portion** is the amount of food you choose to eat. There is no standard portion size and no single right or wrong portion size.

A **serving** is a standard amount used to help give advice about how much to eat, or to identify how many calories and nutrients are in a food.

For example:

- You eat a sandwich with 2 slices of bread.
- The Choose MyPlate **serving size** for bread is 1 slice.
- Your **portion** is 2 slices, which equals 2 servings from the Grains group.
- Your 2 servings are one-third of the recommendation of 6 servings for people needing 1,600 calories per day. (See Chart 1).

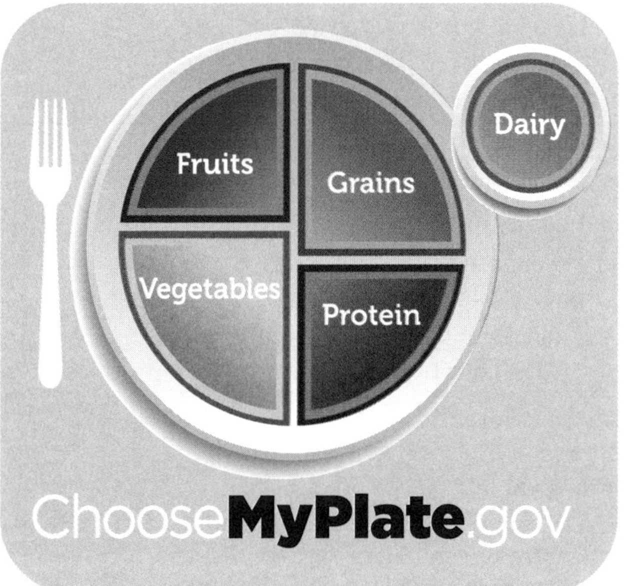

How Much Are You Eating *(Continued)*

Chart 1. How to Use the Food Guide Pyramid

	How Many Servings Do You Need Each Day?		
What counts as a serving?	Children ages 2 to 6, women, some older adults (1,600 calories)	Older children, teen girls, active women, most men (2,200 calories)	Teen boys and active men (2,800 calories)
Grains Group (Bread, Cereal, Rice, and Pasta)—Especially Whole Grain • 1 slice of bread • About 1 cup of ready-to-eat cereal • ½ cup of cooked cereal, rice, or pasta	6	9	11
Vegetable Group • 1 cup of raw leafy vegetables • ½ cup of other vegetables—cooked or raw • ¾ cup of vegetable juice	3	4	5
Fruit Group • 1 medium apple, banana, orange, pear • ½ cup of chopped, cooked, or canned fruit • ¾ cup of fruit juice	2	3	4
Milk, Yogurt, and Cheese Group—preferably fat free or low fat • 1 cup of milk** or yogurt • 1½ ounces of natural cheese (such as Cheddar) • 2 ounces of processed cheese (such as American)	2 or 3*	2 or 3*	2 or 3*
Meat and Beans Group (Meat, Poultry, Fish, Dry Beans, Eggs, and Nuts)—preferably lean or low fat • 2-3 ounces of cooked lean meat, poultry, or fish. These count as 1 ounce of meat: > ½ cup of cooked dry beans or tofu > 2½ ounce soyburger > 1 egg > 2 Tbsp. of peanut butter > ⅓ cup of nuts	2, for a total of 5 ounces	2, for a total of 6 ounces	3, for a total of 7 ounces

* *Older children and teens ages 9 to 18 years and adults over age 50 need 3 servings daily; others need 2 servings daily.*

** *This includes lactose-free and lactose-reduced milk products. Soy-based beverages with added calcium are an option for those who prefer a non-dairy source of calcium.*

(Continued...)

How Much Are You Eating *(Continued)*

Chart 2. Sample Food Portions Larger than 1 Pyramid/Choose MyPlate Serving

This list shows the size of a portion you may choose or be served. They are *not* recommendations. This chart compares these portions to Pyramid servings, so that you can judge how they might fit into your overall daily eating plan.

Food	Sample Portion You Receive	Compare to Pyramid Serving Size	Approximate Pyramid Servings in this Portion
Grains Group			
Bagel	1 bagel 4½" in diameter (4 ounces)	½ bagel 3" in diameter (1 ounce)	4
Muffin	1 muffin 3½" in diameter (4 ounces)	1 muffin 2½" in diameter (1½ ounces)	3
English muffin	1 whole muffin	½ muffin	2
Sweet roll or cinnamon bun	1 large from bakery (6 ounces)	1 small (1½ ounces)	4
Pancakes	4 pancakes 5" in diameter (10 ounces)	1 pancake 4" in diameter (1½ ounces)	6
Burrito-sized flour tortilla	1 tortilla 9" in diameter (2 ounces)	1 tortilla 7" in diameter (1 ounce)	2
Individual bag of tortilla chips	1¾ ounces	12 tortilla chips (¾ ounce)	2
Popcorn	16 cups (movie theatre, medium)	2 cups	8
Hamburger bun	1 bun	½ bun	2
Spaghetti	2 cups (cooked)	½ cup (cooked)	4
Rice	1 cup (cooked)	½ cup (cooked)	2
Vegetable Group			
Baked potato	1 large (7 ounces)	1 small (2¼ ounces)	3
French fries	1 medium order (4 ounces)	½ cup, 10 French fries (1 ounce)	4
Meat and Beans Group			
Broiled chicken breast	6 ounces	2 to 3 ounces	2
Fried chicken	3 pieces (7 to 8 ounces)	2 to 3 ounces	3
Broiled fish	6 to 9 ounces	2 to 3 ounces	3
Sirloin steak	8 ounces (cooked, trimmed)	2 to 3 ounces	3
Porterhouse steak or prime rib	13 ounces (cooked, trimmed)	2 to 3 ounces	5
Ham or roast beef (in deli sandwich)	5 ounces	2 to 3 ounces	2
Tuna salad (in deli sandwich)	6 ounces	2 to 3 ounces	2

How Much Are You Eating *(Continued)*

be 11 servings per day. The full spaghetti dinner might fit easily within his recommended food choices for the day.

One key to making wise food choices is knowing how much you are eating, as well as how much you should eat. This is especially important if you are trying to lose weight or manage your weight.

Don't Be Fooled by Large Portions

Many items sold as single portions actually provide 2 or more Pyramid servings. For example, a large bagel may actually be equal to 3 or 4 servings from the Grains group. A restaurant portion of steak may be more than the recommended amount for the whole day. Chart 2 lists other common examples of foods that are often sold or prepared in portions larger than 1 Pyramid serving.

Nutrition Facts Label Serving Sizes

The serving sizes listed on the *Nutrition Facts label* may be different from *Food Guide Pyramid* serving sizes. Many Pyramid serving sizes are smaller than those on the Nutrition Facts label. For example, 1 serving of cooked cereal, rice, or pasta is 1 cup for the label but only ½ cup for the Pyramid.

Use the Nutrition Facts label to make nutritional comparisons of similar products. The label serving size is not meant to tell you how much to eat, but to help identify nutrients in a food and to make product comparisons easier. To compare the calories and nutrients in two foods, first check the serving size and the number of servings in the package. Serving sizes are provided in familiar units, such as cups or pieces.

The Bottom Line

Choosing sensible portions is a key to controlling calorie intake and getting or keeping your weight in a healthy range. What is sensible for you?

- Each day, choose the recommended amount from the five Pyramid food groups—depending on your calorie needs.
- A Pyramid serving may not be the same as the portion you choose to eat—compare to find out how many servings are in your portion.
- Keep sensible portions in mind at restaurants as well as at home.

Tips to Help You Choose Sensible Portions

When Eating Out:

- Choose a "small or "medium" portion. This includes main dishes, side dishes, and beverages as well. Remember that water is always a good option for quenching your thirst.
- If main dish portions are larger than you want, order an appetizer or side dish instead, or share a main dish with a friend.
- Resign from the "clean your plate club"—when you've eaten enough, leave the rest. If you can chill the extra food right away, take it home in a "doggie bag."
- Ask for salad dressing to be served "on the side" so you can add only as much as you want.
- Order an item from the menu instead of the "all-you-can-eat" buffet.

At Home:

- Once or twice, measure your typical portion of foods you eat often. Use standard measuring cups. This will help you estimate the portion size of these foods and similar foods.
- Be especially careful to limit portions of foods high in calories, such as cookies, cakes, other sweets, and fats, oils, and spreads.
- Try using a smaller plate for your meal.
- Put sensible portions on your plate at the beginning of the meal, and don't take "seconds."

How Much Are You Eating *(Continued)*

Dietary Guidelines for Americans

The Dietary Guidelines offer sound advice that will help to promote your health and reduce your risk for chronic diseases such as heart disease, certain cancers, diabetes, stroke, and osteoporosis. The 10 Guidelines are grouped into the ABC's of nutrition:

A: Aim for Fitness

- Aim for a healthy weight.
- Be physically active each day.

B: Build a Healthy Base

- Let the Pyramid guide your food choices.
- Choose a variety of grains daily, especially whole grains.
- Choose a variety of fruits and vegetables daily.
- Keep food safe to eat.

C: Choose Sensibly

- Choose a diet that is low in saturated fat and cholesterol and moderate in total fat.
- Choose beverages and foods to moderate your intake of sugars.
- Choose and prepare foods with less salt.
- If you drink alcoholic beverages, do so in moderation.

To order Dietary Guidelines publications, call 888-878-3256. Ask for the Dietary Guidelines for Americans (40-page bulletin, $4.75 per copy) or Using the Dietary Guidelines for Americans (5-panel brochure, $.50 per copy).

You can also find out more about the Guidelines and download these publications by visiting USDA's Center for Nutrition Policy and Promotion website at www.cnpp.usda.gov.

The U.S. Department of Agriculture (USDA) prohibits discrimination in all its programs and activities on the basis of race, color, national origin, sex, religion, age, disability, political beliefs, sexual orientation, or marital or family status. (Not all prohibited bases apply to all programs.) Persons with disabilities who require alternative means for communication of program information (Braille, large print, audiotape, etc.) should contact USDA's TARGET Center at 202-720-2600 (voice and TDD).

To file a complaint of discrimination, write USDA, Director, Office of Civil Rights, Room 326-W, Whitten Building, 14th and Independence Avenue, SW, Washington, DC 20250-9410 or call 202-720-5964 (voice or TDD). USDA is an equal opportunity provider and employer.

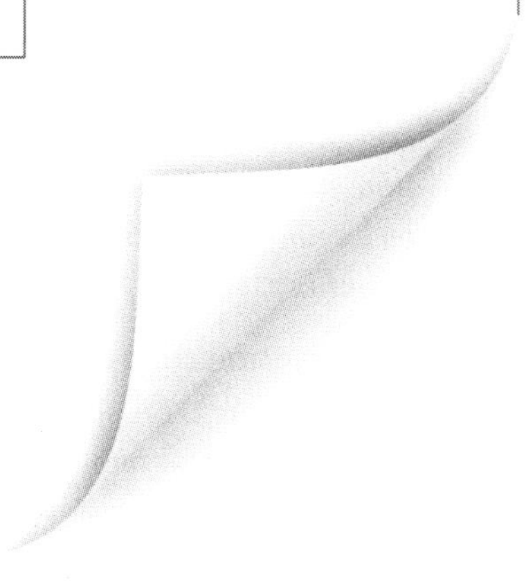

END OF CHAPTER

Putting It Into Practice Questions & Answers

1. Your new chef is anxious to introduce his new recipes to your clients. What would you suggest he do first?
   A. *Work with him to help develop a standardized recipe. Begin by making sure you have all of the necessary equipment and ingredients; ask him to prepare the recipe in its original format. Have him cost out the recipe to make sure it is feasible for your budget. Ask your clients or a client team to evaluate it for appearance, tenderness, texture, flavor, overall quality, and appropriateness for the client audience. Then, follow steps 3-10 in developing a standardized recipe.*

2. Complete this question using Figure 21.4. Your lasagna recipe yields about 24 lbs.; you need 48, 6 oz (1 cup) portions. What would be the best size pan to cook and serve it in? (note: assume that 1 lb. = 1 pint)
   A. *What you know: 24 lbs = 24 pints. There are 2 pints in one quart so you will have 12 quarts. From the chart, you see that a full size, 4" pan usually has 13 quarts and 52 cups. That is the closest to your 12 quarts so you would choose a full size pan (12x20) for the lasagna.*

3. Your chef wants to standardize a new recipe. The old recipe yield is 20 servings and she wants the new yield to be 75 servings. 1) What is the conversion factor? 2) Use that conversion factor to determine how much chicken is needed in the recipe if the old amount was 4 lbs.
   A. 1. *To convert a recipe to a new amount, divide the new amount by the old amount: 75÷20=3.75 Remember N comes before O in the alphabet so the __N__ew amount goes first and is divided by the __O__ld amount.*
   2. *Now, use the conversion factor of 3.75 to multiply each ingredient amount. In this case, there was 4 lbs. of chicken in the old recipe so multiply 4 x 3.75 = 15 lbs. To prepare the new recipe to yield 75 servings, you would need 15 lbs.*

4. 1) Calculate the yield percentage of ground beef if the AP weight is 10 lbs. and the EP weight is 7.5 lbs. 2) Using the yield percentage, calculate the ingredient cost of two pounds of ground beef if the AP price is $1.69 per lb.
   A. 1. *To calculate yield percentage, divide the EP weight by the AP weight: 7.5 ÷ 10 lbs = .75 or a 75% yield percentage*
   2. *To calculate the ingredient cost using the yield percentage, divide the AP price by the yield percentage: $1.69 ÷ .75 = $2.25 for one pound. There are two pounds of ground beef in the recipe so the ingredient cost would be 2 x 2.25 or $4.50.*

5. Your facility is researching the need to expand their computer system and have asked for your input. Currently all you have is a computerized inventory system. How would you justify expanding the computerized inventory system by adding a computerized recipe system?
   A. *Before you add a computerized recipe system, make sure you have done your research. Talk to software vendors and other Certified Dietary Managers who are using this software and ask these questions: How much staff time did you take to implement? What are the advantages of having this software? What are the disadvantages of having this software? Once you have gathered all the data, write up your proposal and submit it to your administrator.*

6. What portion control utensil would be best to list on a standardized recipe for rice pilaf?
   A. *As a starch, the serving size would be ½ c. A disher, #8, would yield a ½ cup serving and also portion the rice into a nice shape.*

Specify Standards and Procedures for Preparing Food

Overview and Objectives

This unit is all about managing production. Standardized recipes are one way to manage production; specifying standards and procedures for preparing food is another important consideration in managing production. The Certified Dietary Manager needs to establish the standards for food and production as part of the quality management initiatives. This chapter will address the production steps involved in the preparation of food. As with all standards, follow-up and continuous coaching of employees will ensure that standards are met.

After completing this chapter, you should be able to:

- ✓ Develop food quality control standards; e.g. appearance, temperature, acceptance
- ✓ Implement procedures to monitor food production
- ✓ Develop procedures for monitoring food waste control

The development of standards for the preparation of food begins with identifying quality standards for raw and prepared foods in your facility. Specifically, you want to identify purchasing, preparation, and storage standards for foods served in your facility. Storage standards are covered in Chapter 16 and 17.

SECTION A Purchasing Standards

Before you purchase foods or write specifications, you want to identify general information and guidelines about the food you purchase. That information can be used to document standards for your facility.

Eggs and Dairy Products

Eggs

Eggs have many uses in most foodservice facilities. You and the chef/cook need to consider what type of eggs best fit the production needs. The type of eggs used will depend upon the number of clients served and the menu. (i.e. do you have an on-site bakery?) There are three different egg products you might use: fresh eggs, processed eggs (frozen eggs and liquid eggs), or dried eggs.

Fresh Eggs. The USDA provides the following information about shell eggs. There are three consumer grades for eggs: U.S. Grade AA, A, and B. The grade is determined by the interior quality of the egg and the appearance and condition of the egg shell. Eggs of any quality grade may differ in weight (size).

U.S. Grade AA eggs have whites that are thick and firm; yolks that are high, round, and practically free from defects; and clean, unbroken shells. Grade AA and Grade A eggs are best for frying and poaching where appearance is important.

U.S. Grade A eggs have characteristics of Grade AA eggs except that the whites are "reasonably" firm. This is the quality most often sold in stores.

U.S. Grade B eggs have whites that may be thinner and yolks that may be wider and flatter than eggs of higher grades. The shells must be unbroken, but may show slight stains. This quality is seldom found in retail stores because they are usually used to make liquid, frozen, and dried egg products.

Frozen, Liquid, and Dried Eggs. Processed eggs save time when using eggs for baking or cooking omelets and scrambled eggs in large quantities. Processed eggs help meet the food safety regulation that prohibits pooling eggs (breaking raw eggs into a container and storing them for later). All processed egg products are processed under sanitary conditions and must display the USDA inspection mark. Processed eggs are broken and separated into yolks and whites and then pasteurized before processing into dried, frozen or refrigerated liquid egg products. There are several different processed liquid egg and dried egg products. Figure 22.1 shows both liquid and dried egg products, how they are packaged for purchase, their uses, and storage and handling guidelines. Pasteurized dried egg white powder should be used for meringues or desserts that are not cooked.

Cheese

Cheese is important because it can add calcium and protein to menu items. With the wide variety of cheeses available, it can also add unique flavors. There are processed cheeses and natural cheeses.

Processed cheeses. When you are selecting cheese for use in hot items, such as heated sandwiches, casseroles, or sauces, select a cheese with a suitable flavor and texture that will melt consistently and easily. Processed cheeses are a combination of natural cheeses that have undergone a heat process. They melt more easily and smoothly but provide less of the variety of unique flavors because they are a combination of cheeses. They melt quickly and smoothly; they work well in casseroles and sauces. Processed cheeses are often used for hot sandwiches because melting is easier to control. If you have a signature hot sandwich, you might have a higher client satisfaction with a natural cheese slice because of the more pronounced cheese flavor. Processed cheeses come in a variety of forms such as sliced, block, or spreads.

Natural cheeses. The flavor of the natural cheese depends upon the type of milk (cow, goat, or sheep) and the length of time the cheese is aged.

Figure 22.1 Egg Products

Refrigerated Liquid Egg Products	
• Whole eggs, white or yolks • Sugared egg yolks • Salted whole eggs or yolks	• Scrambled egg mix • Extended shelf life whole eggs, whites, yolks or scrambled egg mix
USAGE:	Foodservice and the commercial food processing industry.
AVAILABILITY:	Bulk tank trucks, totes, metal or plastic containers, polyethylene coated fiber or laminated foil and paper cartons and hermetically sealed polyethylene bags. Container size from small bags to cartons (8-oz to 5-lb), intermediate size bag in boxes and pails (20- to 40-lb) and larger drums and totes (200- to 3,500-lb).
ADVANTAGES:	Pasteurized, quick and easy to use.
STORAGE/HANDLING:	Store according to processor's recommendations. Normally should be used within six days, except for extended shelf life products for which the supplier's recommendations should be followed.
Dried Egg Products	
• Whole eggs or yolk solids • Dried egg or scrambled egg mix • Egg whites	• Free flowing whole eggs or yolk solids • Stabilized (glucose-free) whole eggs or yolk solids • Blends of whole eggs and/or yolk carbohydrates
USAGE:	Ingredient especially for the commercial food processing industry.
AVAILABILITY:	Foodservice—6-oz pouches, 3- and 25-lb poly packs Commercial—25- and 50-lb boxes, 150-, 175-, and 200-lb drums
ADVANTAGES:	Long shelf life, stable and mixable.
STORAGE/HANDLING:	Keep in dry storage away from extreme temperatures and strong odors. Use pallets.

Source: American Egg Board, used with permission.

There are several varieties of natural cheeses:

✓ Fresh cheese such as ricotta, mozzarella, or feta
✓ Soft cheese such as Brie
✓ Semisoft such as blue or Monterey Jack
✓ Firm cheese such as Cheddar, Provolone
✓ Hard grating cheese such as Parmesan.

Aging does decrease the lactose content so if you have lactose intolerant clients who prefer cheese, they might be able to tolerate an aged natural cheese. Natural cheeses come in a variety of forms such as grated, sliced, and cubed.

There are hundreds of varieties of cheeses and you can determine which type and form to purchase by reviewing your recipes and consulting the chef/cook. There are many Websites that can help you determine the characteristics and purchasing information of cheeses or use a food production book such as *Food for Fifty* by Mary Molt.

Milk

Milk is another staple in the foodservice department and is commonly used in recipes as well as for a beverage.

Fluid milk. Generally, there are four different types of fluid milk used for beverages:

- ✓ Whole milk—contains 8 g of fat per 8 oz cup and the federal standard requires that whole milk be at least 3.25% fat.
- ✓ Reduced fat milk—2% fat and contains 4.7 g total fat per cup.
- ✓ Low-fat milk—1% fat and contains 2.6 g total fat per cup.
- ✓ Skim milk—0.5% fat and contains 0.5 g total fat per cup.

The availability of goat milk is increasing and for Certified Dietary Managers who work in hospitals, you may need to purchase goat milk. Goat milk has a higher concentration of medium chain fatty acids (MCT) and research has shown that clients with various medical conditions such as malabsorption syndrome are more tolerant of goat milk. For infants who are allergic to cow's milk, goat milk may be an acceptable alternative.

Fluid milk products must be **pasteurized** to be served in commercial facilities. Pasteurization means heating fluid milk or cream to a specific temperature for a specified amount of time. Both fluid milk and cream products may also be **ultra-pasteurized**. Ultra-pasteurization takes the pasteurization process to higher temperatures for a shorter period of time. Finally, these products can also be **ultra-high-temperature processed**. The products are heated at a high enough temperature to kill all of the bacteria. Ultra-high-temperature products can be held without refrigeration for up to three months. Once they are opened, they must be treated like all fluid milk or cream products, refrigerated, and used within a few days.

Yogurt. Yogurt is a product cultured with a lactic acid-producing bacteria. It is available with whole milk, low-fat, or skim milk. Some Greek yogurts have a much higher protein content (i.e. 11-14gm as compared to 7gm for the traditional yogurt). For cancer clients or those needing increased protein and calories, consider purchasing a whole milk, Greek yogurt. There are many flavorings, sweeteners, and fruits added to increase client acceptance.

Butter

Butter is considered a dairy product because it is made with pasteurized cream and has an 80% milkfat content. Butter is usually graded according to federal standards with Grades A or AA. Grade B butter is made from sour cream. When butter is churned, salt or a salty brine is added. Unsalted butter is available as well as whipped butter.

Unsalted butter is called for in some baking recipes because the butter flavor is more pronounced. Whipped butter doesn't convert well in baking recipes; it is used more as a spread.

Glossary

Ultra-High Temperature Processed
Products that are treated by flash sterilization and then packed into sterilized, airtight containers, and are shelf-stable for up to three months

Ultra-Pasteurized
Heated to a higher temperature for a shorter period of time

Ultra-High-Temperature Processed
Heated to a temperature to kill all bacteria and are shelf-stable for up to three months

Putting It Into Practice: 1

Coffee is available in your cafeteria throughout the day. You want to make creamers available that don't need refrigeration and can be displayed next to the coffee. What type of creamer should you purchase?

(Check your answer at the end of this chapter)

Grains

Grains are the seeds or kernel of cereal grasses. Grains come in many different forms depending upon the amount of milling:

- ✓ Whole grains—contain the bran (outer shell providing fiber, B vitamins, trace minerals), the endosperm (provides energy—carbohydrate and protein), and the germ (provides antioxidants, vitamin E, B-vitamins). Whole grains that are cracked, crushed, or flaked during milling but still retain the same proportion of bran, germ, and endosperm as the original grain are also considered whole grains.
- ✓ Pearled grains—bran and germ layers are removed resulting in less fiber but faster cooking times; also known as polished grain.
- ✓ Grits—corn or oat kernels cut into smaller pieces so they cook more quickly; they are still considered whole grains. Steel-cut oats is one example.
- ✓ Flakes—whole grains that are rolled into a flattened kernel.
- ✓ Meal—whole grains that are finely ground; corn meal and graham flour are examples.
- ✓ Bran—the outer part of the grain kernel that can be flakes or fibers. Oat bran, wheat bran, and rice bran are examples.
- ✓ Germ—the bottom of the grain kernel that contains the fat and fat soluble vitamins; because of the fat content, it has a shorter shelf life.
- ✓ Flour—kernels that are ground and sifted; not considered a whole grain if the bran and germ are removed.

Cooking with whole grains and serving whole grains should be encouraged in your facility because of the added nutrient content. There are some new grains on the market that will enhance the nutrient content of your menus if used: Amaranth seeds are higher in protein content and can be used with flour in breads or pancakes. Quinoa (pronounced KEEN-wah) is higher in protein, calcium, and iron than any of the other grains. It is a small seed from South America and is used like rice.

The interest in gluten-free products has skyrocketed in the past few years. Gluten is a type of protein found in many grains. As the Certified Dietary Manager, you need to know which products are gluten-free to meet the increased demand from your clients. See Figure 22.2 for a table of grains that are considered whole grains, not whole grains, and gluten-free grains.

Flours

Flours can be made from almost any grain. Besides fiber, one of the characteristics that differentiate flour is the amount of gluten it contains. All-purpose flour is a blended wheat flour with a lower protein content than bread flour. It serves dual purpose for baking, breading, and general cooking needs. Bread flour, being higher in protein, is also higher in gluten. Gluten helps give yeast breads a higher volume. For pastries such as biscuits and cookies where a high gluten content is less desirable, large commercial bakeries use a pastry flour that is a low-protein flour made from soft wheat. Self-rising flour contains leavening agents and added salt and should be avoided with low-sodium diets.

Figure 22.2 Whole Grain Guide

Whole Grains	Not Whole Grains	Gluten-Free Grains
Look for these terms on the label:	**Not whole grain if the label reads:**	
• Cracked wheat	• Flour, white flour, wheat flour	• Quinoa
• Crushed wheat	• All-purpose flour	• Rice
• Whole wheat flour	• Unbleached flour	• Sorghum
• Graham flour	• Bromated flour	• Teff
• Bromated whole wheat flour	• Instantized flour	• Amaranth
• Whole (wheat or corn)	• Self-rising flour	• Buckwheat
• Wheat berries	• Any grain product labeled "enriched"	• Corn
• Oat groats	• Bread flour	• Hominy
• Rolled oats	• Cake flour	• Millet
• Brown rice	• Durum flour	
• Brown rice flour	• Corn or hominy grits	
• Wild rice	• Farina	
• Amaranth	• Semolina	
• Whole barley	• White rice	
• Quinoa	• Couscous	
• Kasha/buckwheat groats	• Pearled barley	
• Whole millet		
• Wild rice		
• Whole rye flour and flakes		

Corn starch is similar to flour in that it is finely ground endosperm, the starchy part of the kernel. It is used as a thickener in place of flour because the final cooked product is translucent rather than opaque. A substitute for corn starch as a thickener is arrowroot or tapioca.

Pasta

Pasta is made from a high-protein wheat flour or a durum semolina flour. Pasta comes in a large variety of shapes, most of which can be used with sauces or in casseroles. Your menu, your recipes, and the chef/cook can help decide which pasta shapes to purchase. Ask your foodservice vendor for a poster with the various pasta shapes or do a quick Web search for a guide to pasta shapes and sauces. Another consideration besides the shape is whether the pasta will be made with an egg product, such as egg noodles, and whether you will purchase fresh or dry pasta. Fresh pasta is highly perishable. Some pasta is available frozen.

Some Asian recipes call for other types of noodles such as rice noodles, made from rice, or chow mein noodles made from wheat. Bean starch noodles or cellophane noodles are made from mung bean starch. Both rice noodles and cellophane noodles can be fried very quickly and added to dishes as a garnish. Asian noodles are usually stir-fried or used as a base or garnish rather than served with a sauce.

You have a client who loves cream soups but is gluten intolerant. Your cream soups are thickened with flour. What change would you recommend so that your client can have the cream soup?

(Check your answer at the end of this chapter)

Meats

Beef, Pork, Lamb, Veal

Meat will obviously be the high dollar item in your food budget. Therefore, knowing about meat quality, how it is handled after delivery, and cooking methods are extremely important. Fortunately, there is help from the National Association of Meat Purveyors (NAMP). They publish a *Meat Buyer's Guide* based on the USDA's Institutional Meat Purchasing Specifications (IMPS). The guide is available for purchase at this URL: http://www.namp.com/namp/Default.asp. Most of the meat today is purchased portioned or a retail cut rather than in wholesale cuts that are broken down into smaller cuts. All meat that crosses state lines is required to be inspected by the federal government; if it is processed and sold within a given state, the inspection must be equivalent to the federal standards. Grading of meat such as prime and choice for beef is not mandatory but it helps to communicate to the client the eating quality of the product. If you are responsible for purchasing meat in your facility or if purchasing of meat occurs in your department, use the *Meat Buyer's Guide* to help you understand the purchasing language and process.

Poultry

The past ten years has seen an explosion in the selection of cooked and processed poultry products available to Certified Dietary Managers. As with the other products, examine your menu and recipes. Together with the chef/cook, decide which poultry products would be the best buy for your facility and clientele. If the chef is skilled at making homemade soups, purchasing whole poultry or cup-up pieces that will yield bones for stock might be a good investment. Would portioned cuts be the best for the skills of the staff? Pulled chicken, rather than uniform diced pieces of chicken, might be needed for salads or casseroles. Before finalizing the purchase order, know what your needs are in terms of the types of poultry cuts.

Poultry has a mandatory inspection for wholesomeness and optional grading. Grade A poultry is most commonly sold to commercial facilities. The grading relates to the fat covering, discolorations, feathers, thickness of flesh and other overall quality criteria.

Grade Stamp

Inspection Stamp

Today, both raw meat and raw poultry products may be irradiated to extend the shelf life. The FDA requires that irradiated meat and poultry be labeled as such.

Fish and Shellfish

When it comes to purchasing fish and shellfish, fresh is not always the best choice. As soon as fish is caught, it loses its ability to fight off bacteria. Most fish today is quickly frozen within hours of being caught and this fresh-frozen choice may be the best choice depending upon your geographic location. If fish are intended for raw or undercooked consumption (such as sushi or cold-smoked salmon), it must be properly frozen before being served to kill worms deeply imbedded inside fish muscle. Look for labeling or other information to assure that the fish was properly frozen.

The U.S. Department of Commerce does voluntary inspection of fish and shellfish. Look for the Packed Under Federal Inspection (PUFI) mark on packages to assure that the fish is safe, wholesome, and properly labeled. There is also grading for fish similar to other meats. The Grade A stamp assures that the product is free from blemishes and defects, and is of high quality with good flavor and aroma.

Fish can be purchased in many sizes and shapes. The following are common examples of what you might purchase:

- ✓ Fish fillet—product is cut the length of the fish parallel to the backbone; it can be an irregular shape and size.
- ✓ Portioned cuts—square or rectangular cuts from a block of frozen fish; fish sticks are one example.
- ✓ Steaks—product is cut across the fish into slices.

See Figure 22.3 for a Seafood Buying Guide. The buying guide only addresses commonly served fish and shellfish. If your facility serves high-cost shellfish, be sure you investigate the proper storage and purchasing information for products such as fresh lobster, oysters, clams, and mussels.

Putting It Into Practice: 3

Your university foodservice has decided to offer Sushi at least once during each menu cycle. What purchasing standard should you consider for Sushi?

(Check your answer at the end of this chapter)

Figure 22.3 Seafood Buying Guide

Fish or Seafood Type	Characteristics to Look for:
Fresh or thawed filets and steaks	Mild odor; firm, elastic flesh; no bruising, blood spots or browning
Fresh or thawed shrimp—sold by the count per pound (e.g. extra large shrimp are 26-30 to the pound)	Flesh completely fills the shell; no strong odors; no black edges or spots; moist but not slimy feel
Surimi	Firm and moist; possess an off-white color; no strong odors; flesh sould have a light pink tint
Frozen seafood	No signs of frost on seafood or package interior; no signs of drying as in white patches; no strong odors; should be solidly frozen
Smoked fish	Clean, smoky odor; firm texture; no signs of mold or salt crystals

Fresh and Canned Produce

Fresh or canned produce is most likely part of every meal served so having purchasing standards will be critical to serving quality meals.

Fresh Produce

There are changes occurring in the fresh produce industry: 1) purchasing fresh produce at farmer's markets is gaining in popularity; 2) pre-cleaned and cut produce is widely available today and in some case may be less expensive than the whole product.

Farmer's Markets. Fresh produce is best at peak harvest and you will have the highest quality and nutritional value if you purchase from local farmers. Farmer's markets rarely sell graded products as the USDA grading program is voluntary. They may sell their products under a different name for a grade such as firsts and seconds. Check your menu and recipe needs to determine what level of quality is needed. If exterior appearance is important (i.e. when you are serving whole or pieces of fresh fruit or vegetables), then pay for the top-quality product. If the product is going to be mashed, chopped, or pureed, then choosing the lower quality grade will be your best buy. Get to know your vendors and how they keep the product fresh between harvesting and market. They might also be willing to deliver products to your facility.

Pre-cleaned and Cut Produce. Again, you have to know your menu and recipes and what staff time and skill level is available to determine the best produce to purchase. If the pre-cleaned or cut produce is cheaper and meets the needs of the facility, go one step farther and make sure vendors have HACCP (Hazard Analysis Critical Control Point) plans in place. Remember the pre-cut lettuce and pre-cleaned spinach foodborne illness outbreaks in the past ten years? Pre-cleaned and cut produce should be processed in clean, cold facilities and delivered in refrigerated trucks.

Canned and Frozen Fruits and Vegetables

Processing slightly reduces nutritional content of canned and frozen products but not enough to abandon the use of them. Frozen products have a higher quality appearance because freezing doesn't cause color and texture changes as much as canning. This is especially true for the **IQF (Individually Quick Frozen)** products. Frozen products can contain more nutrients than fresh because they are processed soon after harvesting. Many fresh products sit in store rooms or produce counters for a long time after harvesting, thus losing nutritional value.

The USDA has voluntary grading of quality for many canned and frozen vegetables and fruits. The most common are U.S. Grade A (Fancy), U.S. Grade B (Extra-select or Choice), and U.S. Grade C (Standard). Grading is paid for by the packer and packers may use different terminology. Grades are based on appearance criteria: color, uniformity of size, shape, lack of blemishes, or lack of stems/leaves. Like fresh produce, purchase only the grade that you need. If you are using canned tomatoes for pasta sauce, you don't need to purchase Grade A or Fancy.

IQF (Individually Quick Frozen)
A process of rapid freezing yielding smaller ice crystals and better color and texture

Your menu calls for a Blushing Pear salad that features canned pear halves. What grade should you consider purchasing for this salad?

(Check your answer at the end of this chapter)

SECTION B Preparation and Quality Standards

Preparation tips indicated below are not meant to be cooking or production instructions. Consider purchasing a book like *Food for Fifty* by Mary Molt to find recipes and full cooking instructions. When preparing standardized recipes, consider adding a quality standard to the recipe. That way, production staff will be reminded what the product should look like when it is completed. You will find more detailed quality standards in *Food for Fifty*.

Eggs, Cheese and Milk

Eggs

Preparation. The two most important principles for preparing egg products are to use low temperatures and minimize cooking time. It is also helpful to review grades and sizes of shell egg products. Grade A or AA is a good choice for eggs that will be prepared whole, such as poached or fried, because the yolks are firm and high. For other uses, Grade B is fine. Eggs are also sized. You will want to match shell egg sizes to sizes specified in any of your standardized recipes.

Menu items featuring eggs can range from scrambled eggs to omelets to frittatas to soufflés. With modified diets, you can use egg whites or egg substitute products that have been modified to reduce cholesterol and saturated fat. Figure 22.4 lists some common egg preparation problems and solutions.

Quality Standards. Quality standards for egg products should include the following:

✓ Fresh egg products such as scrambled, omelets and custards should have a soft-semisolid structure with no water separating from the cooked eggs.

✓ The color should be a soft yellow with no greening.

Cheese

Preparation. Cheese can add calcium, protein, and unique flavor to menu items. When you are selecting cheese for use in hot items, such as heated sandwiches, casseroles, or sauces select a cheese with a suitable flavor and texture. Generally, it should be sliced (for sandwiches), shredded, or cubed. Low temperatures, generally no higher than 350°F, help prevent curdling, toughness, and stringiness. Processed cheese products can be easy to incorporate into soups and sauces because they melt and blend particularly well. For food safety, a foodservice operation should select only pasteurized cheeses.

Quality Standards. A quality product containing cheese will have the cheese evenly distributed and melted with no browning of the cheese on top. The cheese flavor will blend with the other flavors and not be overpowering.

Milk

Preparation. Your menu and recipes will drive what milk products to purchase for cooking. See Figure 22.5 for descriptions of milk products used in cooking.

Glossary

Coagulate
To change a protein liquid into a soft or partially solid mass such as milk, pectin in jams/jellies, melted cheese

Figure 22.4 **Egg Preparation Problems and Solutions**

GREENING

PROBLEM: Cooked eggs may turn green (a natural chemical reaction) if held over heat for an extended period of time.

SOLUTION:

Omelets and Scrambled Eggs

- Use fresh eggs (Grade AA or A). Greening is more likely in older eggs.
- Cook eggs in small batches, no larger than three quarts.
- Substitute a medium white sauce for the liquid in the egg mixture. (One part white sauce to five parts egg.)
- Use temperatures of 135˚F and above for steam table holding.
- Do not hold hot foods on buffet line for longer than 1 hour.
- Use only stainless steel equipment and utensils.
- Try a liquid egg product if greening is frequent. (Many of these contain citric acid which retards greening.)
- Beat in ¼ teaspoon lemon juice for every 18 large eggs, or ¼ teaspoon citric acid crystals for every dozen large eggs.

Hard-Cooked Eggs

- Simmer eggs (185-190˚F) in water. Don't boil.
- Cool immediately in cold water. Peel when cool.

WEEPING

PROBLEM: Water separating from cooked eggs is caused by overcooking or by cooking and holding at high heat or from the addition of watery ingredients.

SOLUTION:

Scrambled Eggs

- Prepare eggs in small batches, no larger than three quarts.
- Substitute a medium white sauce for the liquid in the egg mixture. (One part white sauce to five parts egg.)
- Use temperatures 135˚F and above for steam table holding.
- Use egg products with stabilizers (i.e. gums) added.
- Limit the amount of added ingredients and make sure they are well-drained.

Meringues

- Lack of volume of the foam during beating or cooking:
  - > Beat whites until frothy before adding sugar.
  - > Add sugar slowly.
  - > Stop frequently and lift whites from bottom of bowl to ensure thorough and even beating.
  - > Use a clean metal or glass (not plastic) bowl.
  - > Beat until sugar is dissolved, the peaks barely fold over and whites do not slip from sides when bowl is tilted.
- If the meringue is to be used on a pie, place it on a hot (160˚F or above) filling, and brown immediately at 350˚F for approximately 15 minutes.
- For pie meringues containing a larger number of egg whites, reduce baking temperature and increase baking time to achieve temperature of 160˚F and mixture tests done (knife inserted near center removes cleanly).

RUBBERY AND DRY EGGS

PROBLEM: The problem is the result of overcooking and high heat. It generally follows weeping.

SOLUTION:

Omelets and Scrambled Eggs

- Cook at medium heat until no visible liquid egg remains.
- Cook in small batches, no larger than three quarts.
- Use a medium white sauce as liquid in egg mixture. (One part white sauce to five parts egg.)
- Use temperatures 135˚F and above for steam table holding.

Fried Eggs

- Cook over medium heat on preheated grill or in preheated pan.
- Use the right amount of fat to avoid toughening, about one teaspoon per egg.
- Baste with fat or steam-baste by adding small amounts of water and covering.

Figure 22.5 Milk Products Used in Cooking

Product	Characteristics
Evaporated Milk	Comes as whole milk, low fat, or fat free. Fluid milk with about 60% of the water removed.
Sweetened Condensed Milk	Comes as whole or fat free. It is evaporated milk with added sugar and processed to one-third its original volume.
Dry Milk	Comes as whole or low-fat. Dissolves in cold water; whole dry milk has a shorter shelf life because of the fat content.
Buttermilk	Can be purchased as fluid or dry product. The fluid product has a bacteria added to make it thick and tart. Dry buttermilk is dried from the liquid produced when making butter.
Half-and-Half	A mixture of whole milk and cream with 10.5-17% fat. May be used in place of light cream or table cream.
Light Cream, Table Cream	A lower-milkfat cream; cannot be used for whipping.
Light Whipping Cream	Contains a minimum of 30-36% fat and does work for whipping.
Heavy Whipping Cream	Contains a minimum of 36% fat and is preferred for whipped cream because it whips easily and holds it shape.
Sour Cream	A cultured product like yogurt except it is cultured cream. It contains 18-22% fat.

When cooking or reheating products containing milk or cream, use a low heat setting. Like cheese, milk is high in protein. When heated, protein **coagulates** and if heated too rapidly, the milk product may curdle. The film on the top of cooked milk or custards is an also an example of coagulated protein.

Quality Standards. Products containing milk or cream such as cream soups, sauces, and desserts will appear smooth with a uniform texture and no film. The color will be light and opaque. Products containing cream will also have a rich mouth feel and texture.

Grains

This section will address products made with grains such as sauces, yeast and quick breads, pasta and rice products, and dessert products.

Sauce

Preparation. There are several basic sauces:

- ✓ Simple sauces: A simple sauce is the au jus made from the drippings of roasted meat. The caramelized drippings are dissolved in water by stirring over heat with no thickening added. Concentrated canned soups may be used as a sauce (with no or minimal dilution); simply heat and serve hot.
- ✓ Butter sauces: Butter or margarine adds richness and flavor as a sauce and holds additional seasonings well. To make a butter sauce, stir seasonings into melted butter or margarine.
- ✓ Bread sauces: To prepare dry bread sauce, stir and brown breadcrumbs in a hot skillet with melted butter. For moist bread sauce, use two ounces of dry breadcrumbs to thicken one quart of stock.
- ✓ Sauces thickened with egg: These include mayonnaise and cooked sauces such as Hollandaise. The principles involved in the preparation of these sauces include the absorption of fat into the egg yolk and the ability of the egg yolk to act as an emulsifying agent and hold oil in suspension, as is the case in mayonnaise. Select pasteurized egg products for these recipes.

- ✓ Tart or savory sauces: Examples are barbecue sauce or teriyaki sauce. These sauces are often used on baked, broiled, and grilled meat, poultry, and fish. Marinades can be used to flavor and tenderize meats. Some include acid ingredients to help tenderize meat. If meat is marinated, do it under refrigeration. Discard the excess marinade before cooking.
- ✓ Starch-thickened sauces: These products use starch ingredients such as flour, cornstarch, tapioca, or others to thicken the product while heating. Cereal starch requires a boiling temperature to complete gelatinization, or the swelling of the starch granules which causes thickening to take place. Boiling must continue for five minutes to ensure complete swelling. Root starch begins to gelatinize when heated to 150°-160°F, and complete swelling is accomplished before boiling. If boiling continues, the starch granules will break down; the sauce will lose its thick appearance and become sticky. When preparing a starch-thickened sauce, it's important to stir continuously to prevent lumps.

A basic method for preparing a starch-based sauce begins by mixing the starch with fat. This is called a **roux**. To make a roux, blend an equal weight of melted fat and flour, and cook them together three to five minutes for a white roux, five to seven minutes for a blond roux, and ten minutes for a brown roux. Next, add to hot liquid off the burner, whipping with a wire whip. Continue stirring and heating until it reaches a boil. Cooking thickens the sauce and removes the starchy flavor.

Quality Standards. Quality standards for gravies and sauces should include: smooth texture; not too thick; lightly salted. The appearance and texture depends upon the type of sauce or gravy:

- ✓ White sauce (made with milk): White, opaque color
- ✓ Cream sauce (made with cream): Light yellow, rich mouthfeel
- ✓ Béchamel (made with part milk or cream and chicken or fish stock): Light yellow, rich mouth feel
- ✓ Veloute (made only with chicken or fish stock): Light yellow
- ✓ Brown sauce (made with browned roux): Rich brown color, lightly toasted flavor, have a slight sheen.

Yeast Bread

Preparation. Yeast breads are leavened with yeast and may be a lean dough (using little or no sugar and margarine) or a sweet dough (using sugar, margarine, and/or eggs). Lean dough is appropriate for French bread, sandwich rolls, and similar products; while sweet dough makes good caramel rolls or raisin bread. See Figure 22.6 for preparation problems and solutions.

Quality Standard: Uniform golden brown color, sounds hollow when tapped; crisp, tender crust; uniform grain, moist texture.

Quick Bread

Preparation. Quick breads include biscuits, muffins, and loaves such as banana bread or nut bread. Quick breads can be made from batter (as with muffins) or soft dough (as with biscuits that are rolled and cut).

Glossary

Roux
Used to thicken sauces and gravies that combines equal weights of fat and flour

Figure 22.6 Yeast Bread Preparation Problems and Solutions

Problem:	Coarse, heavy texture
Solution:	Be sure yeast is not killed by water that is too hot in initial stages or excessive equipment-generated heat in processing [use a thermometer; extend kneading time; check proofing time (may be too long or too short)]; check to be sure excessive salt was not used.
Problem:	Loaf is cracked
Solution:	Avoid adding excessive flour when forming the loaf; shape loaf with care, not forcing it.
Problem:	Loaf is too big and light
Solution:	Check flour ingredient (may be too much gluten); check oven temperature (may be too low); check yeast measurement (may be too much)
Problem:	Loaf collapses
Solution:	Re-check and limit proofing time; make sure oven temperature is not too low

For any baked product, it is important to measure flour correctly. Be sure to match the product to the recipe, as presifted flour does not have the same volume as unsifted flour.

Some ingredients require packing. An example is brown sugar. Failure to pack the sugar when specified could reduce the sugar in the recipe by as much as 50 percent and affect the final product significantly.

Note that unlike yeast breads, quick breads do not rely on developing the gluten in flour, so mixing should be limited. Too much mixing causes the gluten to develop, resulting in tunnels in the product.

Biscuits contain similar ingredients, but the proportion of flour is higher. A muffin dough has 2 parts flour to one part liquid, whereas a biscuit dough has three parts flour to one part liquid.

Figure 22.7 lists quick bread problems and solutions.

Quality Standard. Muffins and biscuits should be uniform size and shape; have a tender crumb, even cell structure, rounded, not peaked top, pleasing flavor, moist texture, no tunnels and a uniform golden brown color.

Figure 22.7 Quick Bread Preparation Problems and Solutions

Problem:	Coarse texture with tunnels
Solution:	Avoid over mixing; re-check measurements of ingredients
Problem:	Dry product
Solution:	Avoid over baking; also check flour measurement (may be too much)
Problem:	Quick breads become soggy
Solution:	Remove from pans after about 5 minutes; do not let sit in pans too long
Problem:	Muffin or biscuit texture is tough or rubbery
Solution:	Limit mixing; only moisten dry ingredients
Problem:	Biscuits are dense and don't "rise" much
Solution:	Mix and handle dough a little bit more

Pasta and Rice

Preparation. When preparing rice, macaroni, noodles, and spaghetti, or similar products, general cooking principles are to:

✓ Cook quickly in boiling water until tender. Salt the water if specified in the recipe.

✓ Add a small amount of salad oil to the water to keep pastas and rice from sticking together and foaming. At serving time, there will be no need for additional fat. (Additions of salt and/or oil should be part of the standardized recipe, and amounts should be controlled as required for special diets.)

✓ Drain quickly and stir in fat, if specified. Do not rinse.

✓ Avoid washing rice before cooking or rinsing pasta after cooking, as these procedures wash away valuable nutrients such as B-vitamins.

Quality Standard. Pasta should have some resistance to the bite (called al dente or tender to the tooth); not too soft or mushy. Rice grains should also be tender, not too soft, and separate easily.

Meat, Poultry, and Fish Products

The quality of meat products will depend upon the quality of the ingredients, the equipment in place, and the skill level of the cooking staff. Endpoint cooking standards for meat products are extremely important and are located in Chapter 17.

Beef, Pork, Lamb, Veal

Preparation. When cooking meats, choose *dry heat or moist heat* methods. For example, tender cuts that contain little connective tissue, such as steaks and roasts, do well with dry heat methods. These include roasting, baking, broiling (for individual portions that are 1-2" thick), and frying. Less tender cuts of meat with more connective tissue require moist heat to develop tenderness and flavor.

You can use meat timetables as a general guide for cooking meat. Timetables, available in most cookbooks, are useful in determining production scheduling requirements, i.e. when to start the cooking process so that products will be done in time for service. You can measure doneness with a thermometer placed in the center of the product, not touching bone. The temperature of a roast may continue to rise after it is removed from the oven.

Quality Standards. Meat products should be evenly browned, not burned, tender, and moist. To assure food safety, meat products are cooked to the appropriate time and temperature recommendations.

Poultry

Preparation. Poultry is available in various cuts, from whole birds to cut pieces. Generally, poultry should be cooked at a low temperature (325°-350°F) to produce a tender, juicy product. Preparation options include roasting, broiling, grilling, oven frying, and other frying methods; as well as moist-heat methods such as braising, stewing, or steaming.

As with meats, you can use timetables as a general guide for cooking poultry. It is important to verify end-point cooking temperatures with a thermometer.

The chicken breasts for dinner were dry and tough. They don't meet the standard. What might have happened to cause this?

(Check your answer at the end of this chapter)

Quality Standards. Poultry products should be lightly browned, tender, and moist. To ensure food safety, poultry products are cooked to the appropriate time and temperature recommendations.

Fish

Preparation. Fish should generally be cooked at a moderately high temperature, rapidly enough to retain juices and moisture, but slowly enough to ensure thorough cooking. You can match preparation techniques to the product. For example, fatty fish such as salmon lend themselves to baking and broiling. In general, consider ten minutes cooking time per one inch thickness at 400-425°F.

Quality Standards. Fish products should be juicy, flavorful, and tender. Breaded products should be a uniform golden brown color. To ensure food safety, fish products are cooked to the appropriate time and temperature recommendations.

Fresh Produce

Fresh produce should be prepared as close to serving time as practical to preserve the fresh appearance and nutritional value.

Fresh Vegetables

Preparation. Careful attention to preparation techniques can help preserve nutrient values in produce, as well as flavor, appearance, and overall quality. It's important to consider the needs of the clients served, ensuring that vegetables are tender enough for any clients with chewing limitations. Sometimes, chopping or grating vegetables (as in a coleslaw, for example) is an option for serving fresh vegetables. Cook vegetables in small amounts of water, or steam them until they are tender but firm. As possible, hold prep work for as close to final service time as possible to maintain quality and minimize nutrient losses. In the past, some chefs have used baking soda to brighten the color of cooked vegetables. Not only does this make the vegetable mushy, it also decreases the nutrient quantity of the vegetable. When cooking fresh vegetables, pre-cook only until color brightens and the vegetable is still crisp. Plunge into ice cold water, drain, and store in the refrigerator until ready to complete cooking immediately prior to service. This helps to preserve the color and texture but increases the nutrient loss.

Quality Standards (this is also appropriate for canned fruits). Vegetables are cut into bite-sized pieces as appropriate for the clientele. They are cooked to a tender but firm consistency. Color is pleasing and appropriate for the vegetable.

Fruit

Preparation. Fresh fruits may be served whole, halved, or in pieces. Wash fresh fruits thoroughly before serving. Some, such as peaches and bananas, can turn brown after slicing. To prevent this, you can dip slices in ascorbic acid or diluted lemon juice after peeling or cutting. As with vegetables, you should cut or prepare fresh fruits as close to service time as practical.

Dried fruits may be served as stewed fruit or in pies, cobblers, crisps, whips, and salads. Frozen fruit should be served as soon as it has thawed (preferably before all the ice crystals have melted).

Quality Standards (this is also appropriate for canned vegetables). Fruits are cut into bite sized pieces as appropriate for the clientele or the fruit recipe. Color is pleasing and appropriate for the fruit. Frozen fruit is not watery and has some ice crystals. Flavor is mildly sweet and appropriate for the fruit.

Having standards for purchasing and preparation are only two of the standards needed to control quality. Chapter 21 discussed two others, standardized recipes and portion control. What about special diets? What happens if a product flops? Can these be controlled?

SECTION C Other Food Preparation Standards

Ingredient Substitutions and Monitoring Food Waste

During food production, sometimes things go wrong. An ingredient may be unavailable due to a delayed delivery, a shortage from the supplier, or an error. Or, a recipe may fail due to errors in standardization, changes in ingredients, or errors made by a cook. In each of these situations, a Certified Dietary Manager is likely to be called upon to solve the problem.

Substitutions

When ingredients are not available, the Certified Dietary Manager needs to make a decision about substituting ingredients. A reasonable policy is to have substitutions routinely approved by a manager, rather than left to the cook's discretion. This policy ensures that the manager will become aware of supply problems. In consequence, a manager can further investigate these problems and take steps to ensure against repeated shortages.

Work with the staff to develop a standard ingredient substitution list. Some ingredients do not substitute well. However, many common ingredients can be changed. Figure 22.8 lists examples of common ingredient substitutions that may be acceptable in many recipes.

Occasionally, it may also be necessary to substitute entire products in a menu, due to shortages. To make these decisions, look for the most similar product you can identify. For example, a substitution for breaded chicken strips might be breaded chicken breasts. A substitution for meatloaf might be Salisbury steak or a ground beef patty. A substitution for cooked oatmeal might be cream of wheat. In each of these decisions, double check the intended substitution for each special diet served. Key nutritional components, such as calories, protein, fat, and carbohydrate, should remain about the same. Also give special consideration to any client with unique restrictions, such as food allergies or intolerances.

Beyond the substitution issue, sometimes there is an error in production leading to unacceptable products or recipe flops. Figure 22.9 lists ideas for dealing with common production problems.

Figure 22.8 Common Ingredient Substitutions

These substitutions work in some recipes, but not all. Substitution decisions require culinary experience and sound judgment.

For:	Substitute:
1 lb. butter	1 lb. margarine
1 cup milk	¼ cup dry milk plus 1 cup water
1 cup buttermilk	1 cup plain yogurt or 7/8 cup milk and ¼ cup vinegar or lemon juice
1 tsp. baking powder	1/3 tsp. baking soda plus ½ tsp. cream of tartar
1 cup cracker crumbs	1 cup bread crumbs
1 Tbsp. cornstarch (for thickening)	2 Tbsp. flour
1 clove garlic, minced	1/8 tsp. garlic powder
1 tsp. lemon juice	½ tsp. vinegar or 1 tsp. lime juice
1 lb. dried beans	Approx. 5 cup cooked beans (adjust liquids)
1 cup packed brown sugar	1 cup granulated sugar (may add 1 Tbsp. molasses)

Figure 22.9 Solutions for Common Production Problems

Problem:	Solution:
Soup or sauce curdles	Add milk and beat rapidly
Chips are stale	Heat in oven at 350°F for 10 minutes
Soup is under yield	Add broth, tomato juice, or other liquid as appropriate
Baked product overly browned	Cut off dark edges
Product is too salty	Add a small amount of sugar (if not for special diets) or if its a soup, add potatoes
Product is too dry	Add a small amount of sauce or gravy

Source: Adapted from F&N Training Paks, © 1998, The Grossbauer Group

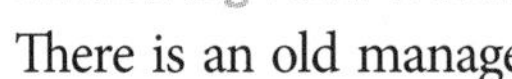

Monitoring Food Waste

There is an old management adage in foodservice: "You can't control what you don't measure." When it comes to controlling food costs and food production, you also need controls for what food is wasted. Implement a waste log and ask employees to record what was wasted and why. This waste is then calculated as part of the food cost. See Figure 22.10 for a Food Waste Standard Policy and Procedure.

It is also important to occasionally monitor what goes out in the trash that is discarded every day. There have been actual incidents where employees have hidden food in the trash bags and then transferred it to their vehicle when the trash was taken out.

Another control is for food waste that is edible, such as leftovers that can't be used for another meal. These can be donated to hunger relief charities.

As follow-up to any problem that arises during food production, investigate the causes and seek to make improvements. Whether the situation relates to inventory management, reliability of suppliers, errors in standardized recipes, or skills of employees, it is up to the Certified Dietary Manager to implement improvements.

Putting It Into Practice: 6

The cream of broccoli soup curdled and there isn't time to make another batch before the meal service. Is there a way to solve this problem?

(Check your answer at the end of this chapter)

Figure 22.10 **Food Waste Standard Policy and Procedure**

Date Effective: ____________________

Date Revised: ____________________

Date Reviewed: ____________________

Approved By: ____________________

Issuing Department: ____________________

Policy

It is the foodservice department's goal to maximize food usage in order to avoid waste. To this end, certain leftover foods are reused, with restrictions.

Procedures

- Do not refreeze thawed food unless it is cooked thoroughly first. Refreezing will not kill the microorganisms present in thawed food.
- Cool foods that are planned for use a second time to 41°F very quickly. Ice baths, vigorous stirring, and transfer to shallow dishes are options for ensuring a quick cooldown.
- Discard most leftovers that are stored in the cooler and not used within 72 hours.
- Use soups with added meat, ground meats and poultry, meat gravies and broths, fresh chicken, fresh turkey, and cooked chicken nuggets or patties that are kept in the cooler within 48 hours.
- Do not use any food that has remained out for 2 hours or more—throw it away.
- Store leftover foods in containers with tight-fitting lids. If food is stored in a zip-top plastic bag, push the air out of the bag before sealing.
- Label all containers clearly with the date and time that the food was first prepared.
- Reheat food to a minimum of 165°F. Reheat gravies and soups by bringing to a rolling boil for at least 1 minute.
- Throw it out when in doubt. Smelling food is not a reliable means of determining whether or not it is still usable. Never taste food as a means of judging freshness.

Review Date 4/08 | G0615

Source: RD411.com

Nutrient Control and Special Diets

If you are serving special diets, you may have special responsibility to supervise the amounts of certain nutrients during food production. Foods served to clients following sodium (salt) limitations, for example, need to provide consistent and reliable amounts of sodium. The same is true for fats, as well as many other nutrients.

Meanwhile, many clients who have no special diet orders may still be following special nutritional guidelines, through personal choices and attention to healthful practices. For these clients, you likewise have a responsibility to standardize and control nutrient content of menu items. Furthermore, if you label foods served by nutritional content, you have an obligation to assure the labeling is truthful on an ongoing basis.

To assure this control, specify salt, fats, and other ingredients in standardized recipes. Avoid using phrases like, "salt and pepper to taste" or "add butter as desired" or "pour olive oil liberally over all." Instead, test and standardize quantities for these ingredients. It is even important to standardize amounts of salt to add to water for pasta, rice, and vegetables (if any is to be added).

Vegetables, stir-fries, hamburgers, and many other products can be produced on a batch basis throughout service. Often, cooking in small, continuous batches minimizes holding times, preserves nutrients, and also boosts final quality of products at the time of service. This is called **batch cooking**.

It is also essential to practice meticulous portion control. Not only does portion control affect the success of standardized recipe yields and food costing plans, it also affects nutrient control. Overportioning a product by 10 percent also increases calories, fat, sodium, protein, and all other nutrients by 10 percent. An accumulation of portion control errors through a one-day menu can seriously violate the controls intended by a special diet.

In producing food, also pay special attention to texture and consistency, especially for products served to clients with swallowing disorders. Variations from standards established for product consistency can make meal time difficult, or even dangerous, for a client with a swallowing disorder.

Making special diets appealing sometimes requires culinary creativity and a flair for presentation. Particularly in a healthcare or a correctional facility, you may be serving clients whose appetites are compromised due to illness, disability, side effects of medications, psychological stress, or even depression. Extra attention to presentation, attractive garnishes, and other visual details can play a strong therapeutic role.

Pureed diets in particular require planning. In a skilled nursing facility, a quarter of clients (or more) may be eating from a pureed menu. Plain pureed foods are uniform in color, and the color can be drab (such as pale brown for pureed meat). Many plain pureed foods offer little visual appeal.

Experienced Certified Dietary Managers use food processors to blend casseroles, rather than serving plain foods. They also emphasize using seasonings, thickening ordinary foods, serving slurries, and adding milk or other ingredients to bring entrees up to required protein and calorie needs. Today, healthcare foodservice managers use specially developed recipes, color combinations, flavor combinations, and safe garnishes to make pureed menu items interesting, attractive, and appealing. Pureed meat products can also be molded to look more like their source foods.

Garnishing

Garnishing foods is a small touch that goes a long way. A simple garnish lends a polished appearance with professional zest and can entice appetites. Garnishes can be part of many standardized recipes, and foodservice staff can benefit from training in how to present foods. An appropriate garnish should always be something edible and safe to eat. Often, it complements the color of the product. Sometimes it adds a complementary flavor, too, such as a lemon wedge on fish or minced parsley on soup. Remember to calculate the cost of garnishes. While possibilities for garnishing are endless, here are a few ideas:

- ✓ Lemon or orange wedge (on fish, chicken, salads)
- ✓ Fruit sliced in a fan shape

Glossary

Batch Cooking
Cooking in small, continuous batches to preserve nutrients and food quality

Garnish
Enhance food appearance by adding edible decorations

✓ Melon balls (with cold plates)
✓ Cucumber and/or carrot curls; cherry tomatoes (with sandwiches)
✓ Croutons (on soups or salads)
✓ Grated cheese (on soups, salads, or hot vegetables)
✓ Parsley, dill, or rosemary sprig (with meat, poultry, or fish entrees)
✓ Minced herbs (on soups or casseroles)
✓ Whipped cream (on desserts or beverages)
✓ Maraschino cherry (on desserts)
✓ Flavored syrup (drizzled on cakes in a zigzag pattern)
✓ Carved vegetables (with entrees or cold items)
✓ Paprika and/or minced chives (on potato products)
✓ Grated summer squash on salads
✓ Hard candy on clear-liquid diet trays.

END OF CHAPTER

Putting It Into Practice Questions & Answers

1. Coffee is available in your cafeteria throughout the day. You want to make creamers available that don't need refrigeration and can be displayed next to the coffee. What type of creamer should you purchase?

   A. *Individual creamers that have been ultra-high-temperature processed do not need refrigeration.*

2. You have a client who loves cream soups but is gluten intolerant. Your cream soups are thickened with flour. What change would you recommend so that your client can have the cream soup?

   A. *Corn starch can also be used as a thickener and it contains no gluten.*

3. Your university foodservice has decided to offer Sushi at least once during each menu cycle. What purchasing standard should you consider for Sushi?

   A. *The fish must be frozen according to the FDA standards and contain a proper label.*

4. Your menu calls for a Blushing Pear salad that uses canned pear halves. What grade should you consider purchasing for this salad?

   A. *Since you are using a pear half that will be the predominant salad ingredient, consider purchasing the Grade A (Fancy). This will showcase your salad without worrying about odd shaped pieces or discolorations.*

5. The chicken breasts for dinner were dry and tough. They don't meet the standard. What might have happened to cause this?

   A. *Poultry contains protein. If it is cooked at too high a temperature, too quickly, the protein strands shorten and become tough and rubbery. If they are held too long on a steam table they may also be overcooked.*

6. The cream of broccoli soup curdled and there isn't time to make another batch before the meal service. Is there a way to solve this problem?

   A. *Add whole milk and beat rapidly to break up the curdles.*

CHAPTER 23

Supervise the Production and Distribution of Food

Overview and Objectives

There are many factors that go into the production and distribution of food. The difference between quality foodservice and poor foodservice is the Certified Dietary Manager. Compare the key standards to current practice and take necessary action to ensure quality production.

After completing this chapter, you should be able to:

- ✓ Check quality/quantity of food served
- ✓ Check adherence to delivery schedules and procedures
- ✓ Keep records for monitoring and accountability

Chapters 21 and 22 have already addressed production controls and standards such as portion control, standardized recipes, purchasing, and preparation standards. Other controls in the production and distribution process that affect the quality of food are time and temperature controls, production planning tools, staff training, and controlling energy usage. Each of these controls produces records for monitoring and accountability.

Time and Temperature Controls

One of the greatest influences on the quality and quantity of food served is controlling time and temperature. So far, examples of quality standards for preparation addressed criteria such as purchasing the appropriate quality of product, using low heat when preparing high protein foods, and comparing end products to standards prior to service. Time and temperature controls should be added to your standardized recipes so that foods are cooked to the proper temperature, within a given amount of time, and then cooled and stored properly. These standards combine with the sanitation standards (FDA Food Code) and provisions to also ensure food safety for your clients. They also help to assure the quality of food.

How do you supervise time and temperature to assure food quality and quantity? Let's assume that you have procedures in place to take the temperature of foods at delivery and before, during, and after service. As the Certified Dietary Manager, your job is to make sure that those procedures are in place, they are working, and you take any necessary corrective action. In this instance, you can do that by checking the temperature documentation and taking the temperature yourself occasionally to compare to the documentation. What if food is being served at an improper temperature? What is the corrective action? The immediate action is to adjust the food temperature. For instance, if the food is too cold, reheat the food to 165°F for 15 seconds and return it to service. The second action is to address the performance problem with the staff member responsible. Deal with the performance issue as early as possible. If the problem occurred because of lack of training, arrange for one-on-one training right away. If the problem occurred because of lack of equipment (thermometers weren't readily available), fix it. If the person can do the job properly and just didn't do it, review the standard and hold the person accountable.

You also have a policy that foods at each meal are tasted prior to service. One way to monitor this policy is to occasionally observe plate waste. Spend some time in the room where plates are being returned or in the dining room. What is on the plate? Are you seeing servings of the same food item uneaten? What is the corrective action? The immediate action is to taste the food on the serving line. If there is something wrong with the quality of the food, either fix it or remove it from service. Then follow up with the person responsible for tasting the food and address the performance problem.

Production Planning Tools

Supervising the production and distribution of food requires using production planning tools. Those tools include forecasting, production scheduling, supervision of quality, and training for production staff.

Forecasting

Have you ever wondered how Certified Dietary Managers know the amount of food to prepare for any given meal or event? **Forecasting** is the process of estimating future needs for food. It tells you both how much food to produce, and how much food to order. Based on your own facility, you will determine how far in advance you need to forecast. About a week ahead is not uncommon. Based on the menu, purchasing systems, and inventory management system, a timetable or schedule for forecasting becomes a routine part of your operation. To create a forecast, there are several types of information you can examine is developed:

Census figures. Many Certified Dietary Managers keep records of the quantity of food served in the past. Depending on the facility, this may be available in one or more forms. In a healthcare environment, a manager may use a census, or a client count of patients/residents receiving each of a variety of menus or diet types on corresponding days of the menu cycle, and then match the figures. In this process, the manager then checks the current census to estimate adjustments. Figure 23.1 shows an example of this process. A census may also be available in a school, a university, and corrections environment. Many complex formulas and options exist for using census data. One facility may average the figures for the past five menu cycles. Another may examine figures from one year ago.

Glossary

Forecasting
Estimating future product needs for menu items

Figure 23.1 Using a Census to Create a Forecast

Background
You serve clients in a skilled nursing facility based on a three-week cycle menu. You are currently forecasting needs for Day 15 of the cycle, coming up in about a week.
Process
1. You examine the census for Day 15 of the previous menu cycle. You see that you served 152 clients on the regular menu, 34 clients on a pureed menu, and 51 clients on a modified fat and sugar menu. The total client count was 237. 2. You check today's census, and see that the client count is 235, with a very similar distribution among diets. 3. You carry over the numbers from the last Day 15 to the future Day 15.

Tally figures. In a computerized menu system, a computer may tally each item selected or served on a menu. These tallies become valuable detail for the next forecast. In this system, a Certified Dietary Manager may essentially transfer the tally figures on the computer from a past menu cycle day to the next one, making any manual adjustments desired.

Using historical data such as census and tallies, a Certified Dietary Manager also has to evaluate whether the predictions were accurate the last time around. For example, did the serviceline run out of food before the service ended? Or, did the cook report large quantities of leftovers of any item? These must be taken into account for the next estimate. A standard procedure is to provide a form for documenting shortages and leftovers. Review these routinely. If there are excessive leftovers, this can be a sign that the forecast needs to be decreased. However, if a particular product runs out before service ends, this is a sign that more should be produced. It is particularly important to encourage employees to complete production records accurately when service ends, and to monitor overproduction and underproduction for continued planning.

Weather plays a big part in how many meals are served for different facilities. Attendance at K-12 schools, a college or university, and a retirement center or senior housing may all be dramatically affected by the weather. Along with your tally figures, make a note about the weather. If you have a record of how many were served on a rainy day, you can use this information for future rainy days. Even though forecasting figures might be pre-set in your electronic software, you can override the system and predict your own forecast on days when weather events may affect your count.

Your school celebrates the return of spring with a week-long celebration that culminates in a large outdoor picnic. You normally serve 450 students and their guests. The day of the picnic arrives and it is cold and rainy. What steps would you take to adjust the forecast for meals?

(Check your answer at the end of this chapter)

Point of sale records. Another source for historical figures is a point of sale (POS) system, or computer-based cash register system that tabulates menu items sold. This is useful in a cafeteria setting. The data may be available as a printout from the POS system, and/or the system may include software for forecasting that electronically accepts sales records. When you use sales figures, it is also important to consider records of service problems. For example, you may find that you sold 143 servings of macaroni and cheese at lunch on Day 12. However, service records tell you that the cafeteria ran out of macaroni and cheese at 11:45 AM, before all clients had purchased lunch. In this case, you need to boost the number for the next forecast.

Specific orders. For a catered event, you generally have an advance client count that can be used in forecasting.

Known changes. There may be certain changes you can predict for the future. In a hospital, for example, what if the upcoming Day 4 of the menu cycle is also a holiday? In this case, you can likely predict that the census will go down, as clients are discharged for the holiday. Likewise, in a campus or business dining environment, schedules can help you predict times when fewer (or more) clients are likely to arrive.

These are just a few examples of records that may be used for determining a forecast. In addition, a common practice is to **pad** or increase forecast figures by a small increment, such as three to ten percent. In the Figure 23.1 example, if you forecast for 235 residents, what happens if three more are admitted to the facility before the next Day 15? You never want to cut the forecast so closely that you cannot serve a few more clients. The amount of padding you need to do depends on how much variation is normal for your client count. On the other hand, you do not want to pad excessively, as this may generate food waste and lost dollars.

To determine a forecasting methodology, ask the following questions:

- ✓ How can I best capture historical figures about the amount of food served?
- ✓ How can I verify whether these figures will carry through to the future?
- ✓ How can I capture and incorporate notes about food shortages or leftovers?
- ✓ How much variation is typical for my facility, and how much do I need to pad the figures?

A forecast is expressed in numbers of servings for each menu item. Products served on multiple menus are totaled for a final count. Figure 23.2 provides a partial example of a forecast.

A forecast is more than number-crunching. It requires a willingness to make good judgments. It is not an exact science. Effective methods for predicting needs are not universal, but vary from one facility to another. Client groups, menus, and service models all affect the forecast. Starting with standard approaches, most Certified Dietary Managers learn much from experience, and refine their forecasting methods to the individual facility. In addition, foodservice facilities with very stable client counts on a cycle menu often devise a standard forecast that is used routinely, with only minor adjustments from cycle to cycle.

The results of effective forecasting include:

- ✓ Smooth operations, as products are available when they are needed
- ✓ Satisfaction, as clients receive the foods they expect
- ✓ Cost control, as accuracy minimizes food waste.

Glossary

Pad
Adding to a forecast by a small percentage to assure adequate quantities of food

Figure 23.2 Partial Forecast for Day 15 Lunch

Product	Predicted Count (Number of Servings)
Mulligatawny soup	124
Macaroni and cheese	78
Turkey salad sandwich on wheat bun	54
Pureed macaroni and cheese	17
Tossed salad	67
French dressing	22
Cottage cheese	2
Fresh banana	81

Production Scheduling

With quantities of food to deliver at single points in time, a Certified Dietary Manager needs to give special attention to advance preparation practices. Advance preparation is a general term that describes any tasks that can or must be completed before main production takes place. To determine what steps of the production of any product should undergo advance preparation, ask questions such as these about each recipe:

✓ What ingredients need to be thawed before a cook will be able to use them in this recipe (and how long will it take to thaw them following safe techniques)?

✓ What sub-recipes have to be produced in order to make the main recipe? A sub-recipe is a distinct recipe routine that must be completed before production of a main recipe is possible. An example of a sub-recipe is the tomato sauce that will be used in lasagna, the pie crust that will be used in chicken pot pie, or the cooked ham that will be used in ham salad.

✓ What pre-preparation processing is required to bring an inventory product into the form required by the recipe? Examples of advance processing include washing lettuce, peeling and slicing apples or potatoes, trimming fat from meat, dicing meat, crushing garlic, chopping onions, soaking dry beans, and many others.

✓ What products need to be pre-portioned before production can begin?

It is not always necessary to perform all possible advance preparation as a separate group of tasks. However, doing work in advance when possible often eases the workload in the few hours before service, and makes it easier to meet service requirements.

Once you have identified tasks that can be performed in advance, it is helpful to establish timetables. For example, thawing frozen meat in the refrigerator may take several days. So, a **production schedule** must indicate the need to transfer it in time. Figure 23.3 lists tips for thawing foods.

Sub-recipes can sometimes be prepared in advance and then held under proper storage conditions until needed. Often, the decision to separate sub-recipes as advance preparation tasks depends on a judgment of quality and food safety. A

Putting It Into Practice: 2

What are the production steps for the recipe below? Indicate with a star the steps that are advance preparation.

Chicken Wrap

- 96 (6-inch) tortillas
- 9 lbs. grilled chicken breast, cubed
- 1 #10 can cooked black beans, drained
- 8 lbs. pre-chopped mixed lettuce (romaine and iceberg)
- 3 lbs. crumbled feta cheese
- 3 lbs. roasted red peppers, chopped
- 1½ qts. commercial Caesar Dressing

(Check your answer at the end of this chapter)

Figure 23.3 Thawing Tips and Times

Tips	Thawing Times
• Schedule thawing so that meat will be cooked soon after thawing is complete. • Do not thaw at room temperature. Use one of the approved thawing methods. • Withdraw from freezer only the amount of meat/poultry needed for one-day use. • Remove from carton and thaw in original wrappings in the refrigerator. • Space packages on refrigerator shelves so that air can circulate around them.	• Timing for large meat roasts: 4-7 hrs. per pound of meat • Timing for small meat roasts: 3-5 hrs. per pound of meat. • Timing for chops, steaks: 12-14 hrs. • Timing for chicken, whole: 1 day • Timing for chicken pieces: 12-14 hrs. • Timing for whole turkey—18 lbs or larger: 4-5 days • Timing for whole turkey—under 18 lbs: 2-3 days • Timing for seafood in blocks: 1-2 days

tomato sauce for lasagna, for example, can readily be made in advance, chilled rapidly, and held for a day. However, a traditional hollandaise sauce cannot be held.

Advance processing of vegetables can be batched for greater efficiency. Consider this example: Cook A needs a total of 4 quarts of chopped onions for beef stew plus 2 quarts of chopped onions for homemade bean soup. For the same production period, Cook B needs 1 quart of chopped onions for a chicken salad plate, and 3 cups of chopped onions for guacamole. The employee responsible for the salad bar needs another 4 quarts of chopped onions.

In this example, each of three employees could requisition and obtain onions for preparation. An employee responsible for issuing inventory would process at least three separate requisitions, and make at least three deliveries. Each cook could wash and peel the onions, set up a food processor, chop the onions, and then clean up. This would generate a lot of work.

Alternately, one person could go through the process one time, and prepare all the chopped onions needed for all three areas. Then, the employee could portion and distribute the chopped onions. Even in a very small operation, consolidation such as this is cost-beneficial.

While consolidation provides greater economy and convenience, the disadvantage of this approach is the burden of predicting exact needs. In some systems, a cook reviews the upcoming schedule and requisitions advance preparation needs. In others, the Certified Dietary Manager establishes a schedule for pre-preparation in conjunction with the forecast.

Here is a situation in which computerized systems can offer support. A well-designed food management software package may:

✓ Handle pre-processed ingredients as a type of inventory item, and requisition them automatically according to established lead times and forecasts

✓ Consolidate needs for pre-preparation and generate a distribution list for each product

✓ Generate labels for products undergoing ingredient room processing or pre-processing

Glossary

Production Schedule
A document that outlines what to produce, how much to produce and who is responsible

✓ Review upcoming needs for thawed products and generate advance thawing schedules that tell a storage clerk when to transfer products to refrigeration.

Use of an automated system makes it more practical to consolidate and manage production schedules without risking oversights and emergencies.

Production Schedule Communication. As you forecast production, plan staffing, and schedule activities, it becomes clear there is another critical piece in the flow of food production. This is communication. Scheduling production is an excellent example of a task that requires clear and precise communications for assigned staff. The main production activities require direction, too. A cook needs to know what to make, how many servings to make, when to have products ready, and where to deliver products.

How this is communicated varies by facility. In some small facilities, actual food tallies or counts reach the cooks before preparation. For example, in a healthcare environment, automated menu tallies may be handed to the cooks with an instruction to add a pad of several servings per item. The tally form identifies meal, product, number of servings, and distribution instructions.

In a manual system, a Certified Dietary Manager maintains a set of production sheet forms for cooks based on a cycle menu. This can require manual editing from cycle to cycle, and become quite burdensome.

In any large, multi-site facility, it is virtually essential today that a computerized production system be used to manage the paperwork and communications involved with food production. A set of computer-generated production sheets can provide a daily, detailed schedule for each cook, along with standardized recipes scaled for the number of servings forecasted. A sample production sheet appears in Figure 23.4.

After production, it is also important to document leftovers and shortages of each product. This information helps with future forecasting, and careful attention to this process can both improve service (supply) and reduce food waste. In some facilities, this documentation is the responsibility of cooks. In others, it is the responsibility of trayline or service personnel. Figure 23.5 illustrates a food production planning and leftover report form.

At the end of each work day, production records such as these should go back to the Certified Dietary Manager or person in charge of forecasting. In a computerized system, this data may be entered into the system for use in automated forecasting for future menus.

At the end of each day, your cooks document production results. What items should they document?

(Check your answer at the end of this chapter)

Supervision of Quality

Another aspect of ongoing food production management is the supervision of quality. A Certified Dietary Manager should look at foods during both production and service. In addition, some facilities set up small taste panels of foods produced, either daily or at periodic intervals. Production and management personnel join together to taste samples of all products, evaluate quality, evaluate texture (especially for texture-modified products), and make suggestions for improvement.

Figure 23.4 Sample Production Sheet

Prepared for HOT FOOD												Sunday, 10/16/XX (Weekly)
Recipe	**Meat/Food**	**Total Required**	**Regular**	**Strained**	**Chopped**	**Ground**	**Pureed**	**Minced**	**Nectar-Like**	**Syrup-Like**	**Honey-Like**	**Pudding-Like**
A.M. Meal												
4	Cream of Wheat (½ cup)	37.0	37.0									
210	Sausage (1 oz.)	32.0	24.0		1.0	4.0	2.0	1.0				
4598	Turkey Sausage (1 oz.)	3.0	3.0									
900	Pancakes (2, 4")	36.0	33.0				3.0					
6748	Coffee (8 oz.)	36.0	33.0						1.0		1.0	1.0
A.M. Meal Substitutions and Alternates												
8124	Super Cereal (4 oz.)	1.0	1.0									
6753	Scrambled Eggs (#16 dipper)	3.0	2.0				1.0					
2640	Toast and Margarine (1 each)	2.0	1.0				1.0					
277	Hot Tea (8 oz.)	2.0	2.0									
Noon Meal												
10984	Beef Brisket with Gravy (3 oz. w/2 oz.)	36.0	28.0		1.0	4.0	2.0	1.0				
13664	Parsley Buttered Potatoes (½ cup)	38.0	34.0				4.0					
12180	Broccoli and Carrots (½ cup)	36.0	32.0				4.0					
6748	Coffee (8 oz.)	35.0	32.0						1.0		1.0	1.0
2588	Hot Rolls and Margarine (1 each)	38.0	34.0				4.0					
Noon Meal Substitutions and Alternates												
2907	Chicken Noodle Soup (6 oz.)	1.0	1.0									
5506	Hamburger on Bun (3 oz. on 1)	1.0	1.0									
8008	Salmon Fillet (3 oz.)	2.0	1.0				1.0					
7915	Lima Beans with Pimento (½ cup)	2.0	2.0									
277	Hot Tea (8 oz.)	2.0	2.0									
P.M. Meal												
14750	Escarole Soup (6 oz.)	35.0	32.0				3.0					
6748	Coffee (8 oz.)	35.0	32.0						1.0		1.0	1.0
P.M. Meal Substitutions and Alternates												
7110	Broth (6 oz.)	2.0	2.0									
277	Hot Tea (8 oz.)	2.0	2.0									

Figure 23.5 Food Production Planning and Leftover Report

Date:			Meal:					
Service Start Time:			Service End Time:					
Item	**Portion Size**	**Qty. of Portions to Prepare**	**Employee Assigned**	**Comments**	**Qty. of Portions Left Over**	**Actual Qty. Served**	**Leftover Disposition**	**Shortage: Ran Out at ____ (time)**

Throughout the food production process, a manager should be highly visible and accessible to cooks. A manager needs to monitor activities and observe practices related to culinary technique, employee safety, and food safety. A manager needs to coach employees who are learning new skills. In addition, a manager should be ready to intervene when it appears that production is behind schedule, and make decisions when problems or substitution needs arise. Finally, a manager needs to listen to the concerns and suggestions raised by preparation staff. For example, a staff member may suggest an improvement to a standardized recipe, an alternate production method, or an idea for presenting food more attractively. An effective manager continually seeks feedback and input from production staff in order to improve quality.

Staff Training for Production Employees

As production employees perform their work, expert technique becomes critical. From careful measuring to preparation techniques to presentation to garnishing, many aspects of final quality rest with the cooks. Not every cook enters a facility with special training. However, someone in the facility should have a high level of culinary expertise. This may be the Certified Dietary Manager, an executive chef, or an experienced production manager. In turn, this person should coach other members of the staff to develop skills and talents. Some facilities have a short production meeting each day to make sure production questions are answered.

Each cook needs some special training about food production. For example, a cook needs to know:

- ✓ The purpose of standardized recipes
- ✓ Standard terms used on each recipe, such as yield, portion size, etc.
- ✓ Ingredient descriptions and the distinctions among products (e.g. the difference between kosher salt and iodized salt; all-purpose flour and self-rising flour, sifted or unsifted flour, etc.)

Figure 23.6 Common Cooking Terms

Al denté: An Italian term literally meaning "to the tooth"; refers to food that is cooked just enough to have a little resistance to the bite.

Bain Marie: A water bath used to warm or cook food. A container of food is placed in another container of water, either in the oven or on the stove.

Baste: To put stock or other liquid over meat while it is cooking (usually roasting) in order to keep it moist.

Beat: To briskly mix ingredients, usually with a whisk, electric mixer, or fork.

Bard: To cover or wrap raw meat with some type of solid fat before cooking.

Blanch: To pour boiling water over food (often fruit, vegetables, or nuts) in order to soften it or to remove the hulls or skins. Other methods include simmering the food and then placing it quickly in cold water, or steaming the food for a short period of time. Often confused with parboiling; see definition below.

Braise: To prepare food by browning it, covering it, and then slowly cooking it in the oven or on the stove with as much as 1/2 inch of liquid.

Brown: To cook food, usually in a small amount of fat, until it is brown; often a first step in another cooking process.

Broil: To cook food by exposing it to direct high heat, usually in the broiler of an oven or on a grill.

Butterfly: To cut a food directly through the center, splitting it almost in half.

Clarify: To remove food particles from grease used for frying, or to remove the top fat from melted butter, by heating and straining and/or skimming.

Coddle: To slowly cook a food (usually eggs) in liquid at a low heat. Usually done by placing it in boiling water and then immediately covering the pot and removing it from the stove.

Cream: To bring solid fat and dry ingredients (usually sugar and butter, margarine, or shortening) to a smooth, creamy consistency with a mixer or large spoon. The fat is creamed first; then the sugar is added gradually.

Cut in: To combine a dry ingredient and a solid fat with a fork, two knives, or a pastry blender (curved wires or thin, dull blades attached to a handle). They are mixed in a gliding cutting motion until they form small, separate pieces.

Dice: To cut a food into tiny chunks or cubes.

Deglaze: To make a sauce or sauce base using the juices and food bits remaining in a pan after cooking (broiling, sautéing, etc.) meat or fish. After some or all of the fat is removed from the pan and liquid is added, the mixture is heated and stirred and the pan is scraped until all of the food particles and juices are mixed.

Dredge: To coat food with a flour mixture or bread crumbs, usually before frying.

Dust: To sprinkle food with a dry ingredient by hand, with a sifter or a can made for dusting.

Fold: To gently blend two ingredients or mixtures, such as whipped egg whites and cake batter. They are layered on top of one another, the bowl is tilted, and the mixing is done with a sweeping top-to-bottom motion.

Fry: To cook food quickly in fat that is usually at a high temperature. If a small amount of fat is used, it is called stir frying, sautéing, or pan frying. If the food is immersed in fat, it is called deep fat frying.

Garnish: An edible item used to decorate a dish, or the process of decorating it. A garnish can be as small and simple as a sprig of parsley, as ornate as a small vegetable sculpture, or as substantial as the starch and vegetables on the plate used to garnish the meat.

Grate: To produce small bits or shavings of a food by rubbing on a grater or using a food processor.

Julienne: Used to describe food that has been cut into matchstick-like pieces 1/8 of an inch thick and 1½ to 3 inches long.

Knead: To develop the gluten in dough by hand or with a kneading attachment on a mixer. When done by hand, it is folded, pressed down, and turned ¼ turn repeatedly until it becomes smooth and pliable.

Macerate: To soak fruit or vegetables in liquid.

Marinate: To soak meat in a seasoned liquid.

Mince: To finely chop food.

Pare: To cut the skin from fruit or vegetables.

Pan-broil: To cook meat on the stovetop using an uncovered skillet and very little or no fat. Each side of the meat is browned, and fat is poured off during cooking.

Parboil: To partially cook food in water that is already at a rolling boil. A large quantity of water is used so that the food does not interrupt the boiling.

Poach: To completely cook a food in liquid just below boiling, usually in a covered pot.

Puree: To process cooked food or soft raw food in a blender,

(Continued)

Figure 23.6 Common Cooking Terms *(Continued)*

food processor, food mill, or sieve until it is semi-liquid and has a relatively even consistency. Also refers to the finished product.

Reduce: To cook a liquid food over high heat, allowing the water to evaporate.

Render: One process is to melt fat off of meat during cooking, with the cooked meat being the product. Another is to separate pieces of tissue from meat fat by heating and then straining it. This prepares the fat as well as the crisped tissue for other uses.

Roast: To cook food, usually meat, in the oven without it sitting in liquid.

Roux: A thickening agent using equal weights of fat and flour.

Sauté: To cook food in a small amount of fat at a temperature high enough to quickly sear it. This is done in an open skillet with constant stirring motion.

Scald: To cook food (usually milk) just below boiling, usually at about 185°F.

Scallop: To cook food in a cream sauce in the oven.

Shred: To process food into long bits and pieces, either by hand or with a grater.

Sear: To quickly brown food (usually meat) and seal in the juices by placing it on a very hot cooking surface. The surface of the food should be relatively dry, and depending on its natural fat content, little or no fat is used.

Simmer: To cook food, or food immersed in liquid, below boiling, usually between 130° and 185°F.

Steam: To cook food in direct contact with steam, either over boiling water or in a pressure cooker.

Whip: To process food rapidly with a spoon, whisk, or mixer. The utensil is swept up and down to incorporate air. This is the same as beating when the object is to thoroughly blend ingredients. Depending on the recipe, whipping may refer to lengthening the process and greatly increasing the volume of the food by incorporating a large quantity of air, as in whipped cream.

- ✓ Utensils and methods for measuring ingredients
- ✓ Abbreviation system for measurements
- ✓ Food safety and/or HACCP standards in place for each recipe
- ✓ Procedures for requisitioning ingredients
- ✓ Cooking terms used throughout the recipe, such as sauté, simmer, bake, broil, roux, etc. A list of common cooking terms appears in Figure 23.6.
- ✓ Employee safety and ergonomic practices that protect the cook and others from injury
- ✓ Proper methods for using all required equipment
- ✓ Methods for portioning and/or panning food
- ✓ Methods for holding food and/or transporting it to service
- ✓ Established timetables for production
- ✓ Procedures for addressing questions and problems.

As a basic work process, a cook can follow several steps to assure an efficient work flow:

- ✓ Read through the production sheet and be sure all assignments are clear. Question anything that is unclear.
- ✓ Read through each recipe, and be sure all instructions are clear.
- ✓ Assemble all needed ingredients.
- ✓ Assure that all needed equipment, bowls, knives, and utensils are available and ready for use.
- ✓ Follow the recipe procedure exactly, taking each step in sequence.

What would you monitor to assure production staff training has been effective? What do you do if you find the training was not effective?

(Check your answer at the end of this chapter)

- ✓ Clean up between tasks and keep the work area orderly.
- ✓ Follow established sanitation guidelines.
- ✓ Group errands (such as trips to the storeroom, dishroom, or trash area) and work as efficiently as possible.

Beyond basic orientation, many foodservice employees enjoy further culinary training. You may ask your in-house culinary expert to present cooking classes, featuring basic techniques, garnishing tips, and more. When a culinary expert is not available on staff, consider inviting a local talent to present a special inservice session or series of classes. Another option for training is to use culinary instructional videos, which are readily available from many sources. Culinary reference information, slide shows, and even video clips illustrating culinary techniques are available free on several Websites. As feasible, schedule production employees to attend food shows and trade shows. Finally, if your facility offers a continuing education program, you may encourage employees to attend seminars or classes in preparation and culinary techniques.

It is important to encourage, acknowledge, and reward advances in knowledge and skill. Follow up to assure the training is implemented. Often, the simple availability of training is enough to motivate employees to challenge themselves and tap into their own talents. Skillful food production brings on the immediate rewards of seeing a product that looks good, tastes good, and generates positive satisfaction ratings.

Controlling Energy Usage

You might wonder how controlling energy usage fits into this chapter on supervising the production and distribution of food. As you think about it, very little can be produced in foodservice without the use of energy. The next decade will be an exciting and probably challenging time as we become more energy efficient. All types of foodservice industries are being encouraged to try new methods for becoming more energy efficient by utilizing food waste for energy, reducing energy consumption through energy efficient equipment, and turning off equipment and lights when not in use. Can you think of other ways to conserve in your department?

Foodservice departments utilize significantly more energy than other departments and this may be a controllable expense worth investigating. Figure 23.7 shows the Commercial Building Energy Cost Per Square Foot and Figure 23.8 shows how this energy use is divided in a restaurant.

How do you begin controlling energy costs?

- ✓ Start with contacting your local energy companies. They may offer design consulting services to help you design and order equipment for maximum efficiency.
- ✓ A local energy company may also conduct kitchen equipment test reports giving you specific information about the energy usage of cooking and food preparation equipment. A local college or university may also have a program where students could provide this service as part of their learning activities.

Figure 23.7 Commercial Building Energy Cost Per Square Foot (Dollars)

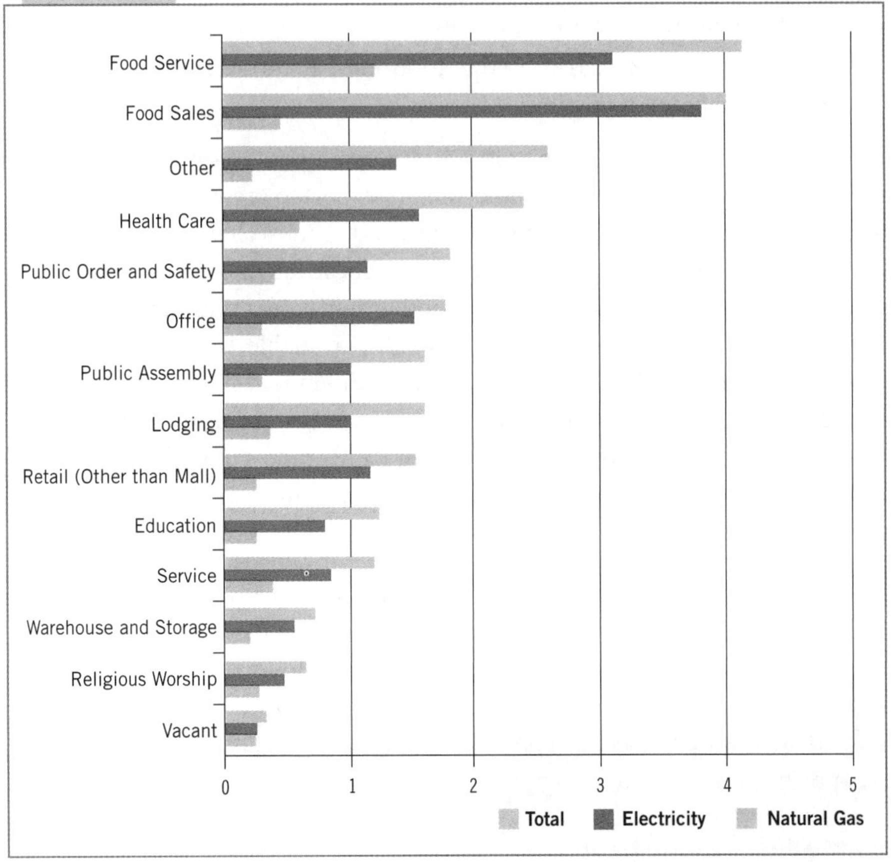

Source: Sustainablefoodservice.com and Energy Information Administration, www.eia.doe.gov. Used with permission.

Figure 23.8 Restaurant Energy Use

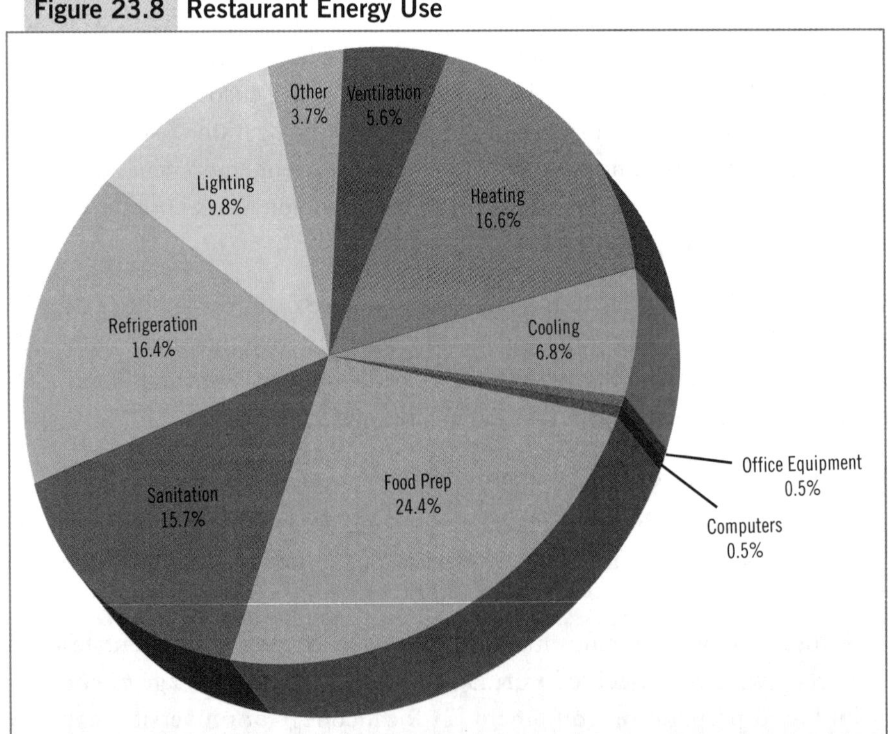

Source: Sustainablefoodservice.com and Energy Information Administration, www.eia.doe.gov. Used with permission.

✓ Your energy company may also conduct an on-site survey resulting in a list of recommended actions to cut energy use and costs.

Figure 23.9 shows energy conservation tips to consider for your facility.

Like the other supervision activities in this chapter, control of energy costs mean keeping records of utility costs and monitoring equipment use. Track your energy/utility costs monthly and look for dramatic changes or trends. Total your water usage each month and ask your staff to help you find ways to conserve water. Use training to get your staff on board with energy conservation and how controlling energy use affects operational costs. Since your staff are the ones using the equipment, they can be the keys to success in monitoring equipment use. Controlling energy costs may well be wiser in the long run than trying to meet your budget by reducing the quality of food.

Figure 23.9 Energy Saving Tips

1. Switch from incandescent EXIT lights to LED EXIT lighting. They last ten times longer with an average annual savings of $40, excluding maintenance costs.
2. Switch from Incandescent Light Bulbs in exhaust hoods and walk-ins to Energy Star Compact Fluorescent Lamps (CFL). Replacing a single 100 watt incandescent lamp, operated 12 hours per day over 365 days with a 23 watt CFL will save approximately $35 in annual operating cost at a utility rate of $0.10/kWh.
3. Turn off door heaters on reach-in refrigerators and freezers. Commercial reach-in refrigerators and freezers have door heaters to help prevent condensation build up around the door frame, however, in dry climates condensate may not be an issue and many refrigerators and freezers have door heaters which can be manually turned off. A single door heater has an approximate annual operating cost of $50 at a utility rate of $0.10/kWh.
4. Use Strip Curtains or plastic doors on walk-in coolers and freezers to prevent warm air infiltration and reduce compressor runtime. Utility studies have shown an annual savings of $100 for a typical 10 x 10 walk-in freezer equipped with a strip curtain assuming a utility rate of $0.10/kWh.
5. Fix all water leaks. A seemingly innocent hot water leak with a flow rate of half a gallon per hour can have an annual cost of $90 if left unabated. Cost assumes a natural gas cost of $1.00/therm and a water/sewer utility cost of $8.00/CCF.
6. Clean dirty refrigeration system—evaporator and condenser coils. They should be inspected monthly for dust, lint and other obstructions and cleaned if necessary.
7. Set Water Heater to Proper Temperature! Only heat water to the temperature required for specific tasks in your operation. Facilities with high temperature dish machine typically require 140° F supply hot water and those with a low temperature machine can require supply hot water as low as 125° F. A water heater set 10°F too high in a typical casual dining restaurant using 2,000 gallons of hot water per day will cost an extra $900 /year, assuming a natural gas utility cost of $1.00/therm.
8. Replace high flow pre-rinse sprayers with high performing, low flow sprayers that have a flow rate no higher than 1.6 gallon per minute. Retrofitting a high flow nozzle rated at 5.0 gpm with a low flow unit rated at 1.2 gpm in a dish room where operated one hour per day over 365 days will save approximately $1,700 in natural gas and water costs.
9. Implement a strict start up and shut down schedule for all cooking appliances. Fryers, ovens, griddles and charbroilers require no more then 20-30 minutes to pre-heat. Pay special attention to charbroiler and manually controlled griddles—shut them entirely off, partially off or down during slow service periods.
10. Install and/or maintain programmable thermostats to manage heating and air conditioning systems. Properly program the thermostat so that during unoccupied periods, cooling is set to 85° F and heating to 55° F. During occupied hours set the cooling set point as high as possible and heating set point as low as possible, but still being mindful to maintain staff and customer comfort. As a rule of thumb, for every cooling degree set point increase and heating degree set point decrease, system operating cost lowers by 3% - 4%.

Source: Fisher-Nickel Inc., Food Service Technology Center –fishnick.com. Costs are based on California rates.

END OF CHAPTER

Putting It Into Practice Questions & Answers

1. Your school celebrates the return of spring with a week-long celebration that culminates in a large outdoor picnic. You normally serve 450 students and their guests. The day of the picnic arrives and it is cold and rainy. What steps would you take to adjust the forecast for meals?

   A. *1. Review any records from previous picnics to determine a normal attendance.*

   2. Check to see if any of the records were picnics on rainy days; then use this number as your starting forecast.

   3. If there are no records from the past on rainy days, you would still be wise to reduce the production amount for the day by at least 10% because of the weather. Guests are less likely to attend in rainy weather. Then track the number you feed, what was predicted, and how much was leftover. Make sure you enter these numbers into your record for the next time.

2. What are the production steps for the recipe below? Indicate with a star the steps that are advance preparation.

   Chicken Wrap:
   - 96 (6-inch) tortillas
   - 9 lbs. grilled chicken breast, cubed
   - 1 #10 can cooked black beans, drained
   - 8 lbs. pre-chopped mixed lettuce (romaine and ice berg)—purchased pre-chopped
   - 3 lbs. crumbled feta cheese
   - 3 lbs. roasted red peppers, chopped
   - 1½ qts. commercial Caesar Dressing

   A. *Production Steps:*

   (Day before service)

   *1. Roast red peppers following supplemental recipe**

   *2. Grill chicken breast to 165°F for 15 seconds; then place in a single layer, cover, vent, and refrigerate**

   (Day of service)

   *1. Chop red peppers into 1/4" dice**
   *2. Crumble feta cheese**
   *3. Dice chicken breasts into 1/2" dice**
   *4. Drain and rinse black beans**
   *5. Rinse and drain mixed lettuce product**
   6. Assemble wraps: toss lettuce product with Caesar dressing. Layer each wrap with 1 oz. (1/3 cup) lettuce; 1/2 oz. feta cheese (1 Tbsp.), 2 Tbsp. black beans, 1 Tbsp. red pepper, 1.5 oz. chicken breast. Roll up securely.
   7. Refrigerate until service time

3. At the end of each day, your cooks document production results. What items should they document?

   A. *They should record the following: 1) Number of servings forecasted; 2) Number of servings produced 3) Number of servings left over; 4) Shortages of any menu item and the time it ran out.*

4. What would you monitor to assure production staff training has been effective? What do you do if you find the training was not effective?

   A. *Monitor the following: 1) Cooking staff is using standardized recipes; 2) They are assembling ingredients and small equipment in advance of preparation; 3) Work space is kept clean and orderly; 4) Prepared products are tasty and attractive; 5) Client satisfaction ratings are increasing.*

   If there is a concern about any of these processes, determine the cause and take corrective action.

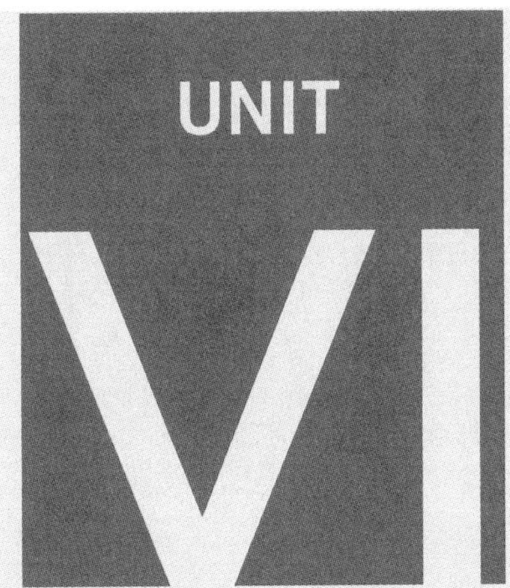

Manage Business Operations

Mike Phillips, a banker for Bank of America, once said, "Money will come when you are doing the right thing." As a Certified Dietary Manager, managing fiscal resources is critical to the success of your operation. This chapter helps you do the "right things" to be successful by using key reports and processes so you can make the best decisions.

Prepare Purchase Specifications and Supervise the Purchase of Food and Supplies

Overview and Objectives

While Certified Dietary Managers may not have to write purchase specifications, they will spend valuable time purchasing food and supplies for their facility, and must be able to differentiate between products when ordering. Once purchasing is completed, the purchasing process continues with receiving and inventory. This chapter reviews all aspects of the purchasing process.

After completing this chapter, you should be able to:

✓ Identify purchasing policies and procedures of department

✓ Establish specifications for ordering and bidding

✓ Evaluate facility needs, budget restrictions, and products available

✓ Gather and evaluate product information

✓ Be familiar with computer applications and create a purchase order

✓ Check inventory and identify purchase needs

✓ Complete purchase order requisition forms

✓ Check supplies received against purchase order delivery slips

✓ Compare product received against order specifications

✓ Maintain inventory records

✓ Recognize inventory management practices (FIFO, par stock, physical, perpetual)

✓ Examine vendor product/selection

Purchasing is a highly specialized process and the topic alone is the subject of many books. This chapter covers only a few of the decisions in the purchasing process. Purchasing has changed significantly in the past 20 years with much of the purchasing today done through prime vendors with computerized ordering. Smaller healthcare facilities belong to multi-unit purchasing co-ops and have enjoyed the benefits of cooperative purchasing to leverage better prices.

The main focus of purchasing is to buy the products needed at the best cost and optimal value—and get them delivered when (and where) they are needed. Through effective purchasing, a Certified Dietary Manager achieves objectives related to quality, quantity, price, supplier, and schedule. Each is described below.

Quality. The purchaser must obtain the right quality products and services. This is not always the highest quality available. Instead, it is a match to the needs and budget of the facility. The relationship between quality and price is called value.

Quantity. Products must be purchased in the right quantity; otherwise, the operation can run out of products, delaying or altering food production and service. Or, the operation can carry excess inventory, with resulting cash flow and loss implications.

Price. The buyer has a responsibility to obtain required quality products at the best price.

Supplier. It is important to select product sources with thought, analysis, and comparison, rather than simply to select a supplier based on random factors.

Schedule. Products must be received at the right time. Delivery times should be within the control of the foodservice operation. While occasional problems must be anticipated, supplier selection should be based in part on reliable delivery schedules.

In large facilities, purchasing may be the responsibility of a specialized foodservice buyer or purchasing agent. In smaller facilities, it is often the responsibility of the Certified Dietary Manager, supervisor, or foodservice director.

The purchasing task is ongoing. Through experience with suppliers, products, and services, the Certified Dietary Manager can develop a very effective system to help control costs and to assure that quality requirements are met.

Purchasing Specifications

Specifications for Food

Management of the purchasing process begins with a specification for each product. A **specification** is a quality statement that spells out what requirements must be met in order for a product to be acceptable. It really describes the suitability of a product for its intended use in your own operation. This is not necessarily top-of-the-line quality.

The purpose of a specification is quality control. You get what you ask for. If you don't ask for it, you are not likely to get it! A specification is used when requesting prices or bids from a list of possible suppliers. A specification helps assure that you are comparing apples to apples, so to speak. In turn, this helps to compare prices meaningfully. It also defines a clear, mutual expectation of what will be received at delivery.

Specification for Equipment

Specifications are also written for equipment and disposable items such as paper and plastic. Equipment manufacturers usually provide a specification sheet with their equipment that details the specific features of the equipment such as:

✓ Equipment type
✓ Model number

Glossary

Specification
Quality statement that lists what requirements must be met in order for a product to be acceptable

- ✓ Capacity
- ✓ Description of construction materials such as stainless steel gauge and finishes (such as polished)
- ✓ Construction and design characteristics
- ✓ Performance characteristics
- ✓ List of standard features
- ✓ Description of safety features
- ✓ List of optional features available at extra cost
- ✓ Laboratory certification and approval symbols (UL, NSF, CSA, AGA)
- ✓ All dimensions—interior, exterior, service, ventilation, air
- ✓ Circulation and clearances
- ✓ Net and shipment (crated) weights
- ✓ Data concerning utilities—gas, steam, water, electric, and ventilating
- ✓ Availability of colors and finishes
- ✓ Manufacturer's address, phone number, and fax number.

This information can be very helpful when writing equipment specifications. Make sure your criteria aren't written to a specific piece of equipment. The specifications should be as generic as possible and include what you need the equipment to do.

Writing specifications comes after the decision about what product best fits your needs. Once you decide what you need, you can describe the specific quality characteristics you will accept. There may be more than one specification written for each product. For example, pre-portioned hamburger patties of several sizes may be necessary for different entrees. If olives are used for garnishes as well as for the salad bar, two different products may be needed. For example, large olives that are perfectly shaped and of uniform size (and also expensive) are not necessary if the olives will be chopped for a salad. A "broken pieces" product is acceptable, and of course, less expensive.

Specifications must be:

- ✓ Accurate and objectively describe quality aspects
- ✓ Realistic. Quality definitions cannot be so strict that few or no products will be acceptable.
- ✓ Stated in clear terms
- ✓ Written so as to make it possible for several suppliers to quote prices and supply products
- ✓ Provide some flexibility for both the supplier and the buyer.

To write a specification, begin with a product name. Then, specify what the product will be used for. Next, provide a description of the product with quality information. Next, indicate how you will test or verify acceptability. Finally, note any special requirements. An example of a specification format appears in Figure 24.1.

Figure 24.1 Product Specification Format

[Name of Foodservice Operation]

1. **Product Name:** ______________________________
2. **Product Used For:** Clearly indicate product use, such as olive for garnish, hamburger patty for grilling, etc.
3. **Product General Description:** Provide quality information about desired product. For example, "iceberg lettuce; heads to be green and firm without spoilage, no excessive dirt or damage. No more than 10 outer leaves; packed 24 heads per case."
4. **Detailed Description:** State other factors that clearly identify the desired product. Examples of specific factors, which vary by product being described include:
    - Geographic Origin
    - Variety
    - Type
    - Style
    - Grade
    - Size
    - Portion Size
    - Brand Name
    - Density
    - Specific Gravity
    - Container Size
    - Edible Yield, Trim
    - Inspection
5. **Check-In Procedures:** Describe what a receiving clerk will do to verify acceptability of the product. For example, products to be delivered at or below 41°F will be tested with a thermometer. Portioned meat patties will be randomly weighed. Lettuce packed 24 heads per case will be counted.
6. **Special Instructions and Requirements:** Any additional information needed to clearly indicate quality expectations can be included here. Examples include bidding procedures, if applicable, labeling and/or packaging requirements, and delivery and service requirements.

Glossary

Grade
A rating that describes the quality and appearance characteristics of a product

Putting It Into Practice: 1

Draft a specification for a crushed tomato canned product. Include the grade, can size, pack size, and other relevant information.

(Check your answer at the end of this chapter)

Along with these details, identify required food safety controls, such as delivery temperatures, acceptable product dating, and any other essential characteristics. In addition, describe the ordering procedures and delivery performance/schedule.

What characteristics can you list in a specification? These vary by product. For certain agricultural products, a USDA grade is an essential tool. A **grade** describes the quality of the product. A grade may describe uniformity, texture, fat content, flavor, maturity, and/or other quality factors. Grade assignments are based on standards established by the USDA for each applicable food. They give you an objective measure or standard with which you can compare your own needs. For example, a Fancy grade of canned vegetables indicates the best flavor, color, and tenderness. It also indicates the product is uniform in size.

In addition, portion and count can be critical. For fish filets, you need to decide what weight you require for each filet in order to match the needs of your recipes and menus. As another example, canned pear halves may be packed with varying counts in a #10 can. On container size, slight variability may exist from one vendor to another. However, if your requirements are rigid, specify them. For example, if you have a product you will only use in very small amounts for individual orders on demand, you do not want to receive it in large units. Common can sizes appear in Figure 24.2. For ideas about other factors to include in specifications for particular products, you can search for the USDA Commercial Item Descriptions, available on the Web at http://www.ams.usda.gov.

In some facilities, the packaging itself is also specified. For example, glass may be prohibited for safety reasons. Today, processing methods may be important as well. Some facilities are also developing specifications that relate to food additives and allergens (factors likely to cause allergic reactions in sensitive individuals). If specific factors are important to your own client group and requirements, include them.

Examples of factors that may be included in a quality statement appear in Figure 24.3.

To identify additional details and options, talk with several suppliers. Many food distributors can provide a detailed specifications manual. Some may also provide their own quality ratings that will help match products to needs. Realize that using known brand-name ingredients is not essential. A distributor's own brand may prove more economical, and may even be the very same product under a unique label.

Use of branded menu items is a growing trend. A school system may serve French fries produced by a recognized fast food chain or chocolate chip cookies manufactured by a well-known company. Or, a cafeteria may serve doughnuts, pizzas, or tacos that have national brand-name recognition. When using branded menu items, a foodservice operation enjoys marketing clout as well as quality control. Costs may be higher, but sales may be too. Thus, a facility needs to base decisions to use branded products on value and impact on the financial bottom line.

Usually the specification should not include the brand of the food or equipment item. However, in some cases where your chef may want specific products such as Heinz® ketchup, the brand would be included in the specification. If you specify a brand, be prepared to defend why that brand must be purchased. In one university setting, the pasta brand that had been purchased was an inferior quality (it fell apart during cooking). That data was used to justify a higher quality brand in the specification.

Finally, if you are writing specifications for specialized dietary products, involve a Registered Dietitian in developing specifications. Simple product names for low-sodium soup, heart healthy convenience entrees, or enteral nutritional supplements do not tell all. A dietitian can specify nutritional content for these products.

Evaluating Products

As suppliers suggest products to match your needs, your next step is to taste and test the products. As a supplier indicates an ability to meet your specification, ask for samples. It is important to taste each product under consideration. Sometimes, it is also important to test it through your recipe production process, and then verify quality and taste. When relevant, ask the supplier to deliver samples of several products that meet your specification so that you can compare them.

Figure 24.2 Common Can Sizes

Size	Net Weight	Measure	Common Pack	Principal Products
#10	6 lbs. 9 oz.	12-13 cups	6 per case	Fruits, vegetables, some other foods
No. 3 Cyl	2.9-3.2 lbs.	5¼ cups	12 per case	Condensed soups, some vegetables, meat and poultry products, fruit and vegetable juices
#2½	1 lb. 13 oz.	3½ cups	24 per case	Fruits, some vegetables
#2	1 lb. 4 oz.	2½ cups	24 per case	Juices, ready-to-serve soups, some fruits
#300	14-16 oz.	1¾ cups	24 per case	Some fruits and meat products
#1 (Picnic)	10½-12 oz.	1¼ cups	48 per case	Condensed soups, some fruits, vegeta-bles, meat, fish
8 oz.	8 oz.	1 cup	48 or 72 per case	Ready-to-serve soups, fruits, vegetables

Sources: National Food Service Management Institute, Food for Fifty

Figure 24.3 Purchase Specification Factors

For Meats:

- Inspection (mandatory)
- Grading (if desired)
- IMPS/MBG Descriptions
- Weight/Thickness Limitations
- Fat Limitations
- State of Refrigeration
- Miscellaneous (tying, boning, packaging, etc.)

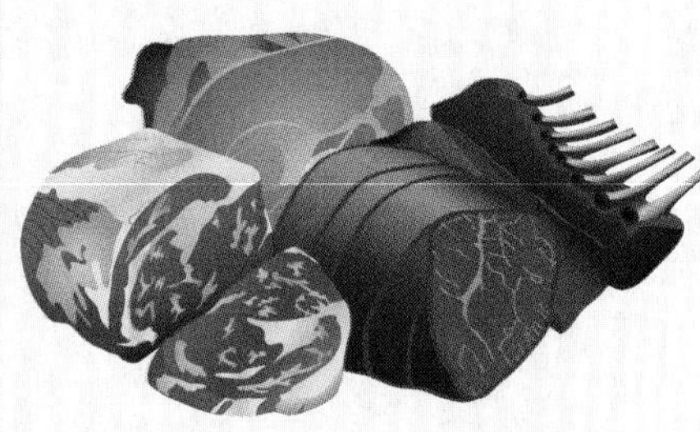

For Seafoods:

- Type (fin fish or shellfish)
- Market Form (whole, eviscerated, etc. fin fish; alive, whole, shucked, etc.)
- Quality Requirements (describe flesh, eyes, skin, gills, etc.)
- Grade (if desired)
- Inspection (voluntary)
- Processing Requirements

For Poultry:

- Kind (chicken, turkey, duck, goose)
- Class (typed by age)
- Grade (if desired)
- Size (weight limitations)
- Inspection (mandatory)
- Style (whole, breasts, breasts with ribs, etc.)
- State of refrigeration

For Fresh Fruits and Vegetables:

- Grade (if desired)
- Variety
- Size
- Type of Pack
- Count per Container
- Growing Area

For Processed Fruits and Vegetables:

- Grade (if desired)
- Drain Weight
- Packing Medium
- Can (container) Size

Some operations use the term **can-cutting** to describe the process of sampling products for possible purchase. To perform a successful taste test, you can involve several key members of your operation. At least one person involved in food production should attend—a manager, chief chef, or head cook. In addition, the person responsible for purchasing must be involved, and should review the product carefully against the written specification. You can use a simple rating card to allow panelists to rate taste, appearance, texture, and other pertinent characteristics. After each person has made an independent evaluation, ask panelists to compare notes and discuss the products. Can-cutting can be done for one product and multiple vendors or multiple grades and products from one vendor.

Generally, there is a difference between package weight and net weight for products. Net weight is the weight of the food product itself, after you have removed all packaging. For canned products, you may also specify a minimum drain weight. This tells you how much product you will have after you drain away the liquid. Ultimately, it affects both yield and price. Figure 24.4 shows an example of how this can make a difference.

Figure 24.4 Impact of Drain Weight

You are comparing two different products for canned peach slices, each packed in #10 cans.

Product #1: Minimum drain weight = 63 oz.
Price: $3.00 per can

Product #2: Minimum drain weight = 75 oz.
Price: $3.10 per can

All other factors being equal, which product represents a better value? To determine this, calculate the price per ounce of usable product:

Product #1: $3.00 ÷ 63 oz. = $0.0476 per oz.

Product #1: $3.10 ÷ 75 oz. = $0.0413 per oz.

In this example, Product #2 is actually a better value if the quality is equal.

Understanding Product Yields

As you specify products and later quantify them for purchase, it is essential to consider product yields. Much like a recipe yield, a product yield tells how much usable food you will obtain from each product you purchase. Knowing the product yields helps you purchase the right quantity for the job. It also helps compare and control costs of competing products.

Purchasing Decisions

As you can see, the person responsible for purchasing is expected to purchase the required products for the best price. There are several buying techniques that may help the purchaser: using manufacturer's rebates, purchasing groups and cooperatives, valuing inventory, and make or buy decisions.

Glossary

Can-Cutting
Procedure of sampling products for possible purchase

Putting It Into Practice: 2

Your facility is deciding whether to change from one cola company to offering a different brand of cola products. Your clientele is requesting this change. The brand you currently use is part of the prime vendor contract. What process should you use to make this change?

(Check your answer at the end of this chapter)

Manufacturers Rebates

In today's foodservice environment, many Certified Dietary Managers have been pressing the limits of budgets for quite some time. As a result, the margin of profit enjoyed by food distributors has decreased to a very minimal level. As managers continue to look for price breaks, a new avenue has evolved—manufacturers rebates. A manufacturers rebate is a refund offered directly from the manufacturer of the product. For example, you purchase ABC brand coffee. The manufacturer of ABC coffee gives a refund of $5 for every case purchased.

This opportunity can provide a significant impact on operating expenses. However, it also requires tracking commitments to see that they come through. Today, some managers accomplish this by using software or online ordering systems that track purchases and automatically claim rebates.

Purchasing Groups and Cooperatives

Often, groups of facilities band together to negotiate both prime vendor contracts and manufacturers rebate agreements. In one model, the facilities work together through a separate organization called a purchasing group. This is a group representing multiple clients. The group standardizes use of many products, completes a bid process, and selects vendors. The group uses its volume to exert buying power and obtain excellent pricing. A purchasing group may involve all supplies to the facility, not just food.

In another model, Certified Dietary Managers work together through a purchasing cooperative (co-op) to achieve volume and buying power. Generally, members of the group work together to specify and select products and suppliers.

If you belong to a purchasing group or cooperative, it is important to participate as fully as possible, buying products on the contract. Otherwise, the clout of the group is diluted. It is equally important to participate in selection of products and vendors to assure they meet your needs.

Valuing Inventory

An essential tool for financial management in foodservice is an **inventory valuation**. This is a dollar figure representing the value of all inventory on hand at the moment. This figure is not only useful in completing operating statements reflecting the department's financial performance; it can also provide useful information to use in managing the purchasing process. Based on accounting procedures in your facility, you may be required to provide an inventory valuation at the end of each month, or at other defined intervals.

To calculate value, you need to track food prices (what you pay) for each product, per purchase unit. Multiply the number of purchase units on hand by the price for that product. Then, add all product values together. An example of a form for valuing inventory appears in Figure 24.5.

Note that in computer-based systems, purchase prices may be maintained in the system. Then, a user enters a physical count for each product, and allows the computer to calculate value.

Glossary

Inventory Valuation
The dollar figure or value of all inventory on hand at a given point in time

Figure 24.5 **Physical Inventory—Valuation Form**

Date: ____________________

Product	Unit Type	Quantity in Storage	Unit Purchase Price	Total Price
				Total Value: ________

Make or Buy?

In developing product specifications and making purchasing decisions, a Certified Dietary Manager often faces the opportunity to use convenience foods. Convenience foods are products that offer convenience in preparation. They may be pre-made, such as a frozen entree. Or, they may have been processed in a manner that reduces labor, such as grated carrots or diced onions. For macaroni and cheese, the manager could purchase a ready-made, frozen product or make it from scratch. Similarly, for a cake, the manager could purchase a frozen cake, a cake mix, or make the product entirely from scratch. Decisions between convenience and from-scratch products can have broad financial implications.

In determining whether to make or buy, consider both financial and quality factors. As you evaluate these decisions, ask questions such as:

- ✓ What is the final quality of the convenience food? Is it acceptable for our needs?
- ✓ What is the labor requirement of the convenience food versus the product we would make from scratch?
- ✓ If you consider both labor and food cost, which product comes out to be least expensive?

If quality is acceptable and total expense is less, convenience foods may be a good choice. A make-or-buy question has become pivotal in foodservice operations in which either of these factors exists:

- ✓ The operation is experiencing a labor shortage, and/or
- ✓ The cost of labor is very high.

An example of high-cost labor comes into play in some union environments. Unionization of kitchen employees may mean that wages are fairly high. To calculate labor costs for any product, start with a union wage for the production staff who would prepare the product. Then, account for the additional expenses of benefits (time off, health insurance, etc.) You can check with your own human resources department to obtain a factor for benefits. From this, set a labor factor, such as 1.50, meaning the real cost of labor is 1.50 times the actual wages. Multiply the labor factor times the number of hours required to obtain a labor cost for the product. Here is an example:

> Chicken soup production from scratch requires 0.25 hours of work by a pre-preparation employee, plus 1.5 hours of work from a hot food cook. Total hours = 1.75.
>
> The union wage for these employees is about $11.00 per hour, and the benefit factor is 50%.
>
> Multiply $11.00 by 1.50 to calculate what the labor really costs per hour: $11.00 x 1.50 = $16.50
>
> Multiply number of hours required by the true labor cost to total the labor expense: 1.75 hours x $16.50/hr = $28.88

In this example, every time you make a batch of chicken soup from scratch, it costs $28.88, in addition to the cost of food you purchase for the recipe. To make a final comparison, you need to calculate food costs, too, and then convert the figure to cost per serving. Compare this with cost per serving of the canned soup, plus the labor cost of producing the convenience product. (This should be minimal.) Finally, evaluate the quality and value for each option.

Glossary

Prime Vendor
A primary supplier who usually provides about 80% of the products

Putting It Into Practice: 3

Your clients are complaining about the quality of the muffin product. Your administrator is asking you to recommend a higher quality product. You are considering making the muffins rather than purchasing them. What steps would you take to make the decision?

(Check your answer at the end of this chapter)

The Bid Process

Once you have specifications ready, the next step is to obtain bids from suppliers. A key purpose of this process is to obtain optimal value at optimal prices, while constraining budget expenditures.

Commonly, a foodservice operation will select one main vendor for the majority of its food items. This primary supplier is called the **prime vendor**. In a prime vendor arrangement, an operation agrees to purchase the majority of its products from a given supplier in exchange for guaranteed pricing for a guaranteed period of time. A prime vendor agreement usually dictates that an operation will purchase a minimum percentage of its relevant products from this vendor. Typically, this is about 80 percent.

Today, a prime vendor agreement is managed beyond the level of individual facilities. Instead, it is negotiated at a corporate level and passed on to the Certified Dietary Manager. The parties responsible for negotiating a prime vendor contract may be the corporate purchasing agents of a healthcare chain, a contract management company, or other organization. Meanwhile, a corporation or individual operation may select additional vendors, often locally based suppliers, for certain perishable items like fresh meats, produce, and dairy products.

To obtain price quotations from any supplier, a Certified Dietary Manager can use a competitive bidding process. **Competitive bidding** allows multiple vendors to submit bids or price quotations for products based on defined specifications. The manager can then accept the lowest quoted price resulting in cost savings to the facility. Competitive bidding is usually required for equipment or budget items over a specified amount.

Competitive bidding will help assure the manager of getting the lowest price when:

✓ The order is large enough to justify the time and expense involved

✓ Specifications are clearly known by all suppliers, and

✓ Several suppliers desire to quote prices on the order.

Competitive bidding can be done through an informal or formal process. An informal process is based on phone calls, e-mails, and information interactions. Some informal negotiation might also be possible. For example, before prices are obtained from suppliers, the buyer may attempt to secure a lower price quotation.

Keys to success for an informal bid purchasing system include:

✓ The quoted price and other terms of the agreement must be clearly understood.

✓ The price quoted by the supplier must remain firm for the length of time needed by the purchaser to make a decision.

✓ All suppliers must quote according to the same specifications for any given product.

✓ All eligible suppliers should be allowed to quote on the order.

✓ Parties document the agreed-upon price and other terms.

In a formal process, the Certified Dietary Manager or purchasing agent invites suppliers to submit sealed bids on a detailed, written prospective order. The manager reviews written responses and makes a selection.

Note that in a competitive bid process for a prime vendor, it is important to provide vendors with projected usage figures for each product, because they will base quotations on the total volume. Then, as you receive bids, examine the bottom line of each one. Prices for individual products may vary, with one lower or higher from one bidder or another. However, the real price comparison is made based on the sum total of all items. This figure helps drive the decision of which vendor to select.

A contrast to a prime vendor approach is a concept called **cherry picking**. In this model, a Certified Dietary Manager purchases each individual product from the vendor with the lowest price. Thus, one facility may place a relatively small number of purchase orders with many different suppliers. An advantage of this method is that the manager presumably obtains the lowest possible price for each item.

Glossary

Competitive Bidding
Asking multiple vendors to submit price quotes for products or equipment based on defined specifications

Cherry Picking
A purchasing concept where the Certified Dietary Manager purchases individual products from individual vendors as opposed to using a primary vendor

Disadvantages of this system include:

✓ The manager forms weaker relationships with vendors and may dilute the facility's clout with suppliers.

✓ Paperwork and administrative load can increase.

✓ Workload for receiving staff can also increase.

In comparison, prime vendor purchasing offers a number of advantages:

✓ It improves the consistency and quality of food purchased.

✓ It locks in predictable pricing and budget control.

✓ It may improve cash flow, as cash flow increases with a known and constant supplier, and lower inventory levels may be established.

✓ It makes the receiving process more efficient.

✓ It often generates excellent vendor performance because of the value of the contract and the commitment of the client.

✓ It may provide an opportunity to enjoy value added services. These are services a distributor adds to its line at a free or reduced cost for customers. Examples include standardized menus, computer software, or training materials.

Prime vendor purchasing can have several disadvantages, too, including the loss of a reliable backup vendor, a limited inventory, and an increase in prices due to lower competition. Two methods a buyer can use to help ensure optimal results with a prime vendor system are to choose an efficient and credible vendor, and to establish a periodic bidding process. This process is essential to maintain low cost, and may serve to retain interest and reliability in the backup supplier.

While price is important, it is not wise to base vendor selection entirely on price. Here are some additional questions to ask before selecting a vendor:

✓ Does the vendor carry the majority of products you need, including any specialized items for modified diets?

✓ What is the vendor's ability to meet scheduling needs for delivery?

✓ What ordering procedures or technology does the vendor provide (such as interfaces with your computer system, or online ordering)?

✓ How reliable is the vendor's service? Can you check references among other customers?

✓ How willing is the vendor to commit to food safety guidelines you have established?

✓ What access will you have to a service representative or sales person to assist with any problems that arise?

Purchasing Mechanics

Once inventory needs have been determined and vendors selected, it is time to place a **purchase order**. A purchase order is a business document that specifies what is being purchased, in what quantity, from whom, for whom, and under what terms. In most facilities, a pre-determined purchase order format and

Glossary

Purchase Order
A business document that specifies what is being purchased

set of related procedures already exist. In most small facilities, a Certified Dietary Manager or purchasing agent bears responsibility for making purchases. In large facilities, purchasing may be handled by a purchasing department, or a buyer serving a number of foodservice operations. Additional information that may appear in a purchase order includes: the vendor's item number, your internal inventory number, and the purchase unit (e.g. case).

Note that it is important to clarify who is authorized to make a purchase order. If you ordinarily hold the authorization, you must also assure that you have designated others to place an order when you are not available, such as during a vacation or an emergency.

There are many methods of placing a purchase order. In a traditional system, a Certified Dietary Manager writes down all needs on purchase order forms, and then calls suppliers to place the orders. Today, managers use Web-based ordering systems. In one, you may connect with a vendor's online ordering system directly. In another, your connection may be built into foodservice management software. In this case, the software may generate purchase orders on screen for your review and approval, and then transfer the order electronically to your designated vendor. See Figure 24.6 for an example of an online purchase order system.

Most software and Web-based options provide detailed reporting of purchasing history. This is very valuable for cost analysis, as well as for determining usage in preparation for a competitive bid process.

Efficient systems can track products through purchase, storage, issuing, and usage (production or service) control points. Systems can convert purchase units (such as case of #10 cans) to production units (such as cups or ounces). After production, an automated system may update inventory records by applying production units used (from standard recipe information) for comparison with quantities of products issued and subsequent reductions in inventory levels.

Purchasing Ethics

With the responsibility of purchasing comes another responsibility—that of ethical practices. Sound ethics assure that purchasing decisions are not influenced by personal factors, but are instead based on objectives of the facility. This is essential to the sound fiscal operation of an facility, as well as to your own professional standing. Most facilities have a policy addressing ethical practices. In your own facility, you should become familiar with this policy and follow it.

Broadly recognized ethical practices dictate that as a purchasing agent, you do not accept meals, gifts, or favors from suppliers. In addition, you treat all suppliers and potential suppliers fairly and equally. For example, in a competitive bid process, you include all possible candidates. Final selections of vendors are based on the criteria described above, including price, value, and service. An ethical Certified Dietary Manager continuously evaluates purchasing choices on an objective basis, and remains open to new opportunities.

Putting It Into Practice: 4

You are attending a foodservice trade show and one of the vendors is offering a 32" flat screen TV if you purchase a year's supply of coffee. You have to make the decision today as the offer won't be good tomorrow. You know that coffee is one of your high dollar items and this would represent a significant savings. You also know that the Activities Department has wanted a new flat screen TV to use with the clients. You decide to sign a purchase agreement for the coffee. Is this ethical?

(Check your answer at the end of this chapter)

Figure 24.6 Purchase Order

Sysco | Market

Welcome Thomas Keller | Close Window
Account: 001827625

Contact My Sales Associate | Customer Support | Feedback | Help

Open Orders | Lists

Products | Orders | Manage Lists | Sysco Market

Active Order: Order Name (54)

Search
Product Search
Search within Results

Today's Activities
Account
Payment Hold!
Order Alerts
Order Name 1: Invalid Deliv. !
Order Name 2: Backord. Item
Order Name 3: Backord. Item
Partial Delivery
Order Name 1: Invalid Deliv. !
Order Name 2: Backord. Item
Order Name 1: Invalid Deliv. !

Promotions

Orders — Your Thurs order restock has been submitted. Import Order | + Create New Order

Open	Pending	Rejected	Submitted
Jan 15 2010	Jan 15 2010	Jan 15 2010	Jan 15 2010
Order Name Continue	Order Name Continue	Order Name Continue	Order Name Continue
Order Total: $1,234.56	Order Total: $1,234.56	Order Total: $1,234.56	Order Total: $1,234.56
Item Total: 72	Item Total: 72	Item Total: 72	Item Total: 72

Open Orders will be saved up to 7 days past the specified delivery date.

Order History | Import Order Queue

Deliv. Date	Status	Order Name	Last Modified	PO No.	Ref. No.	Item Total	Est. Total ($)
03/30/10	Processing	Name 10/01/10 05:36PM	02/01/10	1320753	1324950	150	82.20
02/20/10	Cancelled	Name 10/01/10 05:36PM	02/04/10	1320753	2039485	90	82.20
02/20/10	Delivered	Name 10/01/10 05:36PM	02/09/10	1320753	2384375	203	82.20
02/20/10	Rejected	Name 10/01/10 05:36PM	02/01/10	1320753	2039485	405	82.20

Sysco | Market

Welcome Thomas Keller | Close Window
Account: 001827625

Contact My Sales Associate | Customer Support | Feedback | Help

Open Orders | Lists

Products | Orders | Manage Lists | Sysco Market

Active Order: Order Name (54)

Search
Product Search
Search within Results

Today's Activities
Account
Payment Hold!
Order Alerts
Order Name 1: Invalid Deliv. !
Order Name 2: Backord. Item
Order Name 3: Backord. Item
Partial Delivery
Order Name 1: Invalid Deliv. !
Order Name 2: Backord. Item
Order Name 1: Invalid Deliv. !

Promotions

View Order: Order Name — Edit | Export | Print | Delete

Order Details | Shipping Info — Quick Order

Delivery Date:	06/01/2010	**PO Number:**	123456789	**Created By:**	Tom Keller
Shipping Condition:	Will Call	**Order Number:**	000012345	**Last Modified By:**	John Doe
Invoice Separately:	Yes	**Quantity:**	50	**Last Modified Date:**	06/17/2010

Group By | Column Options

$	Stock	Last Ordered	Product Name	Brand	Sysco UPC	Category	Pack Size	Price ($)	Order Qty	Est. Total ($)
$		01/23	Cheese Sub Amer Yel 160	Citavo	1234567890	Dairy Products	4/5 lb	41.10 cs	6 cs	309.52
$		02/10	Cheese Sub Amer Yel 160	Metz	1234567890	Dry Spices	16 oz	41.10 cs	6 cs	92.35
$		01/23	NEW! Cheese Sub Amer Yel 160	Classic	1234567890	Dairy Products	4/5 lb	41.10 cs	2 cs	309.52
		02/10	Cheese Sub Amer Yel 160	Imperial	1234567890	Dairy Products	4/5 lb	41.10 cs	2 cs	345.89
		01/23	PHASED OUT Cheese Sub Amer Yel 160	Metz	1234567890	Dry Spices	16 oz	41.10 cs	1 cs	12.89
		02/10	LEAVING SOON! Cheese Sub Amer Yel 160	Classic	1234567890	Dairy Products	4/5 lb	41.10 cs	1 cs	246.78
		01/23	Cheese Sub Amer Yel 160	Imperial	1234567890	Dairy Products	4/5 lb	41.10 cs	2 ea	301.34
		02/10	Cheese Sub Amer Yel 160	Metz	1234567890	Dry Spices	16 oz	41.10 cs	3 cs	23.78

Source: Sysco Corporation, used with permission.

From forecast to specification to purchase order, it is clear that there is a great deal of planning, attention to detail, and sound management required to perform effective purchasing.

Inventory

To be effective in placing your order, you have to understand the items in your inventory. From Chapter 22, you decided on the quality of the products to use and earlier in this chapter, you have identified the specific standards (specifications) for the products. Understanding the items in your inventory means knowing the amount of items you have in inventory and what your par levels are.

Inventory Basics

To understand inventory, it's helpful to know a few basic terms:

✓ Inventory item. This is any product routinely supplied to the facility. Both food and non-food products can be inventory items. The food products are generally ingredients for recipes, or items that will be served directly to clients, such as individual cartons of milk or pats of margarine. Just as with a recipe, each inventory item has a unique identity, or its own title. In online systems, each inventory item also has a unique number or identifier.

✓ Inventory category. Inventory may also be managed under categories, just as recipes are. A category is a grouping that is logical and useful to the foodservice operation. For example, some Certified Dietary Managers categorize items according to where they are stored. Thus, a category called frozen foods may refer to foods stored in the freezer. Sub-categories may include names like: Frozen foods—chicken, Frozen foods—ice cream, and others.

✓ Purchase unit. A purchase unit is the package, container, or unit in which a product is purchased. For example, canned peaches may be purchased by the case. Each case contains 6 cans. The purchase unit is a case. Other purchase units include: pounds (as in pounds of meat), bags (as in large bags of flour), drums (as in drums of fat for deep-fat frying), and others.

✓ Issue unit. An issue unit is the package, container, or amount in which a product is issued from the inventory storage area. Sometimes, the issue unit is identical to the purchase unit. Other times, it is different. For example, the canned peaches purchased in whole cases of 6 cans each are issued by single #10 cans to food production staff. So, the issue unit for this example is: #10 can.

- A cake mix may be purchased in cases of three boxes. However, when a cook needs cake mix, the cook withdraws it as some number of individual boxes. So, in this case, the purchase unit is a case; the issue unit is a box.
- Fresh apples may arrive in cartons, but be used individually. In this case, a carton is the purchase unit, while each is the issue unit.
- Bulk items may be purchased in large containers and issued by weight. Flour, for example, may come in 20-pound bags and be poured into a bin. As needed, the cook withdraws flour. In systems where withdrawals are tracked and accounted for, the Certified Dietary Manager may set the issue unit in pounds.

✓ Storage areas. Storage areas are defined locations where products are stored. Each product in an inventory list must have a defined storage area or location so that you can manage and control it. Storage areas include freezers, refrigerators, deep-chill units, pantries, storerooms, and small supply carts kept in the kitchen or serving areas.

✓ Inventory list. A complete and up-to-date list of inventory is necessary at all times. The inventory list defines the products you have specified as ingredients for recipes and direct-serve products for menus. A typical inventory list identifies: name, inventory number, inventory category, storage location, purchase unit, issue unit, and source (supplier from whom it is ordered).

✓ Physical inventory. A **physical inventory** is an actual count of products on hand at the current time. Counting products is often called taking inventory. A physical inventory is an essential control tool. How often you do it depends on the method you use for determining inventory requirements.

As you count a product, you typically count by purchase units and/or fractions of purchase units. A count is recorded on an inventory form, which has columns for noting date and amount on hand. Review Figure 24.5.

One computer-based tool for taking an inventory uses bar codes to identify products. A handheld scanner "reads" a bar code representing each item on the inventory list, and then the user keys in a number to indicate quantity on hand. This can speed up the process of taking inventory. When it is complete, the user can then apply the figures to determine inventory requirements. In addition, a user can typically print a report showing the current physical inventory.

Inventory Management Tools

Some items are needed only for immediate and one-time use. However, most inventory products for a foodservice operation tend to repeat themselves. Planning what to purchase for each of these needs requires a different process.

Let's say you are planning a Volunteer's Dinner for next week. You have developed a special menu for this meal, which will require beef tenderloin. This is an item you do not routinely use in any menu cycles. So, the filet mignon is a one-time need. To determine requirements, you count the expected number of clients, pad this figure as you see fit, and then order according to the needs dictated by the recipe you will use.

Routinely, though, the vast majority of products you maintain need to be on hand over and over, based on the menu cycle. There are several ways to manage ongoing inventory needs, including the minimum/maximum system, the par level system, and the perpetual inventory system, and just-in-time purchasing. Each of these is described below.

Minimum/Maximum system. A minimum/maximum inventory system is one in which inventory levels are maintained within established ranges for each product. It is based on two reference points for each product in the inventory:

1. The minimum quantity for the product. Minimum quantity is the minimum amount that must be available; inventory levels should not fall below this figure.

Glossary

Physical Inventory
A physical count of items in inventory that occurs weekly, monthly, quarterly, or annually

Figure 24.7 Terminology in a Minimum/Maximum System

The following terms and established values apply to each product you manage in a minimum/maximum system.

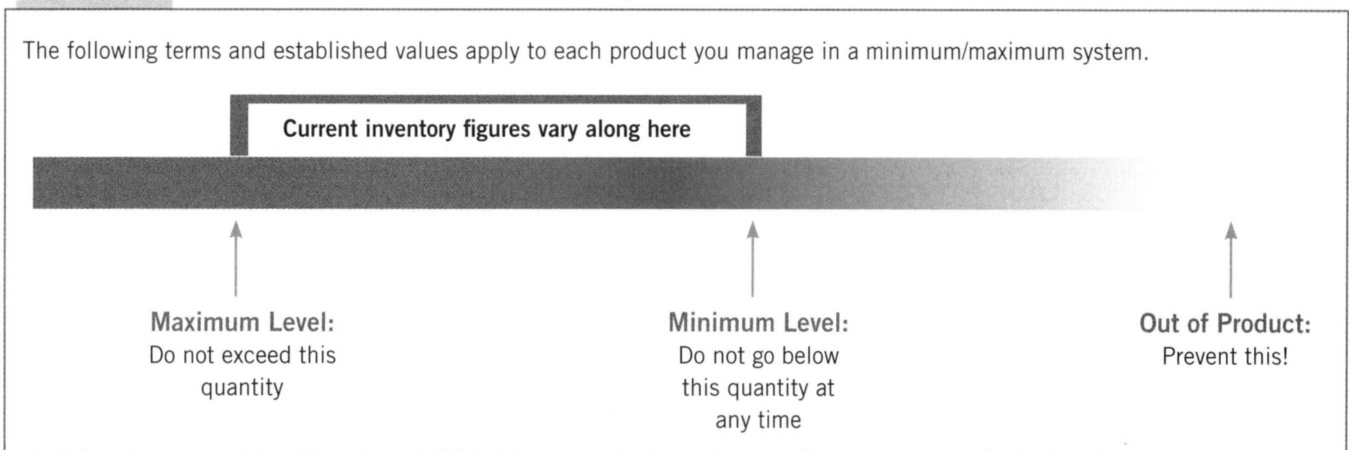

2. The maximum quantity of the product. Maximum quantity is the maximum amount of this product that should be carried in stock at any given time; inventory levels should not rise above this figure.

Quantities for inventory products are expressed in purchase units. To determine how much to order, you can take a current count of purchase units on hand for an item in inventory (physical inventory). You then subtract the current count from the maximum quantity. Here is a simple example:

- ✓ The maximum level for canned peaches is 4 cases.
- ✓ The operation currently has 2 cases on hand.
- ✓ The order would be: 4 - 2 = 2 cases.
- ✓ You would order 2 cases.

However, the system can become a bit more complex, based on how long it will take an order to arrive, and how much product may be used during that interim. In the above example, what happens if while waiting for the 2 cases of peaches just ordered, you use an additional 2 cases? Now, you are totally out of peaches. Whether this is a serious issue for any given product depends on:

Lead time: how long it takes from the time you place an order until it actually arrives, and

Usage rate: how much product you typically use during a defined time interval.

So, to account for these factors, you can calculate lead units. Lead units is a special factor representing the number of units you need to subtract from current inventory to determine how much to order.

Each time you take inventory counts, you can subtract lead units from the amount on hand. If the answer is below the minimum, you order. If it is not, you wait. Figure 24.7 illustrates how several key terms relate to each other, and Figure 24.8 illustrates how to calculate lead units and purchase quantity.

A minimum/maximum system of inventory management works well for non-perishable products, or products that can remain in storage for extended

Figure 24.8 Calculating Lead Units and Purchase Quantity

Background: You are setting values for canned, stewed tomatoes in a minimum/maximum inventory system. Tomatoes are purchased in #10 cans, as 6 cans per case.

Purchase Unit: Case

Based on predictions, volume of usage, and experience, you have set the following figures.

Maximum Quantity	6 cases. You do not want to carry more than this amount at any time.
Minimum Quantity	4 cases. You do not want to fall below this minimum, or you may risk running out.
Lead Time	3 days. From the time you place an order, it takes 3 days for you to receive the product.
Usage Rate	1 case per day. You generally use about 1 case of stewed tomatoes every day.
Lead Units	This is lead time multiplied by usage rate or 3 days X 1 case/day = 3 cases If you place the order for stewed tomatoes today, you expect to use another 3 cases of stewed tomatoes while you are waiting for the order to arrive.
Purchase Quantity	You take an inventory count today and discover that you currently have 5 cases of stewed tomatoes in stock. You calculate purchase quantity as follows: Maximum Quantity - (Current Quantity - Lead Units) = Quantity to Order, *or* 6 cases - (5 cases - 3 cases) = 6 - 2 = 4 cases You order 4 cases of stewed tomatoes today.

periods of time. Examples of such products include canned goods, dry goods, spices, condiments, and the like. In addition, it is appropriate for items you routinely keep in stock, not for an occasional item ordered for a special event.

Notice that in this system, how you set minimum and maximum quantities can have a great impact. If you set the minimum quantity too low, you risk running out of products. If you set the maximum quantity too high, you may be carrying excess inventory. Excess inventory poses several disadvantages. It incurs storage costs, ties up cash flow, and increases the risk of losses through spoilage or product expirations.

Today, most Certified Dietary Managers attempt to maintain the smallest quantities of inventory products feasible, while still assuring that supplies will be adequate to produce and serve food reliably. Look carefully at lead units and also consider the reliability of your supplier. Sometimes, a supplier runs out of products. Fulfillment of your order may be delayed. Or, a weather emergency may prevent deliveries. As with menu forecasting, inventory forecasting requires ongoing monitoring and refinement. If you run out of a product when there are no unusual delays or other circumstances, this is a clue that your minimum level is set too low.

Par level system. A simpler inventory management concept is the **par level** concept. In this, you set par levels, or minimum quantities you wish to maintain for each product. You take physical inventory on a scheduled basis. After each count, you compare the amounts on hand with the established par. If the

Glossary

Par Levels
A minimum quantity to be maintained in inventory

Perpetual Inventory
A running count of inventory items that is updated continuously, usually with an electronic order entry or point of sale system

on-hand figure is lower, you order more to bring it up to par. This system can work for facilities with very stable menus and forecasts.

Perpetual inventory system. While minimum/maximum and par systems require you to take physical inventories quite often, a perpetual inventory system does not. Instead, a **perpetual inventory** represents a running count of products on hand. In many respects, it operates just like a bank checkbook. The process works like this:

- ✓ You begin the system with a balance for each product. The balance is how many purchase units are on hand.
- ✓ When you purchase and receive more product, you add this to the balance.
- ✓ When you withdraw products for use, you subtract them from the balance.
- ✓ At any given time, you can examine the balance and determine purchases required to replenish supplies. Generally, you total withdrawals over the period since the last order, and order this quantity.
- ✓ Periodically, you reconcile the perpetual balance by taking a physical inventory, and comparing the actual figures for amounts on hand with what you have calculated you *should* have on hand for each item. This is just like balancing a checkbook. An example of a form for maintaining perpetual inventory appears in Figure 24.9.

Good practice dictates that one person take responsibility for maintaining the balance sheet, while someone else conducts the physical inventory for reconciliation. Just as in an accounting system, a reconciliation is a type of audit. Involving different people imposes control and helps prevent the opportunity for theft.

An advantage to the perpetual inventory system is control. Based on orders received and units issued, you know what should be in stores. If the figures do not match, you may have valuable information that can help control inventory shrinkage.

Shrinkage is a decline in inventory counts through anything other than withdrawals that have been accounted for. What can cause shrinkage? Here are some examples:

- ✓ A cook is opening a jar of pickles and drops it. The product is cleaned up and discarded.
- ✓ A visitor or employee walks through a storage area and pockets a product for personal use.
- ✓ A storage clerk does not rotate product effectively, following a first-in, first-out (FIFO) system. A case of sandwich meat becomes outdated and is thrown away.
- ✓ A purchaser purchases food in excess quantities, and again, food expires and is thrown away.

Figure 24.9 **Perpetual Inventory Form**

Product Name: ______________________ **Purchase Unit Size:** ______________________

Date	In	Out	Balance Carried Forward	Date	In	Out	Balance Carried Forward

Furthermore, discrepancies may arise from documentation errors in the receiving process. For example:

- ✓ A purchase order specifies 40 pounds of ground beef.
- ✓ The delivery is only 38 pounds, but no one notices and documents this fact.
- ✓ The figure of 40 pounds is added to the perpetual balance. In fact, though, only 38 pounds have been added to the physical inventory. The running balance for ground beef is now incorrect.

In a related example, the distributor runs out of a product and is unable to supply it. If no one documents this error, the anticipated delivery may be added to the perpetual balance. In fact, though, no product was added to the physical inventory.

Any discrepancy discovered through reconciliation merits investigation. Often, by following up on discrepancies, a Certified Dietary Manager can pinpoint problems, make improvements, and better control inventory. Through this process, the manager may contain unnecessary expenditures as well.

Just-in-Time Purchasing. As mentioned above, there are many advantages to limiting supplies on hand for each product. Limiting excess inventory limits a number of costs. The challenge, though, is to keep inventory totals low while assuring adequate supplies are available as they are needed. A growing trend today is to shorten the timetable from purchase order to use. This is called

JIT Purchasing
Purchasing items as needed or Just In Time

just-in-time purchasing or **JIT**. In this concept, a Certified Dietary Manager purchases products just in time for use.

How is it possible? Computerized systems are a great help in this regard. Automated calculations of purchasing needs streamline the time requirement for doing the paperwork before placing an order. In addition, technologies exist for placing and processing orders quickly through Internet-based systems and databases. Some managers have made arrangements with suppliers to honor deliveries with short turnaround times, such as 24 hours.

Inventory Control Tools

Receiving Process. It is essential that the right products in the right quantity at the right price and from the right supplier be received at the right time. Thus, attention to the receiving process is critical to controlling inventory. Review Chapter 16 for food safety indicators in the receiving process.

What makes a receiving process work well? There are several components in an effective system. Trained staff must be available to perform required tasks. Employees with receiving duties must:

✓ Know quality specifications for each product

✓ Recognize required quality

✓ Recognize food safety indicators to assure food received is wholesome

✓ Know how to handle discrepancies in quality or quantity

✓ Know how to complete receiving records.

In small facilities, the Certified Dietary Manager may perform the receiving tasks. In larger facilities, there may be one or more employees whose duties are devoted to receiving and storage. A basic receiving process follows the steps described below.

Step 1: Check against purchase records

- ✓ The quantity of all items must be verified against what was purchased; count items that come by count; weigh items that are ordered by weight.

Step 2: Inspect against specifications

- ✓ Compare products against written specifications, especially meat products.

Step 3: Accept or reject products; contact the manager for the following:

- ✓ Wrong product is delivered or product does not meet specifications
- ✓ Product was not ordered
- ✓ The supplier has made an unacceptable substitute
- ✓ Food safety indicators are unacceptable
- ✓ Product was not delivered on time.

The assistant manager is the person who checks in deliveries in your facility. She is in a hurry today because they are short one staff person in the kitchen. The following day, there aren't enough chicken breasts for the production of the noon meal. What might have happened?

(Check your answer at the end of this chapter)

Step 4: Issue a credit memo if necessary:

✓ This occurs if only a partial order is delivered OR

✓ The required items are not available (see Figure 24.10 for a credit memo example).

Step 5: Inspect against delivery invoice before signing it

✓ It is important that items appear on the delivery invoice in the correct quantity and the correct price.

✓ Contact the Certified Dietary Manager if an unauthorized substitution is made or corrections are needed.

Step 6: Complete the receiving report

✓ Large facilities that have a designated person receiving the products will require a signed, completed receiving report.

Furthermore, prompt storage secures the inventory. Conversely, deliveries left standing in hallways become invitations to theft. Depending on the layout of your own facility, a delivery may be stored in an area where many people are walking. Some may not even be foodservice employees. So clearly, quick action is essential.

Figure 24.10 Credit Memorandum

To: ______________________ Number: __________

Address: ______________________

City: ______________________ State: __________

Please send credit for the following:

Invoice	Item	Quantity	Unit of Sale	Unit Price	Extension

Reason:

Delivery Person: ______________________ Authorizing Signature: ______________________

Equipment for Receiving. A receiving area must have adequate space for completion of the steps outlined above. In a large facility, there may be a receiving dock connected with a special entrance for trucks. Generally, the receiving area should be located near the delivery door.

Necessary equipment may include: tools to open containers, an accurate scale, carts or dollies, containers to hold ice removed from fresh poultry or seafood, a thermometer, a calculator, marking and tagging equipment, and any needed office equipment (computer, file cabinet, clipboard, etc.).

Food Storage Process

After products are received, they must be transferred immediately to the proper secure storage area. Prompt storage assures food safety and a more secure inventory. Deliveries left standing in hallways become invitations to theft and improper holding temperatures.

There are three basic concerns to address to manage storage:

✓ Ensure that product quality and wholesomeness is retained during storage

✓ Manage inventory records needed for accounting purposes

✓ Prevent theft of items in storage.

An initial step in managing storage is to organize storage areas effectively. Some of this organization is influenced by the existing physical layout of the facility. Food storage areas may include one or more rooms for dry storage, as well as refrigerated units, freezers, and possibly deep-chill units. In some facilities, a major storeroom is supplemented by a smaller storage area close to food preparation and service areas for small items needed routinely. This is simply a time-saver.

Organization ties in with your procedures for issuing inventory. Based on the authorization you assign for making withdrawals from inventory, you can decide where to locate many products. In general, items of high value should have the strongest controls and the most limited access.

Where to place products within any storage area depends on how you need to use the food. Generally, you want to place like items together—all canned fruits in one location, followed by all canned vegetables, etc. The organization you choose should streamline the amount of work required by both receiving personnel and production personnel to accomplish their jobs, while also promoting security. Organization may differ from one foodservice operation to another. The essential idea is that organization must make sense for your efficient workflow and inventory controls. Some storerooms are organized according to the order sheet to facilitate ordering.

Quality can deteriorate or food can become unsafe if items are not properly stored. Thus, it is important to rotate food so that items in storage the longest will be used first. A standard approach to rotation is called **First in, First Out (FIFO)**. This means the first item to go into storage is the first item to come out of storage. So, older products move to the front; new deliveries are placed behind them. Failure to follow a FIFO system can

Glossary

FIFO (First In, First Out)
A storage method to assure that older products are used first

Putting It Into Practice: 6

Your foodservice department is planning a very special meal next week. You order extra-large shrimp (12-15 per pound) for this party. You checked it into the freezer three days ago. On the day of the party, the only shrimp available is small shrimp, (72-75 per pound). What might have gone wrong?

(Check your answer at the end of this chapter)

result in inventory loss. An outdated product will have to be discarded, which represents expensive food waste.

To implement FIFO, some facilities mark packages with dates as they are received. One approach is to use a marker to indicate receiving date on every package. Another is to use labels or dots to mark packages. For example, a label saying "use first" can be placed on older products at the time that new products are added to inventory. For cans, specially designed can racks—where new product goes in the top and oldest comes out the bottom—can help.

Items must be stored at the proper temperature and humidity. Certified Dietary Managers should use accurate thermometers to check that temperatures for refrigerated items are kept at 41°F or below, that dry storage area temperatures range between 50°F and 70°F, and that frozen foods are kept between 0°F and -10°F. Storage records need to include temperature of storage units taken at regular intervals.

Storage areas must also be kept clean. Routine cleaning for all frozen, refrigerated, and dry storage areas is important. Effective storage practices also require proper ventilation and air circulation. Ongoing programs to control rodent and insect infestation are necessary. Typically, items should be stored in their original containers, and items that absorb odors (such as flour) should be stored away from items that give off odors (such as onions). Most food should be stored in airtight containers, and all products should be covered.

Food Issuing Practices

A controlled process for withdrawing products from storage for use is called **issuing**. The idea here is that not just anyone can go take what is needed. Instead, someone has to issue a product. The active process of issuing denotes control, responsibility, and accountability. An effective food issuing system does three things:

- ✓ Matches items removed from storage with those required for actual food production
- ✓ Supports security procedures
- ✓ Documents the quantities of items issued for record-keeping and accounting.

Clearly, these objectives require basic controls and documentation. Many facilities use a **food requisition**. This form organizes requests for issues, and it documents the transactions. An example appears in Figure 24.11. Unit price and food cost may or may not appear on the form, depending on how your accounting system is structured.

The process of issuing is managing the movement of ingredients to production and service areas. Each facility must establish policies about inventory issues. For example, who may complete the requisition and authorize inventory withdrawal? When should products be issued? A basic plan may be that the cook completes a food requisition for recipes to be prepared for the next meal period. A standardized recipe will indicate the types and quantities of necessary

Your facility is small and you do not have a formal requisition process. Kitchen staff members just sign a sheet of paper in the storage room when they take products out. Lately you have noticed that inventory for some products seem to be short. What should you do?

(Check your answer at the end of this chapter)

Figure 24.11 Food Requisition

Date: ______________ Location: ______________

Quantity	Unit	Description	Unit Price	Extension

Authorized: ______________ Received By: ______________

ingredients. In computerized food production systems, a printout may show what withdrawals will be needed.

After the food requisition is completed, it goes to the storeroom for issuing. An employee assigned to storeroom management withdraws and counts the products, and delivers them to designated areas. The person who receives the withdrawal verifies the delivery, and signs off that everything has been received. In another example, a service employee requisitions ready-to-use products from inventory. For example, a cafeteria employee stocking the cold service area may request cartons of milk, fresh fruit, and other items. The same steps hold—the cafeteria employee completes a requisition; the assigned employee fills it; and the cafeteria employee checks and signs off on it. In many ways, this process is similar to the initial receiving process. Each person involved in the transaction is responsible for accuracy and verification, and is accountable for the products.

Controlling access to storage areas is a prime concern in security at the time of food distribution. After items are issued and transferred to food production or service areas, the issuing process is complete.

In a very large facility, some food may be stored off-site in a warehouse. Again, the process follows the same principles. However, the requisitions must be organized and communicated well in advance of need. Assigned employees withdraw products and deliver them to the requesting location.

Requisitions can be used by the Certified Dietary Manager to match the quantity of items withdrawn from inventory with that used in actual food production as a method of monitoring product movement and control. The objective in issuing is to distribute needed items for production efficiently, safely, and economically. Related to this first objective is to keep food stocks secure from theft and pilferage. Record-keeping is a supportive service, but not an objective unto itself. The end result is effective food distribution throughout the operation.

Glossary

Issuing
Process for withdrawing products from storage

Food Requisition
A form that documents storage transactions

In another scenario, some foodservice facilities accommodate issuing systems for areas that maintain par inventory levels. Consider, for example, items on nourishment carts in nursing stations, or supplies in a decentralized pantry where rethermalization of trays takes place just before meal service. As items in these areas are reduced to a predetermined level, a specified quantity of additional products is issued to build the inventory levels to a predetermined par level.

A modification of this system is the exchange cart process. In this model, an employee stocks a cart with required supplies (following a predetermined list), and wheels it to a pantry. Then, the employee exchanges this cart for an old cart. He takes the old cart back to the kitchen for restocking.

Some foodservice facilities use computerized issuing systems. Some facilities use optical reading devices that read information from bar codes and enter it into computerized information systems. Software calculates the quantity of products leaving storage areas and maintains an ongoing count of products in inventory, supporting a perpetual inventory system.

Some facilities use stockless inventory systems. For example, a satellite unit may have no or little inventory on hand. Products to be prepared/served are brought to the facility daily. Any remaining products are taken back to the central preparation area at the end of the serving period. While not practical in many facilities, this system is useful when satellite facilities have very minimal food storage areas. In this system, very frequent deliveries of necessary products are essential.

Even small facilities can implement the basic principles of issuing control. Perhaps expensive and/or theft-prone items can remain in locked storage. Management staff can be present for issuing these relatively few items at specific times preceding production. Other items can remain available in storage areas for request on an as-needed basis by production personnel.

Consistently enforced policies regarding storage areas being off-limits to unauthorized personnel can reduce the number of employees who issue products to themselves. Use of a perpetual inventory system to manage selected items and matching of production records with changes in inventory volumes can also help the small facility monitor the effectiveness of issuing procedures.

Small foodservice operations may not find it practical to use a formal food requisition system. These facilities might, however, require that a Certified Dietary Manager be physically present at the time withdrawals are made from inventory. Small facilities can also use a requisition taped to the wall or door of each storage area. Staff members authorized to withdraw products from storage can then enter information onto the form. Close supervision is necessary to assure that personnel adhere to this procedure.

ABC Analysis

Most Certified Dietary Managers recognize that the greatest dollar value of an inventory investment is represented by a relatively small number of items. If, for example, a facility purchases 400 products, perhaps only 100 or fewer of these items, such as meats, represent the greatest cost. The concept of **ABC analysis** helps a manager focus inventory controls where they are most needed. In an ABC analysis, you follow these steps:

- ✓ Study purchases to determine which products are most costly. Categorize these as "A" items. Then group products that are next most costly. Categorize these as "B" items. Finally, identify items that are least costly, and categorize them as "C" items. The idea of cost here refers to the price of an individual item in a typical usage unit, not the total dollars spent on any item during the course of a week or month. In other words, while breads, cereals, and dairy items may represent a significant cost because of the quantity used, it is the use of costly "A" items that is of interest in ABC analysis.
- ✓ Categorize items in this manner to set priorities in purchasing, receiving and storing. Costly "A" items must be carefully controlled; less expensive "C" items need less control.

If you use an ABC approach to managing inventory:

- ✓ You can expend your time and efforts to control the most costly inventory items.
- ✓ You can minimize inventory investments, carrying smaller quantities of "A" products in inventory.
- ✓ You can develop specific policies and procedures to control, purchase, receive, and store top-priority items.

How can the concept of ABC analysis be used in storage? Small facilities might designate one section of a reach-in refrigerator or freezer for storage of most expensive items. These units can be kept locked and a perpetual inventory system can be used to monitor the quantity of "A" items in these areas. While not essential, the perpetual inventory system imposes an additional control, because you can find out when discrepancies occur and follow through on them. The *precious room concept*—locked storage within a locked storage area—can be useful to store the most expensive dry items, including chafing dishes, buffet utensils, alcoholic beverages, and other expensive supplies and materials.

Ways to Reduce Inventory Costs

Cash flow problems can occur when inventory levels are too high. Steps you can take to reduce inventory costs include the following:

- ✓ Reduce the quantities of products purchased. To make the transition when stocks are too great, you may be able to "live on inventory" for some time period and achieve a reduction.
- ✓ Reduce turnaround time on deliveries. In other words, work with suppliers to obtain products more quickly from the time you place an order until it is received. Computerized ordering systems can greatly support this practice.

✓ Obtain more frequent deliveries in smaller quantities by negotiating with suppliers.

✓ Adjust inventory minimums when practical.

✓ Be sure that purchase units are well suited to your usage needs. For example, a product you use in very small amounts should be purchased in small units, not large ones. For instance, purchase very small amounts at a local grocery store.

✓ Streamline the list of products carried. For example, perhaps you carry three sizes of ground beef patties. Through critical analysis, you may be able to whittle this down to one size of ground beef patties.

✓ Examine special dietary products for possible consolidation with regular products. In facilities serving a number of special diets, there may be a tendency to carry two types of each fruit, vegetable, bread, frozen entree, baked product, and so forth. One product may be for clients requiring modification of salt, sugar, or fat. Another may be for clients with no dietary restrictions. By reviewing dietary needs and product options, you may be able to select one product to serve both needs. Examples are: a juice-packed canned fruit, a sodium-reduced soup, or a "healthy" convenience food.

✓ Refuse early deliveries to avoid making payments sooner than you really need to.

✓ Refuse to accept excess quantity on any delivery.

Security and Controls

Throughout the process of purchasing, receiving, storing, and issuing food, there are ongoing security concerns. Many relate to the flow of procedures from one task to the next.

The first concerns come into play in the purchasing process, where a form of theft or error can occur. Here are some of the issues:

Kickbacks. Kickbacks involve the purchaser working in collusion with someone from the supplier's company. In one type of kickback scheme, products are purchased at higher than necessary prices; the two thieves split the difference between the real and inflated price. The payment can be in money or gifts. Either way, the foodservice operation is the loser. Routine review of invoices and competitive bids can identify this unethical practice.

Padding the invoice. This means adding items that were not received, and/or increasing the invoice by adding unreasonable "handling" or other charges. Since this scheme works well when the employee who purchases also does the receiving, the Certified Dietary Manager should design a system that separates purchasing and receiving tasks.

Fictitious companies. Personnel who purchase can steal by setting up a "dummy" company to submit invoices for products that were never received. To identify this, you can periodically review payees' names on company checks and assure that they are valid.

Duplicate invoices. Suppliers may send an invoice through twice if the facility does not have an internal system to verify which invoices have not been paid and cancel invoices that have been paid. This type of problem may happen unintentionally, and is not necessarily a sign of bad faith or malicious intent. What's important here is to have basic accounting practices in place to address any failures or errors.

Credit memo problems. Financial loss can occur when products are not delivered and no credit memo is issued to reduce the original delivery invoice accordingly. A similar problem can occur if a product is rejected and the supplier fails to process a credit memo. Certified Dietary Managers can require that a credit memo be issued, and attach it to the delivery invoice whenever shortages or related problems occur.

Delivery invoice errors. Intentional or unintentional arithmetic errors, short weight or count, quality deviations, and similar mistakes can cost foodservices money. It is important to check the arithmetic on invoices. Regardless of whether these are innocent errors or intentional frauds, the bottom line is the same. The facility loses money.

Quality substitutions. Downgrading a product with the hope that it won't be noticed is a type of theft that can sometimes occur. Paying more for a lower-quality product can be prevented by proper receiving practices.

Security concerns become important at time of receiving, too. There are many opportunities for employee and supplier theft. Consider the following examples:

- ✓ Your facility receives the wrong item, such as ground beef at 30% fat instead of 20% fat. If the employee does not catch this error, you are paying a higher price for a lower-quality product (and you may not have enough ground beef for scheduled preparation).
- ✓ Your facility receives a short weight or count and fails to notice. Now, your foodervice operation pays for a product it does not even have (and again you may not have enough food for scheduled production).
- ✓ You receive a product containing a filler, such as ground meat to which ground ice has been added.
- ✓ A similar scenario gives you meat that has not been trimmed to specifications. In this case, weight of the product may match the invoice, but edible yield factor is lower, so you are paying more per ounce of edible portion.

To help guard against loss at the time products are received, you can focus on some basic principles. First of all, schedule deliveries to allow adequate time for careful check-in of products. Next, make the investment in training for receiving staff. Recognize staff for their role as gatekeepers, and assure they understand the details and mechanics of how to accomplish their mission.

In the receiving area itself, the receiving door should be locked. An audio signal can be installed to permit delivery staff to signal when they have arrived. With this plan, delivery persons will be under visual supervision of receiving staff during the entire time they are in the facility, and access to possible deliveries is controlled.

In storage, yet additional problems can arise. The most common is theft, either by foodservice employees or outsiders to the facility. Theft is also called pilferage. Several practices can help reduce pilferage. A critical step is to manage the flow of products from receiving to storage. Move them as quickly as possible, and assure that schedules are set up to expedite this process.

As an additional control, prohibit access to storage areas. Locking all storage areas and controlling access to keys is a generally accepted practice. Whether areas are locked or not, you need to have a clear policy about who may or may not enter the storage areas. Post signs on storage areas to reinforce the policy. As with any other policy, however, words are not enough. Walk through the operation with alert eyes, and investigate any situation that does not look right.

Another storage concern relates to small items needed in production or service areas. For example, a cook may keep a stock of herbs and spices (or much more). Or a service employee may keep bundles of condiments and cans of juice. Realize that once products are distributed to high-traffic areas, your ability to exert control diminishes. Thus, it is helpful to minimize the decentralized stores you permit. Handle as much inventory as possible from secured storage areas, and/or transfer decentralized stores back to secure areas at the end of each work day.

Finally, consider how you will manage personal items in your facility. In some facilities, foodservice employees may be permitted to store their own lunches in the operation. Or, a nurse may ask for space to store a cake for a client's birthday. Or, you may have a policy allowing employees to take certain leftovers home with them. However, at any time when an employee walks out of your kitchen carrying food, it may not be evident whether he is authorized to do so or not. These are just a few examples of situations in which the distinctions between your facility's property and someone else's can become unclear. Any time they are unclear, you set up the opportunity for someone to walk away with a product, claiming it is his own when it is not.

To control these issues, some facilities designate a special refrigerator, away from other storage areas, specifically for personal items. There may be a requirement for an employee to check in products before placing them in this area. A control mechanism that helps with removal of products from an operation is a materials pass. This is a document stating that the employee is authorized to remove this item from the building. It names the item(s), and contains a date and authorized signature. In some facilities, all employees leaving the building are asked to show their property to a security guard on the way out the door.

An additional consideration in securing storage is off-hours access. At certain times of day or night, there may be only one or two employees working, such as a late night clean-up employee, or an early morning storeroom employee. When possible, secure areas that do not require access during these times. In addition, you may need to coordinate with a security manager, an evening administrator, or someone else in your facility to ask for assistance in monitoring security.

Paying for Purchased Products

The role of the accounting department deserves special attention in this discussion because all products received must be paid for. Designing a system that makes the accounting function as an integral part of the purchasing task is very important.

In small foodservice operations, the owner or Certified Dietary Manager may be both the purchaser and the bill-payer. As facilities become larger, these tasks are split between operations and accounting or office personnel. As foodservice operations grow bigger still, purchasing responsibilities may be assumed by the accounting department in an increased effort to separate duties. Typically, a flow of documentation is used to help the manager, accountant, and supplier communicate with each other. This documentation may be paper-based, or it may be maintained in a computer system.

One type of document is a source document. This means it is a source of original entry for financial information into the accounting system. For example, a time card may be a source document for payroll. A purchase order is a source document, as is a signed invoice.

Figure 24.12 identifies the source documents and flow of accounting information in a small facility, from the time that an order is placed until the supplier is paid.

At the end of the day or shift, purchase orders and delivery invoices are forwarded to the designated manager or bookkeeper. This person must:

- ✓ Assure that there are no differences in quantity and/or price between items ordered (purchase order) and received (delivery invoice).
- ✓ Assure that arithmetic extensions on the delivery invoice are correct.
- ✓ File the invoice for payment.

Procedures may be modified by larger foodservice facilities.

Responsibility for purchasing tasks may vary from one facility to another. It is most common for a foodservice operation to bear responsibility for purchasing food. This is because the specification and selection process requires an in-depth knowledge of food and foodservice.

There are generally two methods used to pay suppliers for purchased products. One is managed by invoice, while another is managed by statement. An **invoice** is a document designating what has been purchased and accepted, and at what price. The purchases are totaled as the amount due. A **statement** is an accounting document that summarizes all invoices, credits, and payments for a given time period and provides the bottom line, such as amount due.

With the by-invoice plan, the Certified Dietary Manager takes the following steps:

- ✓ Review invoices from receiving daily. Question and correct any matters of concern. Be sure that the final figure on each invoice reflects all discrepancies, credits, or adjustments noted by the receiving clerk.
- ✓ Mark invoice "approved for payment" and sign them.
- ✓ File invoice by due date.

Invoice
A document designating what has been purchased and accepted

Statement
A document that summarizes all invoices, credits, and payments for a given time period

Figure 24.12 Source Document Flow in a Small Facility

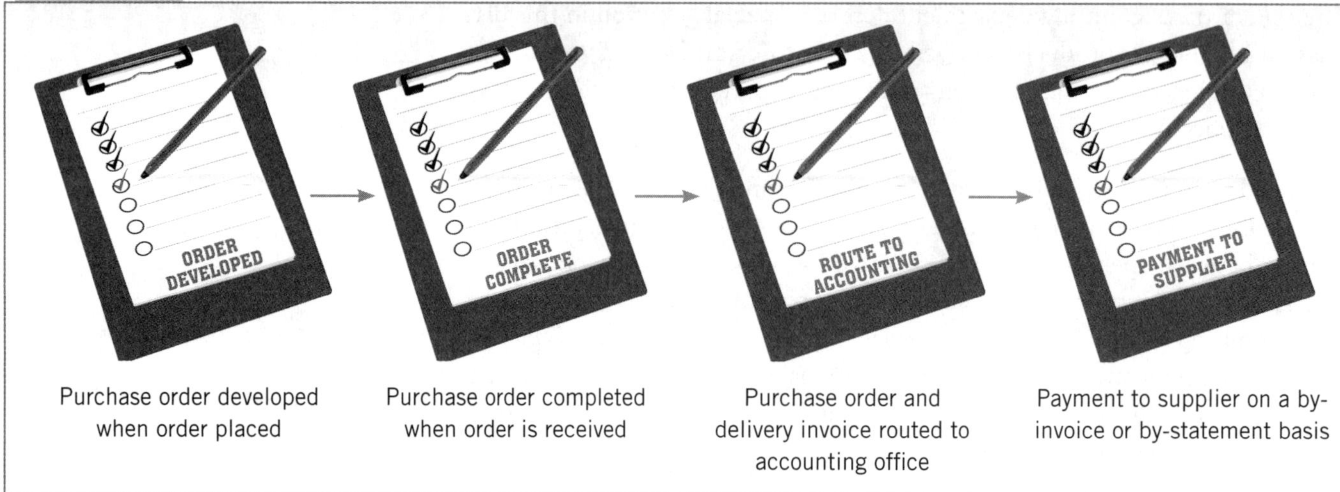

- ✓ On a scheduled basis (such as once per week), pull invoices about to come due and process them for payment. For example, if an approved bill is due on August 10, it may be pulled on August 6 and processed for payment. It might be signed and mailed on August 7 to allow adequate time for delivery.

With the by-statement plan, the Certified Dietary Manager begins as above, but then follows a slightly different process. Here are the steps:

- ✓ Review invoices from receiving daily. Question and correct any matters of concern. Be sure that the final figure on each invoice reflects all discrepancies, credits, or adjustments noted by the receiving clerk.
- ✓ Mark invoice "approved for payment" and sign them.
- ✓ File invoice by supplier, in an organized date sequence. For example, all invoices from Axl Distributors go into the "Axl" file, with oldest invoices in the front, and newest in the back.
- ✓ Wait for a statement from each supplier to arrive.
- ✓ When the statement arrives, pull all invoices from this supplier's file. Verify the statement against your invoices. If there are any discrepancies, contact the supplier for clarification or adjustment. Then, process the statement for payment.

In most facilities, documents approved for payment then go to a business office or accounting office, where designated personnel actually cut the checks and mail them. Regardless of whether you manage payments by-invoice or by-statement, similar procedures are necessary to prepare the documents for payment.

Management in the News

Smart Purchasing Practices for Foodservice Supplies

by Kenneth Donhauser and Martha Braunbach

In most long-term healthcare facilities, the foodservice department accounts for half of the supply spend of the whole operation. It is critical to the success of the foodservice department that systems are in place, followed, and staff understand the purpose. Technology is a great tool to create a better and more efficient department.

Recently a nursing facility in North Carolina implemented systems to help lower costs and watch purchases closer. In the past, staff would just call the distributor and order products without regard to what was on the menu or in inventory and essentially there were no controls. Because of this new system, a staff member was caught ordering a case of cheesecakes at a cost of around $200 and trying to leave the building with it. We have to wonder how long things of this nature were occurring prior to them putting the ordering systems in place.

Keep these practices in mind to help prevent loss and pilferage:

- Product theft will cost your operation. Implement procedures and systems to reduce this risk.
- An order guide should be followed based on what is on the menu. Items that are ordered and are not on the menu need to be questioned.
- There should be controls on all exit doors and delivery areas both inside and out, so that someone cannot walk out to their car with product, or hide it nearby.
- A scale should be used for all appropriate deliveries.
- All orders need to be inspected and verified.
- Place orders electronically and use reports available to improve your operation.
- Don't allow suppliers to substitute products without your permission.

Suppliers offer promotions on a regular basis to boost their sales. The sales representatives are provided with incentives to boost their sales during this timeframe. The incentives can be cash, prizes, or trips. One area within the facility that needs to be monitored is soaps and chemicals that are dispersed through an automated system. During one holiday promotion in December, the sales reps were given incentive to sell more of their products to move them out of the supplier's inventory. One method of selling more products was to increase the amount of product being dispersed. For example, even though it called for one ounce, the representative increased it to two ounces; therefore, the facility ran out faster and had to order more of the product. The sales rep reasoned that for a period of about 6-8 weeks, the facility would not catch that they were using more product. This became known as "Christmas titration."

To safeguard against these types of unethical practices, gain knowledge of costs and follow these guidelines.

- Do not allow sales reps to place their own orders.
- Know your overall costs per resident day, as well as by area within your department.
- Know your costs compared to other facilities.
- Make sure staff knows how to use equipment and does not use excess products/supplies, thinking if one is good, two must be better.
- Having too much inventory is just as bad as running out all the time.

(Continued...)

Smart Purchasing Practices for Foodservice Supplies *(Continued)*

The price being paid for the products you use is very important, but there are many other factors that weigh on your cost per resident day.

A number of years ago, a distributor sales rep came to the foodservice manager with a special on ground beef. The deal was well below what she had been paying so she ordered double the quantity. The product came in and it was fine. The foodservice manager was very proud of herself for saving her facility quite a bit of money. What was not so good is that the foodservice manager never verified that she received the price quoted. We uncovered this at the business office while looking at the invoices and noticed a lot more ground beef than usual had been ordered. Of course, the price on the invoice was the normal price, but with the foodservice manager we were able to get a credit from the distributor.

Be mindful of these things when ordering, receiving, and signing invoices for products.

- The lowest price may not be the best value.
- Systems must be in place to verify prices.
- Understand how your distributor prices your account by "mark up" or "margin." There is a big difference in the prices you pay between a 10 percent markup vs. a 10 percent margin.
- Use a Group Purchasing Organization (GPO) to help lower your costs.
- Verify that supplier credits are received.
- Ask your distributor to let you know about any specials and closeouts.
- Evaluate products by doing blind cuttings.
- If using a manual tray card system, consider upgrading to an electronic version.
- If you are performing resident care functions manually, consider upgrading to an automated system to manage your residents' needs.
- Don't assume larger sizes are less expensive than smaller sizes on a comparable basis, like per ounce.

Performing intake studies can help significantly lower costs by identifying what residents are not eating and placing items on menus that they will find more agreeable. At one facility in New York, nourishments were their second largest expenditure. This can happen if residents are not being fed properly or they don't like what's on the menu. Make sure you take advantage of the electronic reports available to you from your distributor to help you identify areas that may need closer scrutiny.

When residents are not eating their meals in order to keep weight on, your expenses in other areas like nutritional supplements will also increase. In a study of nursing facilities that we did during the second half of 2008 and the first half of 2009, we found the median average of what was spent on nutritional supplements per resident day was $0.48. The median average means that there are an equal number of facilities above and below that average. Do you know your costs per resident day for key product areas like nutritional supplements, and are these costs appropriate?

Most of the above ideas and suggestions can be implemented at a nominal cost and without too much hassle. Implementation of these ideas and your own will contribute to a more efficient, less costly, and higher quality operation.

Kenneth Donhauser is CEO and Martha (Marti) Braunbach is Corporate Director, Nutrition and Food Service for PRIME Services, a supply cost management company focused on removing costs from the supply chain while increasing operational efficiency and increasing cash flow. To learn more about PRIME Services, or to sign up for the free email series "Controlling Costs," visit www.primeservicesinc.com.

END OF CHAPTER

Putting It Into Practice Questions & Answers

1. Draft a specification for a crushed tomato canned product. Include the grade, can size, pack size, and other relevant information.

   A. *All purpose crushed tomatoes, #10 can, 80 oz net weight, 6 per case.*

2. Your facility is deciding whether to change from one cola company to offering a different brand of cola products. Your clientele is requesting this change. The brand you currently use is part of the prime vendor contract. What process should you use to make this change?

   A. *Conduct a "can-cutting" and offer a blind taste test meaning that all samples have generic labels. Use kitchen staff as well as a client panel to complete the taste test. Each taste panel participant has a form to rank the products. If a different brand is selected by the taste panel, you have data to support your purchase outside of the prime vendor contract. If the panel selects the same brand as is currently served, you can inform all of your clientele of the taste test results.*

3. Your clients are complaining about the quality of the muffin product. Your administrator is asking you to recommend a higher quality product. You are considering making the muffins rather than purchasing them. What steps would you take to make the decision?

   A. 1. *Make a list of the options available (i.e. purchase a different brand, make them from a mix, make them from scratch)*
   2. *Prepare the mix and the scratch product and record the amount of time it takes to make each product. Also record the amount of time to prep the purchased product.*
   3. *Have a taste panel of clients and kitchen staff rate all alternatives.*
   4. *Complete a spreadsheet with the basic costs of each, the labor cost of each, and the final rating of each.*
   5. *Make a decision based on your data.*

4. You are attending a foodservice trade show and one of the vendors is offering a 32" flat screen TV if you purchase a year's supply of coffee. You have to make the decision today as the offer won't be good tomorrow. You know that coffee is one of your high dollar items and this would represent a significant savings. You also know that the Activities Department has wanted a new flat screen TV to use with the clients. You decide to sign a purchase agreement for the coffee. Is this ethical?

   A. *First, you need to know what your facility policy says about accepting premiums from vendors. Often, it is not ethical to accept a premium over a certain dollar amount such as $25.00. Second, what is the storage cost to store a year's worth of coffee? Can you afford to tie up storage space for a year? Third, what kind of an example are you providing to your staff and your facility by accepting such an expensive premium?*

5. The assistant manager is the person who checks in deliveries in your facility. She is in a hurry today because they are short one staff person in the kitchen. The following day, there aren't enough chicken breasts for the production of the noon meal. What might have happened?

   A. *Perhaps the assistant manager failed to count the packages of chicken during delivery and the delivery was short a package. Unfortunately, it is too late to get credit at this point for a partial delivery. Review the procedures for receiving with the assistant manager and then follow-up.*

(Continued)

Putting It Into Practice Questions & Answers *(Continued)*

6. Your foodservice department is planning a very special meal next week. You order extra-large shrimp (12-15 per pound) for this party. You checked it into the freezer three days ago. On the day of the party, the only shrimp available is small shrimp, (72-75 per pound). What might have gone wrong?

   A. *It is easy to mix up packages of shrimp in storage. Whoever issued the shrimp for an earlier recipe may have taken the wrong package or a theft has occurred. Either way, it will be important to investigate, review the procedures for issuing food with your staff, and retrain if necessary.*

7. Your facility is small and you do not have a formal requisition process. Kitchen staff members just sign a sheet of paper in the storage room when they take products out. Lately you have noticed that inventory for some products seem to be short. What should you do?

   A. *Meet with your department staff to discuss the problem. Ask for suggestions for a new procedure to issuing food such as having the store room locked and whoever needs supplies has to check out a key. Review the cost of food that is missing and how that impacts the department budget. Some type of control is needed and soliciting the help of your staff may be the start of solving the problem.*

CHAPTER

25

Manage Revenue Generating Services

Overview and Objectives

Foodservice departments in most facilities are expected to break even or bring in a profit. As a Certified Dietary Manager, you may be expected to find ways to offset operational expenses or enhance profits by increasing revenues to the department. In this chapter, we will examine ideas for generating and managing revenue, including the most common approach, catering.

After completing this chapter, you should be able to:

- ✓ Research revenue generating opportunities
- ✓ Analyze revenue generating opportunities
- ✓ Supervise cash activities and reports
- ✓ Calculate cost and set prices for catered events
- ✓ Plan foodservice and menus for catered events
- ✓ Estimate price-per-unit serving for catered events
- ✓ Use cost-control techniques to balance revenue budget
- ✓ Prepare business plan and justification for new revenue generating programs
- ✓ Promote existing and new revenue generating programs

Throughout this textbook, you have read many times about the importance of talking to your clients, surveying your clients, involving your clients in panels, and in general, determining your client needs and wants. In so doing, you are marketing your department services. Marketing is much more than advertising and promoting products; it is also about meeting your client's wants and needs. Marketing is also one aspect of managing revenue generating services.

What are revenue generating services? Money that is coming in to your facility is considered revenue. Revenue generating services from your department are the activities you do that bring in revenue/money:

- ✓ The meals you serve every day to clients in the dining room
- ✓ Catering jobs
- ✓ The cafeteria
- ✓ Serving meals to community groups.

Revenue Generating Services

The key objective of implementing revenue generating services is to increase gross revenue in the operating statement. Depending on the overall financial plan of your facility, this revenue may increase profits or fund other activities. Opportunities for generating revenue abound in any foodservice department, and generally draw upon the resources you have in place, such as physical facilities for producing food, a ready client base, culinary talent, and business support services within your facility. Thus, the possibilities are limited only by your imagination and resourcefulness as a Certified Dietary Manager.

Some options may employ special merchandising techniques in a cafeteria, while others may require creating new systems and services. Some may use the existing client base, such as employees of your organization, while others may extend your client reach further into the community.

Here are some examples of revenue generating services used in foodservice departments:

- ✓ Ice cream sundaes available at break times
- ✓ An espresso bar for specialty coffees
- ✓ Vending machines
- ✓ Point-of-sale merchandising for specialty items (see Figure 25.1 for examples)
- ✓ A snack shop
- ✓ Home meal replacements for take-out, for busy employees on their way home
- ✓ Take-out holiday specialties, such as deli trays, pies, holiday cookies, etc.
- ✓ Sunday brunch services in the cafeteria
- ✓ Payroll deduction service for employees to charge meals and take-out (improves sales)
- ✓ Take-out pizzas
- ✓ Gourmet meals (at a price) for clients and their families/friends
- ✓ Catering (discussed later in this chapter).

Glossary

Revenue Generating Services
Any service that brings money into a business

Figure 25.1 Point-Of-Sale Merchandising Ideas

Freshly baked cookies—small cookie oven
Ice cream and confectionery frozen products—ice cream freezer
Hot soft pretzels—pretzel machine
Chips—chip racks
Nachos—nacho dispenser
Coffee—coffee maker
Instant cappuccino or specialty coffee drinks—specialty beverage machine
Rice bowls, burritos, etc.—tabletop freezer

Source: Der Garabedian, Carrie. 77 Ways to Increase Revenue. DMA, 2003.

The Certified Dietary Manager can use a variety of techniques to manage revenue generating services: supervising cash activities and reports, business planning including a profitability analysis, calculating costs for services such as catering, and promoting revenue generating services.

Supervising Cash Activities and Reports

Each foodservice operation needs to have specific operating procedures for the cash register or POS (point of sale). At the beginning of the work shift, the cashier should count the cash bank assigned to the register and verify the cash amount. During all cash counting operations, two people should be present: a cashier and a supervisor or Certified Dietary Manager. These two verify each other's work.

At the end of the shift, the cashier may be required to complete applicable cashier records. A cashier and supervisor or manager count the cash, record the sum, and sign or initial the cash record. During the cafeteria operation, there may be times when the cashier must void a transaction or make other corrections. A manager or supervisor should authorize this. Standard operating procedures should be developed for handling issues such as these.

While cash-handling procedures vary by operation, some basic procedures generally apply:

- ✓ Keep the cash drawer closed when not in use.
- ✓ Give each new cashier his or her own bank.
- ✓ At the end of a shift, check out the cashier. Count the cash in the drawer, and compare it with sales records. Document the checkout, and note any amount over or under.
- ✓ Have policies and procedures in place for addressing discrepancies between cash in the drawer and actual sales, such that if a cashier consistently makes errors in cash handling, these are addressed and corrected.
- ✓ Train each cashier on use of the system, and keep a reference or manual available.
- ✓ In a POS system, be sure that register keys keyed to specific items match the menu, and that cashiers know on which key to enter each item.
- ✓ Be sure that pricing is up-to-date in the system.

Business Planning

While it is not practical to implement a long list of revenue generating services all at once, a Certified Dietary Manager can carefully weigh the strengths of in-house resources along with the opportunities to decide on the best options. It is important to conduct some financial analysis to decide which is most likely to meet the revenue objectives.

The most simple approach is to build these services without significantly increasing your operating costs. For example, you may be able to weave production of homemade cookies for takeout into the existing routine of your bake shop cook. This means your only added cost is the raw food cost for the cookie ingredients. You may be able to work with a food supplier to obtain merchandising equipment at no cost, for as long as you are purchasing the related food products. Then, each sale (if priced appropriately) generates added revenue for your department.

Some revenue generating options pinpoint high-profit menu items. Specialty coffee is an excellent example. Taking the cue from the foodservice marketplace, you can observe that specialty coffees are very popular, and clients are willing to pay extra for a cup of premium latte, cappuccino, or iced coffee. The revenue comes in from excellent ingredients and technique, along with creative merchandising, while the raw food costs are relatively low.

The cash drawer has been short $5.00 the past three days. What steps would you take to address this?

(Check your answer at the end of this chapter)

Some revenue concepts may require extra labor time along with a boost in raw food expenses. Providing take-out holiday foods is an example. For this idea, you may need to schedule some additional staff time, while also purchasing additional raw ingredients. Any time your idea begins to incur extra costs, a profitability analysis is warranted. A **profitability analysis** is a financial calculation that compares costs with revenues to determine whether an idea is profitable. To create one, you need to detail your costs, set a selling price, project a sales volume, and then calculate the bottom line. Figure 25.2 provides an example for take-out deli trays. Another type of financial calculation is a **break-even analysis**.

Figure 25.2 Profitability Analysis: Take-Out Deli Trays

Costs:

1. Food	
Ham	$0.60
Turkey	1.20
Soft Cheese	0.72
Gouda Cheese	0.51
Jack Cheese	0.37
Crackers	0.93
Garnish	0.14
Food Total	*$4.47 per tray*
2. Packaging	
Packaging Materials	*0.19 per tray*
3. Labor	
30 minutes—1 employee@ $12.70/hr., including benefits	*$6.35 per tray*
	$11.01 per tray
4. Advertising	
Advertising Cost	**$120.00 total**

Revenue:

Selling Price per Tray	$21.95
Total Production Cost per Tray	− $11.01
Gross Profit per Tray	$10.94

# Trays Sold		Gross Profit		Net Revenue
5	X $10.94 =	$ 54.70	-$120 =	($65.30)
10	X $10.94 =	109.40	-$120 =	(10.60)
11	X $10.94 =	120.34	-$120 =	0.34
15	X $10.94 =	164.10	-$120 =	44.10
20	X $10.94 =	218.80	-$120 =	98.80
25	X $10.94 =	273.50	-$120 =	153.50
50	X $10.94 =	547.00	-$120 =	427.00
75	X $10.94 =	820.50	-$120 =	700.50
100	X $10.94 =	1094.00	-$120 =	$974.00

For some ideas, you may determine that you need to make an investment, e.g. purchasing new equipment or building a snack shop or purchasing a kiosk for mobile food sales. If there is a significant budget cost to an idea, the next step is to create a **business plan**.

A business plan is a formal document that includes the following:

✓ Goal

✓ Overall description of the revenue generating service including your proposed products and/or other services

✓ Description of your target market (who will purchase the products and/or services)

✓ Pricing strategy that includes a review of the competition for the products and/or services

✓ Detailed timeline including the management team responsible for each task

✓ Financial projections with pricing, sales volume, costs, expenses, payback period, and net revenues.

In essence, a business plan is a blueprint for all aspects of the business you are embarking upon. Thus, you need to expand the profitability analysis to show capital expenditures. Project all other related costs, such as advertising. Project what you will sell, at what price, and in what numbers over defined periods of time. You can project what level of sales will be required to break even, i.e. pay off the investment—and estimate a timeframe to reach this level of sales. Then project profitability beyond that point. It is not unusual for a break-even point to occur 12 or 18 months down the line on a business investment. However, because of the financial risk involved, you will need to plan realistically and cost justify the required budget. You will need to survey your resources within the facility and ensure that you have all the required business support to launch a venture. Within your facility's accounting systems, a new business venture is likely to become a subset of your budget, with its own cost center. This allows you to track and evaluate revenues, expenses, and profitability specific to your revenue generating endeavor.

Calculating Costs for Services Such as Catering

Catering represents a specialty service you provide based on demand, and it is typically a revenue generating service. Your target market may be clients internal to your facility, or you may choose to promote a catering service within the community to generate revenue to the department. For in-house clients, the revenue is typically a transaction that occurs in your organization's bookkeeping, indicating an expenditure on one department's budget that becomes revenue in the foodservice department's budget.

Planning a Catered Event. What should you do when you receive a request to cater an event? First, think about a menu. Most foodservice departments develop a set of catering menus to suit various occasions. For example, there may be several menus for breakfasts—one for a continental self-serve breakfast and another for a buffet breakfast. There may be a set of menus for luncheons—one with cold foods and sandwiches (casual), one or more for an elegant

Glossary

Profitability Analysis
Financial calculation that compares costs with revenues to determine whether an idea is profitable

Break Even Analysis
Financial calculation that compares costs with revenues to determine if a profit is possible

Business Plan
A formal document that provides details for a proposed revenue generating service

luncheon...and so forth. A Certified Dietary Manager will meet with the client to review menu choices and select a specific menu.

The advantage of working with pre-defined catering menus is that, as you've already discovered, a menu drives the remainder of the planning. By using catering menus (with minor adjustments and customization), you can minimize your managerial time in working out pricing, recipes, purchasing needs, production plans, and service needs. Depending on the request, though, there may be situations in which you must develop a specialty menu for a distinguished event.

Beyond the menu, you need to ask questions to continue planning. Your steps should include:

- ✓ Make the business arrangements through a work order (for in-house requests) or a contract (for outside clients). A written document is important for confirming the order and related details. Later, it is also used for invoicing or accounting
- ✓ Confirm date, time, and location of the event.
- ✓ Determine the number of people to be served.
- ✓ Define service expectations. Is this for a fine dining event or a casual snack? Is this for a buffet or tabled-waited service?
- ✓ Plan the work schedule, responsibilities, supervision, and staffing to include adequate time before, after, and during the event to cover setup, preparation, service, and clean-up.
- ✓ Plan and request the physical support you will require, such as room setup.
- ✓ Plan the ambiance, food presentation, and table setting (if applicable).
- ✓ As relevant, plan and order flowers, linens, uniforms, special equipment rental, and any other needs.
- ✓ Forecast food and any special beverage needs; place orders.
- ✓ Train employees as needed to carry out set-up and service expectations.

These steps need to be taken in some form for all catering, even if it is just delivering coffee to a meeting.

Costing and Pricing a Catered Event. Catering may have the potential to be your largest revenue generating service. It is important to plan pricing for catering to ensure it meets your facility's financial objectives. There are different pricing options; what you use may depend upon the type of catering you do.

- ✓ **Fixed Pricing.** If your catering activities consist of in-house catering such as meals for staff, board meetings, and training sessions, you may prefer to use Fixed Pricing. Fixed Pricing is where you have established in advance a fixed cost for a variety of menu items. Figure 25.3 is an example of a requisition to be completed by those requesting in-house catering services, followed by a fixed menu for catering items.

You are establishing the selling price for a catered event. Your Chief Financial Officer (CFO) suggested you use 21% as the profit percentage on top of your costs. Your total costs are $427.00. You are expecting 40 people for this event. What will be the selling price per person?

(Check your answer at the end of this chapter)

Figure 25.3 **Sample Special Function Requisition**

Date: ___________ Location of Special Function: ___________________________ Time of Special Function: __________

Contact Name: ______________________________ Contact Phone Number: ______________________________

Special Function Name: ______________________ School: ______________________________

Today's Date: ___________ Budget Account #: ___________________________ Payment by Cash or Check: __________

○ Delivery or ○ Pick-up

Items Needed: [(Be specific) Ex. 3 dozen oatmeal raisin cookies, 30 waters, 1 large fruit tray, 42 bacon/onion sandwiches, 35 forks, 35 plates, 50 napkins, 30 BBQ Chicken, Potato Salad, Baked Beans, and Roll Dinners, etc.]

Quantity	Complete Description of Item	Unit Cost	Total Cost
	Total Requisition	$	$

Originator's Signature: ______________________________ Date: __________

Administrator's Signature: ______________________________ Date: __________

Notice: Without Budget Number, Payment Due upon Delivery

THIS SECTION FOR FOOD SERVICE USE ONLY

○ Check Attached Charge Budget Number: __________

Cost of Special Function: $ ______________________

(Continued)

Source: Foodservice Director Donna Freyaldenhoven, Meridian Public Schools, Meridian MS

Figure 25.3 Sample Special Function Requisition Form *(Continued)*

Description	Quantity	Price	Quantity	Price
Cookies, Regular (Chocolate Chip, Peanut Butter, Oatmeal Raisin, Sugar, Snickerdoodle)	1 dozen	$2.50		
Cookies, Gourmet (Macadamia Nut, Cranberry Oatmeal)	1 dozen	$3.00		
Drummettes	96 pieces	$30.00	192 pieces	$50.00
Chicken Salad Sandwiches	42 in fourths	$25.00		
Tuna Salad Sandwiches	42 in fourths	$25.00		
Bacon and Onion Sandwiches	42 in fourths	$32.00		
Ham and Cheese Sandwiches	24 in thirds	$25.00		
Turkey and Cheese Sandwiches	24 in thirds	$25.00		
Grape and Cheese Tray	Seasonal	Call for price		
Fruit Platter	Small	$25.00	Large	$40.00
Vegetable Platter	Small	$25.00	Large	$40.00
Soup and Sandwich Combo (Loaded Potato, Vegetable, White Chicken Chili, Chili)	Min. of 20	$5.00		
Grilled Ribeye Steak Sandwich with Chips and Fruit	Min. of 20	$7.00 each		
Club Sandwich with Chips and Fruit	Min. of 20	$6.00 each		
Homemade Quiche Plate with Grits and Fruit		$5.00 each		
Scrambled Eggs with Meat, Grits and Biscuit		$4.00 each		
Biscuit with Sausage, Ham or Chicken	1 dozen	$12.00		
Cinnamon Rolls	1 dozen	$6.00		
Donuts	1 dozen	$5.50		
Wildcat Mini Fried Donuts (Glazed with Cinnamon or Dusted with Powdered Sugar)	24 pieces	$3.00		
Progressive Salad (Pimento Cheese Bowl, Chicken Salad Bowl, Fruit Salad, Lettuce, Tomato with Basket of Bread)	Min. of 25	$6.00 each		
Salads: Chef Salad, Chicken Salad, Tuna Salad, Fried Chicken Salad, Chicken Tenders Salad	Min. of 25	$6.00 each		
Blackened Grilled Ribeye with Salad	Min. of 25	$7.00 each		
BBQ Chicken Potato Salad, Baked Beans, with Roll	Min. of 25	$6.00 each		
Fried Chicken, Mashed Potatoes, English Peas with Roll	Min. of 25	$6.00 each		
Loaded Baked Potato with Grilled Chicken, Peppers, Onion, Salad with Roll	Min. of 25	$6.50 each		
Ribeye Steak, Mashed Potato Supreme, Salad with Roll	Min. of 25	$7.50 each		
Brownies	Sheet	$15.00		
Cakes (MS Mud, Pumpkin, Spice, Banana, Strawberry, Yellow Cake with Chocolate Frosting, others as requested)	Sheet	$20.00		
Coffee	25 cups	$3.50	50 cups	$7.00
Tea	2 gallons	$3.00		
Lemonade	2 gallons	$3.00		
Juice	4 oz. carton	Call for price	11.5 oz. can	Call for price
Water	8 oz.	Call for price	16 oz.	Call for price

All prices subject to change without notice. *Source: Foodservice Director Donna Freyaldenhoven, Meridian Public Schools, Meridian MS*

- ✓ **Custom Pricing.** Custom pricing is mainly used for external events where you determine the cost of the catering after they have given you all of the details about the event. Figure 25.4 shows a catering cost form that you might use to determine the cost of a catered event. This example is using the actual cost so you will have to determine the actual food cost, labor cost, supply cost, fixed cost and know your profit percentage. Once you have basic expenses tallied, you can price your event by using a percentage that meets your financial objectives. Some facilities use a food cost percentage method, some use a total cost percentage method, and others use the factor method. Figure 25.4 uses a total cost percentage method. Many software packages today can help you determine your menu prices by just entering the menu item and the portion size. The software is set up to calculate your cost percentage and determine your selling price.
- ✓ **Factor Method.** A less accurate method of determining the markup on menu items is to multiply the food costs by a set number or factor such as three (3). With this markup, you will make about a 67 percent margin on your event and that may or may not represent your real costs. You are much better off to work with your financial officer to establish a set profit percentage and use the cost sheet in Figure 25.4.

Figure 25.4 **Catering Cost Worksheet**

Event: Board Luncheon **Date:** May 8, xxxx **Number of Meals:** 68

Expenses

Actual Total Food Cost $ ____________________

Total Labor Cost $ ____________________

Total Supplies Cost $ ____________________

1) Total Fixed Cost $ ____________________

2) Total Meal Expense $ ____________________

3) Total Meal Expenses x 1 + Profit Percentage = Total Meal Cost

Profit percentage can be determined as a percentage of sales from your profit-and-loss statement and should be a number you can get from your Chief Financial Officer (CFO).

Cost per catering client: Divide the total meal cost from 2) above by the total number of people expected at the event.

Example

Expense:

Actual Total Food Cost: $391

Total Labor Cost: $167

Total Supplies Cost: $ 25 (cloth napkins, placemats)

Total Fixed Cost: $ 20 (room rental)

1) Total Meal Expense $603

Profit Percentage: 5% or .05

2) Total meal Cost = $603 x 1.05 = $633

3) Cost per Catering Client = $633 ÷ by 68 (people attending event) = $9.31

You would probably change this to $9.50 per person.

Whatever pricing option you use, you want to calculate your food, labor, and supply costs in order to accurately determine a catering charge for the event. Once you have basic expenses tallied, you can price your event by using a percentage that meets your financial objectives.

Promoting Revenue Generating Services

Let's say that you have chosen to expand catering as your revenue generating service. How will clients, either internal or external, know about your expanded service? **Marketing** is part of doing business today, especially in the foodservice industry.

Marketing and Image. Have you ever been responsible for selecting a nursing home for someone you care about? Many healthcare consumers today follow advice from a number of organizations, such as the American Association of Retired Persons (AARP), the National Council of Senior Citizens, and others when they look for a facility. A specific tip offered by these organizations is simple and consistent: Visit the facility during meal time.

This is powerful information. What it tells us is that in a healthcare environment, the foodservice department may have significant impact on the decisions of others to use the facility's services. This is just one example of why marketing is important in a foodservice operation.

More specifically, marketing activities can have great impact on the immediate sales within a foodservice department, such as sales of the lunch special in an employee cafeteria, or sales of products in a convenience store. Thus, a Certified Dietary Manager needs to consider marketing on two levels: the role of foodservice marketing in fulfilling facility objectives, and the role of marketing in fulfilling the objectives of the foodservice operation.

Let's take a closer look at the process of marketing. So far, we know that marketing has to do with presenting products or services to persuade people to buy. What do we need to do to make this happen? There are several parts: advertising and promotion, and direct communications with clients or potential customers. However, before we can tackle these, it is essential to examine image itself. Image is the view or perception of products and services, as presented in the marketplace.

Every successful business creates an image of what its products or services represent. Often, this image comes directly from the corporate vision. It always relates to the idea of taking care of customers or meeting client's needs. All marketing activities stem from this image, and help to convey this image.

Here is an example: Axl Hospital has a vision to provide state-of-the-art healthcare, blending technology with human compassion to meet clients health needs. From this vision, you might guess that Axl Hospital would want to build an image in the marketplace that:

✓ Focuses on caring for people

✓ Relates the technical excellence of the hospital's resources

✓ Explains the benefits of this combination to potential clients.

Glossary

Marketing
Presenting products or services to clients (and potential clients) in a way that persuades them to buy

Now, any marketing activities Axl conducts are likely to revolve around these ideas. When Axl Hospital produces a billboard for local highways or places a radio advertisement, you can be sure that at least one of the themes listed above will be reflected. Figure 25.5 lists some examples of specific images that might be defined by a foodservice operation.

Figure 25.5 **Images a Foodservice Department Might Convey in Marketing Efforts**

Setting	Example of an Image
Employee Dining	Provides the freshest food with quickest service
Hospital	Provides highly personalized meal service with respect for individual needs
Nursing Home	Offers home-style food in a home-like environment
School	Provides the most nutritious meals at the best price, with a commitment to the well-being of students

Clearly, the image you define for your own foodservice operation will not be identical to one defined for another facility. The image is somewhat specific to each facility, and becomes part of its corporate "personality".

Before pursuing marketing efforts, it is very helpful to define and focus your own facility's image. The more consistently a facility uses and supports a cohesive image, the more various campaigns and communications will work together in synergy to generate powerful results.

Advertising and Promotion. Once image is established, a facility can begin conducting effective advertising and promotion. What do these terms mean? Advertising means placing persuasive announcements in the marketplace to generate sales. These announcements may take the form of newspaper ads, radio ads, television commercials, or even banner ads on the Web. Advertising is also done through direct mail campaigns, e-mail campaigns, and other techniques.

Promotion is a little more general, referring to any activity that is designed to publicize a product or service. It may take the form of press releases sent to a local newspaper, or even menus posted in a dining area.

Interestingly, promotion can have a secondary effect beyond support for sales. For example, in a healthcare facility where your mission is to promote the nutritional well-being of clients, part of your task may simply be to persuade clients to eat. How you present the menu and the food may make a big difference. The dining environment and the service you provide have an impact too. Hence, the ability to promote food becomes a clinical care concern as well as one of business development.

Following are some examples of advertising and promotion activities a foodservice operation might use.

Posted menu. One of the most basic tools for promotion in any foodservice operation is the menu. This simple document offers a superb opportunity to call attention to the food, to reinforce a defined image, and to build sales and/

How would you promote a culture change from trayline service to dining room service to your internal clients?

(Check your answer at the end of this chapter)

or acceptance. A menu is always of interest to foodservice clients. As available, it may be studied far in advance of meal service times.

What makes a menu an effective promotional tool? First of all, it must be easy to read. A clear layout groups offerings by days and meals that are readily identified. It uses a font that is easy to read and adequately sized. Often, it uses clip art, borders, or images to draw attention to its contents.

Here are a few specific tips used by graphic designers:

- ✓ Use consistent alignment, generally to the left. Do not center everything, as this is difficult to read.
- ✓ Use a consistent design for menu headings that is larger type, bold type, and/or a unique font. Often, a good choice is a sans serif font (one in which the strokes contain no decoration).
- ✓ Select and use one font for the remaining contents of the menu.
- ✓ Use ALL CAPS sparingly, as it is difficult to read. Generally, it works best only for brief headings.
- ✓ Use clip art sparingly, to draw attention to menu contents. Do not let it compete with the words on the menu.
- ✓ Select pieces of clip art that are compatible with each other in style. They should look like they were all drawn by the same artist, even if they weren't.
- ✓ Use colors carefully. Generally, dark type is easiest to read. It should have good contrast. For example, black type printed on dark blue paper will not be very readable. Dark blue type on white paper will.
- ✓ Use each design element for a purpose, such as to highlight an important idea. Do not over-decorate, as this actually impairs readability and makes the menu difficult to understand.

Distributed menu. In a facility that serves long-term clients, such as a school or a retirement community, Certified Dietary Managers often create a copy of the menu for distribution to clients. Clients may keep this menu as a reference for the time period it covers. The same presentation ideas addressed above apply to this distributed menu. In addition, this menu may include some general information about the facility, such as locations, hours of service, payment options, a phone number or hotline number, a Website address, or other useful reference. This menu also provides an excellent opportunity to relate a clear message about your organizational commitment.

In a healthcare facility where clients complete a selective menu, the promotional opportunity is on the menu form distributed to clients. Once again, readability issues are very important. The type should be large, clear, and dark, with good contrast to the paper on which it is printed.

Catering menu. If you offer standard catering menus, consider the appearance of these as well. They are a marketing tool. Some Certified Dietary Managers print them attractively, add photos from real events, and place them in a booklet or notebook for review by potential clients.

Glossary

Promotion
Activity designed to publicize a product or service

Naming products. What do you call the items you offer on a menu? This is a subtle but forceful choice. For instance, which of these products would you be more tempted to select from a menu—coffee cake or scrumptious coffee cake? Tossed salad or garden green salad? Vegetable soup or Autumn minestrone?

The name you choose is a promotional activity. Furthermore, the name you choose can go a long way in conveying the image you have defined. Figure 25.6 lists some examples of product names that relate directly to the image a food-service department might wish to convey.

Figure 25.6 Naming Products to Convey an Image

Image	Product Names
Fresh Food	• Garden Green Salad • Fresh Diced Apples • Harvest Fritata • Wholesome Cornbread
Home-Style Food	• Down Home Biscuits • Home-Style Beef Stew • Martha's Apple Pie • Robust Bean Soup
Upscale Food	• Portabella Pastry Puff • Authentic Bruschetta • Spinach Roulade • Blackened Salmon

Definitely, the choice of a name builds an image about the food. There is a caution here, however. A name should still be clear and as descriptive as possible. The challenge is to communicate clearly and creatively at the same time. For example, the name double fudge delight sounds interesting, but we don't know what it is—a drink? A cake? A cookie? An ice cream sundae? So, a name should convey enough information to avoid confusion or surprises, which can backfire and disappoint a client. This is especially important in a setting where clients order their food without seeing it, e.g. from a hospital bed. Many Certified Dietary Managers also add brief descriptions to menu listings to tell more about the food.

Where can you go to obtain inspiration for naming products? Cookbooks, restaurant menus, trade magazines, and recipe websites can all be good sources for ideas. Of course, you will want to customize names, and certainly avoid using the unique product names of other commercial establishments.

Meal deals. Special deals or meal packages often constitute a way of promoting food. Many operations have a creative name for a lunch special. The special, dubbed Chef's Choice or Incredible Edibles or something like this, may include a group of menu items and bear a value-oriented price tag. The price tag usually reflects a cost savings. In marketing, this approach is called bundling. It means that a group of products are joined together with one price tag to encourage the sale of all of them. Bundling can increase sales. At the same time, it can often speed up the service in a restaurant or cafeteria, as clients make their choices more quickly.

Discounts and coupons. Discounts can be a way of encouraging greater volume of sales. A example of a discount in a convenience store might be an offer to purchase one deli sandwich, and receive the second one at half price. This type of offer is often short-term, and of course pricing must be calculated to be cost effective for the operation.

For a new product or service, a promotional special or coupon can be a valuable marketing tool. A promotional special at a low price or a coupon for a free introductory trial can motivate clients to try something new without feeling that they are taking risks. For example, to advertise a new meal delivery service for clients of an independent living community, you might offer a coupon good for one free home-delivered meal.

Loyalty programs. Another approach is to reward clients for loyalty or repeat business. You may choose to do this with a punch card that earns a punch (or stamp) for every cup of specialty coffee or take-out meal purchased. Ten punches earn a free one. For this strategy, you can select a high-profit item you wish to promote. In debit card systems, a client may earn so many "points" for every $100 placed on the card. The value is added to the debit balance. There are many possibilities, but the objective is always to encourage a client to continue using your service. Continued business is valuable and can contribute significantly to revenues.

Special signage. As food is displayed, special signs can draw attention to products and advertise them. A cafeteria offering healthy fare items, for example, may develop a special graphic to identify these products throughout the service area. A sign may also be used to highlight a featured item, or a special price. A sign should be simple, clear, and easy to read. It should be attractive, but should not detract from the visual impact of the food itself. It should not block view of the food products.

Newsletter. A newsletter can be a simple tool for telling clients more about your operation. It may also reach people who are closely involved with customers, such as family members of nursing home clients, or visitors to a hospital, or parents of students in a public school. Quite often, the most effective newsletters are very short, such as one page. A set of two or three brief articles can address new offerings, new services, the mechanics of interacting with the foodservice department, the ways in which foodservice staff can be reached to discuss clients' needs, and much more. Here again is an opportunity to support your defined image by including content that tells more about what you do, how you do it, and why you do it.

Some foodservice operations offer nutrition tips in a newsletter, too. They may also include a signature recipe from an in-house culinary expert. Ultimately, the emphasis of a newsletter designed for marketing purposes should be to build image, to help clients, and to advertise products or services through editorial content.

Specific product promotions. On a rotating basis, a Certified Dietary Manager may promote specific items on the menu. This can encourage clients to try new fare, and may thus expand sales and establish new loyalties. If you use any branded food items, you have a ready opportunity for promotion. Brand names should be featured prominently in menus and on signs.

Some operations use self-branding concepts. This means they create their own special product line based on a theme or identity, and create a unique name for this line of products. This can be an excellent way to hone an image and to promote food items.

An operation that offers home meal replacements or take-out items or gift baskets can most certainly promote these products uniquely, too. Signage, fliers, community advertising, and public announcements can all support this effort.

Theme meals and events. Particularly in situations in which a client group represents repeat business over extended time periods, there is a genuine need to break up the monotony of cycle menus, and produce renewed excitement in meal service. One way to do this is to present theme meals. Theme meals are built around a theme, such as a holiday, a season, an event, a type of food, a destination, an ethnic cuisine, a cultural custom, a famous character, a cooking style, or almost any idea you can cook up! Figures 25.7 and 25.8 present ideas for theme celebrations.

The success of a theme meal is more than food alone. Dining is a sensory experience that encompasses not just flavor, but ambiance, sounds, and sights, too. In a skilled nursing facility, a theme meal is often a full-blown event, and it becomes an interdisciplinary project. Recreation therapists often become very involved and help to plan the themes, the decor, and the activities that will turn a meal into an experience. Some of the details that can make a theme meal successful include:

- ✓ Decoration of the dining area
- ✓ Special entertainment
- ✓ Games and activities
- ✓ Background sound or music
- ✓ Theme-related serviceware and napkins
- ✓ Characters/servers dressed in special costumes.

Theme weeks. A related idea is a theme week, in which a special theme may work its way through an entire week. For example, a holiday season theme may include specialties each day of the week, such as eggnog, holiday cookies, and more. Ideas for full weeks can also piggyback on publicized recognition weeks/months, such as National Nutrition Month, Pride in Food Service Week, or many of the health-related promotional weeks that occur throughout the year.

Needless to say, theme dining ideas require menu creation and advance planning. Some Certified Dietary Managers save their holiday menus, theme menus, and other materials for re-use in the future.

You have a new baker who is receiving many compliments. You decide to develop a brand for your bakery products that represent the home-made and healthy characteristics of her products. How would you market these products?

(Check your answer at the end of this chapter)

Figure 25.7 Theme Example: Halloween Dessert

Figure 25.8 Theme Example: Luau Entree

Open houses. An open house is often a way to help the families and significant others of your clients become more familiar with your service, and try the food themselves. In addition, an open house can bring in potential clients.

Press releases. An inexpensive way to promote products and services is through the use of press releases. For example, an open house may be announced in a press release issued to local newspapers, radio stations, and television stations. A press release is a brief document developed specifically for the media. When writing a release, keep these tips in mind:

- ✓ Write a clear headline that tells what this is about.
- ✓ Write a lead sentence that gives the key point.

✓ Add further description about the announcement, followed by more information about your facility.

✓ Provide contact information for more information, and invite inquiries.

✓ When possible, provide a photo for print media.

✓ Clear your announcement with your in-house marketing or media relations department, or your own superior.

Media representatives do not always use a press release as is. They may call to obtain more information or conduct interviews, and write the story according to their own editorial guidelines and needs.

Website. Many foodservice operations use a website to communicate with clients and promote products and services. A website may include your upcoming menus, a few featured recipes, profiles of your culinary experts, contact information (address, phone, fax, and e-mail), and descriptions of special offerings. Some foodservice websites offer online ordering, too.

To make use of this medium, always keep the site fresh and up-to-date. Menus, for example, should always be current. In some facilities, it is appropriate to offer special coupons on a website to promote sales.

Brochures and fliers. A printed piece can be available in your service areas to promote special products and services. Printed pieces may also be used to promote catering, home meal delivery, nutritional counseling, or other features. As with printed menus, a promotional brochure should also be neatly designed without excessive decoration. It should be easy to understand, and should always include identity and contact information.

With a desktop publishing program and a color printer, a Certified Dietary Manager may produce many pieces in small runs from a simple computer system. Some managers use pre-printed, specialty papers to make design a little easier.

A basic approach for writing a promotional piece is to follow these steps:

✓ Identify your audience. Who will read this piece? Make sure that everything you write is directed to this group.

✓ Write a brief sentence describing the concerns or needs your product or service will meet.

✓ Then tell how your product or service will help.

✓ Briefly describe the features of the product or service. Bullet points are often effective for this part.

✓ Summarize the benefits the client will enjoy as a result of using your product or service.

Catering services. While catering is a service mechanism, it also doubles as a promotional vehicle for many operations. Every time you provide catered food, you also place your food and service in front of potential clients. If your facility caters within the community, there is an ongoing chance to build your image and generate interest in your facility. This can be a superb way to support the broader marketing efforts of your facility, while also generating revenue.

Informal promotion. This is one of the most effective marketing techniques of all times. It is better known as word of mouth. A client who enjoys a positive experience tells others about it. This is inexpensive, honest marketing, and it is a natural byproduct of simple, ongoing attention to clients' needs. A personal recommendation for your products or services will likely have a profound impact.

END OF CHAPTER

Putting It Into Practice Questions & Answers

1. The cash drawer has been short $5.00 the past three days. What steps would you take to address this?

   A. *Review your cash handling policies and procedures regarding discrepancies. Observe the cashier at the beginning, during, and at the end of the shift to make sure he is keeping the cash drawer closed when not in use; he has his own cash drawer; he is counting his drawer with a manager at the end of the shift. Retrain if needed on the use of the point of sale system. If the discrepancy continues, and it is just one cashier, follow your policy and procedure for handling discrepancies.*

2. You are establishing the selling price for a catered event. Your Chief Financial Officer (CFO) suggested you use 21% as the profit percentage on top of your costs. Your total costs are $427.00. You are expecting 40 people for this event. What will be the selling price <u>per person</u>?

   A. *1. The first step is determine your total price = total costs x the profit percentage.*
   $427 x 1.21 = $516.67 or $517.

   2. To determine the price per person, divide the total cost including the profit percentage by the total number of people: $517 ÷ 40 = $12.925 or <u>$12.95</u>

3. How would you promote a culture change from trayline service to dining room service to your internal clients?

   A. *There are a number of ideas you could use. Build up anticipation by starting a few weeks before you actually implement the change. Add a note each week to the menu and to signage in the dining room with something like:*

   Week 1: Culture Change is coming

   Week 2: Culture Change means having more choices

   Week 3: Culture Change means table service—"What would you like to eat today?"

   Week 4: Culture Change will begin next Monday—Are you ready?

   Make sure your staff understands the changes and can answer questions from your clients and other staff.

4. You have a new baker who is receiving many compliments. You decide to develop a brand for your bakery products that represent the home-made and healthy characteristics of her products. How would you market these products?

   A. *You might begin with a contest to develop a name for the self-brand. This will raise interest and inform at the same time. Once you have chosen a brand name, use that name in special signage so clientele can easily locate the items. If you serve external customers in a cafeteria, write a short article for a local newspaper about the new brand that features the baker. Use the brand name on menus and brochures for catering.*

Monitor/Review Cost of Menus Against Budget and Guidelines

Overview and Objectives

Most Certified Dietary Managers are expected to manage money as part of their job. That includes making sure that a budget is monitored. Certified Dietary Managers have an increasingly important role in helping their facility maintain the bottom line. This is the first of three chapters that focus on financial control techniques—specifically you will review menu pricing, prepare a simple budget and calculate food cost per client patient day.

After completing this chapter, you should be able to:

- ✓ Compute cost of menus
- ✓ Conduct a product price-comparison study
- ✓ Prepare a budget
- ✓ Calculate daily cost per patient/client day

From the information on forecasting, purchasing, and inventory, you know that part of the Certified Dietary Manager's job is to manage the cost of food coming in and going out. Budgeting is a tool to help you manage those costs. You have to calculate raw food costs and in some cases menu costs in order to develop your food budget.

Calculating Raw Food Costs

This information is the basis of a Professional Practice Standard for Certified Dietary Managers. See the full standard at the end of this chapter in *Management in the News.* Two very important tools for planning, monitoring, and adjusting the financial performance of a foodservice department are calculating raw food costs and calculating labor costs. Labor costs will be addressed in the next chapter. You may examine raw food costs per meal per client or the total cost you incur by producing and serving one meal to all clients. More specifically, a Certified Dietary Manager may determine a cost per meal for each meal separately. Managers also talk about cost per client day or cost per patient day (cost/ppd). (Note: For purposes of this textbook, the word client is being used rather than patient, resident, inmate, or child. However, the industry measure for food costs in healthcare is referred to cost per patient day. For this measure, patient also means client). As you begin this chapter, review the financial terms in Figure 26.1.

Figure 26.1 Financial Terminology*

Term	Definition	Example
FTE—Full Time Equivalent	The equivalent of one person working full time at 40 hours per week. Or it may mean two or more people whose hours together add up to 40 hrs/wk Labor Budgets are usually based on FTEs.	To determine FTEs per year for one full time person: 8 hrs./day x 5 days/wk x 52 wks/yr = 2080 hr/yr or one FTE.
Pay Period	A defined cycle for documenting hour worked and processing the payroll to issue paychecks.	If you are paid every other week, your pay period is two weeks long.
Overtime	The time an employee works beyond a regularly scheduled work day or pay period.	An employee who works 83 hours in one pay period (40 hrs/wk for 2 weeks) would be entitled to three hours of overtime.
Exempt Employee	An employee who is exempt from overtime pay. This person is on salary and receives a standard rate of pay.	In most organizations, managers are classified as exempt.
Non-Exempt Employee	An employee who is **not** exempt from overtime pay.	Most foodservice staff positions
Census	The number of clients or client count on a given day. How this is determined depends upon the type of foodservice.	Healthcare, Corrections/Schools: Managers will receive a daily census count Cafeteria or Restaurant: Census is determined from the point of sale (POS) records.
Cost per Meal	Raw food cost for one meal may also be called cost per patient day or cost/ppd	
Food Cost Percentage	This is a number that may be used to determine menu costs. It is calculated by dividing the food costs for a specified period such as one month, by the total sales for that month.	In Figure 26.2, the total sales or revenues are $33,245. The total food cost is all of the food costs added up: Meat, Produce, Dairy, Staples = $12,500. To calculate the food cost percentage: $12,500 ÷ 33,245 = .3759 or 37.6%
Gross versus Net	Gross means a sum of money, as is, before any deductions are applied. Net is the amount of money that remains after all needed expenses have been deducted.	$1220/month; Your net incomes might be $875 after all of the deductions.
Break-Even	When revenues and expenses are equal	There is no loss or profit.
Subsidies	External funding for foodservice activities	School Foodservice: Usually refers to funding and/or food received from the USDA. Healthcare/University: Meals for staff may be subsidized by the facility as a benefit. A portion of the food cost for employee meals would be covered by a budget other than the foodservice department.

** Some of these terms have been defined in preceding chapters.*

In healthcare, corrections, K-12 schools, and college and universities, you may be given a budgeted amount per person per day. In this situation, it is especially critical to assure that your cost per meal fits within the budget. You are responsible for providing a certain number of meals to a certain number of clients, without cash transactions.

You would also apply the cost-per-meal or cost-per-day figure in planning a budget for operations. Then you would use this figure in menu planning, costing the menu as you plan to assure it fits within the budget. This is called precosting the menu. Next you would apply this per-day figure in your purchasing management. Raw food costs are determined using several different methods.

Inventory Method

This method requires you to count your inventory each month and determine the dollar value of the inventory. It is the most accurate method of determining monthly raw food costs. The formula for calculating monthly raw food costs using this method is:

> Beginning Inventory Value (the ending inventory value from the previous month)
>
> + purchases (for the month)
>
> - Ending inventory
>
> = Monthly Food Costs

See Figure 26.2 for an example of calculating monthly food costs and the cost/ppd. Computerized inventory systems have made calculating monthly food costs much easier because purchases are recorded automatically. You will still have to complete a monthly physical inventory each month to calculate your ending inventory.

Figure 26.2 **Fiscal Measurements to Calculate Food Cost in Foodservice Departments**

Measurement	Formula	Example	
Monthly Food Cost	Beginning Inventory + Purchases - Ending Inventory	Beginning Inventory Purchases Ending Inventory **Monthly Food Cost**	18,345.00 + 15,267.00 - 21,112.00 **= $12,500.00**
Food Cost Percentage	Monthly Food Cost + Sales	Monthly Food Cost Sales **Food Cost %**	12,500.00 + 33,245.00 **= .3759 or 37.6%**
Raw Food Cost Per Patient Day (PPD)	Monthly Food Cost ÷ Total Patient Days (Patient Days = number of patients x number of days in month)	Monthly Food Cost Total Patient Days **Food Cost PPD** (Total Patient Days = 100 patients x 30 days)	12,500.00 ÷ 3,000.00 **= $4.17**
Raw Food Cost per Meal	Monthly Food Cost ÷ Total Patient Days x 3	Monthly Food Cost Total Patient Days x 3	12,500.00 ÷ 9,000.00 **= $1.3888 or $1.39**

Requisition Method

If your facility uses storeroom requisitions, then you would add your total direct purchases to the daily storeroom requisitions.

Recipe Method

This method is based on determining the total cost of food for each standardized recipe. The cost of each ingredient is added together and divided by the number of servings to calculate the cost per client of the recipe. Recipes must be used exactly as written (ingredients carefully measured and recipe portioned exactly). Most facilities need computer software to assist in this method.

Record of Purchases Method

This method uses a simple tabulation of the current month purchase invoices to give the total cost of purchases for a specified time period. This represents an estimate of costs and does not take into account the cost of food in storage.

Menu Cost Report

A menu cost report is another very valuable tool. This report shows what it costs to produce a particular menu. A menu may be pre-costed, which means its costs are calculated during the planning phase. A tool such as this ensures that you are planning menus that can, realistically, meet your budget.

In addition to a pre-cost report, some operations run a post-cost report, or one that shows what the menu actually cost when production and service have been completed. This helps to identify operational variances. It shows where the planning may have fallen short, where food is unaccounted for, or where other factors need better control.

There are many formats and options for a menu cost report. An example of a menu pre-cost report appears in Figure 26.3. This report indicates that, as planned, the menu for regular diets served on day 1 of a cycle breakfast menu

Figure 26.3 Menu Pre-Cost Report for One Meal

Meal: Breakfast Menu, Cycle Day 1, Regular Diet		
Menu Item	**Portion Size**	**Cost per Portion**
Orange Juice	6 oz.	$0.31
Cheese Omelet	1 each	0.35
English Muffin	2 halves	0.12
Margarine	2 pats	0.05
Jelly	1 pak	0.04
Coffee	12 oz.	0.19
Skim Milk	4 oz.	0.17
Condiment Pack	1 each	0.09
	TOTAL	$1.32

Putting It Into Practice: 1

Calculate the monthly food cost and the cost per patient day given the following data:

Beginning Inventory... $15,000

Purchases................. $25,000

Ending Inventory $17,500

Census for the month of April: 118

(Check your answer at the end of this chapter)

Figure 26.4 Menu Cost Report for All Diets, One Day

Diet	Per Client					Number of Clients	Total for Diet
	Breakfast	Lunch	Dinner	Snacks	Total Cost		
Regular	$1.32	$1.77	$2.14	$0.32	$5.55	100	$555.00
Diabetic	1.36	1.65	2.11	0.35	5.47	43	235.21
Heart Healthy	1.47	1.55	2.08	0.19	5.29	23	121.67
Pureed	0.98	1.64	2.09	0.31	5.02	13	65.26
Tube Feeding*					6.12	21	128.52
					DAILY TOTAL	200	$1105.66

costs $1.32 per client. The cost of each item has been calculated based on the portion size used and actual food costs. Some of these costs have come directly from purchasing records. For example, a Certified Dietary Manager examining pricing for skim milk has determined that the facility pays $0.17 per 4 ounce carton of skim milk. Other numbers for a report such as this one come from a calculation of costs for each serving of each standardized recipe.

A manager may also extend a report such as this for additional meals and (if applicable) additional special diets. A more complete costing report for the cycle day also indicates how many clients are actually being served on each diet. A sample menu cost report showing these extensions appears in Figure 26.4.

What is the impact on your budget compliance if one diet costs more or less to serve than you anticipated? As you can see from a report such as this one, the answer depends on how many clients receive this particular diet. In this example, a variation in meal cost for Regular diets will have the greatest bottom line impact because there are more clients receiving this meal.

Budgeting

Monitoring or reviewing your costs is something that should be a continual process in your department. This allows you to control costs because you know what category is costing the most. Comparing costs to the budget gives an idea of where you should be with your costs.

What is a Budget

In any business, sound management dictates that there is a plan for financial management. This is an essential component that helps protect an organization against suddenly running out of money. It helps a Certified Dietary Manager plan and make decisions about purchasing food and equipment, hiring workers, scheduling overtime, and much more. In essence, a budget provides a road map for financial management.

The two most basic components of a budget are:

Revenue, which is money coming in, or income.

Expenses, which is money going out, or costs.

Glossary

Budget
A written plan or prediction for income and expenses

Fiscal Year
The 12-month period for which a budget applies

Revenue
Money coming in, or income

Expenses
Money going out, or costs

So, a **budget** is a written plan for income and expenses. Typically, a budget covers a one-year period. This period may follow a calendar year, such as January through December, or it may follow a different 12-month period, such as July through June. The 12-month period for which a budget applies is called a **fiscal year**. A fiscal year is set by the financial managers of a facility, and applies to the entire facility.

In any organization, the budget is arranged according to a hierarchy, or set of categories. Each department or section of the organization has its own budget. A composite of all the individual budgets becomes the budget for the facility as a whole. Thus, a foodservice budget feeds into the comprehensive financial plan for the facility. A Certified Dietary Manager plays a role in assuring the financial viability of the organization.

As an aid in both planning and implementing a budget, financial planners break a budget into smaller pieces, called categories. A budget for a foodservice operation, for example, may list expenses as an annual total, and then also list specific groups of expenses, with a projected dollar figure for each. The same concept applies to revenues. Figure 26.5 illustrates how budget categories may be presented.

This is a simplified example of a foodservice budget. In this example, revenues come from sales in three categories: a cafeteria, a convenience store, and catering. The budget represents a projection or estimate of the income the operation expects to receive from each of these. Meanwhile, expenses are grouped by: food, miscellaneous supplies, labor, repairs and services, and capital equipment.

Figure 26.5 Sample Budget Categories

Revenues		
100	Sales	
101	Sales - Cafeteria	$330,000
102	Sales - Convenience Store	210,000
103	Sales - Catering	51,000
	TOTAL REVENUES	**$591,000**
Expenses		
500	Food	
501	Meat	$90,000
502	Produce	40,000
503	Dairy	19,000
504	Staples	121,000
550	**Miscellaneous Supplies**	43,000
600	Labor	
601	Wages	190,000
602	Overtime/Premiums	11,000
603	Benefits	49,000
700	Repairs and Services	11,000
800	Capital Equipment	14,000
	TOTAL EXPENSES:	**$588,000**

Note that in this example, each category in the budget has a number. Meat purchases, for example, are in budget category #501. Numbering of categories is common, and it helps financial planners identify categories clearly.

Another common practice with budgets is to break them down into smaller time increments. This makes it much easier to monitor revenues and expenses. In a foodservice operation, a typical unit of time is one month. There are two ways to determine a monthly budget. If you expect revenues and expenses to accumulate evenly throughout the year, you prorate all the figures. This means you adjust each figure according to a specified increment of time. So, to determine a one-month budget, divide each figure of an annual budget by 12. In the example in Figure 26.5, wages paid to employees in a one-month period should be approximately: $190,000 ÷ 12 = $15,833.

A more complex budgeting model says that revenues and/or expenses will not be the same from month to month. Imagine you are operating a dining service for students in a university. You know that your client/customer count, or number of students receiving meals, will drop sharply for the summer months, when enrollment is very low. Your budget for revenue from student meal plan payments will drop for this period, too. At the same time, you can be sure you will be spending less on food and labor, at least for this component of your department's operation. In a budget such as this one, a specific figure is planned for each category for each month.

Types of Budgets

The two most common budgets that Certified Dietary Managers may use are an operating budget and a capital budget.

Operating Budget. This is an estimate of costs incurred in the process of generating meals. So it would be an estimate of the food costs, beverage costs, and labor costs. The operating budget is a financial plan for the period of time it covers. That time period might be one month, six months, or one year.

Capital Budget. A capital budget is a plan for building improvements and additions or replacement of equipment. Your facility will need a capital budget plan from each department in order to complete an overall capital budget for your facility. Figure 26.6 a-c shows an actual operation budget for a public school system that includes the capital budget line.

Developing a Budget

When you create a budget, you are creating an estimate for the future financial performance of your operation. In almost any facility, managers in their respective areas are called upon to submit budgets for an upcoming fiscal year, often months in advance. How much of the process is done by financial managers, versus how much is done by department managers, varies from one operation to another. In general, though, the following steps are useful in budget preparation:

1. **Clarify your objectives within the framework of the facility.** Are you aiming to operate at break-even, or at a profit? If it is a profit, how great? What revenues are expected from your operation?

Glossary

Operating Budget
A financial plan that includes food, beverage, and labor costs and expected revenue

Capital Budget
A financial plan that includes projected building improvements and additions or replacement of equipment

Putting It Into Practice: 2

Using the sample budget in Fig. 26.5, did the department have a loss in revenue, a profit, or break even?

(Check your answer at the end of this chapter)

Figure 26.6a **Metro Nashville Public Schools Food Service Fund 2010-2011 Fiscal Year**

Estimated Cash Reserves July 1, 2010	$	8,170,934
2010-11 Budgeted Revenue:		
USDA Meal Reimbursements	$	26,566,154
Lunch Sales		2,696,082
Breakfast Sales		252,852
A la Carte Sales		4,578,351
State Matching		320,130
Interest & Miscellaneous		70,862
Estimated Commodities		1,753,920
Total Budgeted Revenue	**$**	**36,238,351**
Funds Available for 2010-2011	**$**	**44,409,285**
2010-11 Budgeted Expenditures:		
Salaries	$	12,271,362
Social Security & Medicare Match		858,995
Retirement Match		1,671,003
Employee Insurance Match		3,697,783
Food Purchases		11,946,237
Warehouse and Vendor Supplies		952,933
Other Supplies		104,976
Equipment		757,674
Equipment Maintenance		393,501
Freight and Storage		367,839
Uniform Rental & Laundry Services		166,270
Mileage		85,995
Other Expenses		255,263
Utilities		954,600
Estimated Commodities		1,753,920
Total Budgeted Expenditures	**$**	**36,238,351**
2011 Estimated Change in Cash Reserves	**$**	**—**

Used with permission.

Figure 26.6b **Metropolitan Nashville Public Schools Fiscal Year 2010-2011 Budget**

Account Number		Account Name	2009-2010 Positions	2009-2010 Budget	2010-2011 Position Changes	2010-2011 Budget Changes	2010-2011 Proposed Positions	2009-2010 Proposed Budget	Remarks
1440		FOOD SERVICE							
1440	0	Salaries, Certificated	3.0	$ 237,638		$ (2,731)	3.0	$ 234,907	Food Service Certificated Coordinators
1440	1	Salaries, Clerical	10.0	343,575	1.0	(12,364)	11.0	331,211	Senior Secretary, Senior Account Clerks, Account Clerks
1440	2	Salaries, Support	768.0	11,972,206		(266,962)	768.0	11,705,244	Director, Coordinators, Field Managers, FS Managers and FS Workers
1440	3	Food		11,781,619		164,618		11,946,237	Dairy, Produce, Frozen Food and Food Staples
1440	4	Supplies and Materials		1,097,352		(39,773)		1,057,579	Vendor & Warehouse Purchases, Fuel, Truck Repairs, Office Supplies
1440	5	Other Expenses		2,215,539		(77,736)		2,137,803	Equipment Repair, Telephone, Commodity Freight, Uniforms, Laundry, Training Permits, Utilities, Technology Vendor Support
1440	6	FICA, Pension & Insurance		5,698,978		528,803		6,227,781	Pension, Insurance, FICA
1440	7	Equipment		739,038		18,636		757,674	Large Equipment, Smallwares, Technology Hardware
1440	8	Travel/ Mileage		78,583		7,412		85,995	Mileage
		Function Total	**781.0**	**$ 34,164,528**	**1.0**	**$ 319,903**	**782.0**	**$ 34,484,431**	
		USDA Commodities		**1,369,545**		**384,375**		**1,753,920**	
		Total Budget and Commodities	**781.0**	**$ 35,534,073**	**1.0**	**704,278**	**782.0**	**$ 38,238,351**	

Meal Prices	2009-2010	2010-2011
BREAKFAST		
Elementary and Secondary Adult Priced by Al a Carte Item	$ 1.25	$ 1.25
LUNCH		
Elementary	$ 2.00	$ 2.00
Secondary	2.25	2.25
Adult (MNPS staff or working volunteer)	3.00	3.00
Adult (parent visitor)	3.50	3.50
Adult (parent/visitor holiday meal)	4.00	4.00

Used with permission.

Figure 26.6c Metropolitan Nashville Public Schools Fiscal Year 2010-2011 Budget

Position	2009-2010 Work Calendars				2010-2011 Work Calendars			
	Serving Days	Paid Time Off Days (Vacation-Holidays)	Training/ Clean-Up/Set-Up/ Closing Days	Total Paid Days	Serving Days	Paid Time Off Says (Vacation-Holidays)	Training/Clean-Up/Set-Up/ Closing Days	Total Paid Days
K-8 Cafeteria Managers	174	16	11	201	172	16	9	197
9-12 Cafeteria Managers	171	16	11	198	172	16	7	195
K-8 Cafeteria Workers	174	16	6	196	172	16	5	193
9-12 Cafeteria Workers (on exam days, select employees will work half days)	168	16	6	190	171	16	3	190
*Field Managers, Technology Support, Central Office Support				221				218
*Director, Coordinators, Warehouse, Central Office Support				261				258

** Central Administration reduction in work days*

Used with permission.

2. **Break your budget into sections.** For example, if you are operating a dining room at a profit, you may need to break this into its own budget. This way, you can estimate costs and revenues for this area uniquely. Sometimes, an area that is tracked uniquely is assigned its own cost center for accounting and budgeting purposes. Work with your financial officer to establish your budget categories.
3. **Estimate your revenues.** Look at your current budget and examine each source of revenue. Do you anticipate any changes? Estimate revenues from any new services, or any predicted changes in volume or pricing of existing services.
4. **Estimate your operating costs.** This can be one of the most time-consuming aspects of budget preparation. In this step, you need to examine food costs and labor costs, among others. For food costs, most Certified Dietary Managers budget for a modest increase. How much this should be varies by product, by season, by market conditions, and by revisions in your own purchasing agreements. You may speak with some of your vendors, research food price trends, and examine your prime vendor agreement to gain further information.

   Also realize that most operating costs relate directly to client counts or census. So, you may need to consult others in your organization to obtain census estimates for the coming year. If you work in a skilled nursing facility, for example, you need to have an estimate of how the census may change. Scale all your operating costs accordingly.

   For labor, you need to consider any major changes that may have an impact, such as an upcoming contract negotiation with a labor union, an across-the-board pay increase for employees in your operation, and similar information. Also consider your FTEs. Is there any change in services planned that might affect this number?

Figure 26.7 illustrates some of the calculations that may be required to project changes for a new food budget based on projected changes.

5. **Estimate your capital expenses.** Capital expenses fall into a unique category for budgeting purposes. Review your own equipment as it stands, and study repair records. If you have any piece of major equipment that may be reaching the end of its life cycle, you may need to list a replacement in your capital budget. Other considerations include planned changes in service or delivery that may require capital expenditures, and proposals for capital expenditures that may save operating expenses. An example of the latter might be a computer system that will save clerical labor and allow you to reduce your labor budget by one FTE.

Clearly, there is an element of crystal ball reading in this process, and this is not an exact science! You may not really know what capital items you will or will not need to purchase. Some facilities handle this by placing certain capital items in a budget on contingency. On contingency means that if the specified replacement is required, these budget funds will be spent. Otherwise, they will not.

Generally, a budget goes through several rounds of discussion and revision in most facilities. You may draft your first budget, and then discuss it with your superior and/or a financial officer. At a higher level, a financial officer has to piece together all the budgets and make the bottom line turn out satisfactorily. To do this, the financial expert may go back to a number of individual budgets and look for ways to reduce expenses and/or increase revenues, tweaking until the total budget for the facility becomes acceptable.

So, be prepared to adjust a budget in a negotiation process. For example, someone may ask you where you can cut $10,000, and you may need to respond. When capital expenses are involved, also be sure you have done your homework and that you are prepared to cost justify any recommended expenditure. For example, if you feel you will need to replace an oven next year, you may need to provide documentation and repair records indicating the rationale. You will also have to provide price quotations in order to assure that the budget figures you are proposing are realistic.

After a budget review process, you will receive a finalized or "approved" budget for the coming fiscal year. Now, it will become your responsibility to use this as a tool to help the facility meet its financial objectives.

What would the operating budget for food be if the current budget is $147,560 and the cost of living is expected to increase by 2.3%?

(Check your answer at the end of this chapter)

Figure 26.7 **Annual Budget Preparation**

Budget Category	Current Budget	Projected Changes	New Budget
Staples	$146,000	+1.5% (multiply by 1.015)	$148,190
Meats	132,000	+2% (multiply by 1.02)	134,640
Bakery	12,000	-no change-	12,000
Dairy	27,000	+0.5% (multiply by 1.005)	27,135
Produce	69,000	+3% (multiply by 1.03)	71,070

Management in the News

Last Updated September 2010

ANFP Practice Standards: Calculating Food Costs

by Susan Davis Allen, MS, RD, CHE

Knowing accurate costs and evaluating cost per patient meal or patient day will help the CDM address budgetary concerns quickly, and help prevent an adverse budgetary outcome at the end of the month. To accurately estimate costs, one must determine the cost per meal, or more often, a 'meal equivalent.' A simple method of doing that is dividing total food cost by the number of patient meals including calculated meal equivalents. The standard that follows will help you accurately determine your total meals/meal equivalents and total food costs.

Standard

The Certified Dietary Manager (CDM) assures that raw food costs are calculated per patient day and stays within the department budget.

Criteria

1.1 Raw food costs are determined using one of the following methods.

Inventory Method: This is the most accurate method of determining monthly raw food costs. It is done by accurately counting the inventory in all storage areas and determining the dollar value of the inventory. The formula for determining raw food costs using this method is:

Beginning inventory (the ending inventory from the previous month)

+ Purchases (for the month)

- Ending Inventory

= Monthly Food Costs

Many foodservice departments keep storeroom cost records on their computer, to aid in easily updating prices on storeroom inventory costs.

Requisition Method: For facilities that use storeroom requisitions, this method involves adding total direct purchases to the total value of the daily storeroom requisitions.

Recipe Method: This method is based on determining the total cost of food for each standardized recipe. The cost of each ingredient is added together and divided by the number of servings. Recipes must be used exactly as written (ingredients measured and correct portion sizes). Most facilities need computer software to assist in this method.

Record of Purchases Method: This method uses a simple tabulation of the current month purchase invoices to give the total cost of purchases for a specified time period. This represents an estimate of costs and does not take into account the cost of food in storage.

1.2 Calculate total meals or trays delivered to patients/residents, and Meals on Wheels or Home Delivered Meals trays per day, counting all three meals in a day.

1.3 Calculate 'meal equivalents' by adding together the following total food costs: Cafeteria, floor stock, catering to outside groups, staff meals, tube feedings, and nourishments. Divide this total by a 'market-basket' price (average price for a typical cafeteria meal). This will yield the total 'meal equivalents.'

(Continued...)

ANFP Practice Standards: Calculating Food Costs *(Continued)*

1.4 Add together total meals (1.2) and meal equivalents (1.3) to get total meals/equivalents.

1.5 Divide total food cost (1.1) by the meals/equivalents (1.4) to determine food cost per patient day.

1.6 Divide food cost per patient day (1.5) by 3 (three meals per day) to get food cost per patient meal.

1.7 Dietary managers have access to their department budget.

1.8 Dietary managers compare their monthly food costs to their monthly budget and make adjustments accordingly.

1.9 Dietary managers forecast for an upcoming budget year using past numbers, the Consumer Price Index, or other projected figures.

1.10 Dietary managers have input into the projected upcoming year's food cost and budget.

Assessment

1.1 The CDM prepares a written summary of the monthly budget.

1.2 The CDM follows up on increases in monthly food costs by checking variances in the following procedures:

a. Ordering practices

b. Receiving practices

c. Storage practices

d. Production practices (includes portion control, menu substitutions, following standardized recipes)

e. Increases in food prices

f. Waste

g. Unexpected special events

1.3 The CDM designates an employee trained in these procedures to act in their absence.

Summing it Up

These guidelines offer help for CDM, CFPPs responsible for calculating food costs in the nutrition services department. Refer to them as needed.

REFERENCES

1. Allen, SD. 'Measuring Meal Production and Calculating Meal Equivalents.' Dietary Manager Magazine, Jan. 2010. p 25.
2. CD-HCF/DMA 'Survival Skills for Nutrition Services.' 2006 p. 92-94.
3. Palacio, J., Thies, M., Introduction to Foodservice, Eleventh Edition. Pearson Prentice Hall, 2009.

Susan Davis Allen, MS, RD, CHE, is Director of Institutional Advancement at Southwest Wisconsin Technical College in Fennimore, WI. She serves as an advisor to the Certifying Board for Dietary Managers and has authored many publications for ANFP and other professional groups.

END OF CHAPTER

Putting It Into Practice Questions & Answers

1. Calculate the monthly food cost and the cost per patient day given the following data:

Beginning Inventory	$15,000
Purchases	$25,000
Ending Inventory	$17,500
Census for the month of April	118

A. 1. *Add the Beginning Inventory to the purchases.*
   a. *$15,000 + $25,000 = $40,000*

2. *Subtract the Ending Inventory from the total in #1.*
   a. *$40,000 - $17,500 = $22,500 = Monthly Food Cost*

3. *Multiply the census for April times the number of days in April.*
   a. *118 x 30 = 3540*

4. *Divide the monthly food cost by the patient/client meals in a month.*
   a. *$22,500 ÷ 3540 = $6.3559 or $6.36 = cost per patient day*

2. Using the sample budget in Fig. 26.5, did the department have a loss in revenue, a profit, or break even?

A. *To determine the answer, look at the Total Revenues and the Total Expenses. If the Total Revenues is greater than the Total Expenses, the department made a profit. If the Total Expenses is greater than the Revenue, there was a loss. If both numbers are the same, the department broke even. In this case, the Total Revenues was higher than the Total Expenses so the department made a small profit of $3000.*

3. What would the operating budget for food be if the current budget is $147,560 and the cost of living is expected to increase by 2.3%?

A. 1. *Multiply the current budget by the expected percentage increase*
   a. *$147,560 x .023 = 3392.5 = 3393*

2. *Add the increase to the current budget.*
   a. *$147,500 + 3393 = $150,893 = projected food budget*

Administer Salary and Wage Adjustments for Employees

Overview and Objectives

Controlling food and labor costs are the two of the most important controls the Certified Dietary Manager has. This chapter looks at controlling labor costs and how legislation and unions impact control.

After completing this chapter, you should be able to:

- ✓ Prepare an estimate of personnel costs for a foodservice department
- ✓ Compare actual costs to budget costs
- ✓ Identify laws, regulations, and agreements regarding employee compensation
- ✓ Utilize guidelines for salary scales and merit raises
- ✓ Provide insurance, tax, and other forms for personnel

Years ago, food used to be the big budget item in foodservice departments. However, labor costs, especially employee benefit costs, have increased dramatically. Your employees are your greatest assets. Budgeting for salaries is a necessary task so you can justify your payroll and keep your employees content!

Estimating Labor Costs for Budget Purposes

For facilities that have a daily census (hospitals, long-term care, corrections, schools, universities) the census is a useful planning tool for estimating personnel costs. Since census drives labor costs, you can use the average census to help estimate personnel costs for the upcoming operational budget period. The human resources department might be able to provide you with the necessary salary information as well.

There are other factors that impact the labor hours in a foodservice department:

- ✓ Number of menu items
- ✓ Type of menu
- ✓ Type and extent of services offered
- ✓ Type of equipment
- ✓ Layout of equipment and department in relation to dining rooms
- ✓ Seasonal variations in staffing
- ✓ Number of hours the foodservice department is open for business.

Once you have identified the factors affecting labor, you can begin estimating labor costs by completing a form such as that shown in Fig. 27.1.

As you are planning the labor budget, review these factors. Do you plan on changing the menu items or type of menu? For instance, will you implement a culture change and how will this impact labor needs? If the equipment is outdated, does equipment down time affect labor hours or slow down production? Do you have seasonal variations in staffing that need to be included in the budget? Do you plan to change the length of time the foodservice is open and if so, how will this affect labor hours? Once you have answers to these questions, you can begin to build your budget for labor. Figure 27.2 shows a sample budget with salary and employee benefit categories.

Managing the labor budget means monitoring it on a very regular basis. Overtime hours can quickly get out of hand if you are not monitoring the labor budget. If you are just starting out, you might want to monitor the budget every week. If your budget is computerized, you should be able to easily access your budget with the year-to-date figures. Be sure and review the *Management in the News* section, Keeping Labor Hours in Check, at the end of this chapter to see additional tips on controlling your labor budget.

Figure 27.1 Estimating Labor Cost Form

Category	# of Employees	Rate ($)	Hours/ Week	Weekly Estimate ($)	Fiscal Year Estimate ($)
Management (Examples/Salaried Positions)					
Certified Dietary Manager	1		40		
Subtotal for Management	**1**		**40**		
Foodservice Production					
Chef	1		40		
Cooks	2		80		
Kitchen Help	4		60		
Sanitation/Dishwashers	2		60		
Subtotal for Production	**9**		**240**		
Cafeteria					
Servers	2		40		
Cashiers	2		40		
Waitstaff	2		40		
Subtotal for Cafeteria	**6**		**120**		
TOTALS for Management, Production, and Cafeteria.	**16**		**400**		

Figure 27.2 **Sample Budget With Salary Categories**

Salaries	2012	Year-to-Date	2013
Administrative	$ 53,257	$ 45,001	
Managers	84,412	78,581	
Employees (Includes waitstaff, kitchen staff, sanitation staff)	183,645	165,247	
Call-in Staff	2,780	2,649	
Total Salaries	**$ 324,094**	**$ 291,478**	
Employee Benefits	**2012**	**Year-to-Date**	**2013**
Health/Life/Dental	$ 139,360	$ 139,760	
Retirement	18,797	19,001	
FICA	20,418	20,067	
Unemployment	3,214	2,978	
Workers Compensation	6,482	5,189	
TOTAL EMPLOYEE BENEFITS	**$ 188,271**	**$ 186,995**	
TOTAL LABOR COSTS	**$ 512,365**		

Labor Financial Measurements Used in Foodservice Operations

Labor Costs Per Meal. Just as in Chapter 26, where you calculated food costs PPD or per meal, you should also calculate labor costs per meal. Use the formula listed below:

> **Example:** Use the Total labor costs from Figure 27.2 and Total Meals Served of 191,118
> $512,365 ÷ 191,118 = $2.68 labor cost per meal

Labor Costs per Meal Served = Labor Costs ÷ Total Meals Served

See the example in Figure 27.3 for a sample calculation.

It is important to control both food cost and labor cost per meal to meet the fiscal objectives of your facility.

Meal Equivalents. In foodservice, especially in facilities where you have a predetermined clientele, such as healthcare, corrections, schools, and universities, it is essential to count the meals you serve. While that might seem simple when you serve three meals a day to a set population, it hardly covers all of the "meals" you serve. What if you also provide cafeteria service? Or, foodservice is constantly called upon to provide coffee and cookies or muffins, extra supplements, a staff luncheon, etc. Not only do these extra activities affect food cost, they may also significantly affect labor costs. If those 'food activities' are not counted as meals in the labor costs per meal served, it may appear as if your labor costs are too high. If your labor costs are too high, you may be expected to decrease FTEs for the next budget period.

For cafeteria service, floor stock (food taken to other locations for clients), catering to outside groups, staff meals, tube feedings, coffee and snack times, and nourishments, it is important to calculate a meal equivalent. Total the food cost for each of these activities and divide this figure by a "market basket" price (average price for a typical cafeteria meal). Add these meal equivalents to your total meals and then refigure your labor cost per meal. You will see a difference that is a more accurate reflection of your labor costs. See the example in Figure 27.3.

Figure 27.3 Including Meal Equivalents into Labor Cost per Meal

Total Meal Equivalents Costs for March

Cafeteria Sales for the Month of March	$18,562.00
Floor Stock Requisitions for March	415.00
Catering for Coffee, Snacks, Activities	219.00
Staff Meals for March	1,405.00
Tube Feedings and Nourishments	5,637.00
Average Price for a Typical Cafeteria Meal	3.21

Meal Equivalents for March: $26,238 ÷ $3.21 = 8,174 Meal Equivalents

Recalculate the Labor Cost per Meal from the Example in Figure 27.2:

Total Labor Cost for March: $512,365

Total Meals 191,118 + Meal Equivalents 8,174 = 199,292

Divide the Labor Cost by the Total Meals Served: $512,352 ÷ 199,292 = $2.57

Note: While a decrease in labor cost per meal by 10 cents may not seem dramatic, it can make a huge difference in your overall labor costs. What if your administration said your labor cost per meal could not be more than $2.50 per meal? You could lower the cost by 10 cents per meal just by counting all of the food you are producing.

Other Labor Cost Considerations

Part-time Staff. Another way to lower costs in foodservice is through the use of part-time employees. The use of part-time staff to replace full-time staff has increased significantly in the past 10 years. Part of the reason is because part-time staff can dramatically decrease labor cost. How much savings is dependent upon the wage differential from full-time staff and the benefit package offered to part-time staff. Let's look at an example of a university foodservice that currently employs 10 full-time cooks to cover 14 shifts per week. The university employees receive an average wage of $16/hr plus employee benefits equivalent to an additional 50 percent.

Calculate the labor cost per meal if the total labor costs for the past month were $6927 and the census was 60 for the month of March.

(Check your answer at the end of this chapter)

Wages:	10 cooks x 40 hrs x $16 per hour	= $6400
Benefits:	$6400 x 50%	= $3200
	Total labor cost	**= $9600/week**

Now, the university decides to cover some of the shifts with LTEs or Limited Term Employees who work only part-time for $10/hr and qualify for only 20 percent benefits.

Full-time Cooks:

Wages:	6 cooks x 40 hrs x $16/hr	= $3840
Benefits:	$3840 x 50%	= $1920
	Total Labor Costs	**= $5760**

Part-time Cooks:

Wages:	8 cooks x 20 hrs x $10	= $1600
Benefits:	$1600 x 20%	= $320
	Total Labor Costs	= $1920
	New Total Labor Costs	**= $7680/week**

If you decide to increase the number of part-time employees, you should make sure they feel a part of the department and are included in all of the training.

Labor Legislation. The effect of labor legislation can be significant when considering your labor budget. Unfortunately, labor legislation varies from state to state. There are some general terms that apply to all states: minimum wage and provisions for overtime. Both of these are set by the Fair Labor Standards Laws that were discussed in Chapter 8.

Minimum Wage. Minimum wage is the least amount that you can pay nonexempt employees, before deductions. Remember, nonexempt employees are those who are paid hourly and are not on a set salary. The current Federal Minimum wage effective July 24, 2009 is $7.25 per hour. Many states have their own minimum wage. (e.g. Washington State minimum wage is $8.67.) In cases where an employee is subject to both the state and federal minimum wage laws, the employee is entitled to the higher of the two minimum wages. There are different minimum wage rates for tipped employees and for employees who are younger than 20 and have worked less than 90 days. Work with your human resources department or administrator to make sure you have the current information for your state.

Equal Pay. The Equal Pay Act of 1963 ensures that there are no sex-based wage differentials between men and women employed in the same establishment who perform jobs requiring equal effort, skill, and responsibility. These provisions are enforced by the Equal Employment Opportunity Commission (EEOC).

Provisions for Overtime. According to the Department of Labor, "an employer who requires or permits an employee to work overtime is generally required to pay the employee premium pay for such overtime work. Employees

Glossary

Minimum Wage
The minimum dollar wage for nonexempt employees before deductions

Putting It Into Practice: 2

You just hired a new male cook. He has come to you about his salary because he believes he should be paid more. He is supporting his family of four on his salary and is insisting that he deserves more than the female cook who does the same work. How would you respond to his request?

(Check your answer at the end of this chapter)

covered by the Fair Labor Standards Act (FLSA) must receive overtime pay for hours worked in excess of 40 in a workweek of at least one and one-half times their regular rate of pay. The FLSA does not require overtime pay for work on Saturdays, Sundays, holidays, or regular days of rest, unless overtime hours are worked on such days. Extra pay for working weekends or nights is a matter of agreement between the employer and the employee (or the employee's representative). The FLSA does not require extra pay for weekend or night work or double time pay."

Working with Human Resources (HR) Department

If the Certified Dietary Manager is fortunate enough to have an HR Department, many of the tasks regarding labor will be completed by that department. For instance, HR personnel will help determine where to place an employee on the salary schedule. HR will keep all employee records. They will provide the insurance, tax, and other forms for personnel.

If you do not have an HR Department, you may be expected to maintain salary records, provide insurance and tax forms, and provide other forms for personnel. Work with your administrator to determine what forms are required and what salary should be offered.

Working With Labor Unions

Labor contracts will always be an important factor affecting labor costs. Labor contracts impact wages, benefits, and other aspects of human resources management. Unionization provides certain advantages to employees. It also imposes certain requirements on the Certified Dietary Manager who must comply with a union agreement.

The decision for employees to form or join a union is made through a voting process. A **union** forms an agreement with an organization on behalf of the group of employees.

Reasons for an employee desiring to join a union sometimes relate directly to relationships with management. In addition, employees may form or join unions in order to attain better working conditions, improved safety, better pay, or specific benefits. However, membership in a union is not a guarantee that employees will receive everything they want or expect.

In some situations, Certified Dietary Managers can discourage efforts to unionize by following sound management practices. Implementation of procedures to address employee concerns can be helpful in eliminating many of the reasons for affiliating with a union. Certified Dietary Managers need to keep in touch with employees' needs and wants. Some techniques used to do this include a suggestion box, employee survey(s), "employee relations rounds" conducted by the human resources department (or by the manager in small facilities), employee meetings, and effectively conducted employee appraisal programs. Whenever these or other techniques are used to assess employee concerns, management must then take concerns and suggestions seriously and attempt to make improvements.

Glossary

Labor Union
Formal organization representing employees and designed to advance the needs and interests of its members

Putting It Into Practice: 3

You are hiring an entry level person to work full-time. Your salary scale starts entry level people at the minimum wage. your state minimum wage is $8.25 but the federal minimum wage is lower. What salary level do you use for this new employee?

(Check your answer at the end of this chapter)

Other reasons for joining a union include a desire to be heard, the appeal of a formal means of expressing concerns to administrators, and a feeling that group attachment brings security. A formal group of employees is perceived as stronger than an informal group.

Impact of Unions on the Administration

Once employees are represented by a union, the administration will probably have to alter operations several ways. It will no longer be able to make decisions or deal with individual employees on a special basis. You will have to follow the contract for salary rather than decide at what level to place a new employee. Regardless of an employee's ability or skills, each must be treated equally if he or she is in the same (or similar) job classification. Frequently, seniority—rather than other factors which might distinguish employees' qualifications and performance—may become the most important factor in matters affecting personnel-related decisions.

There can be advantages to unionization. The presence of a union prompts development and/or improvement of policies or procedures that affect relationships with employees. A facility that does not have well-developed policies and management tools is likely to benefit. On certain issues, administrators will also be able to deal with only one representative of unionized employees rather than with various individual staff members. Finally, top levels of administration may need to recover much decision-making responsibility that had previously been delegated to supervisors, since the actions of a single supervisor may have facility-wide implications in a unionized environment. To the extent that centralized decision-making is beneficial, it is another advantage to union affiliation.

The Collective Bargaining Process

Many people define collective bargaining as negotiations between union and facility representatives leading to a contract. More generally, however, the term **collective bargaining** applies to routine communications and negotiations involving contract agreements, interpreting contract clauses, and resolving disputes (grievances) between union and administrative officials. A great deal of time can be spent in negotiating a union agreement. It is common for union contracts to apply for a period of three or more years. To prepare for the negotiation, administrative officials in a facility must obtain information about prevailing wage and salary rates and fringe benefit provisions. They must also assess the facility's financial position, resources, and ability to commit to specific wages and other terms. Furthermore, they must analyze existing contracts, communicate with union representatives, and consider probable union concerns.

With the political battles over collective bargaining in 2011, collective bargaining in the future may look very different.

Through discussion and negotiation, the union and the employee reach a final agreement about relevant issues including wages and salary. This agreement is signed and formalized, with each party committing to honor it for the time period specified.

Glossary

Collective Bargaining
Communications and negotiation between union and administration regarding wages, benefits and other issues

The Union and Labor Costs

According to the U.S. Bureau of Labor Statistics, the median weekly wage for all union employees in 2009 was $901, versus $710 for all workers who were not union employees. That statistic clearly shows that labor costs in union facilities will be higher. How can the Certified Dietary Manager prepare for these increased costs? When administration is negotiating a new contract, make sure that the labor costs you provide the administration are accurate. If you can survey other union foodservice departments to determine their wage scale, that information will also be helpful.

Work with the union steward to improve communications about labor costs and the impact they have on your department budget.

Utilize guidelines for salary scales and merit raises. Every facility should have a salary schedule. If your staff is represented by a union, you are bound by their contract to follow that salary schedule. If there is no union in your facility, there should still be a salary schedule and policies about merit increases. Another resource that might help you with salary guidelines is The Association of Nutrition & Foodservice Professionals/Dietary Managers Association Annual Salary Survey. Figure 27.4 shows the 2010 Salary Survey results. While this information focuses on salaries for Certified Dietary Managers, it can still be a reference for your facility because it contains benefit information and represents the entire United States.

Geographic Regions for ANFP/DMA 2010 Salary Survey

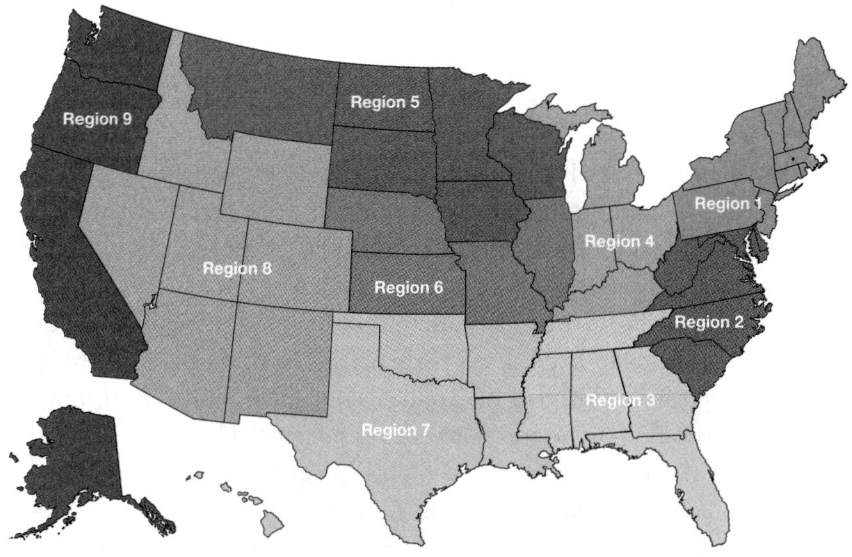

Figure 27.4 ANFP/DMA Salary Survey*

Category	Subcategory	2010 Survey Sample Size	2010 Survey Average Value	2008 Survey Average Value	2006 Survey Average Value	2005 Survey Average Value
As of August 1, 2010, what was the annual salary or wage for this position?						
ALL		**3,287**	**$45,423**	$42,786	$40,374	$39,201
CDM, CFPP	Yes	**3,161**	**$45,342**	$42,733	$40,420	$39,321
	No	**98**	**$48,575**	$44,220	$39,690	$36,956
Education	Associate Degree	**423**	**$49,504**	$46,855	$44,197	$43,477
	Bachelor's Degree	**461**	**$56,651**	$53,685	$47,914	$46,653
	Dietary Managers Course Completion	**88**	**$55,291**	$38,807	$36,741	$35,617
	Culinary Arts	**112**	**$44,344**	$53,488	$47,511	$48,425
	Technical School	**2,030**	**$40,975**	$42,384	$38,496	$36,632
	Other	**146**	**$53,389**	$48,749	$47,597	$44,516
Years of Industry Experience	0 - 5 years	**238**	**$34,464**	$31,591	$30,992	$30,307
	6 - 10 years	**375**	**$37,958**	$35,777	$35,716	$34,029
	11 - 15 years	**436**	**$41,561**	$40,438	$39,270	$37,563
	16 - 20 years	**548**	**$44,963**	$43,473	$40,440	$39,640
	21 - 25 years	**517**	**$47,682**	$44,723	$42,414	$41,275
	26 - 30 years	**559**	**$49,832**	$46,647	$43,274	$41,762
	Over 31 years	**585**	**$51,805**	$48,566	$45,426	$44,432
Type of Facility	Long Term Care/Nursing Home	**1,406**	**$41,382**	$38,690	$37,890	$36,581
	Long Term Care/Assisted Living	**153**	**$42,607**	$42,107	$38,957	$38,207
	Long Term Care/Hospital	**145**	**$43,946**	$41,634	$38,526	$36,222
	Hospital	**698**	**$51,013**	$46,605	$42,885	$42,393
	Continuous Care Retirement Community	**287**	**$54,713**	$53,498	$48,654	$47,809
	Assisted Living Facility	**85**	**$43,265**	$40,442	$39,378	$36,028
	School	**116**	**$40,982**	$39,214	$34,314	$32,785
	Correctional Facility	**42**	**$47,929**	$43,751	$38,644	$35,828
	Military	**14**	**$60,470**	$50,052	$45,099	$48,315
	Other	**311**	**$46,344**	$44,450	$41,803	$40,067
Location of Facility	Major City or Suburb	**1,159**	**$53,137**	$49,742	$46,587	$44,731
	Small Town/Rural *(population under 100,000)*	**1,958**	**$40,764**	$38,384	$36,247	$35,428
Employment Status	Full-time	**2,993**	**$45,714**	$43,205	$40,565	$39,723
	Part-time	**96**	**$32,838**	$25,699	$30,261	$20,470
Position	Exempt *(salaried)*	**2,090**	**$50,431**	$47,327	$44,265	$43,530
	Non-exempt *(hourly)*	**997**	**$34,175**	$32,857	$31,490	$29,638
Number of Employees Reporting to You	0	**160**	**$35,693**	$34,583	$33,814	$28,107
	1 - 5	**222**	**$37,425**	$35,353	$34,161	$31,985
	6 - 10	**641**	**$37,791**	$36,172	$33,411	$32,250
	11 - 15	**666**	**$41,472**	$39,355	$37,956	$37,606
	16 - 20	**381**	**$46,009**	$42,240	$38,967	$38,372
	21 - 30	**413**	**$47,417**	$45,085	$42,720	$40,783
	31 - 50	**275**	**$55,298**	$52,661	$48,931	$46,703
	51 - 100	**199**	**$67,620**	$62,523	$57,964	$56,675
	Over 100	**64**	**$79,000**	$76,112	$64,818	$64,515
Geographic Region (See map following this chart.)	1	**420**	**$52,454**	$49,790	$46,325	$43,938
	2	**355**	**$48,405**	$45,549	$41,322	$41,086
	3	**440**	**$49,605**	$44,631	$42,821	$41,547
	4	**439**	**$41,883**	$40,788	$37,831	$38,319
	5	**518**	**$39,974**	$38,264	$36,429	$35,175
	6	**423**	**$39,605**	$38,508	$35,056	$35,433
	7	**328**	**$39,224**	$36,950	$34,401	$33,180
	8	**132**	**$45,458**	$45,189	$41,912	$37,957
	9	**211**	**$60,443**	$53,986	$48,608	$45,807
	Non-US	**10**	**$48,019**	$35,986	$43,903	$35,506

** 2010 with comparison to 2005, 2006, and 2008.*

Source: ANFP/DMA 2010 (see full summary at www.anfp.org/jobs/salary_survey.shtml

Management in the News

Managing Labor Hours

by Denis O'Connor, CDM, CFPP

As a dietary manager, you know that the greatest asset in your department is your employees. Your department would not run without them, and they can make you look so good in the eyes of administration. The flip side is that you must be able to manage your department using the appropriate number of labor hours so that you can justify your payroll amount. This latter challenge can make a huge difference in how successful you are in maintaining the payroll budget, specifically as it relates to overtime. This article will highlight the concepts and processes I utilized to eliminate overtime in a department of 60 employees.

Create Your Labor Plan

Without a plan you will face a greater challenge. First, determine how many labor hours are needed to complete various assignments. You may be starting from scratch in the case of expanding your department, or in most cases you have come into a department that has pre-existing labor hours established. My advice is to question everything. Just because they "have done it that way for years," does not necessarily make it the most efficient way of doing something. A key point at this stage is to be an effective listener and a good observer. Listen to your employees. Let them tell you what they are doing and the time it takes them to do it. Then observe for yourself. Doing this will let staff know that you are serious about making sure they have the appropriate time needed to perform their tasks.

Set Your Labor Plan Parameters

Now that you know the number of hours needed, the next step is to set parameters to reach your goal. This can be achieved by doing the following:

Create a manageable schedule—Following your research by observing the staff, you should now be able to create a schedule that is realistic and manages your labor hours without running any overtime.

Meet with your leadership staff—Be clear in your goal and make sure these people know they will be held accountable. If there is overtime, they need to explain why. Of course if the department is smaller and you are the only supervisor, then the responsibility lies with you.

Meet with all of your staff—As simple and straight forward as this point is, if you fail to accomplish it you will have great difficulty being successful. Communicate effectively and honestly with your staff. Explain to them why overtime dollars are so excessive compared to straight time rates. Employees know budgets; give them the information they need to better understand where you are coming from. Tell them you are holding your leadership staff accountable, and challenge them to be accountable also. When I did this, my staff took it on and set about monitoring their hours worked on their own to make sure they did not work any overtime. They would approach their supervisor and ask to have their hours checked to make sure they were on target. This told me I had communicated effectively to them and they understood the goal.

(Continued...)

Managing Labor Hours *(Continued)*

Cross train your staff—The more people you have to share the work and share in the tasks, the more flexibility you have as a manager. If an employee needs a day off and you can move another employee into the slot because they have experience and training in the area, you are much more likely to fill that spot without overtime. Again, it is very important that you communicate with staff so they know why you are cross training. Doing this will eliminate any fears they may have about other people taking over their job.

Be prepared to pitch in—When staff sees me pitching in, they feel that I care about *them* getting the work done as opposed to feeling that I care about getting the work done myself. There is a distinct difference in this point. Each employee must have the sense that what they do contributes to the organization's overall success. Pitching in only because the employee can't get the job finished is much less effective than pitching in to show you are willing to help them. In my experience, I might pitch in when there is no deadline or things are running smoothly. This gives me the opportunity to chat with staff and make sure they are happy.

Monitor, monitor, monitor—To be successful managing labor hours you must monitor your hours closely to make sure you are not running over. There is no hard and fast rule as to how often you do this, but you must know when you are going over. If that means checking payroll numbers daily, then be prepared to do it. After a while it will become second nature. You need to know early in the week if you are running over so you can creatively adjust schedules to stay within budget.

Communicate to your staff and highlight your successes—Meet with your staff regularly to let them know that your plan (with their help and support) is working. Don't be afraid to share the budget dollar amounts with them. Doing this will give them ownership in the plan and they will feel empowered to help even more. Also, depending on your circumstances, be prepared to reward your staff. You may find that your administrator is happy to sponsor a department party, as this is a very small price to pay compared to overtime labor dollars. If you are not able to do this, then make every effort to let your staff know that you appreciate their efforts. This will go a long way in maintaining an overtime-free department.

Summing it Up

Bringing all staff on board in the plan, communicating with them every step of the way, and holding them accountable has led to successfully eliminating overtime in my department. In these budget strapped times, this helps our organization—and it may help yours, too.

Denis O'Connor, CDM, CFPP is director of dining services at Bay Village of Sarasota, a CCRC in Sarasota, FL. He manages a department of 60 employees.

END OF CHAPTER

Putting It Into Practice Questions & Answers

1. Calculate the labor cost per meal if the total labor costs for the past month were $6927 and the census was 60 for the month of March.

   A. *The formula to determine labor cost per meal is:* ***Labor Costs ÷ Total Meals Served***

      1. *Determine your total labor cost ($6927)*
      2. *Determine your total meals served.*
         a. *60 clients x 3 meals/day x 31 days in March = 5580*
      3. *Divide $6927 by 5580 =* ***$1.24/meal***

2. You just hired a new male cook. He has come to you about his salary because he believes he should be paid more. He is supporting his family of four on his salary and is insisting that he deserves more than the female cook who does the same work. How would you respond to his request?

   A. *Explain to your male cook that it is against the law to pay different sexes different salaries if they are doing the same work. You should explain the law is The Equal Pay Act of 1963.*

3. You are hiring an entry level person to work full-time. Your salary scale starts entry level people at the minimum wage. Your state minimum wage is $8.25 but the federal minimum wage is lower. What salary level do you use for this new employee?

   A. *All employees who are paid the minimum wage are entitled the higher level wage if the state wages differs from the federal wage. By law, you must start your new employee at the $8.25/ hour wage.*

CHAPTER 28

Implement Cost-Effective Procedures

Overview and Objectives

Achieving your department goals while staying within budget depends on setting realistic goals and understanding how funds are allocated. It also requires flexibility. Review cost-saving principles, recommend cost-saving purchasing practices and analyze program changes based on actual cost versus budget.

After completing this chapter, you should be able to:

- ✓ Review bids or purchasing programs
- ✓ Recommend cost-saving purchasing practices
- ✓ Recommend cost-saving department practices
- ✓ Review actual costs with budget estimate to identify problem areas

Financial Tools

Throughout this unit, you have prepared purchasing specifications, managed revenue generating services, and monitored the cost of food and labor. Specifically, you have repeated the control process from other chapters throughout this textbook by setting standards and measuring performance. Now it is time to complete the control process by comparing performance with standards and taking corrective action. Let's examine some of the financial reporting tools you will use. See Figure 28.1 for an overview of common financial documents.

Balance Sheet

The balance sheet for not-for-profit organizations is a statement of the facility's assets, liabilities, and net assets. A balance sheet showing for-profit financial activities would include investor or stockholder information. The balance sheet presents a snapshot in time (on the day it was generated, usually the last day of the accounting period). Different facilities have different account periods; the most common are quarterly, semi-annually, and annually.

The balance sheet may show both the current reporting period and a comparison to the same reporting period the year before. Balance sheets are usually used for accounting reports and may help compare department activity from one year to the next. The tool that helps compare the actual department operational performance is the operating statement.

Figure 28.1 Comparisons of Financial Documents

Budget	Balance Sheet	Operating Statement
A financial planning document that predicts where you want to be in the next year.	A snapshot showing assets, liabilities, and net assets on a given day in time—usually the last day of the period.	Shows your department's monthly financial performance compared to what was budgeted.

Operating Statement

You have a budget. It has been approved, and both you and financial managers of the facility believe it will work. Now, your job is to use the budget as a tool to manage revenues and expenses in your department. How can you go about doing this?

A number of reports help you keep the pulse on finances. Where these reports come from varies by facility. The most common model uses a centralized accounting system, which is almost always managed on a computer. In a centralized accounting system, accounting functions are managed by one accounting office for the entire organization. What this means for a foodservice department is that:

- ✓ Invoices for food, services, repairs, capital, and other items are paid by Accounting and entered into the pertinent foodservice budget categories on a master ledger.
- ✓ You submit time sheets for each pay period. As payroll is processed, paycheck totals for the foodservice department are entered into foodservice budget categories for labor expenses. (Some employee benefits may also be entered in your budget, or they may be handled through a separate budget for human resources. This varies by organization.)
- ✓ If you have any cash operations, such as dining rooms, cafeterias, or vending, you deposit cash in the accounting office. Accounting personnel transfer the deposit to a bank account, and credit the funds to a revenue category in your budget.

An advantage of this model is that financial managers responsible for the entire facility can keep track of the bottom line.

In this common model, the accounting office typically runs an operating statement for each department or cost center. Often, this is done shortly after the end of each month. So, on January 5, you may receive an operating statement that is current through December. An **operating statement** is a financial report that shows your financial performance (revenues and expenses), as compared with the budget. This statement may also be called a budget report.

Operating Statement
A financial report that shows financial performance (revenues and expenses), as compared with the budget

From one facility to the next, specific formats for financial reports vary. The statement or report typically shows figures for a given period of time, along with a report for year to date. Year to date means a cumulative total of revenues and expenses in each budget category for the portion of the fiscal year that has been completed so far. Let's consider what this report may look like. Figure 28.2 provides an example.

In this example, several labels appear at the tops of columns. Here is a closer look at what they are and what they mean.

Current Period. This section totals expenses and revenues for the time period that was just completed, such as the month that just ended. On this sample report, the current period is identified in the left corner of the page. It is July. Under the current period heading are three columns: Actual, Budget, and Variance.

✓ **Actual:** This column identifies what revenues were actually received in each of these budget categories, and what expenses were actually paid out during the current period of July.

✓ **Budget:** This column shows what the monthly budget was for these budget categories for the reporting period. This budget was established in advance for this fiscal year. In this example, a one-month budget for any category is the annual budget divided by 12.

✓ **Variance:** This column shows how the actual figures compare with the budget as planned. A variance of zero means that the budget is precisely on target; there is no variance. For example, in the Revenue section for the current period in Figure 28.2, you can see that total revenue exceeds the budget by $1,627. This shows that the department received $1,627 more in revenue than anticipated for the month. Where or how? The detail shows that board plans, coffee shop, catering, and vending all brought in more revenue than budget.

✓ Now, look at the variance for the restaurant. The budgeted amount was $5,437. However, actual revenues for July were only $4,558. Parentheses ( ) are used to show places where the actual values represent an operating loss for this budget category. In this case, the restaurant revenue was $789 below the amount budgeted or projected.

✓ Now, look at the Expenses section. You will notice the wages paid to employees during July exceeded the budget. Thus, the report shows a variance of ($236). As you review the list of expense categories, you will notice some are under budget and some are over budget.

Year to Date. In the right-hand section of this report, we see a major heading called year to date. Beyond only July, this section of the report is identifying how the revenue and expense categories of the budget total from the beginning of the fiscal year until now. It is showing cumulative figures. Under the year to date heading are three more columns, Actual, Budget, and Variance. These are identical with the three labels explained above, except that they cover a different time period, giving a cumulative report on financial performance for the year to date.

Putting It Into Practice: 1

How would you explain the difference between a budget and an operating statement? Which one would you use if you were told to reduce your costs?

(Check your answer at the end of this chapter)

Figure 28.2 Sample Operating Statement (Budget Report)

	CURRENT PERIOD			YEAR TO DATE		
	Actual	Budget	Variance	Actual	Budget	Variance
Revenue						
Board Plans	$9.752	$8,264	$1,488	$103,200	$99,169	$4,031
Coffee Shop	5,033	4,521	512	56,231	54,250	1,981
Restaurant	4,558	5,347	(789)	57,622	64,169	(6547)
Catering	2,000	1,750	250	23,965	21,000	2,965
Vending	750	583	167	7,120	7,000	120
TOTAL REVENUE	**22,093**	**20,465**	**1,628**	**248,138**	**245,588**	**2,550**
Expenses						
Food—Meat	2,178	2,285	107	23,048	27,419	4,371
Food—Dairy	520	535	15	5,269	6,419	1,150
Food—Bakery	295	258	(37)	2,500	3,094	594
Food—Produce	1,093	1,108	15	1,357	13,300	11,943
Food—Staples	3,826	3,597	(229)	38,145	43,169	5,024
Wages	7,042	6,806	(236)	78,650	81,669	3,019
Benefits	1,352	1,352	0	14,000	16,219	2,219
Education and Travel	100	146	46	1,489	1,750	261
Consulting Fees	200	121	(79)	1,475	1,456	(19)
Repairs and Maintenance	325	258	(67)	2,500	3,094	594
Advertising and Printing	0	88	88	789	1,050	261
Office Supplies	215	194	(21)	1,867	2,331	464
Clearing Products	153	292	139	2,568	3,500	932
Linens and Dishes	297	438	141	4,566	5,250	684
TOTAL EXPENSES	**17,478**	**17,477**	**(118)**	**178,223**	**209,720**	**31,497**
NET GAIN/LOSS	**$4,497**			**$69,915**		

The example in Figure 28.2 shows that so far, the revenue has been $248,138, and this is $2,550 more than expected in the budget planning. This report also shows that even though the operation was over budget for expenses for July, in the cumulative year to date, the operation is under budget for expenses by a very large amount: $31,497.

Net Gain/Loss. At the bottom of this report, you see the bottom line, which shows how revenues and expenses balance out. For example, the month of July shows a net gain (or "profit") of $4,497. It has performed quite well financially.

Preparing and Using an Operating Systems Statement. You probably won't have to prepare your own operating statement. However, you can see what goes into preparing an operating statement and you need to carefully check the accuracy of the report. The sections of the operating statement include the main sections (food costs and labor costs) from the budget and are calculated according to the information in the previous two chapters. If your facility uses patient days, the operating statement may also include the patient days and total meals. No doubt, this statement provides a great deal of information. How can you use it? When you receive an operating statement, the following process represents sound management:

✓ **Review:** First, review the performance in each category. To review each category, you will need the following records:
  - Meals served
  - Revenue or sales report from cafeteria, catering, clientele
  - Monthly raw food costs
  - Monthly labor costs
  - Production records
  - Overhead costs such as office and cleaning supplies, linens, dishes, repairs.

✓ **Compare.** Note where your financial performance has been over or under budget for the time period being reported. You may also decide to compare this with last year's budget figures to analyze seasonal trends and overall operating trends.

✓ **Ask why.** Where your figures are over or under budget, do you know why? Review each budget category, and look for reasons. This helps you assure that you are in control of any trends, changes, or issues you need to manage. The better you understand reasons for variances, the better able you will be to exert financial control. Sometimes unexpected jumps in business, such as increased catering or snack shop sales, can also generate increased expenses (to purchase more food and pay for more employee hours in order to honor heightened service demands). This is not a bad thing. It can be a sign of business growth. The important figure to monitor in this situation is the net gain or loss.

✓ **Recommend Cost Saving Practices.** Use this financial feedback to target action to assure that your operation remains under sound financial management. Is your labor expense too high? Are your overtime hours excessive? You might look carefully at your schedules and find a way to cut back. Is your cafeteria showing a drop in revenue? Check your sales records, examine specific items on the menu, and try some adjustments in offerings, menu mix, pricing, or other areas.

Is it desirable to be over budget or under budget? In some facilities, there may be a standard for how far your actual operations can vary from the budgeted figures. This may be 5-10 percent. If you do not know exactly what is expected of you, talk this over with your superior. In general, you want to be close to budgeted figures. However, if you are under budget for any expenses, you are in essence saving money. This is generally positive. If you are over budget for revenues, this is also a positive situation.

If you are over budget for expenses—or under budget for revenues—you may be contributing to a cash flow issue for your facility. Either of these situations is potentially troublesome. Either of these situations represents a scenario you want to analyze and change as quickly as possible. Your responsibility in managing a budget is to help meet the financial objectives of the facility and assure financial viability.

Food Cost Report

Another report of value is a food cost report. Keeping in mind that food costs represent a large portion of your budget, you probably want to monitor expenditures in this area in significant detail. This information may be available from a centralized accounting system, and may appear on your operating statements.

Alternately, you may be using a foodservice computer system to monitor purchases and receipts. Most computer systems designed to handle these functions also provide a food cost reporting feature. Sometimes, your prime vendor may also be able to provide food cost reports.

When you receive a food cost report, you want to review and verify the figures, compare them with your expectations, and ask questions about significant trends. For example, you may find that your expenditures for meat have just jumped. Do you know why? If not, you may actually pull purchase orders and receiving records to determine this. Here are some examples of possible reasons for the jump in meat costs:

✓ Your receiving clerk signed off on 50 cases of meat, while the delivery was only 25 cases.

✓ Your supplier substituted higher-priced products for several items on the purchase order. A higher price was charged without authorization, and you were not aware of this.

✓ Pricing for many meat products has risen, and you do not have prices locked in for this time period.

Your department operating statement shows your actual food costs are higher than what was budgeted. What steps would you take to address this variance?

(Check your answer at the end of this chapter)

✓ You served a number of special catered events. You had to purchase much more meat to do so. Your operation charged for the catering service, and you expect a corresponding increase in revenue figures for the same time period.

✓ Your census has undergone a rapid increase of about 30 percent over recent weeks. In reviewing food cost figures, you are noticing that all of them have risen by about 30 percent.

In the first three examples, you have identified a control issue that requires your immediate intervention. In the last two, you have a justification that makes sense. You need to be aware of this, and be prepared to interpret your operating statement accordingly. If, through departmental reports that you generate, you know about these variances before your superior does, you may also want to bring them to the attention of your superior and discuss them.

Another common factor that increases food costs are employees eating without recording as a meal. Employee theft may also be happening or employees may produce extra to take home as leftovers. Make sure you have well documented policies for employee meals and food.

When should you review food cost reports? The practical answer in many operations is to review a report as it becomes available through a centralized accounting system, such as once per month. However, some Certified Dietary Managers say that if they wait until a month is over, they have already lost a critical opportunity to exert financial control. Thus, a growing trend in both large and small facilities is to use foodservice computer systems to obtain reports on a more frequent basis. This may be daily or weekly. Frequent monitoring often provides an opportunity to better control food costs, and comply more closely with a budget.

Cost-saving Purchasing Practices. In addition to reviewing your food cost reports, you should be staying current with market trends. If there has been a freeze in Florida and you are dependent upon Florida orange juice, you may want to review your product specifications and change your order. You can also use current market trends to negotiate with your vendors. There are Websites where you can track market trends such as http://www.foodservice.com/marketprices/ Figure 28.3 shows a sample of the information you can track from this Website. When you notice your food costs increasing, start monitoring the market trends for your most expensive items such as meat and produce, work with your vendors, and make sure you are getting the best prices.

Sales Report

Another report that can be extremely useful to a Certified Dietary Manager is a sales report for cash operations such as a cafeteria, a restaurant, a C-store (Convenience store), or others. A sales report provides a pulse on daily revenues. In addition, it can provide a basis for comparison of food sold with food prepared.

A common way to receive a sales report is through the reporting feature of a point of sale (POS) system. This is a computer-based cash register system. It records transactions and maintains very detailed records of sales. Information may be reported by location, date, meal period, menu item, and much more.

Figure 28.3 Weekly Produce Market Report

The weekly Produce Market Report is separated into categories. This example is produce; each category contains commentary such as the paragraph below followed by a substantial listing of foods, source of the food, how it is packed, and the cost.

California lettuce crop has experienced heavy rainfalls over the past week which could result in quality issues and reduces yields. California broccoli still experiencing gaps due to rains 3 months ago. Expect market to stay steady over the next week. California carrot growers continue to struggle with undersized carrots and light production; Georgia carrot season is over. California carrot production will remain light throughout the month of May with little to no jumbo carrots until early June. California celery continues to struggle with seeder issues. Santa Maria has started production which will increase volumes. California cauliflower production volumes will continue to be variable due to planting gaps due to rain 3 months ago.

Food	Source	How Packed		Cost
Broccoli	California	bunches 14s	cartons	$17.00
Carrots	California	ibo	50 lbs. sacks loose	$29.00
Celery, Organic	Florida	2½ oz.	cartons	$41.75
Onions—Dry, Yellow	Texas	ibo	50 lbs. sacks	$11.00
Peppers—Bell Type, Green	Florida	medium	1 1/9 bushel cartons	$16.00
Peppers—Bell Type, Green	Florida	large	1 1/9 bushel cartons	$17.00

Source: http://www.foodservice.com/marketprices/, May 29, 2011

Most POS systems provide a broad range of reporting options. It is worthwhile to become familiar with the POS system in your own facility, examine options, and specify the reports you need to review.

The Certified Dietary Manager has an important role in the control of sales generated from cash operations. For effective control, the manager needs to know what the amount of sales should be. The manager needs to know what sales actually were. Finally, a manager needs to compare these, and investigate and correct discrepancies.

Let's take a look at each of these control points.

1. **Know what the amount of sales should be:** In a cafeteria or dining room situation, there can be errors in portioning, errors in ringing up food, and other situations that lead to poor control. Regardless of whether mistakes are intentional or accidental, the impact on the foodservice operation will be the same: Sales revenues that should be collected will not be collected. To control cash in a foodservice operation, a Certified Dietary Manager has to examine some basic information, and reconcile accordingly. Using a food usage record, as shown in Figure 28.4, is one way to do this.

   This form provides a control mechanism, because it shows what food has been issued to the serving area, what is left over, and what has actually been used. In this example, mashed potatoes is a menu item featured in the cafeteria line. As the line opened, one half-pan of potatoes was issued to the line. During the meal period, two additional half pans were sent to the line. A total of three half pans were issued. At the end of the meal period,

Figure 28.4 **Food Usage Record—Cafeteria**

Date: ______________________ Serving Period: ______________________

Item	Quantity Issued				Amount Left	Total Used	Sales Income Per Pan	Total Income
	#1	#2	#3	Total				
Mashed Potatoes	.50 pan	.50 pan	.50 pan	1.50 pan	.25 pan	1.25 pan	$18.00	$22.50

Projected Income: ______________________ Actual Income: ______________________

one-quarter of a pan remained. Therefore, one and one-quarter pans of mashed potatoes have been used.

If each pan contained 30 servings, then the total number of servings that should have been sold is:

1.25 pans x 30 servings per pan = 37.5, which you round down to 37 servings.

If each serving should have sold for $0.60, then total revenue that should have been collected for mashed potatoes is:

37 servings x $0.60 per serving = $22.20.

So now, you have both an item count and a dollar figure for what should have happened with mashed potatoes in the cafeteria.

2. **Know what actual sales were:** At the end of the serving period, you can find out what the real item count and dollar figures were for mashed potatoes for the same time period.
3. **Compare expected with actual:** Now that you have both figures, simply compare. For example, let's say that you discover the following information:

Sales for Mashed Potatoes	Projected	Actual
# of servings	37	33
total revenue @ $0.60	$22.20	$19.80

Here, you can see a discrepancy. Your operation has not brought in the sales it should have, based on the amount of food expended. What might cause this? Perhaps the cook did not produce or obtain the intended yield from a recipe, and/or did not properly fill the pans before service. Perhaps the servers over-portioned the potatoes, giving a little too much to each

Your census has dropped significantly over the past month increasing your labor costs. You administrator has just informed each department that they have to cut one FTE. What steps would you take?

(Check your answer at the end of this chapter)

person. Perhaps several servings were dropped and discarded. Perhaps, at checkout, a cashier neglected to notice potatoes on several plates and did not ring them up.

These are just a few examples of how discrepancies can occur in sales. To manage costs in your operation, you can investigate causes of discrepancies such as these, and implement finer controls. To exert the greatest impact, you can focus on menu items with the highest costs, prices, and volume.

Realistically, these figures will not be perfect matches all the time. However, a Certified Dietary Manager needs to exert control by:

- ✓ Establishing a standard for the variance that will be permitted (e.g. 2-3%)
- ✓ Making the routine comparisons
- ✓ Investigating discrepancies
- ✓ Making corrections as warranted.

Census Variations

By now, you are very familiar with the measure of census or client count. Monitoring this number is part of the key to sound financial management. Why? Because many of your operating costs are based on projected census figures. Your revenues may be directly related to census, too. As the census changes, you need to adjust your expenditures accordingly in order to keep the budget on track.

Consider this example: You work in a facility where the census may vary and your census has dropped from 200 to 160. Your budget for both food and labor is based on a census of 200. Understand that with a lower census, your facility will be experiencing a decrease in revenues, because it will receive less reimbursement for services. This revenue figure may not be in your budget. However, the facility's financial managers know that they need to make adjustments in order to manage the bottom line.

In many foodservice arenas, reimbursement is tight and even volatile. Expenses are managed with tight control. It is not uncommon for a facility that depends upon a censusn to experience budget cuts, even during a fiscal year whose budget has already been approved. For example, you may be asked to reduce labor by eliminating overtime, or leaving an open position unfilled, or cutting back hours for employees. Layoffs may occur, too.

A Certified Dietary Manager can keep control of the budget and support the facility's financial goals at the same time. How? By working proactively to respond to changes in census. Figure 28.5 outlines a process for doing this.

According to Kathleen Deckard, a Certified Dietary Manager, who has consulted across the USA, this approach can prevent you from falling into a situation where you are asked to eliminate positions.

Deckard also offers the following tips.

- ✓ Spread out the adjustments whenever possible, so that each employee works a little less. For example, let a breakfast cook leave early.

Figure 28.5 Proactive Labor Adjustment

Procedure		Example
Step 1	Determine the usual number of labor hours required in one work day. This is a total of all hours worked by all employees in one day.	You operate with 50 hours.
Step 2	Determine your usual census.	Your census is 200.
Step 3	Calculate a ratio of daily labor hours to census.	Your ratio is: 50 ÷ 200 = .25
Step 4	Monitor census. When it changes significantly, determine an adjusted number of labor hours that will keep the ratio stable.	Your census has dropped to 150. To maintain a ratio of 0.25, multiply your new census by the ratio you established in Step 3 0.25 x 150 = 37.5 hours
Step 5	Adjust labor	Now, adjust your daily schedules to use about 37.5 hours of labor per day, instead of your usual 50.

- ✓ Do not send night shift employees home early. Instead, bring them in a little later than usual.
- ✓ Take advantage of shift overlaps, when morning employees are near the end of their work days, and evening employees are just starting.
- ✓ Look for small parts of jobs that an employee can pick up, such as labeling nourishments.
- ✓ Explain to employees what you are doing and why. Ask for help.
- ✓ Post a copy of the census and your calculations where employees can see them; let employees monitor figures along with you.

Aside from labor, realize that with census changes, you also need to adjust food production quantities. In particular, if census declines, you want to scale your production forecast downwards to avoid food waste.

Cost Containment Techniques

By now it is clear that Certified Dietary Managers are constantly challenged to accomplish more with less. The above approach is a very proactive method for controlling operational costs. In addition, a number of specific cost containment techniques can help to minimize costs. Here are some examples:

Menus

- ✓ Adjust menus seasonally to take advantage of food prices that fluctuate by time of year. For example, strawberries may be inexpensive in June, but very expensive in February.
- ✓ Cost each menu.
- ✓ If you are serving multiple diets, consolidate menu offerings as possible so that one suits all needs. This minimizes production labor, and increases volume on certain inventory items, giving you purchasing clout. It also limits the inventory list, which reduces administrative overhead. (Note: You may want to work with your Registered Dietician when consolidating diets)

- ✓ Examine ways to consolidate items produced at any one meal for multiple service areas. For example, consider whether a soup produced for dining room meal service may also be used for client service or a catered event at the same time.
- ✓ Perform a cost comparison of condiments that arrive pre-packaged in individual service units with condiments that are pre-portioned by employees. Also consider the portion size of each condiment that is pre-packaged in individual service units.
- ✓ Carefully evaluate make-versus-buy decisions, and determine the cost effectiveness of using convenience foods.

Food Purchasing

- ✓ Obtain and use competitive bids for products.
- ✓ Establish a schedule for re-bidding and re-negotiating volume purchasing agreements.
- ✓ Investigate options with purchasing groups and co-ops.
- ✓ Examine opportunities for product rebates; track and obtain rebates.
- ✓ Ask a Registered Dietitian to help evaluate use of nutritional supplements and tube feeding products. Determine whether supplementation is provided in the most cost effective manner possible.
- ✓ Research grade and quality for products carefully. Avoid specifying premium quality when it is not necessary for a particular recipe. For example what grade of napkins are you using and what volume? Sometimes purchasing a higher grade napkin means clients use less.

Receiving and Storage

- ✓ Verify that receiving procedures are being enforced so that deliveries match purchase orders.
- ✓ Check invoices to be sure they are correct.
- ✓ Assure that perishable foods are put away quickly.
- ✓ Monitor storage conditions, such as temperature, to be sure product shelf life is optimized.
- ✓ Monitor food that is wasted due to spoilage, and intervene to prevent waste.
- ✓ Evaluate purchasing schedules for perishable foods such as fresh fruit. If needed, adjust the schedule or the quantities purchased.
- ✓ Evaluate the purchase unit of any product you are not able to use before part of it spoils.
- ✓ Monitor use of FIFO inventory rotation.
- ✓ Establish procedures for identifying inventory shrinkage (e.g. perpetual inventory).
- ✓ Practice security measures to protect inventory from theft.

How would you minimize costs if you are noticing an increase in food waste?

(Check your answer at the end of this chapter)

Food Production and Service

- ✓ Cost each recipe.
- ✓ Take the time to calculate the labor element for each recipe to obtain a more refined analysis of cost.
- ✓ Monitor compliance with portion control guidelines.
- ✓ Examine ingredients in recipes. Ask whether a similar ingredient could also work. Compare costs. (Example: Which is less expensive for the unit required to prepare the recipe: ketchup or tomato paste?)
- ✓ Forecast production quantities effectively on a dynamic basis.
- ✓ Monitor leftovers and make adjustments.
- ✓ Use leftovers for other points of service when possible, to avoid food waste.
- ✓ Scale standardized recipes to required needs on an on-going basis.
- ✓ Monitor compliance with standardized recipes.
- ✓ Analyze time-intensive tasks in production, and seek alternative methodologies. For this, use work simplification techniques; evaluate whether pre-prepped products may save money; and examine time-saving equipment.
- ✓ Evaluate options for providing move self-service items to reduce labor requirements.
- ✓ Examine service and delivery systems for efficiency; streamline as possible.
- ✓ Analyze ordering processes or individual menu systems for efficiency; streamline as possible.

Non-Food Supplies

- ✓ Check to be sure all chemical products are being used in proper amounts and concentrations.
- ✓ Investigate use of alternative products; compare costs per usage unit.
- ✓ Cost the use of disposable products against the cost of reusable products.
- ✓ Assure that disposable containers are not over-sized for their intended uses.
- ✓ Check storage and display of disposable products. For example, a bundle of straws or a stack of disposable cups is knocked from a service area and wasted because of unstable arrangement.
- ✓ Train staff about when to use (or not use) disposable products. For example, to wipe a spill, an employee should probably use a washable rag, rather than a stack of paper napkins.
- ✓ Examine dispensers for paper goods to make sure they easily distribute a single-use item without waste.

Using these cost containment techniques a Certified Dietary Manager can positively contribute to the financial success of the facility.

END OF CHAPTER

Putting It Into Practice Questions & Answers

1. How would you explain the difference between a budget and an operating statement? Which one would you use if you were told to reduce your labor costs?

   A. *A budget is a financial plan for the future. The operating statement is a monthly performance report of the previous month for your department. If you are told to reduce your labor costs, you would need to review the labor records, including your monthly labor costs from your operating statement.*

2. Your department operating statement shows your actual food costs are higher than what was budgeted. What steps would you take to address this variance?

   A. *1. Determine if the difference is significant enough to warrant corrective action (e.g. It would be if it was more than 10% different in some facilities)*

   2. It may be that standards are not being followed such as portioning, production reports, purchasing, receiving, storage, or standardized recipes. Follow-up with appropriate staff for corrective action.

   3. Sometimes increased food costs may be due to inadequate supervision, or poor vendor scheduling. These are management problems that should be addressed immediately.

3. Your census has dropped significantly over the past month increasing your labor costs. You administrator has just informed each department that they have to cut one FTE. What steps would you take?

   A. *1. Remember that one FTE is 40 hours per week. Meet with your staff and explain what you have been asked to do.*

   2. Review the union contract for contract language regarding decreasing hours if applicable. Follow the union contract.

   3. Give your staff some options such as:

   a. Ask if anyone would be willing to take a cut in hours.

   b. Spread out the adjustments whenever possible.

   4. Decide with your staff on the corrective action.

   5. Post a copy of the census and your calculations where employees can see them so they can monitor figures along with you.

4. How would you minimize costs if you are noticing an increase in food waste?

   A.
   - *Verify that perishables are being refrigerated as soon as possible after they arrive*
   - *Make sure that you are purchasing correct amounts*
   - *Monitor leftovers and make adjustments to the production schedule or make sure leftovers are being utilized to the fullest*
   - *Discuss with any cooks who have over or undercooked an item to see if additional training is needed*

Chapter References and Resources

Chapter 1

- Handy, Linda, *Dietary Manager Magazine*, "Culture Change in Dining and Regulatory Compliance, June, 2010, pgs. 14-19
- http://www.olemiss.edu/depts/nfsmi/Information/financial%20management/Answer%20Packs/Ch%205%20Meals%20Per%20Labor%20Hour.pdf
- http://www.dmaonline.org/Resources/DMAResources/standard12.shtml
- http://www.choosemyplate.gov
- http://www.calculturechange.org/services-dining.html

Chapter 2

- http://codes.ohio.gov/oac/3701-17-60
- http://www.olemiss.edu/depts/nfsmi/Information/r12-94/maintext.pdf

Chapter 3

- http://www.dmaonline.org/Publications/articles/2009_06_QAA_QI_CQI.pdf
- http://www.dmaonline.org/Publications/articles/2009_02_FiveStarQuality.pdf
- http://www.ncbi.nlm.nih.gov/pmc/articles/PMC1022402/pdf/westjmed00067-0065.pdf

Chapter 4

- Service, Disney Style, DISNEY INSTITUTE, 220 Celebration Place, 3rd Floor, Celebration, FL, 34747, 407.566.2665, www.disneyinstitute.com
- Eck Mills, Linda S, *Dietary Manager,* "The Diamond Approach to Quality Improvement in Food Service, May, 2010, pg. 25-27.

Chapter 5

- http://www.rd411.com/index.php?option=com_content&view=article&id=76:food-likes-and-dislikes&catid=71:conversation-starters&Itemid=350
- http://vskeducation.org/menu-design

Chapter 6

- http://dietarymanagementsoftware.com/index.php

Chapter 7

- http://www.dpa.ca.gov/personnel-policies/workforce-planning/presentations/html/workforce-analysis.htm
- http://assisted-living-seattle.com/4_8_en.html#
- http://www.ahrq.gov/research/shuttered/shuthosp4.htm
- http://www.cmaj.ca/cgi/reprint/172/5/645

Chapter 8

- http://www.eeoc.gov/facts/qanda.html
- http://www.uniformguidelines.com/
- http://integrity-training.com/foodservice1.html

Chapter 9

- http://pubs.niaaa.nih.gov/publications/aa44.htm
- http://www.hrworld.com/features/25-employee-rewards/
- http://pubs.niaaa.nih.gov/publications/economic-2000/index.htm

Chapter 10

- http://chefcallahan.com/index.php?option=com_content&view=article&id=135:ykhc-dietary-department-general-haccp-plan&catid=34:chef-blog&Itemid=18
- http://www.diversityjournal.com/corporate/marketing/diversity-employees-are-marketing-tools-too/
- http://www.unc.edu/world/Action%20Plan%20Booklet.pdf

Chapter 11

- http://www.dentistryiq.com/index/display/article-display/276571/articles/dental-economics/volume-96/issue-10/features/how-to-make-staff-meetings-work.html
- http://humanresources.about.com/od/meetingmanagement/a/meetings_work_3.htm

Chapter 12

- http://sop.nfsmi.org/sop_list.php
- https://www.itbusinessedge.com/cm/docs/DOC-2014
- http://www.danielhoang.com/2009/02/21/social-media-policies-and-procedures/

Chapter 13

- Gregoire, M & Spears, M., *FoodService Organizations—A Managerial and Systems Approach,* Pearson/Prentice Hall, 2007.
- Brown, D & Henkel, Shri. *The Non-Commercial Food Service Manager's Handbook: A Complete Guide for Hospitals, Nursing Homes, Military, Prisons, Schools, and Churches*, Atlantic Publishing Group, Inc., 2007.
- http://blink.ucsd.edu/safety/resources/training/food.html
- http://krex.k-state.edu/dspace/bitstream/2097/806/1/RobertsFPTApr2008.pdf
- http://www.fsmec.org/pdf/JFSR&E_Manuscript_2004002.pdf

Chapter 14

- http://www.smartcommunities.ncat.org/buildings/gbprinc.shtml
- http://www.eere.energy.gov/topics/buildings.html
- http://sustainablefoodservice.com/cat/equipment.htm
- http://www.cee1.org/com/com-kit/com-kit-equip.php3
- http://www.osha.gov/SLTC/youth/restaurant/strains_foodprep.html
- http://www.fishnick.com/saveenergy/tools/calculators/

Chapter 15

- Ventura, Steve, and Templin, Michelle. "Five Star Teamwork—How to Achieve Success Together."
- "Walk the Talk" Resource from Performance Systems Corporation, 2005.

Chapter 16

- http://oregon.gov/ODA/FSD/program_shellfish.shtml
- http://www.gchd.org/NFSEM/fttmilk.html
- http://www.clemson.edu/extension/hgic/food/food_safety/handling/hgic3510.html

Chapter 17

- http://www.fightbac.org/component/content/article/303
- http://www.fsis.usda.gov/News_&_Events/NR_052411_01/index.asp
- http://ohioline.osu.edu/hyg-fact/5000/index.html

Chapter 18

- http://blink.ucsd.edu/safety/occupational/ergonomics/awareness.html
- http://www-ehs.ucsd.edu/ergo/mcergo/backinj.pdf

Chapter 19

- http://www.osha-slc.gov/SLTC/etools/hospital/dietary/dietary.html
- http://www-ehs.ucsd.edu/ergo/fisher.htm

Chapter 20

- Gregoire, M & Spears, M., *FoodService Organizations—A Managerial and Systems Approach,* Pearson/Prentice Hall, 2007, Safety, Sanitation & Maintenance.
- U.S. Public Health Service, FDA Food Code Annex, 2009, Annex 5, Conducting Risk-Based Inspections.
- http://www.roughnotes.com/rnmagazine/2006/october06/10p026.htm
- http://hubpages.com/hub/Risk-Management-In-The-Food-Industry
- http://www.leon.k12.fl.us/Public/RiskMgmt/FoodSvc.htm
- http://blink.ucsd.edu/safety/resources/training/food.html
- http://www.aft.org/pdfs/psrp/workshouldnthurt2004.pdf
- http://www.osha.gov/SLTC/etools/hospital/dietary/dietary.html
- http://www.bb.go.th/Evaluation/Part_in_Foreign/PARTmgt/A%20systems%20approach%20to%20measuring%20productivity%20in%20health%20care%20foodservice%20operations.htm

Chapter 21

- http://www.austincc.edu/vlawrenc/prodstdrecipes.htm
- http://www.olemiss.edu/depts/nfsmi/Information/stdrecipes/process.pdf

Chapter 22

- http://www.goatworld.com/articles/goatmanagement.shtml
- http://www.ilovecheese.com/cheeses.asp?Search=A-C
- http://teamnutrition.usda.gov/HealthierUS/wholegrainresource.pdf
- Molt, Mary. *Food for Fifty*, 13th edition, Pearson, 2011.
- http://www.simplyseafood.com/newsletters/summer_special_06/guide.html

Chapter 23

- http://sustainablefoodservice.com/cat/energy-efficiency.htm
- http://www.pge.com/fstc/

Chapter 24

- http://www.olemiss.edu/depts/nfsmi/Information/GuideForPurchasingEquipment/chapter6.pdf
- http://www.olemiss.edu/depts/nfsmi/Information/PurchasingGuide.html
- http://www.nal.usda.gov/fnic/pubs/foodservice.pdf
- http://www.epa.gov/epp/pubs/case/cafeteria.htm

Chapter 25

- http://www.mpsd.k12.ms.us/21221010713816333/lib/21221010713816333/_files/special_function_requisition_form_REVISED.pdf
- http://www.fns.usda.gov/cnd/breakfast/toolkit/Calculating.pdf

Chapter 26

- http://www.olemiss.edu/depts/nfsmi/Information/fmis-part5.pdf
- http://fcps.schoolwires.com/152910915135110310/site/default.asp?152910621164642803Nav=|&NodeID=545
- http://www.mnps.org/Page67757.aspx

Chapter 27

- http://www.dol.gov/opa/aboutdol/lawsprog.htm

Chapter 28

- http://www.foodservice.com/marketprices/
- http://www.blackwellpublishing.com/zelman/chapter02.pdf
- Puckett, Ruby. *Food Service Manual for Health Care Institutions*, 3rd edition, Jossey-Bass publisher for American Hospital Association Company, 2004.
- Warner, Mickey. *NonCommercial Institutional and Contract Foodservice Management*, John Wiley & Sons, 1994.
- Gregoire, Mary B., and Spears, Marian C. *Foodservice Organizations—A Managerial and Systems Approach*, Pearson/Prentice Hall, 2007.

Types and Descriptions of Foodservice Equipment

Equipment for Receiving

The typical receiving equipment found in foodservice operations includes scales, moving equipment, and miscellaneous items such as calculators, desks, chairs, and file cabinets. Scales must give accurate weights down to ounces. Large receiving scales are usually able to weigh items in the range from 50 to 1,000 pounds. To determine what scale capacity you need, consider the weight units you typically order. Also consider the need for a small portion scale to verify weights of pre-portioned items. Dollies, hand trucks, and other mobile equipment may be needed to move purchases from the receiving dock to storage. The shelving used for storage should be suited to the receiving equipment used.

Equipment for Cold Storage

Adequate storage capacity in refrigerators, deep-chill units, and freezers is necessary to protect food, ensure proper sanitation, and maintain high quality. The storage area should be designed to receive and hold the specific food stored in it. Refrigeration temperatures typically range from 28°F to 40°F, while freezers range from -10°F to 0°F. Units offering these temperatures come in a variety of types: walk-in, reach-in, and roll-in models. Some of the features available on refrigerators include electronic temperature monitoring, automatic door closers, adjustable shelving, and air curtains to reduce loss of cold air and save energy. For rapid chilling of food products, many operations use a blast chiller, which can be a standalone floor unit or an under-counter piece. Most blast chillers automatically record temperatures and produce reporting essential for monitoring food safety. This is a key piece of equipment in cook-chill operations. There are also specialized units for the point of service, such as a display freezer for ice cream novelties.

Equipment for Dry Storage

Overall design of dry storage areas must protect food from contamination and support environmental controls. The key equipment need in this area is shelving. By NSF standards, shelving for food storage must be constructed of materials that will not rust and are safe for contact with food. They must also be durable and able to withstand significant weight. Shelving units are rated for load. Shelving may be stationary or mobile. On mobile units, castors allow you to move or rearrange shelving as needed. Specialized shelving systems are another option. These may be mounted on tracks on the wall for adjustment to height requirements and easy cleaning beneath the units. Design and equipment for dry storage areas must provide for a separate area for storing chemicals in order to prevent contamination of food with chemicals.

Mixers, Cutters, and Slicers

The list of equipment for pre-preparation tasks is ever-expanding as manufacturers attempt to ease the tasks of cleaning and cutting fruit and vegetables, cutting and trimming meats, and much more. Needs for preparation equipment are greatly driven by production models. Basic essentials may include:

- *Food mixers*, which may vary in size from 5 to 140 quarts, and may be counter or floor models. A wide variety of attachments are available for various needs, from bread dough making to pastry blending. Some have attachments for slicing vegetables or dicing for French fries. Many today feature programmable controls. Figure B.1 illustrates mixers and some of the available attachments. A mixer must have a blade guard to prevent accidental injury.

- *Food cutters*, known traditionally as buffalo choppers, which consist of a rotating bowl that moves food into the path of a spinning blade. The vertical cutter and mixer (VCM) chops, cuts, mixes, blends, emulsifies, purees, and homogenizes foods in a matter of seconds, working similarly to a home blender with two knife blades whirling at the bottom of a deep bowl. A smaller version of the VCM is a food processor, which has become a common piece of preparation equipment in most kitchens today.
- *Food slicers*, vegetable peelers, and meat-processing equipment. Slicers may be manual or motor-driven, and some feature auto-shutoff capability. Some models also have built-in portion control scales.
- Other smaller pieces of equipment such as blenders, breading machines, can openers, coffee grinders, knife sharpeners, and waste collection and disposal systems.
- *Scales* for measuring ingredients and/or portioning foods.

Figure B.2 illustrates a food slicer and food cutter, and Figure B.3 illustrates a portion control scale.

Steam Equipment

Steam is a popular means of cooking food, because steam heat penetrates food quickly and efficiently. Steam-cooking units include cabinet-style steamers, steam-jacketed kettles, and braising pans. A *cabinet-style steamer* brings steam into a chamber where it comes directly into contact with the food. The food is typically managed in 12" X 20" pans, which can then be transferred to a steam table for service. A *steam-jacketed kettle* works much as a double boiler, with steam surrounding the food, which is contained in a separate compartment. Both countertop and floor models are available. A kettle is a common choice for preparing soups and stews. *Tilting braising pans* or skillets are highly versatile and can do the job of a range top, griddle, small steam kettle, stock pot, or fry pan. They are often used for braising, sautéing, or simmering meat. They tilt up to 90 degrees on a horizontal axis. Figure B.4 presents two pieces of steam equipment.

Figure B.1 Mixers

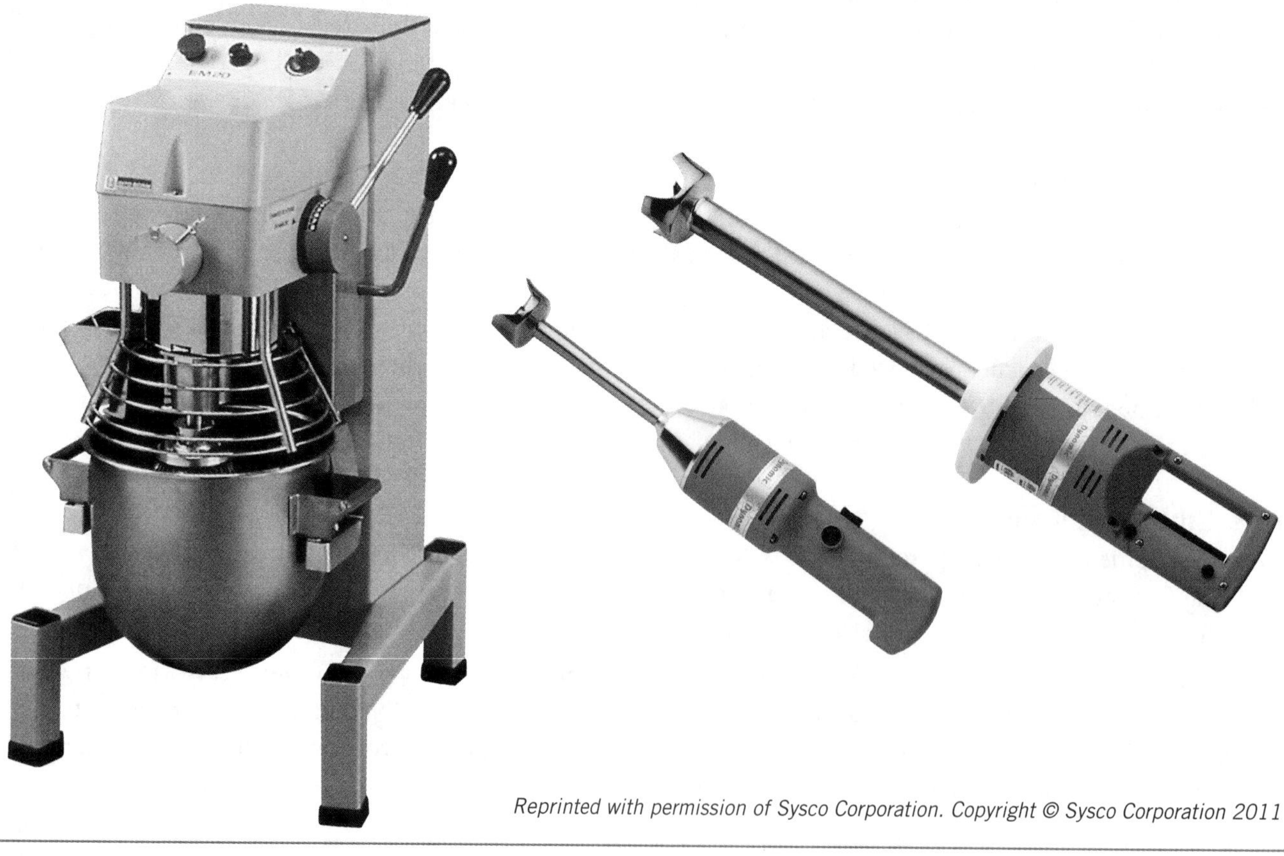

Reprinted with permission of Sysco Corporation. Copyright © Sysco Corporation 2011

Figure B.2 Food Slicer and Food Cutter

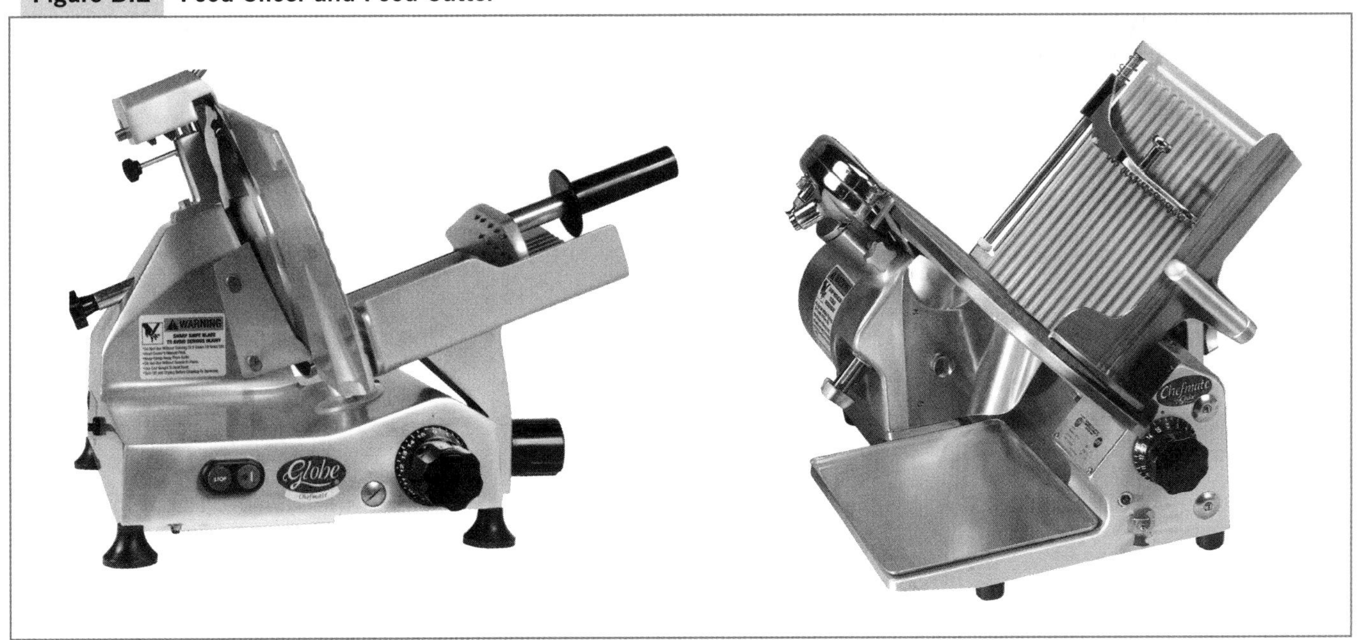

Figure B.3 Portion Control Scales

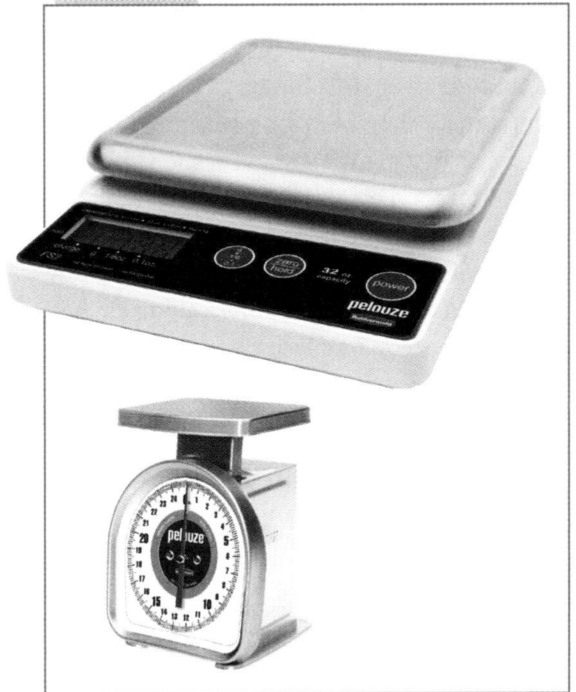

Figure B.4 Steam Kettle and Convection Steamer

Steam equipment must have a water connection and a means of heating the water to generate steam. Some equipment operates with steam under pressure, measured in pounds per square inch (psi), while other pieces of equipment use turbulent steam that is pressureless. Steam equipment may also need a water treatment system to minimize mineral buildup and enhance the life of the equipment.

Ovens

Types of ovens include:

- *Deck oven*, which stacks separate cooking chambers on top of each other. Each can have its own temperature settings, for easy simultaneous production of a variety of menu products in one piece of space-saving equipment.
- *Revolving tray* or *rotary ovens*, both of which rotate food within the oven while it is cooking.
- *Conveyor oven*, which moves food through the heating process on a conveyor belt.
- *Microwave oven*, which uses electromagnetic energy to heat the food quickly. When microwaves penetrate food, molecular activity or movement takes place within the food, creating friction that heats the food internally. When appropriately used, a microwave oven offers flexibility and speed for bringing small quantities of frozen and chilled food to a hot state in minutes.
- *Convection oven*, which circulates heat within an enclosed cooking chamber. Compared with a conventional oven, a convection oven heats food about 30% more quickly, using less energy. Because of the forced air circulation, a convection oven typically provides even heating and baking. A convection oven may be fueled by gas or electricity. A convection oven can be used for roasting, baking, holding, or even rethermalizing food. A typical standard oven has five racks. Double-stacked ovens provide more racks, using the same amount of floor space. Some models of large convection ovens provide a roll-in feature. Racks hold standard size pans that may then transfer to a steam table.
- *Combi oven*, a combination of a convection oven and a steamer. Like a convection oven, this can be gas or electric. It offers three different cooking methods: steam, hot air, or steam and air combined ("combi"), for a versatile range of production options. In its "combi" mode, a combi oven cooks food 50% faster than a convection oven, speeding production with an impact on labor as well. A combi oven can steam, bake, or reheat food quickly, with excellent quality. It can brown baked goods, bake pizzas, steam vegetables, and cook roasts with minimal shrinkage/water loss. In all, it is regarded as the most versatile piece of cooking equipment available for foodservice operations today, and is rapidly gaining popularity. Some operations choose a combi oven to replace a convection oven plus a steamer, saving kitchen space. Using programmable controls, a cook may set a combi oven to apply various cooking techniques in sequence, or set the oven to cook and hold food. Figure B.5 illustrates convection and combi ovens.
- *Broiler*, which uses radiated heat energy to cook. Most broilers heat from above the product, although some cook from the side or even the bottom of the unit.

Many of today's foodservice ovens allow users to pre-program cooking instructions for specific menu items, program different sections of the oven to cook at different temperatures, roast and then hold meat (automatically decreasing the temperature setting after a desired period of time), perform self-diagnostic functions, and conduct other technology-driven intelligent functions.

Fryers

Fryers cook food in a bath of hot oil, producing a browned, crisp outer coating with a tender, moist interior, and are appropriate for French fries, breaded shrimp, eggrolls, onion rings, chicken nuggets, and other products. Food is placed into the fryer in a basket, and then removed and drained for service.

Fryers are available as free-standing units or countertop units, either gas or electric. Capacity is identified by the amount of fat they hold. In a conventional deep-fat fryer, thermostatic controls maintain the oil at an even temperature. Programmable functions and settings for common production items may also be an option. To maintain integrity of flavors,

Figure B.5 Convection Oven

Reprinted with permission of Sysco Corporation. Copyright © Sysco Corporation 2011

it is important to fry separate menu items in separate fryer tanks. A fryer requires an exhaust hood with adequate ventilation, as well as routine changing of the oil.

Ranges and Griddles

A cooking range, gas or electric, often includes a combination of an oven and cooking top within one unit. A range may be classified as medium weight (for intermittent light use) or heavy duty (for continuous volume production). Ventilation is important. A griddle, a flat-topped cooking surface, is available as the top of a range or as a standalone unit. Food is cooked on the griddle surface in a small amount of fat, much as it would be cooked in a fry or sauté pan. A griddle is appropriate for pancakes, hot sandwiches, stir-fried entrees, burgers, and other menu items. Some of today's ranges have auto shut-off features, turning off the heat when the weight of a pot or pan is absent.

As you evaluate ranges, griddles, ovens, and steam equipment, you will probably notice that for some menu items, you may have several equipment choices. Depending on the recipe you are producing, you may find differences in product quality and timing requirements depending on equipment choices. In selecting equipment, it is a good idea to aim for versatility, selecting equipment that can adapt to your menu needs.

Equipment for Holding and Serving

Holding equipment is critical to service models that rely upon hot or cold holding. From a food safety perspective, holding equipment must maintain food temperatures to safety specifications (generally, below 41°F or above 135°F). Cooks may use warming units to keep hot food hot until the time of service. These can be stationary or rolling cabinets.

Serving equipment includes chafing dishes, steam tables, and display cases. Coffee machines, ice machines, and beverage dispensers may also appear in a serving area. As a trend of display cooking takes hold, more and more small equipment for preparation is taking the limelight in serving areas, too.

Transport equipment is also a consideration and is dependent on service models. For example, a trayline service uses a conveyor belt in the kitchen for tray assembly, which integrates with conveyor belts or cart systems to transport trays to service areas. A mobile cart may feature temperature controls, with hot sections and/or refrigerated sections for maintaining food temperatures.

In a cook-chill model, trays may be transported in temperature-controlled carts, and then rethermalized at the point of service, such as in remote pantries in nursing units, through conduction or convection technologies. Some equipment connects to a docking station in pantries for rethermalization. Rethermalization systems typically use specially designed dishes and cups.

Alternately, cook-chill products may be transported in bulk for rethermalization and service in a dining room or cafeteria setting. As with a great deal of modern foodservice equipment, options to program controls and collect food temperature data for food safety (called data logging) are common.

Mobile kiosks are a growing trend as well. A kiosk is a cart, typically about 10-12 feet in width, that serves as a movable, self-contained serving unit. At times, it accommodates simple production and clean-up tasks as well. Kiosks can be rolled through service areas, such as patient units in a hospital, or sidewalks on a university campus. Many are moved into position and then remain stationary during service.

Pots, Pans, and Utensils

Pots and pans are available in a variety of sizes, shapes, weights, and construction materials. Some of the common construction materials include anodized aluminum, which is economical, lightweight, and easy to clean. Anodized aluminum has been chemically processed to make the aluminum less reactive with foods. Stainless steel, an alloy (blend) of metals, is another common choice. It is durable and conducts heat evenly. Lined copper is among the most expensive cookware options. Copper conducts heat very well and promotes even cooking. It has to be lined with another material, such as stainless steel, because direct contact of copper with food can cause toxicity. Another option is treatment of pots and pans with non-stick cooking surfaces. In choosing pots and pans, it is important to match the size to intended recipe volume, and to select a shape that supports the cooking process, such as a pot for soups or a shallow pan for sautéing.

In addition to large equipment, food production requires a number of pieces of smaller equipment, utensils, and other small tools.

Clean-Up and Dishwashing

Cleaning up is an ongoing process that begins before each meal and continues throughout preparation, cooking, and service. Equipment for waste removal may include disposers, compactors, and pulpers. Dishwashing equipment, as in Figure B.6, includes counter and under-counter models, free-standing models, door models, rack conveyor models, and flight-type models (designed for the highest volume). Features on dishwashers may include prewash cycles, automatic dish scraping, integrated waste disposal system, automatic dispensing of chemical products, dryer attachments, side-loading options, and automatic loaders/unloaders. Specialized pot and pan washers are another piece of equipment designed to handle the more intense needs of heavy cookware. Typically, these have a very long wash cycle.

Figure B.6 Dishwashing Equipment

Reprinted with permission of Sysco Corporation. Copyright © Sysco Corporation 2011

Food Storage Guidelines

ANFP/DMA Practice Standards

by Susan Davis Allen, MS, RD, CHE

Professional Standards of Practice serve as the basis for quality dietetic practice for dietary managers. The standards that follow provide guidelines for dietary managers to use in the proper storage of food.

You may ask yourself, "Why do we need a standard for food storage?" Do you track the cost of food that is discarded each week because of improper storage? Can you be sure that in the event of a disaster, your food storage practices would be adequate?

With the increase in healthcare costs, your ability to control costs may come down to your ability to control the shelf stability of both raw and cooked foods. Besides reducing waste, properly stored food maintains its nutritional quality and decreases the risk of foodborne illness. In addition, with the threat of terrorist and natural disasters, properly storing water and other appropriate emergency supplies is becoming increasingly important.

STANDARD 1:

The certified dietary manager (CDM) shall ensure that standards for refrigerated, frozen, and dry foods are put into practice.

Criteria for Refrigerator Storage

1.1 Refrigerator storage temperature meets FDA or state standards (usually a maximum of 35°-41°F) and is recorded once each shift.

1.2 Refrigerators are used for short-term storage (usually a maximum of 7 days).

1.3 Food storage procedures are followed to diminish environmental and cross-contamination. (example: All foods are covered and raw meat items are stored below cooked items.)

1.4 Refrigerator storage areas meet FDA or state standards (e.g. 6 inches off the floor, clean, slatted shelving).

1.5 Ready-to-eat refrigerated foods are labeled according to FDA or state standards (e.g. the date or day by which the food should be consumed, sold, or discarded).

1.6 Refrigerated ready-to-eat food that is not labeled is discarded.

1.7 A refrigerated food storage timeline chart is in place and followed. (See sample.)

1.8 Staff receives training on the proper refrigerator storage time and temperature.

1.9 All discarded refrigerated food is recorded with food item, amount, date, and reason.

1.10 Blast chillers, if available, are used to quickly cool foods to safe refrigeration temperatures.

1.11 Refrigeration unit is cleaned and inspected on a regular basis.

1.12 Only food purchased from approved vendors is refrigerated.

1.13 Refrigerated food stock rotation follows the FIFO (first in, first out) principle.

(Continued)

Professional Practice Standards: Food Storage Guidelines *(Continued)*

1.14 Personnel look for and follow "Use by" dates. (For example: "Use by" dates mean that a product cannot be used after that date, even if it appears and smells good. Products can be safely frozen before the "use by" date. Follow guidelines on the Freezer Storage Chart.)

Criteria for Freezer Storage

2.1 Freezer storage temperature meets FDA or state standards (usually a minimum of -10° - 0°F) and is recorded once each shift.

2.2 Freezers are used for long-term storage and not used for cooling foods. (Usually a maximum of 12 months.)

2.3 Freezer storage areas are designed and maintained to promote proper air circulation.

2.4 A freezer food storage timeline chart is in place and followed. (See sample.)

2.5 Frozen food stock rotation follows the FIFO principle.

2.6 Staff receives training on the proper freezer storage time and temperature.

2.7 All discarded frozen food is recorded with food item, amount, date, and reason.

2.8 Freezers are cleaned and inspected on a regular basis.

2.9 Only food purchased from approved vendors is frozen.

Criteria for Dry Food Storage

3.1 Dry food storage temperature meets FDA or state standards (usually a maximum of 50° - 70°F).

3.2 Dry food storage areas are kept dry, clean, and are well lighted and ventilated.

3.3 Dry food storage has a two-foot ceiling clearance to avoid high temperatures at ceiling.

3.4 A dry food storage timeline chart is in place and followed. (See sample.)

3.5 Dry food stock rotation follows the FIFO principle.

3.6 Working containers holding dry food or ingredients that are removed from their original packages are identified with the common name of the food, unless the food is easily recognizable, such as dry pasta.

3.7 All discarded dry food is recorded with food item, amount, date, and reason.

3.8 Staff receives training on the proper dry food storage time and temperature.

3.9 Storage area is kept clean, secure, and is inspected regularly.

3.10 Only food purchased from approved vendors is stored in dry storage.

3.11 There are separate storage compartments for chemical storage.

3.12 Personnel look for and follow "best before" dates. They also honor "store in a cool dry place" or "keep in the refrigerator once opened." (Note: "Best before" dates mean personnel must look for additional instructions on the label; "best before" dates also mean the item is no longer at its best quality but may still be safe to eat.)

Assessment for Standard 1

1.1 Storage temperatures are tracked and data is used for continuous improvement and/or corrective action.

1.2 Refrigerators are monitored daily for proper food labeling.

1.3 Discarded food record is checked weekly and cost is tracked.

1.4 Data from discarded food record is used for cost control planning purposes.

1.5 Inspection forms for all food storage are used for continuous quality improvement purposes.

1.6 Training records are evaluated to make sure all cooking staff has received training in the proper storage of dry foods; training records are maintained in the foodservice department.

STANDARD 2:

The certified dietary manager shall ensure that standards for water storage and emergency supplies are put into practice. (Note: This information is taken from recommendations of FEMA—Federal Emergency Management Agency.)

(Continued)

Professional Practice Standards: Food Storage Guidelines *(Continued)*

Criteria

1.1 A minimum of a three-day supply of drinking water is stored in appropriate containers. Appropriate containers are clean, sanitized, plastic containers that are food quality.

1.2 Water supplies are labeled and replaced every six months.

1.3 Emergency food supplies equivalent to three days are stored in appropriate storage areas.

1.4 Emergency foods are properly labeled and replaced every six months.

1.5 A three-day menu using common emergency foods is available and made up of foods from the following list:

- Canned condensed meat and vegetable soups
- Canned fruits, fruit juices, and vegetables
- Ready-to-eat cereals and uncooked instant cereals (stored in metal containers)
- Peanut butter
- Jelly
- Hard candy and canned nuts

1.6 Staff receives training on the proper emergency food and water storage time procedures.

Assessment for Standard 2

1.1 Rotation of emergency food and water supplies are recorded and used for continuous improvement and/or corrective action.

1.2 Training records are evaluated to make sure all cooking staff has receiving training in the proper storage of dry foods; training records are maintained in the foodservice department.

Summing it Up

These standards are designed to help you store foods safely and ensure that your clients are receiving wholesome foods. It may be useful to post these guidelines in your kitchen where they can be consulted frequently—near your refrigerator, freezer, and food storage areas.

Recommended Maximum Refrigerator/Freezer Storage Times (Potentially Hazardous Foods)		
Dairy Products	**Refrigerator[1] @ 36°-40°F**	**Freezer[2] @ 0°F**
Fluid milk	5-7 days after sell-by date	1-3 months
Nonfat dry milk (NFDM)	5-6 months	10-12 months
Reconstituted NFDM	3-5 days	Freezes poorly
Buttermilk	1-2 weeks	Freezes poorly
Cheese spread, opened	2 weeks	Freezes poorly
Condensed milk, opened	3-5 days	1 month
Evaporated milk, opened	3-5 days	Freezes poorly
Whipping cream	10 days	2 months
Whipped cream	<1 day	1 month
Cream cheese	2 weeks	Freezes poorly
Cream—half and half	3-4 days	4 months
Margarine	4-5 months	12 months
Butter	1-3 months	6-9 months
Pudding	Package date; 2 days after opening	Freezes poorly
Sour cream	7-21 days	Freezes poorly
Yogurt	1 week after sell-by date	1-2 months

(Continued)

Professional Practice Standards: Food Storage Guidelines *(Continued)*

Recommended Maximum Refrigerator/Freezer Storage Times (Potentially Hazardous Foods)		
Dough	**Refrigerator[1] @ 36°-40°F**	**Freezer[2] @ 0°F**
Tube cans of rolls, biscuits, pizza dough, etc.	Use-by date	Freezes poorly
Ready-to-bake pie crust	Use-by date	2 months
Cookie dough	Use-by date unopened or opened	2 months
Fish	**Refrigerator[1] @ 36°-40°F**	**Freezer[2] @ 0°F**
Lean fish (cod, flounder, sole, haddock)	1-2 days	6 months
Fatty fish (bluefish, mackerel, salmon)	1-2 days	2-3 months
Cooked fish	3-4 days	4-6 months
Smoked fish	14 days or date on vacuum pkg.	2 months in vacuum pkg.
Shellfish	**Refrigerator[1] @ 36°-40°F**	**Freezer[2] @ 0°F**
Shrimp, scallops, crayfish, shucked clams, mussels and oysters	1-2 days	3-6 months
Live clams, mussels, crab, and oysters	2-3 days	2-3 months
Live lobster	1-2 days	2-3 months
Cooked shellfish	3-4 days	3 months
Processed Meats	**Refrigerator[1] @ 36°-40°F**	**Freezer[2] @ 0°F**
Hot dogs, opened package	1 week	1-2 months
Hot dogs, unopened package	2 weeks	1-2 months
Luncheon meats, opened package	3-5 days	1-2 months
Luncheon meats, unopened package	2 weeks	1-2 months
Bacon	7 days	1 month
Sausage, raw	1-2 days	1-2 months
Smoked breakfast links, patties	7 days	1-2 months
Hard sausage	2-3 weeks	1-2 months
Summer sausage, labeled "keep refrigerated", opened	3 weeks	1-2 months
Summer sausage, labeled "keep refrigerated", unopened	3 months	1-2 months
Ham, Corned Beef	**Refrigerator[1] @ 36°-40°F**	**Freezer[2] @ 0°F**
Corned beef, in pouch with pickling juices	5-7 days	Drained, 1 month
Ham, canned—labeled "Keep refrigerated", opened	3-5 days	1-2 months
Ham, canned—labeled "Keep refrigerated", unopened	6-9 months	1-2 months
Ham, fully cooked vacuum-sealed at plant, undated, unopened	2 weeks	1-2 months
Ham, fully cooked vacuum-sealed at plant, dated, un-opened	Use by date on package	1-2 months
Ham, fully cooked, whole	7 days	1-2 months
Ham, fully cooked, half	3-5 days	1-2 months
Ham, fully cooked, slices	3-4 days	1-2 months

(Continued)

Professional Practice Standards: Food Storage Guidelines *(Continued)*

Recommended Maximum Refrigerator/Freezer Storage Times (Potentially Hazardous Foods)		
Fresh Beef, Veal, Lamb, Pork	**Refrigerator[1] @ 36°-40°F**	**Freezer[2] @ 0°F**
Hamburger and stew meat	1-2 days	3-4 months
Steaks	3-5 days	6-12 months
Chops	3-5 days	4-6 months
Roasts	3-5 days	6-12 months
Pre-stuffed, uncooked chops or chicken breast stuffed with dressing	1 day	Freezes poorly
Soups or stews with meat	3-4 days	2-3 months
Meat Leftovers	**Refrigerator[1] @ 36°-40°F**	**Freezer[2] @ 0°F**
Cooked meat and meat casseroles	3-4 days	2-3 months
Gravy and meat broth	1-2 days	2-3 months
Poultry	**Refrigerator[1] @ 36°-40°F**	**Freezer[2] @ 0°F**
Raw chicken or turkey, whole	1-2 days	1 year
Raw chicken or turkey, pieces	1-2 days	9 months
Cooked poultry casseroles	3-4 days	4-6 months
Fried chicken	3-4 days	4 months
Pieces covered with broth or gravy	1-2 days	6 months
Eggs	**Refrigerator[1] @ 36°-40°F**	**Freezer[2] @ 0°F**
Fresh, in shell	3-5 weeks	Freezes poorly
Raw yolks, whites	2-4 days	1 year
Hardcooked	Up to 7 days	Freezes poorly
Liquid pasteurized eggs, egg substitutes, opened	3 days	Freezes poorly
Liquid pasteurized eggs, egg substitutes, unopened	10 days	Freezes poorly
Fruit Beverages	**Refrigerator[1] @ 36°-40°F**	**Freezer[2] @ 0°F**
Juices in cartons, fruit drinks, punch, opnened	7-10 days	8-12 months
Juices in cartons, fruit drinks, punch, unopened	3 weeks	8-12 months

1. Table adapted from Refrigeration & Food Safety, USDA Food Safety and Inspection Service (www.foodsafety.gov), May 2010.
2. Table adapted from "Recommended Food Storage Times, Cold & Dry, Refrigerated & Frozen Foods," University of Kentucky, Cooperative Extension Service, College of Agriculture, (www.ca.uky.edu/HES/fcs/factshts/FN-SSB.085.PDF), July 2007.

Professional Practice Standards: Food Storage Guidelines *(Continued)*

Recommended Maximum Storage Times (Fresh Fruits and Vegetables)		
Fresh Fruits	**Refrigerator[1] @ 36°-40°F**	**Freezer[2] @ 0°F**
Apples	1 month	8-12 months
Apricots	3-5 days	8-12 months
Avocados	5 days	8-12 months
Berries, cherries	2-3 days	8-12 months
Cranberries	1 week	8-12 months
Grapes	5 days	10-12 months
Mangos	Ripen at room temperature	8-12 months
Nectarines	5 days	8-12 months
Peaches	2-3 days	8-12 months
Pears	5 days	8-12 months
Oranges	2 weeks	4-6 months
Pineapples	5-7 days	4-6 months
Plums	5 days	8-12 months
Watermelon	3-5 days	6-8 months
Canned fruit, opened	2-4 days	2-3 months
Fresh Vegetables	**Refrigerator[1] @ 36°-40°F**	**Freezer[2] @ 0°F**
Beets	2 weeks	8-12 months
Bok choy, broccoli, brussels sprouts	3-5 days	8-12 months
Cabbage, carrots	1 week	8-12 months
Cauliflower, celery, cucumbers, green beans	1 week	8-12 months
Corn	1-2 days	8-12 months
Greens (e.g. collard)	3-5 days	8-12 months
Lettuce and salad greens	3-5 days	Freezes poorly
Mushrooms	1-2 days	8-12 months
Green onions	3-5 days	Freezes poorly
Peppers	1 week	8-12 months
Squash, hard	Store in a cool, dry place	8-12 months
Tomatoes	1 week	8-12 months
Zucchini, summer squash	3-5 days	8-12 months
Canned vegetables, opened	1-4 days	2-3 months

1. Table adapted from Refrigeration & Food Safety, USDA Food Safety and Inspection Service (www.foodsafety.gov), May 2010.
2. Table adapted from "Recommended Food Storage Times, Cold & Dry, Refrigerated & Frozen Foods," University of Kentucky, Cooperative Extension Service, College of Agriculture, (www.ca.uky.edu/HES/fcs/factshts/FN-SSB.085.PDF), July 2007.

Professional Practice Standards: Food Storage Guidelines *(Continued)*

Recommended Maximum Storage Times—Dry Goods	
Food Product	**Shelf Storage**
Baking powder or soda	18 months
Barley	2 years
Bread crumbs	6 months
Cereal, ready-to-eat, unopened	6-12 months
Cereal, ready-to-eat, opened	2-3 months
Chocolate, baking	6-12 months
Cornmeal and hominy grits	12 months
Cornstarch	18 months
Flour, bleached	6-8 months
Flour, whole wheat	6-8 months
Honey and syrup	1 year
Noodles, egg	6 months
Noodles, plain	1-2 years
Olive oil	6 months
Pasta	2 years
Rice	2 years
Rice, brown or wild	6 months
Sugar, granulated	2 years +
Sugar, powdered	18 months
Yeast, dry	Expiration date
Canned foods and juices with high acid content (tomatoes, grapefruit, apple products, mixed fruit, berries, pickles, sauerkraut, and vinegar-based products)	1 year
Canned foods with low acid content, including meat and poultry products, vegetable soups (except tomato), spaghetti products, potatoes, corn, carrots, beans, beets, peas, pumpkin	2-5 years

Susan Davis Allen, MS, RD, CHE wrote this Standard in 2005. It was updated in July 2010 by Becky Rude, MS, RD, CDM, CFPP. Allen is an advisor to the Certifying Board for Dietary Managers. Rude serves as chair of that board. Both have authored many publications for ANFP and other professional groups.

Management Math and Formulas

Management Math	Formula	Example
Edible Yield Factor Used to calculate edible yield from produce or meat	Edible portion (EP) ÷ As purchased (AP)	16 lbs. of broccoli (AP) After cleaning yields 13 lbs: 13 ÷ 16 = 81% yield
FTE Full Time Equivalent	1 person @ 8 hrs./day x 5 days/wk x 52 wks/yr. = 2080 hrs	If you have six employees who work full-time, you have 6 FTEs; if you have 10 employees, two work full-time, two work ¾ time; and 6 work ½ time, how many FTEs are there? 2 x 1 FTE = 2 2 x .75 FTE = 1.5 6 x .5 FTE = 3 Total FTEs = 6.5
Inventory Valuation The value of all of your inventory	Number of purchase units on hand x product price, then added together	In a cooler: 1 bag lettuce x $8/bag = $ 8.00 10 lbs. carrots x .39/lb. = 3.90 25 # onions x .25/lb. = 6.25 Inventory Valuation = 18.15
Productivity Rate Used to measure the productivity of foodservice employees	A measure of work such as trays assembled ÷ Measure of time	14 trays assembled in 7 minutes 14 ÷ 7 = 2 minutes/tray
Recipe Cost Used to determine the cost of a standardized recipe	List of ingredients with price per amount of ingredient, added together ÷ by the recipe yield = price per portion	Recipe: Scrambled Eggs for 12 clients: 18 eggs @ $1.5/doz. ($1.5 ÷ 12 = $.124/egg); 18 x .125 = **$2.25 for 18 eggs** 1/4 cup milk @ $4.00/gal (16 cups/gal and 4 ¼ cups/cup) $4.00 ÷ 16 = $.25/cup ÷ 4 = **$.0625 for 1/4 cup milk** **Total cost/client = $2.25 + .0625 = $2.31 ÷ 12 = .19/client**
Scaling a Recipe Used when increasing or decreasing the amount a recipe serves	Divide the New yield by the Original yield. Remember it by the fact that N comes before O in the alphabet so the formula is always N/O to get the conversion factor. Then multiply the ingredients in the recipe by the conversion factor.	Let's use the Scrambled Eggs above. You want to increase this recipe to serve 50 people. 1. Determine the conversion factor: 50 ÷ 12 = **4.167** 2. Multiply that by each ingredient: 18 eggs x 4.167 = **75 eggs** .25 cup milk x 4.167 = **1 cup milk**

(Continued)

Management Math and Formulas

Management Math	Formula	Example
Tray Accuracy Used to determine the number of errors in assembling trays	1. Count the total numbers of items on the menu 2. Count the number of errors you discover on one tray 3. Divide the number of errors by the total number of items	For today's noon meal, there are seven items including drink and condiments. You discover two errors. 2 ÷ 7 = .29 x 100 = 29%
Monthly Food Cost Used to determine food cost for the month	1. Record beginning inventory valuation 2. Add total purchases for the month 3. Subtract ending inventory valuation	For the month of June: 1. Inventory valuation as of June 1: $7456 2. Purchases for the month of June: + 10,914 3. Subtract ending inventory on the 30th - 9002 Monthly Food Cost: $9368
Monthly Food Cost Percent A percentage used to track food costs and may be used to determine meal prices	1. Record the monthly food cost 2. Divide by the sales for the month (or the raw food cost PPD x number of clients)	June monthly food cost $9368 Sales for the month: 27,398 Food cost % for June: $9368 ÷ $27,398 = .342 x 100 or 34.2%
Turnover Rate Used as a measure of stability in the foodservice department	1. List the number of employees who have left over a defined period of time 2. Divide this by the total number of positions you have	Turnover rate for 2012: 1. 12 employees have left the department in 2012 2. The total number of positions is 99 3. 12 ÷ 99 = .12 x 100 = 12%
Raw Food Cost (PPD) Per Patient Day Used as a financial measurement for tracking and benchmarking	Monthly Food Cost from above ÷ total days in the month ÷ total clients	June monthly food cost $9368 ÷ 30 days ÷ 74 clients = $4.16/day
Raw Food Cost per Meal The cost of the raw ingredients to produce a meal	Monthly Food Cost from above ÷ total patient days x 3 meals/day	June monthly food cost: $9368 ÷ 90 = $104
Meals per Labor Hour Used as a measure of productivity and for tracking and benchmarking	Total meals served ÷ total hours worked (Note total meals served includes regular meals plus any catering)	**June meals:** 1. Regular meals: 30 days x 3 x 74 clients = 2220 meals 2. Catering meals: (total food cost ÷ average meal cost) = $648 ÷ $4.16 = 156 additional meals 3. Total meals: 2220 + 156 = 2376 meals ÷ 485 = 5 meals per labor hour
Labor Cost per Meal Served Used as a financial measurement for tracking and benchmarking	Total labor costs ÷ total meals served	Using the example from above for total meals: 2376 Total labor costs for June: $6305 6305 ÷ 2376 = $2.65/meal

Commonly Referenced Foodservice Temperatures

Activity	Temperature
Cooking	
Beef or Pork Roasts	145˚F (15 seconds)
Beef Steak	145˚F (surface temperature on top and bottom)*
Poultry, Game, Stuffed Foods	165˚F (15 seconds)
Chopped or Ground Meat	
Fish and Seafood	145˚F (15 seconds)
Eggs, Cooked to hold	155˚F (15 seconds)
Eggs, Single serving, Cooked to order	145˚F (15 seconds)
Fruits and Vegetables	135˚F
Food in Microwave	165˚F (2 minute standing time after cooking)
Reheating Food	165˚F (Within two hours)
Washing	
Handwashing, Water temperature	100˚F
Dishwashing, Manual—wash water	110˚F - 120˚F
Dishwasing, Mechanical—wash water • Stationary Rack, single temperature • Stationary Rack, dual temperature • Single Tank, conveyor, dual temperature • Multi-tank, conveyor, multi-temperature	 165˚F 150˚F 160˚F 150˚F
Santizing	
With Hot Water	171˚F (a minimum of 30 seconds)
Chemical Sanitizer, water temperature • Iodine • Chlorine • Quats	 70˚ - 120˚F 75˚F - 155˚F 75˚F minimum
Dishwashing, Mechanical • Stationary Rack, single temperature • Stationary Rack, dual temperature • Single Tank, conveyor, dual temperature • Multi-tank, conveyor, multi-temperature	 165˚F 180˚F 180˚F 180˚F

** Not recommended for highly susceptible populations*

(Continued)

Commonly Referenced Foodservice Temperatures

Activity	Temperature
Holding	
Hot Holding	Above 135°F
Cold Holding	Below 41°F
Cooling	
PHF/TCS Cooling from Hot	135°F to 70°F in 2 hours, then 70° F to 41°F in 4 more hours
PHF/TCS Cooling from Room Temperature	70°F to 41°F in 4 hours
Thawing	
Under Refrigeration	41°F or below
Under Running Water	70°F or below
Receiving	
PHF/TCS (refrigerated)	41°F or below
PHF/TCS (frozen)	0°F or below
Ice Cream	6°F - 10°F
Storage	
Dry Storage	50°F - 70°F
Refrigerated	41°F or below
Deep Chill	26°F - 32°F
Frozen	0°F or below
Utensil Storage Between Uses	135°F water
Hazard Zone	**41°F - 135°F**

Complete Glossary

A	
AND	Academy of Nutrition and Dietetics
Aerobic	Requires oxygen to survive; many microorganisms are aerobic
Agenda	Planned outline and timetable for a meeting; should include the meeting objective
Air Gap	An unobstructed air space between an outlet of drinkable water and the flood rim of a fixture or equipment
Al Denté	An Italian cooking term meaning cooked until still firm but tender to the tooth, not soft. Even though it was originally intended for pasta, it also applies to vegetables
Anaerobic	Can grow without the presence of oxygen
As Purchased (AP)	As purchased, or raw weight, without any preproduction
B	
Back-Siphonage	When water is siphoned back into potable water supply after a loss in water pressure
Backflow	When contaminated water flows back into potable water
Batch Cooking	Cooking in small, continuous batches to preserve nutrients and food quality
Benchmarking	Comparing, on some standard scale, the operation of key departments
Biological Hazards	A living organism such as bacteria, virus, parasite, fungi, that can cause harm to humans
Brainstorming	Asking all participants to suggest ideas for solving a problem
Break Even Analysis	Financial calculation that compares costs with revenues to determine if a profit is possible
Budget	A written plan or prediction for income and expenses
Business Plan	A formal document that provides details for a proposed revenue generating service
C	
Can-Cutting	Procedure of sampling products for possible purchase
Capital Budget	A financial plan that includes projected building improvements and additions or replacement of equipment
Capital Equipment	Large equipment with a long life that usually costs over $1,500
Carrier	An individual who may 'carry' or transmit pathogens without having any symptoms of illness
Centralized (Delivery) Meal Service	Foods are prepared and portioned onto trays or plates at a central location in or adjacent to the main kitchen
Chain of Command	The flow of formal power through organizational lines
Cherry Picking	A purchasing concept where the Certified Dietary Manager purchases individual products from individual vendors as opposed to using a primary vendor

Complete Glossary

Clean	Free of visible soil
Cleanability	The ability of a piece of equipment to be easily accessible for cleaning, soil removal, sanitizing, and inspection
Closed Question	A question with a limited number of answers such as one easily answered with yes or no
Coagulate	To change a protein liquid into a soft or partially solid mass such as milk, pectin in jams/jellies, melted cheese
Collective Bargaining	Communications and negotiation between union and administration regarding wages, benefits and other issues
Comfort Food	Any food that imparts a unique sense of emotional well-being, such as chicken soup
Competitive Bidding	Asking multiple vendors to submit price quotes for products or equipment based on defined specifications
Conditional Employee	A potential foodservice employee to whom a job offer is made conditional on responses to subsequent medical questions or examinations
Consensus	General agreement within a group
Contamination	The presence of biological, physical, or chemical substances in food that could cause harm
Control Point	Point in the flow of food where a hazard can be controlled, a step can be taken to minimize the risk of foodborne illness
Conversion Factor	The number by which you adjust each recipe ingredient to arrive at a new yield
Corrective Action (Employee)	An action taken by a supervisor to correct an employee performance problem
Corrective Action (HACCP)	The procedure to follow when monitoring shows that a critical limit has not been met
Critical Control Point (CCP)	Step in the flow of food which, if not controlled, could lead to an unacceptable health risk for consumers of the food
Critical Limits	Specified limits or characteristics of a physical, chemical, or biological nature that help you measure whether you have adequately controlled a hazard at a CCP
Cross-Connection	A dangerous link between an outlet of drinkable water system and unsafe water
Cross-Contamination	The transfer of pathogens from any item or human to food
Cross-Training	Training an employee to do more than one job
Cycle Menu	Changes to a menu daily over a period of time or cycle, such as three days or three weeks
D	
Decentralized (Delivery) Meal Service	Bulk quantities of prepared foods are sent hot or cold to other locations (either within or outside the facility) for finishing and service
Delegation	Passing authority for tasks or assigning duties downward through the organization chart
Disability	A physical or mental impairment that substantially limits one or more major life activities of such individuals; a record of such an impairment; or being regarded as having such an impairment.
Discrimination	Treatment or consideration based on class or category, rather than individual merit
Disher/Portion Scoop	A portion control utensil used for dishing vegetables, fruits, desserts, or starchy products such as rice and potatoes. It is also commonly known as a portion scoop.
Diversity	Describes the many ways in which people differ from each other

Downward Communication	Used to convey policies, procedures, directives, objectives and other information to subordinate personnel and follows the chain of command
Dry Lab	Recording temperatures without actually taking them
E	
Equal Employment Opportunity Commission (EEOC)	Provides oversight for federal employment legislation
Employee Assistance Program (EAP)	Provides support to employees in solving personal problems such as drug and alcohol abuse, family problems, teamwork problems
Empowerment	When management gives power to an employee to take action
Endpoint Temperatures	The temperature a food reaches at the end of cooking
Enteral Nutrition	Supplemental feeding, by mouth or by tube, of formulas or food that contain essential nutrients
Equipment Specification	A detailed description providing information needed to purchase a piece of equipment
Ergonomics	The science of fitting the work environment to the employee
Exclude	Prohibit employees from coming to work
Exempt Employee	An employee who is salaried and does not qualify for overtime compensation
Exit Interview	An interview with an employee who is leaving the organization
Expenses	Money going out, or costs
F	
Facultative	Can grow with OR without the presence of oxygen
Feedback	Providing information to employees about how they are doing
FIFO	First in, first out. A storage method to assure that older products are used first
Fiscal Year	The 12-month period for which a budget applies
Flow of Food	Movement of food through a foodservice facility including purchasing, receiving, storage, preparation, transport, holding, service, cooling, and reheating
Food Requisition	A form that documents storage transactions
Foodborne Illness	A disease that is transmitted by food
Foodborne Illness Outbreak	Occurs when two or more cases of a similar illness results from eating a common food
Foodborne Infection	When pathogens enter the body in an active state and continue to grow (e.g. Salmonella)
Foodborne Intoxication	An illness that occurs from the toxin or poison left from bacteria that are no longer alive (e.g. Clostridium botulinum)
Foodservice Employee	An individual working with unpackaged food, food equipment or utensils, or food contact surfaces
Forecasting	Estimating future product needs for menu items
FOTTWA	Acronym for the conditions needed for bacterial growth: food, oxygen, temperature, time, water, acidity
Full-Time Equivalent (FTE)	The number of standard hours for one full-time employee
Fungi	Molds or yeast that can cause an illness or produce a toxin that causes the illness

G	
Garnish	Enhance food appearance by adding edible decorations
Goal	A statement that outlines an outcome or result
Grade	A rating that describes the quality and appearance characteristics of a product
Grading	A voluntary process providing a descriptive term or number to designate quality
H	
Hazard Analysis Critical Control Point (HACCP)	A management system in which food safety is addressed
Hazard Communication Standard	Also referred to as the "Right to Know" Law; requires informing employees about chemicals they work with and to design and institute employee protection program
Hazard or Danger Zone	The temperature range in which most bacteria grow rapidly (41˚F-135˚F)
Hazards	Biological, chemical, or physical property that may cause an unacceptable consumer health risk. Hazards must be controlled.
Highly Susceptible Population	Persons who are more likely to experience foodborne disease because they are immunocompromised (already ill), preschool age children, or older adults
I	
Inspection	A mandatory process that addresses wholesomeness and safety of fresh meats, dairy products, and produce
Insubordination	Direct refusal to do what the supervisor asks
Integrated Pest Management (IPM)	A coordinated approach with pest control and foodservice to manage pests
Inventory Valuation	The dollar figure or value of all inventory on hand at a given point in time
Invoice	A document designating what has been purchased and accepted
Individually Quick Frozen (IQF)	A process of rapid freezing yielding smaller ice crystals and better color and texture
Issuing	Process for withdrawing products from storage
J	
Just In Time (JIT) Purchasing	Purchasing items as needed, or Just In Time
Job Analysis	An individual schedule, by day, for each staff position
Job Description	Detailed job list including hours and location of the job, qualifications and salary range
Job Sharing	Dividing a full-time position into two or more positions
K	
Kosher	Fit, proper or in agreement with religious law; Kosher meat means the animal has been slaughtered in a special way. Usually, Kosher foods have been blessed by a rabbi.
L	
Labor Hours Per Meal	Total labor hours per meal divided by the total meals served
Labor Union	Formal organization representing employees and designed to advance the needs and interests of its members

Lateral Communication	Occurs among peers and may involve discussion and meetings to solve problems and/or accomplish tasks
Likert Scale	A common rating technique that uses words or numbers
M	
Marketing	Presenting products or services to clients (and potential clients) in a way that persuades them to buy
Meals Per Labor Hour	A productivity standard that is a calculation of the total meals divided by the total number of labor hours for a given time such as a week, month, or year (total meals ÷ total labor hours for a given time = meals per labor hour)
Minimum Wage	The minimum dollar wage for nonexempt employees before deductions
Minutes Per Meal	A productivity standard that is a calculation of the total minutes in producing meals divided by the total meals served (total minutes to produce meals ÷ total meals served = minutes per meal)
Modified Atmosphere Packaging (MAP)	A type of packaging that extends the life of the product by maintaining a reduced oxygen environment
Monitoring	Checking that a processing or handling procedure does not exceed the established critical limit at each critical control point. It involves systematic observation, measurement, and/or recording. More than one observation may be necessary at a particular critical control point. The monitoring procedures chosen must enable action to be taken to correct an out-of-control situation or to bring the product back into acceptable limits.
Material Safety Data Sheet (MSDS)	Required for every chemical that addresses the safe use of the chemical
N	
Non-selective Menu	One in which clients do not have the opportunity to make choices for main dishes
Nutrition Support	General term describing providing foods and liquids to improve nutritional status
O	
Objective	The steps to achieve the goal or the actions to get there
Open-Ended Question	Allows the participant to answer freely, saying whatever comes to mind
Operating Budget	A financial plan that includes food, beverage, and labor costs and expected revenue
Operating Statement	A financial report that shows your financial performance (revenues and expenses) as compared to the budget
Organization Chart	A graphical management tool that shows job relationships in a facility
Occupational Safety and Hazard Administration (OSHA)	Responsible for enforcing chemical safety standards
Outcome	End result of work
P	
Pad	Adding to a forecast by a small percentage to assure adequate quantities of food
Par Levels	A minimum quantity to be maintained in inventory
Parasite	A small organism that lives within another living organism such as Trichinella that lives in pork or wild game

Parenteral Nutrition	Administration of simple essential nutrients into a vein
Pasteurized	Heating to a specific temperature for a specified amount of time
Plan, Do, Check, Act (PDCA)	Cycle of process improvement
Performance Review	A formal, structured meeting between employee and supervisor about the individual employee's performance
Performance Standard	Specific statements describing the outcomes of the work to be performed
Permit Holder	The entity that is legally responsible for the operation of the foodservice facility such as the hospital, nursing facility, or school district
Perpetual Inventory	A running count of inventory items that is updated continuously, usually with an electronic order entry or point of sale system
Person in Charge	The manager of the foodservice operation who is accountable for developing, carrying out, and enforcing procedures aimed at preventing foodborne illness
Potentially Hazardous Food/Time/ Temperature Control for Safety (PHF/TCS)	Designation of foods that require control of time and temperature for safety
Physical Hazards	Foreign materials that enter food accidentally
Physical Inventory	A physical count of items in inventory that occurs weekly, monthly, quarterly, or annually
Policy	Describes an organization's approach to a certain situation
Portion Control	Control of serving sizes so they are standardized
Potable Water	Water that is safe to drink
Preventative Maintenance	An organized routine of cleaning, inspecting and maintaining equipment
Prime Vendor	A primary supplier who usually provides about 80% of the products
Procedure	Details the steps in carrying out a policy
Production Schedule	A document that outlines what to produce, how much to produce, and who is responsible
Profitability Analysis	Financial calculation that compares costs with revenues to determine whether an idea is profitable
Progressive Discipline	A series of defined steps taken when an employee does not correct a performance problem
Promotion	Activity designed to publicize a product or service
Purchase Order	A business document that specifies what is being purchased
Q	
Quality Assessment	The evaluation of processes and/or outcomes to determine if a defined standard of quality is being achieved
Quality Assurance	Sum total of structure, processes, and procedures designed to ensure that clients feel that both food and services are excellent and the facility meets or exceeds an expected standard of quality
Quality Improvement	The ongoing process to improve the delivery of food, services, and resident outcomes
Quality Indicator	Measures of outcomes
Quality Standard	Your facility's definition of what constitutes quality for a product such as food or service
Quantitative	A measure of productivity that measures quantity such as labor hours, time, number of transactions, staff turnover, and overtime usage

R	
Request for Proposal (RFP)	A written description of large dollar items that is then sent to suppliers to obtain a competitive bid
Restrict	To limit an employee's activities so there is no risk of transmitting foodborne illness (such as to reassign the employee to a non-food related position)
Rethermalize	Reheat previously prepared food
Revenue	Money coming in, or income
Revenue Generating Services	Any service that brings money into a business
Risk Management	Managing the possibility of dangerous situations to employees or to the organization
Risks	The likelihood of a potentially dangerous situation
Roux	Used to thicken sauces and gravies that combines equal weights of fat and flour

S	
Sanitary	Free of harmful levels of microorganisms
Sanitizers	Chemicals that destroy microorganisms
Satisfaction Survey	A series of questions designed to elicit feedback from clients in a systematic fashion
Scaling	Adjusting standardized recipes upward or downward to provide a specific yield
Selective Menu	One in which clients have the opportunity to make choices or selections in advance of or immediately prior to meal service
Shellfish Identification Tags	Special labels that can be used to trace a product such as oysters, mussels, clams, back to the source in the event that illness occurs
Special or Single Use Menu	A menu planned for service on a special day such as a Mother's Day Tea
Specification	Quality statement that lists what requirements must be met in order for a product to be acceptable
Split Shift	Two short shifts separated by a period of time off in one day
Staff Position	Provides advisory or consulting support
Staggered Scheduling	Scheduling staff so they come in at different times instead of several coming in and leaving at the same time
Standardized Recipe	A recipe that contains detailed specifications and has been tried, adapted and retried in your facility
Statement	A document that summarizes all invoices, credits, and payments for a given period of time
Static Menu	A fixed menu that doesn't change such as a room service menu

T	
Time/Temperature Indictor (TTI) Strip	A smart label that shows the accumulated time and temperature history of a product
Toxin-Mediated Infection	When live bacteria enter the body and produce a dangerous toxin (e.g. E. coli bacteria)
Tray/Plate Accuracy	How accurately staff have followed the menu, tray card, or tray ticket in assembling the tray
Tray Per Minute	A measure of efficiency of a trayline foodservice system

U	
Ultra-High Temperature Processed (UHT)	Products that are treated by flash sterilization and then packed into sterilized, airtight containers, and are shelf-stable for up to three months
Ultra-Pasteurized	Heated to a higher temperature for a shorter period of time
Upward Communication	Used to communicate ideas, requests and opinions to supervisors
V	
Verification	The use of equipment to determine that the HACCP system is in place and achieving the desired objectives
Virus	Source of foodborne illness that does not grow in food but is transmitted from people, animals, or fish/shellfish
Work Simplification	Simplifying a task so that it is performed as efficiently as possible
Work-Related Injury	Injury that occurs at work that results in days away from work, restricted work activity, medical treatment, loss of consciousness, or death
Y	
Yield	The number of servings a recipe will produce at a given portion size
Yield Percentage	Edible portion weight divided by the as purchased weight

Index

A

B

Page numbers followed by an '*f*' indicate figures

C

D

E

Page numbers followed by an 'f' indicate figures

F

G

H

I

J

K

L

M

Page numbers followed by an '*f*' indicate figures

N

O

P

Page numbers followed by an '*f*' indicate figures

Q

R

Page numbers followed by an 'f' indicate figures

S

Page numbers followed by an *'f'* indicate figures

T

U

V

W

Y

NOTES

NOTES